AN INTRODUCTION

TO

THE ALGEBRA OF QUANTICS

AN INTRODUCTION

TO THE

ALGEBRA OF QUANTICS

BY

EDWIN BAILEY ELLIOTT, M.A., F.R.S.
WAYNFLETE PROFESSOR OF PURE MATHEMATICS, AND
FELLOW OF MAGDALEN COLLEGE, OXFORD

SECOND EDITION

CHELSEA PUBLISHING COMPANY
BRONX, NEW YORK

THE FIRST AND SECOND EDITIONS OF THE PRESENT WORK WERE PUBLISHED BY OXFORD UNIVERSITY PRESS

First Edition, 1895
Second Edition, 1913
Second Edition Reprinted, 1964

Library of Congress Catalog Card No. 63-11320

Printed in the United States of America

PREFACE

THE present work is an expansion of a course of lectures which I have annually delivered for some years past at Queen's College, Oxford.

Its primary object is, as was the case in the lecture room, that of explaining with all the clearness at my command the leading principles of invariant algebra, in the hope of making it evident to the junior student that the subject is attractive as well as important, and that its early difficulties are only such as he can readily surmount. Lucidity in mathematical works has often suffered from undue compression. My constant aim has been to guard against such a possibility here. In a book of moderate size dealing with a great subject much must remain unsaid, if the fundamental considerations are to be presented with the thoroughness and the perspicuity necessary to enable the student adequately to realize them, and give him the interest in them which will prepare him to pursue for himself the study to which they introduce him.

But, while the interests of the beginner have thus been given precedence, I am not without hope that the mathematician who is not new to the higher algebra will, especially in the chapters near the middle of the book, find in its pages matter of value to him as an aid to his researches. In some branches of the theory, which though of really elementary character are of comparatively recent investigation, as for instance in much of the algebra of differential operators, it is believed that a welcome supplement to previous treatises is offered.

The title 'Algebra of Quanties' is perhaps one of my own introduction. It probably needs no defence, and can hardly fail to convey the right meaning. The mathematical world has now for half a century associated the algebra of invariants and covariants with the name of Cayley, and with his 'Memoirs on Quantics,' so that it may perhaps be regarded as appropriate that a new work, appearing in the year which has seen the close of the labours of the renowned author of those memoirs, and dealing with their subject, should bear a name which recalls his memory.

To Salmon's *Higher Algebra* and his other works it is impossible to say how much I am indebted, both for direct reference and for guidance to the use of other authorities. Faà de Bruno's *Formes Binaires* has also been constantly before me. Of Clebsch's *Binäre Formen* and Gordan's *Invariantentheorie* less use has been made, as their symbolical method, and their successful application of it to the great problem of the investigation of complete irreducible systems, have been reluctantly passed over with little more than an allusion in the following pages. A scanty chapter or two on this subject would have been utterly inadequate, and inconsistent with the general plan, as stated above, of an introductory treatise which prefers to omit rather than to obscure by condensation. A whole work which shall present to the English reader in his own language a worthy exposition of the method of the great German masters remains a desideratum.

The reader will not, however, find that the present work is a compilation from others which have preceded it, great as has been the help which those others have afforded. Constant recourse has been had to the original authorities, particularly of course to Cayley's series of memoirs, and to Sylvester's writings in the Cambridge and Dublin Mathematical Journal, the American Journal of Mathematics, and elsewhere.

No bibliography of works and memoirs on the subject has been introduced. All mathematicians who wish to go deeply into the study of original authorities will have in their hands

Dr. F. Meyer's 'Bericht über den gegenwärtigen Stand der Invariantentheorie' in the 'Jahresbericht der Deutschen Mathematiker-Vereinigung' for 1890–91, which is so full and thorough a bibliography and analysis of what has been done, especially in the later period of the history of the invariant theory, that it is hard to see how more can be desired. With regard to the originators of particular results, the difficulty continues, and has grown with the multitude of investigators, which was felt by Dr. Salmon when he wrote, 'I can scarcely pretend to assign to their proper authors the merits of the several steps; and, as between Messrs. Cayley and Sylvester, perhaps these gentlemen themselves, who were in constant communication with each other at the time, would now find it hard to say how much properly belongs to each.' To the difficulty with regard to Cayley and Sylvester may in particular be added that of discriminating between what in Salmon's work should be ascribed to them or others at all and what to Salmon himself. Throughout the following pages discoverers' names are very frequently attached to results; but it is too much to hope, though all care has been taken, that there are not cases in which the names given are those of authors in whose writings the results in question have certainly occurred, rather than those of the authors who first gave them.

I am indebted to several friends for suggestions and other help. Among them there is one, Mr. J. Hammond, M.A., one of the most distinguished of living researchers in the higher Algebra, to whom my especial thanks are due for a manuscript on the binary quintic which has been exceedingly helpful.

Some students, approaching the subject for the first time, will be advised to omit Chapters VII to XI till part of what follows them has been read.

E. B. ELLIOTT.

OXFORD,
September, 1895.

PREFACE TO THE SECOND EDITION

In preparing this new edition my aim has been, as before, to express principles clearly, with a directly didactic purpose, and to exhibit salient conclusions which have been derived from the principles by the use of those methods which are often characterized as distinctively English. The old arrangement, and the old numbering of articles, have been nearly always retained. A good deal has been added; and the additional has sometimes been stated with a brevity which in the original matter was deliberately avoided in the effort never to be obscure. Pains have been taken to insert the additions in places where they assist the argument, or at any rate do not impede its flow. When this has been found impossible or seriously difficult, a practice much resorted to in the first edition has been further adopted; and facts of interest or utility have been stated, with guidance to ways of obtaining them, in examples.

In two Chapters, V and XV, rearrangement has not been avoided. In the former I had neglected an important consideration; and in the latter stress has now been laid on facts of which the importance has only begun to be appreciated since the first edition appeared.

Altogether, fully one-eighth has been added to the book; but the skill of the staff of the University Press has kept the volume within its old bulk—without, as I trust, making it difficult to read.

A need to which I called attention in the preface to the first edition has been satisfied by Messrs. Grace and Young in their *Algebra of Invariants*. I have therefore, with easy conscience, said little more than before about the powerful symbolic method which, in its parallelism to the English method of always keeping in view explicit forms, and bringing to bear upon them knowledge about linear differential operators and about enumerative arithmetic, has been called distinctively German. In such additions as I have made to my mention of that method I have as a rule adopted, not the usual symbolism, but a modification of it which stands in direct relationship to the calculus of differential operations.

My hope is that the work will still appeal, as I am glad to think it has in the past, to the beginner in Higher Algebra; will give him real interest in the subject, and provide him with sound knowledge in one of its departments. In endeavouring to improve this second edition, which is the last I shall live to produce, and is probably definitive, I have continued to think mainly for him, and to picture him as one better prepared for being led on from the simple—it may be the crude—to the elaborate, than for first receiving, and then applying, comprehensive theory. But I further trust that the book will retain, for some time to come, a certain value as one to be referred to by men and women who, while occupied with the continued advancement of Pure Mathematics, will need to look back upon and utilize the labours of those pioneers of modern Algebraic Theory, who adorned the latter half of the nineteenth century, and have now passed away.

E. B. ELLIOTT.

May, 1913.

TABLE OF CONTENTS

CHAPTER I

PRINCIPLES AND DIRECT METHODS

	PAGE
Definitions (Arts. 1–4)	1
Invariants and covariants to be expected (5–7)	5
Jacobians, Hessians, eliminants, and discriminants (8–13, 15)	9
The modulus irresoluble (14)	17
A theorem on powers of the modulus proved and applied (16, 17)	18
Intermediate invariants and covariants (18–20)	23

CHAPTER II

ESSENTIAL QUALITIES OF INVARIANTS

Homogeneity (Arts. 21, 22)	27
The factor a power of the modulus (23, 24)	28
Isobarism (25–28)	31
Absolute invariants (29)	34
Number of independent invariants limited (30)	35
Invariants of more quantics than one (31–33)	37

CHAPTER III

ESSENTIAL QUALITIES OF COVARIANTS

Homogeneity (Arts. 34–36)	40
The factor a power of the modulus (37)	41
Isobarism (38–40)	42
Absolute covariants (41)	45
Number of independent covariants limited (42, 43)	46
Covariants of more quantics than one (44)	48
Invariants and covariants of covariants (45)	49

CHAPTER IV

COGREDIENT AND CONTRAGREDIENT QUANTITIES

PAGE

Cogrediency of $\frac{\partial}{\partial y}$ and $-\frac{\partial}{\partial x}$ with x and y (Arts. 46-50) . . . 51
Cogrediency defined (51) 55
Emanants (52, 53) 56
Geometry of binary systems (54, 55) 59
Covariants derived from emanants (56-58) 60
Symbolical representation: Hyperdeterminants: Transvectants (59-61) 64
Contragrediency (62-65) 74
Contravariants and mixed concomitants: Evectants (66, 67) . . 76
Covariants of a binary quantic as contravariants and as invariants (68, 69) 79

CHAPTER V

BINARY QUANTICS. INVARIANTS, ETC., AS FUNCTIONS OF DIFFERENCES

Convention as to numerical multiples (Art. 71) 82
Covariancy of the factors of a binary quantic (72, 73) . . . 83
Invariants as functions of differences (74-76) 86
Discriminants (77, 79) 89
Invariants of a quadratic, of a cubic, and of a quartic (78, 80, 81) 89, 92
Covariants as functions of differences (82, 83) 94
Covariants of a quadratic, and of a cubic (84-86) 97
Several binary quantics (87) 100
Theorems as to functions of differences (88, 89) 101

CHAPTER VI

BINARY QUANTICS CONTINUED. ANNIHILATORS. SEMINVARIANTS

The annihilators Ω and O of invariants (Arts. 90-94) 108
Symmetry of invariants: Skew invariants (95, 96) 112
Sufficiency of conditions of annihilation (97) 113
Differential operations which effect a linear transformation (98-100) 114
Formation of invariants by aid of Ω (101, 102) 118
Invariants of several binary quantics (103) 120
Annihilators of covariants (104-108) 122
A covariant is given by one of its coefficients (109, 110) . . . 125
Seminvariants, and the covariants which they lead (111, 112, 115) . 127
Determination of seminvariants (113, 114) 129

Additional examples 134

CHAPTER VII

FURTHER THEORY OF THE OPERATORS Ω AND O. RECIPROCITY

PAGE

Gradients, and the differential equations they satisfy (Arts. 116, 117) . . . 138
Seminvariants and invariants as classes of gradients (118–120) . 139
Repeated operations with Ω and O: Alternants (121–125) . . 141
There are no seminvariants of negative excess (126) 146
The exact number of given positive excess (127, 128) 147
Separation of gradients into seminvariant and other parts (128 *bis*) 150
Arithmetical conclusions: Reciprocity: Hermite's law (129–131) . 153
Gradients in more sets than one (132) 157

CHAPTER VIII

GENERATING FUNCTIONS

Generating functions for numbers of partitions and of seminvariants (Arts. 133–137) 159
Irreducible concomitants of linear form, of quadratic, and of cubic (138–141) 164
Irreducible invariants of quartic, of quintic, and of sextic (142, 143) 169
Generating functions for concomitants of given degree and order (144) 171
Reduced and representative generating functions (145–147) . . 172
Real generating functions (148) 179

CHAPTER IX

HILBERT'S PROOFS OF GORDAN'S THEOREM

Lemmas on solutions of Diophantine equations (Art. 150) . . 182
Proof of Gordan's theorem for invariants of one binary quantic (151–154) 186
Proof for covariants of one binary quantic (155, 156) . . . 192
Proof for several binary quantics (157) 193
Hilbert's second proof (157 *bis*, *ter*) 195
Syzygies and syzygants (157 iv) 198

CHAPTER X

PROTOMORPHS, ETC.

PAGE

Recapitulation (Art. 158) 199

Substitution of derived quantics for arguments in seminvariants, &c. (159, 160) 200

A seminvariant is given by its non-unitary terms (161, 162) . . 202

Systems of protomorphs (163, 164, 167, 168) 204

The protomorphs of lowest degrees (165, 166) 207

Irreducible systems of concomitants: The cubic and quartic (169–171) 212

The seminvariants with given non-unitary terms (172, 173) . . 215

Non-unitary terms of invariants are determinate (174, 175) . . 217

Seminvariants as quantics in $a_p:1$. (176–179) 221

Operators which generate seminvariants (180–182) 224

CHAPTER XI

FURTHER THEORY OF SEMINVARIANTS. THE BINARY QUANTIC OF INFINITE ORDER

Expressions for Ω, &c.: Roots and sums of their powers (Arts. 183–187) 229

Non-unitary symmetric functions (188) 236

Generating functions: Perpetuants: Reciprocity (189, 190) . . 238

Power ending products (191) 241

Annihilators of all gradients (192, 193) 242

Generators of all seminvariants (194, 194 *bis*) 243

Additional Examples (Miscellaneous) 247

CHAPTER XII

CANONICAL FORMS, ETC.

Principles and definitions (Arts. 195–198) 253

Canonical form of binary cubic (199-202) 255

Canonical forms of binary quantics of odd order (203–205) . . 260

Canonizants (206) 263

Apolarity (207) 266

Quantics of even order: Catalecticants (208–210) 267

Canonical form of binary quartic (211–220) 269

Solution of a quartic equation (221, 222) 280

Geometry of concomitants of quartic (223) 282

Binary sextics, octavics, and $2n$-ics (224-228) 284

Canonical form of ternary cubic (229) 290

Catalecticants of ternary, quaternary, &c. quartics (230, 231) . 293

CHAPTER XIII

INVARIANTS AND COVARIANTS OF THE BINARY QUINTIC AND SEXTIC

PAGE
The twenty-three concomitants of a quintic (Arts. 232, 234, 235) . 296
Hammond's canonical and semi-canonical forms (233, 235) . . 297
Discriminant of Quintic (236) 302
Syzygy among invariants of Quintic (237) 302
Hermite's Formes-types (238, 240) 304
Quintics which satisfy invariant conditions (239–243) . . . 305
The twenty-six concomitants of a sextic (244, 245) 311

Additional examples 314

CHAPTER XIV

SEVERAL BINARY QUANTICS

Concomitants of several binary quantics (Art. 247) 318
Linear form and p-ic (248, 249, 252) 319
All gradients lead pure or mixed concomitants (248 *bis*) . . . 320
Cases of $p = 1$ and $p = 2$ (250, 251) 323
Irreducible system for linear form and cubic (253, 254) . . . 325
Linear form and quartic (255) 328
Several linear forms (256) 329
System of two quadratics (257, 258) 330
Linear form and two quadratics (259) 334
Quadratic and cubic (260–262) 335
Seminvariants as invariants of systems (262 *bis*) 338
Quantics of orders descending by units (263) 339
Quantics of one order: Combinants (264, 265) 340

CHAPTER XV

RESTRICTED SUBSTITUTIONS. BINARY QUANTICS IN CARTESIAN GEOMETRY

The substitutions of Cartesian geometry (Art. 266) 343
Boolian and orthogonal invariants, &c. (267–269) 344
Orthogonal cogrediency and contragrediency identical (270) . . 346
Annihilators of absolute orthogonal, and Boolian, concomitants (271, 272) 349
Boolian complete systems for quantics of low orders (273) . . 352
All products lead absolute orthogonal covariants (274) . . . 354
An annihilator of all forms (275) 355
Non-absolute orthogonal concomitants (276–278) 356
Orthogonal complete systems (278 *bis*) 361

CHAPTER XVI

TERNARY QUANTICS. THE QUADRATIC AND CUBIC

	PAGE
Triple arrangement of a ternary quantic (Art. 280)	364
The annihilators of invariants and covariants (281–283, 288, 289)	365
The alternants of these annihilators (284–287)	368
The invariant of a ternary quadratic (290)	373
The invariants of a ternary cubic (291–295)	374
Covariants of ternary quantics (296–299)	382
Has a ternary quadratic covariants? (300)	390
Covariants of a ternary cubic (301–304)	391
Ternary covariant sources (304 *bis*)	396
Contravariants (305)	399
Contravariants of ternary quadratic and of ternary cubic (306–308)	400
Mixed concomitants (309, 310)	403
Quantics in more than three variables (311, 312)	406

AN INTRODUCTION

TO

THE ALGEBRA OF QUANTICS

CHAPTER I

PRINCIPLES AND DIRECT METHODS.

1. **Quantics or Forms.** A function of any number of variables $x, y, z, \ldots$, which is rational, integral, and homogeneous in those variables, is called a *quantic* in $x, y, z, \ldots$. The coefficients in a quantic are constants as far as $x, y, z, \ldots$ are concerned. The idea of the variability of $x, y, z, \ldots$ is rarely introduced. We call them variables only to have a distinctive name for them.

If there are only two variables x, y, the quantic is spoken of as a *binary* quantic; if three x, y, z, as a *ternary* quantic; if four, as a *quaternary* quantic; and so on. If there are q variables, where q is any number, we may call it a *q-ary* quantic.

The degree of a quantic in the variables $x, y, z, \ldots$ is generally spoken of as its *order*. Quantics of the first, second, third, fourth, ..., pth orders are called briefly *linear*, *quadratics*, *cubics*, *quartics*, ... p-*ics*.

Thus for instance $ax^3 + 3bx^2y + 3cxy^2 + dy^3$ is a binary cubic, and $ax^2 + by^2 + cz^2 + 2fyz + 2gzx + 2hxy$ is a ternary quadratic.

By some English and most foreign writers the word *Form* is used as synonymous with and instead of the word *Quantic*. Both words being well established, they will be used almost indiscriminately in this work.

Attention will often be concentrated on *binary* quantics alone. The binary p-ic will almost invariably be considered in the form

$$a_0x^p + pa_1x^{p-1}y + \frac{p(p-1)}{1\,.\,2}a_2x^{p-2}y^2$$
$$+ \frac{p(p-1)(p-2)}{1\,.\,2\,.\,3}a_3x^{p-3}y^3 + \ldots + pa_{p-1}xy^{p-1} + a_py^p,$$

which it is usual shortly to symbolize by

$$(a_0, a_1, a_2, a_3, \ldots a_p)(x, y)^p.$$

It is of course clear that, if $a_0, a_1, a_2, a_3, \ldots a_p$ are capable of receiving any values whatever, this is neither more nor less general than the form

$$b_0x^p + b_1x^{p-1}y + b_2x^{p-2}y^2 + b_3x^{p-3}y^3 + \dots + b_{p-1}xy^{p-1} + b_py^p,$$

which it is the custom to denote by

$$(b_0, b_1, b_2, b_3, \dots b_p)(x, y)^p.$$

The advantages gained by use of the first form, in which the numerical coefficients 1, p, $\frac{p(p-1)}{1 \cdot 2}$, ... in the pth power of a binomial are explicitly introduced as factors of the coefficients in order in the binary p-ic, will become apparent in the sequel.

Analogous advantages are gained in general, when quantics in higher numbers of variables are being dealt with, by the explicit introduction of multinomial coefficients. Thus in the general q-ary p-ic in the variables $x_1, x_2, \dots x_q$ it is convenient to consider each coefficient to be the product of a factor denoted by a letter, to which any value whatever may be assigned, and the coefficient of the corresponding term in the expansion of $(x_1 + x_2 + \dots + x_q)^p$.

When speaking of the *coefficients* in a binary quantic $(a_0, a_1, a_2, \dots a_p)(x, y)^p$, we as a rule mean $a_0, a_1, a_2, \dots a_p$, and not $a_0, pa_1, \frac{p(p-1)}{1 \cdot 2}a_2, \dots$; and analogously for quantics in higher numbers of variables.

2. **Linear transformation.** If in a quantic we replace each of the variables by a sum of multiples of first powers of an equally numerous set of new variables—if for instance, the variables originally involved being $x, y, z, \dots$, we substitute for them according to the scheme

$$\begin{aligned} x &= l\,X + m\,Y + n\,Z + \dots, \\ y &= l'X + m'Y + n'Z + \dots, \\ z &= l''X + m''Y + n''Z + \dots, \\ &\cdot\ \cdot\ \cdot\ \cdot\ \cdot\ \cdot\ \cdot\ \cdot\ \cdot \end{aligned}$$

where there are just as many of $X, Y, Z, \dots$ as of $x, y, z, \dots$— we are said to make a *linear substitution* in the quantic, or to *linearly transform* the quantic; and the new quantic in $X, Y, Z, \dots$ which we obtain is spoken of as a *linear transformation* of the original quantic.

The determinant

$$\begin{vmatrix} l, & m, & n, & \dots \\ l', & m', & n', & \dots \\ l'', & m'', & n'', & \dots \\ \cdot & \cdot & \cdot & \cdot \end{vmatrix},$$

whose constituents are the coefficients, in their natural order, of the new variables X, Y, Z, ... in the expressions for the old ones x, y, z, ..., and which accordingly consists of as many rows and columns as there are variables in either set, is called the *determinant* or *modulus* of the substitution or of the transformation. It will often be convenient to denote it by a single letter. The letter which will as a rule be chosen is M.

The original variables x, y, z, ... are as a rule taken to be all independent. It is unlawful then to substitute for them any expressions in terms of new variables which are not all independent. Now if X, Y, Z, ... are all independent the linear expressions

$$\begin{array}{l} l\,X + m\,Y + n\,Z + \ldots, \\ l'X + m'Y + n'Z + \ldots, \\ l''X + m''Y + n''Z + \ldots, \\ \cdot\quad\cdot\quad\cdot\quad\cdot\quad\cdot\quad\cdot\quad\cdot\quad\cdot\quad\cdot \end{array}$$

are or are not all independent according as the modulus M does not or does vanish. We must impose then on the generality of the coefficients in a lawful scheme of linear substitution the one limitation that the modulus M do not vanish.

We are now in a position to define invariants and covariants.

3. Invariants and Covariants.

An *invariant of a single quantic* is such a function of the coefficients in that quantic, that it needs at most to be multiplied by a factor which is a function only of the coefficients in any scheme of linear substitution, to be made equal to the same function of the corresponding coefficients in the quantic into which the given quantic is transformed by that scheme.

An *invariant of two or more quantics* in the same variables is such a function of the two or more sets of coefficients in those quantics, that it needs at most to be multiplied by a factor which is a function only of the coefficients in any scheme of linear substitution, to be made equal to the same function of the corresponding coefficients in the quantics into which the given quantics are transformed by that scheme.

A *covariant* of a single quantic, or of two or more quantics in the same variables, is a function of the variables and of the coefficients in that quantic or those quantics which has the like property; namely that of needing at most to be multiplied by a factor which is a function only of the coefficients in any scheme of linear substitution to be made equal to the same function of the new variables and of the corresponding coefficients in the quantic or quantics into which the given quantic or quantics are transformed by that scheme.

For instance, let the binary p-ic

$$(a_0, a_1, a_2, \dots a_p)(x, y)^p$$

be transformed by the linear substitution

$$x = lX + mY, \quad y = l'X + m'Y,$$

and become

$$(A_0, A_1, A_2, \dots A_p)(X, Y)^p,$$

where $A_0, A_1, A_2, \dots A_p$ are functions of $a_0, a_1, a_2, \dots a_p$, and l, m, l', m': then $f(a_0, a_1, a_2, \dots a_p)$ will be an invariant if an identity holds of the form

$$f(A_0, A_1, A_2, \dots A_p) = \phi(l, m, l', m') f(a_0, a_1, a_2, \dots a_p),$$

and $F(a_0, a_1, a_2, \dots a_p, x, y)$ will be a covariant if an identity holds of the form

$$F(A_0, A_1, A_2, \dots A_p, X, Y) = \phi(l, m, l', m') F(a_0, a_1, a_2, \dots a_p, x, y).$$

Again if the same substitution transforms another binary quantic in x, y

$$(a_0', a_1', a_2', \dots a'_{p'})(x, y)^{p'}$$

into

$$(A_0', A_1', A_2', \dots A'_{p'})(X, Y)^{p'}$$

$f(a_0, a_1, \dots a_p, a_0', a_1', \dots a'_{p'})$ will be an invariant of the p-ic and the p'-ic jointly if an identity holds of the form

$$f(A_0, A_1, \dots A_p, A_0', A_1', \dots A'_{p'}) = \phi(l, m, l', m') f(a_0, a_1, \dots a_p, a_0', a_1', \dots a'_{p'}),$$

and $F(a_0, a_1, \dots a_p, a_0', a_1', \dots a'_{p'}, x, y)$ will be a covariant if an identity holds of the form

$$F(A_0, A_1, \dots A_p, A_0', A_1', \dots A'_{p'}, X, Y) = \phi(l, m, l', m') F(a_0, a_1, \dots a_p, a_0', a_1', \dots a'_{p'}, x, y).$$

It will be noticed that covariants include invariants as a particular case.

4. In every case the factor depending only on the coefficients in the scheme of substitution in the identity which expresses the fact of invariancy or covariancy is as a matter of fact a power of the modulus M. In particular for any invariant or covariant of a *binary* quantic or *binary* quantics the $\phi(l, m, l', m')$ above is a power of $lm' - l'm$. It is a departure from usual practice not to state this as a requirement in defining invariants and covariants. It will probably be granted that the departure is a proper one, for the necessity is a proposition which can and will be proved hereafter, and,

were there any functions such as contemplated in the definitions for which the factor was other than a power of the modulus, their property would be none the less appropriately described as invariantic. The fact that there are not really such functions is one of sufficient interest in itself and of sufficient importance in its applications to deserve proof and prominence.

No limitation requiring functions defined as invariants and covariants to be rational and integral has been imposed in the definitions. There are in fact irrational and fractional functions which have the property of invariancy and covariancy, as well as others which are rational and integral. The main quest in this work will be however for invariants which are rational and integral, and for covariants which are rational and integral both in the coefficients and in the variables, and the words *invariant* and *covariant* will as a rule be used as meaning *rational integral invariant* and *rational integral covariant*.

There is a greater completeness in a system of rational integral invariants and covariants than is at first sight apparent, in that all invariants and covariants can be expressed in terms of such as are rational and integral. The present is not the stage at which to attempt to prove this fact, but the case of covariants of a single binary p-ic may be mentioned as an instance. It will be seen in Chapter III that there cannot be more than p independent covariants, including the p-ic itself and invariants. In terms of p which are independent any other can be expressed. Also in Chapter X a system of p independent covariants will be found which are all rational and integral. It will follow that all other covariants, including such as are irrational or fractional, can be expressed in terms of them.

5. A little careful consideration will show that we ought not to be surprised at the existence of invariants and covariants. Consider for instance a binary quantic. It is equivalent to a product of linear factors, to grant which is only to grant the fundamental theorem of algebra that every rational integral equation has a root, and therefore p roots if its order is p. A relation in the coefficients of the quantic will be equivalent to the expression of some special fact with regard to those linear factors. In particular there will be some relations which express kinds of interdependence among two or more factors which are not altered by the application of a linear transformation of the variables. Such a relation will necessitate the corresponding relation among the co-

efficients in the transformed quantic. In other words the function of the coefficients of the given quantic whose vanishing gives the relation in question must be a factor of the same function of the corresponding coefficients of the transformed quantic.

Thus in particular the vanishing of the discriminant of a binary quantic is the condition, sufficient and necessary, that the quantic may have two identical linear factors. Now, if it has, so clearly must the result of replacing in it x and y by $lX+mY$ and $l'X+m'Y$. Consequently, if the discriminant of the given quantic vanishes, so too must that of the linearly transformed quantic. In other words the first discriminant must be a factor of the second. That the remaining factor must be a function of l, m, l', m' only is to be expected because, the discriminant being homogeneous, and each coefficient in the transformed quantic being linear in the coefficients of the untransformed, the degrees of the two discriminants in the coefficients of the untransformed quantic are the same. It will presently be proved that the discriminants of all quantics, and not of binary quantics only, are invariants.

Again, by thinking of the eliminant or resultant of two binary quantics we can realize that invariants of two or more quantics jointly are with equal reason to be expected. The vanishing of the eliminant of two binary quantics is the necessary and sufficient condition for those quantics to have a common factor. If they have, so equally must their linear transformations. In other words, if the eliminant of two binary quantics vanishes, so must that of the two transformed quantics. The former eliminant is then a factor of the latter.

6. To convince ourselves of the a priori reasonableness of expecting *covariants* to exist, we shall do well to avail ourselves of geometrical representation.

Let us take axes of Cartesian coordinates inclined at any angle, which it is best to regard as unknown, since otherwise we may be in danger of introducing or implying its value in functions with which we deal, and so bringing in ideas not afforded by the quantics and transformation that are before us. The factors of a binary quantic or quantics correspond each to a straight line through the origin, the straight line in each case whose equation is obtained by equating to zero the factor under consideration.

Let us now consider what is effected by the linear substitution $x = lX+mY$, $y = l'X+m'Y$, regarding the substitution not as implying a change of axes but as expressing the coordinates of one point (x, y) in terms of those of another (X, Y) with regard to the same axes. The first point (x, y) being definite, so is the second (X, Y). Moreover to different points (x, y) on a straight line through the origin correspond different points (X, Y) on another line through the origin, for Y/X is uniquely determined in terms of y/x. In fact we have

$$\frac{y}{x}=\frac{l'+m'.Y/X}{l+m.Y/X}, \quad \text{so that} \quad \frac{Y}{X}=\frac{l.y/x-l'}{m'-m.y/x}.$$

Now the student of geometry will recognize from this that the two lines on which (x, y) and (X, Y) lie have a definite homographic or projective correspondence for given values of l, m, l', m'. The effect then of the linear transformation is to replace points on lines through the origin by corresponding points on projectively corresponding lines through the origin.

The pencil of lines representative of any given binary quantic or quantics is accordingly replaced by any linear transformation by a projectively corresponding pencil of lines. Is there any other pencil of lines associated with the first pencil, whose projective correspondents are associated with the second pencil exactly as they themselves are with the first? If so, then the equation of their correspondents may be formed either by applying the linear transformation to their equation or by forming an equation from the transformed quantic or quantics in precisely the same way as their equation was formed from the given quantic or quantics. In other words, the derived quantic which equated to zero gives their equation, and that derived in like manner from the transformed quantic or quantics, are identical, but for a possible factor independent of the coordinates. Such a derived quantic will be a covariant if only the factor involve merely the constants l, m, l', m' of the transformation and not also the coefficients in the quantic or quantics. But the factor must be of no dimensions in the coefficients of the quantic or quantics, for each coefficient in the transformed quantic or quantics is homogeneous and of one dimension in them. Thus it is to be expected that what is required will be the case.

Now as a rule there are of course lines associated with a given pencil in such a way that if they and the pencil are replaced by others by projective transformation the character of the association is preserved. In particular harmonic properties are unaltered by projective transformation.

Thus, for instance, it suggests itself that a binary quadratic and a linear form have jointly a linear covariant, namely the harmonic conjugate of the linear with regard to the quadratic

—see Ex. 6 below: or again that two binary quadratics have jointly a quadratic covariant, their common pair of harmonic conjugates—see Ex. 7 below: or once more that a binary cubic has a cubic covariant, composed of the three harmonic conjugates of the three factors singly each with regard to the other two factors—a fact which will be established later.

7. We have now suggested to us a number of classes of functions which are likely to be invariants and covariants, and which may be examined by the direct method of substitution.

Ex. 1. To verify that $ac-b^2$ is an invariant of the binary quadratic $ax^2+2bxy+cy^2$, of which it is the discriminant.

If by the substitution $x=lX+mY, \quad y=l'X+m'Y$,

$$ax^2+2bxy+cy^2 \text{ becomes } AX^2+2BXY+CY^2,$$

we have

$$\begin{aligned} A &= al^2+2bll'+cl'^2, \\ B &= alm+b(lm'+l'm)+cl'm', \\ C &= am^2+2bmm'+cm'^2. \end{aligned}$$

Hence at once

$$\begin{aligned} AC-B^2 &= (l^2m'^2-2ll'mm'+m^2l'^2)(ac-b^2) \\ &= M^2(ac-b^2). \end{aligned}$$

Ex. 2. Verify that the eliminant $ab'-a'b$ is an invariant of the two binary linear forms $ax+by$, $a'x+b'y$.

Ans. $AB'-A'B=M(ab'-a'b)$.

Ex. 3. Verify that the eliminant $ab'^2-2ba'b'+ca'^2$ is an invariant of the quadratic and linear forms $ax^2+2bxy+cy^2$, $a'x+b'y$.

Ans. $AB'^2-2BA'B'+CA'^2=M^2(ab'^2-2ba'b'+ca'^2)$.

Ex. 4. Verify that $ac'+a'c-2bb'$ is an invariant of the two binary quadratics $ax^2+2bxy+cy^2$, $a'x^2+2b'xy+c'y^2$.

Ans. $AC'+A'C-2BB'=M^2(ac'+a'c-2bb')$. The vanishing of this invariant is the condition that the two quadratics denote pairs of harmonic conjugates, or that if the first quadratic be written $a(x-ay)(x-\beta y)$, the second must be of the form

$$a''(x-ay)^2+b''(x-\beta y)^2.$$

Ex. 5. Verify that $ae-4bd+3c^2$ is an invariant of the binary quartic $ax^4+4bx^3y+6cx^2y^2+4dxy^3+ey^4$.

Ans. $AE-4BD+3C^2=M^4(ae-4bd+3c^2)$.

Ex. 6. Verify that $b'(ax+by)-a'(bx+cy)$ is a covariant of the binary quadratic and linear forms $ax^2+2bxy+cy^2$, $a'x+b'y$.

Ans. $B'(AX+BY)-A'(BX+CY)$

$$= M\{b'(ax+by)-a'(bx+cy)\}.$$

This covariant is the harmonic conjugate of the linear with regard to the quadratic form.

Ex. 7. Verify that $(ab'-a'b)x^2+(ac'-a'c)xy+(bc'-b'c)y^2$ is a covariant of the two quadratics $ax^2+2bxy+cy^2$, $a'x^2+2b'xy+c'y^2$.

Ans. $(AB'-A'B)X^2+(AC'-A'C)XY+(BC'-B'C)Y^2$
$$=M\{(ab'-a'b)x^2+(ac'-a'c)xy+(bc'-b'c)y^2\}.$$

This covariant is the common pair of harmonic conjugates with regard to the two quadratics.

Ex. 8. Verify that $(ac-b^2)x^2+(ad-bc)xy+(bd-c^2)y^2$ is a covariant of the binary cubic $ax^3+3bx^2y+3cxy^2+dy^3$.

Ans. $(AC-B^2)X^2+(AD-BC)XY+(BD-C^2)Y^2$
$$=M^2\{(ac-b^2)x^2+(ad-bc)xy+(bd-c^2)y^2\}.$$

8. Several of the above examples are particular cases of general facts, the proof of which will next occupy us.

Thus Example 1 is a particular case of the general theorem that the discriminant, or eliminant of the various first partial differential coefficients, of any quantic whatever, is an invariant of that quantic.

Again, Examples 2 and 3 are cases of the general fact that the eliminant or resultant of any number of quantics in as many variables is an invariant of those quantics jointly.

Examples 6 and 7 are cases of the theorem that the Jacobian or Functional Determinant (§ 10) of any number of quantics in as many variables is a covariant.

Once more, Example 8 is a case of the fact that the Hessian of a quantic, i.e. the Jacobian of its first partial differential coefficients, is a covariant of the quantic.

9. **Eliminant of linear forms.** We may at once prove a first extension of Example 2, that the eliminant of any number of *linear* forms in that same number of variables is an invariant of those linear forms.

Let there be n variables $x_1, x_2, x_3, \dots x_n$, and let the n linear forms be

$$\begin{array}{l} a_{11}x_1+a_{12}x_2+\dots+a_{1n}x_n, \\ a_{21}x_1+a_{22}x_2+\dots+a_{2n}x_n, \\ \cdot\quad\cdot\quad\cdot\quad\cdot\quad\cdot\quad\cdot\quad\cdot\quad\cdot \\ a_{n1}x_1+a_{n2}x_2+\dots+a_{nn}x_n; \end{array}$$

and let the scheme of linear substitution

$$\begin{array}{l} x_1=l_{11}X_1+l_{12}X_2+\dots+l_{1n}X_n, \\ x_2=l_{21}X_1+l_{22}X_2+\dots+l_{2n}X_n, \\ \cdot\quad\cdot\quad\cdot\quad\cdot\quad\cdot\quad\cdot\quad\cdot\quad\cdot \\ x_n=l_{n1}X_1+l_{n2}X_2+\dots+l_{nn}X_n, \end{array}$$

transform them into

$$\begin{array}{l} A_{11}X_1 + A_{12}X_2 + \dots + A_{1n}X_n, \\ A_{21}X_1 + A_{22}X_2 + \dots + A_{2n}X_n, \\ \cdot \quad \cdot \quad \cdot \quad \cdot \quad \cdot \quad \cdot \quad \cdot \quad \cdot \quad \cdot \quad \cdot \\ A_{n1}X_1 + A_{n2}X_2 + \dots + A_{nn}X_n. \end{array}$$

Then we see at once that, each of r and s being any number between 1 and n inclusive,

$$A_{rs} = a_{r1}l_{1s} + a_{r2}l_{2s} + a_{r3}l_{3s} + \dots + a_{rn}l_{ns};$$

so that, by the ordinary theorem for the multiplication of determinants,

$$\begin{vmatrix} A_{11}, A_{12}, \dots A_{1n} \\ A_{21}, A_{22}, \dots A_{2n} \\ \cdot \quad \cdot \quad \cdot \quad \cdot \quad \cdot \quad \cdot \\ A_{n1}, A_{n2}, \dots A_{nn} \end{vmatrix} = \begin{vmatrix} a_{11}, a_{12}, \dots a_{1n} \\ a_{21}, a_{22}, \dots a_{2n} \\ \cdot \quad \cdot \quad \cdot \quad \cdot \quad \cdot \\ a_{n1}, a_{n2}, \dots a_{nn} \end{vmatrix} \times \begin{vmatrix} l_{11}, l_{12}, \dots l_{1n} \\ l_{21}, l_{22}, \dots l_{2n} \\ \cdot \quad \cdot \quad \cdot \quad \cdot \quad \cdot \\ l_{n1}, l_{n2}, \dots l_{nn} \end{vmatrix}$$

$$= M \begin{vmatrix} a_{11}, a_{12}, \dots a_{1n} \\ a_{21}, a_{22}, \dots a_{2n} \\ \cdot \quad \cdot \quad \cdot \quad \cdot \quad \cdot \\ a_{n1}, a_{n2}, \dots a_{nn} \end{vmatrix}.$$

10. **Jacobians are covariants.** If $u, v, w, \dots$ are any number of quantics in that same number of variables $x, y, z, \dots$, the Jacobian or Functional Determinant of $u, v, w, \dots$ is the determinant

$$\begin{vmatrix} \frac{\partial u}{\partial x}, & \frac{\partial u}{\partial y}, & \frac{\partial u}{\partial z}, & \dots \\ \frac{\partial v}{\partial x}, & \frac{\partial v}{\partial y}, & \frac{\partial v}{\partial z}, & \dots \\ \frac{\partial w}{\partial x}, & \frac{\partial w}{\partial y}, & \frac{\partial w}{\partial z}, & \dots \\ \cdot & \cdot & \cdot & \cdot \end{vmatrix},$$

which it is usual more shortly to write

$$\frac{\partial (u, v, w, \dots)}{\partial (x, y, z, \dots)}.$$

That it is a covariant of $u, v, w, \dots$ may be seen as follows. If in any function u of $x, y, z, \dots$ we substitute for these variables according to the linear scheme

$$\begin{aligned} x &= lX + mY + nZ + \dots, \\ y &= l'X + m'Y + n'Z + \dots, \\ z &= l''X + m''Y + n''Z + \dots, \\ &\dots\dots\dots\dots, \end{aligned}$$

in this way expressing it as a function of $X, Y, Z, \dots$, we have at once

$$\begin{aligned} \frac{\partial u}{\partial X} &= \frac{\partial u}{\partial x} \cdot \frac{\partial x}{\partial X} + \frac{\partial u}{\partial y} \cdot \frac{\partial y}{\partial X} + \frac{\partial u}{\partial z} \cdot \frac{\partial z}{\partial X} + \dots \\ &= l\frac{\partial u}{\partial x} + l'\frac{\partial u}{\partial y} + l''\frac{\partial u}{\partial z} + \dots, \end{aligned}$$

all the differential coefficients being partial.

Similarly

$$\begin{aligned} \frac{\partial u}{\partial Y} &= m\frac{\partial u}{\partial x} + m'\frac{\partial u}{\partial y} + m''\frac{\partial u}{\partial z} + \dots, \\ \frac{\partial u}{\partial Z} &= n\frac{\partial u}{\partial x} + n'\frac{\partial u}{\partial y} + n''\frac{\partial u}{\partial z} + \dots, \end{aligned}$$

&c., &c.

Thus, by the rule for multiplication of determinants of the same order,

$$\begin{vmatrix} l, & m, & n, & \dots \\ l', & m', & n', & \dots \\ l'', & m'', & n'', & \dots \\ . & . & . & . \end{vmatrix} \times \begin{vmatrix} \frac{\partial u}{\partial x}, & \frac{\partial u}{\partial y}, & \frac{\partial u}{\partial z}, & \dots \\ \frac{\partial v}{\partial x}, & \frac{\partial v}{\partial y}, & \frac{\partial v}{\partial z}, & \dots \\ \frac{\partial w}{\partial x}, & \frac{\partial w}{\partial y}, & \frac{\partial w}{\partial z}, & \dots \\ . & . & . & . \end{vmatrix}$$

$$= \begin{vmatrix} l\frac{\partial u}{\partial x} + l'\frac{\partial u}{\partial y} + l''\frac{\partial u}{\partial z} + \dots, & m\frac{\partial u}{\partial x} + m'\frac{\partial u}{\partial y} + m''\frac{\partial u}{\partial z} + \dots, & \dots \\ l\frac{\partial v}{\partial x} + l'\frac{\partial v}{\partial y} + l''\frac{\partial v}{\partial z} + \dots, & m\frac{\partial v}{\partial x} + m'\frac{\partial v}{\partial y} + m''\frac{\partial v}{\partial z} + \dots, & \dots \\ . & . & . \\ . & . & . \end{vmatrix}$$

$$= \begin{vmatrix} \frac{\partial u}{\partial X}, & \frac{\partial u}{\partial Y}, & \frac{\partial u}{\partial Z}, & \dots \\ \frac{\partial v}{\partial X}, & \frac{\partial v}{\partial Y}, & \frac{\partial v}{\partial Z}, & \dots \\ \frac{\partial w}{\partial X}, & \frac{\partial w}{\partial Y}, & \frac{\partial w}{\partial Z}, & \dots \\ . & . & . & . \end{vmatrix}.$$

And this, transposing the right and left-hand sides, is

$$\frac{\partial (u, v, w, \ldots)}{\partial (X, Y, Z, \ldots)} = M \frac{\partial (u, v, w, \ldots)}{\partial (x, y, z, \ldots)},$$

where on the right $u, v, w, \ldots$ are expressed in terms of $x, y, z, \ldots$ i.e. in their original forms, and on the left in terms of $X, Y, Z, \ldots$, i.e. in their transformed forms. Thus the Jacobian of $u, v, w, \ldots$ is a covariant.

Covariants, as stated already, include invariants as a particular case. When the Jacobian does not involve the variables it is an invariant. This is the case when $u, v, w, \ldots$ are all of the first order in $x, y, z, \ldots$. Thus the present result includes that of the preceding article.

Ex. 9. Obtain from this result examples 2, 6 and 7 of § 7.

Ex. 10. Obtain a linear covariant of the ternary quadratic and two linear forms

$$ax^2 + by^2 + cz^2 + 2fyz + 2gzx + 2hxy,$$
$$a'x + b'y + c'z,$$
$$a''x + b''y + c''z;$$

and interpret it geometrically, by taking for X and Y the two linear forms, or otherwise.

Ans. $(b'c'' - b''c')(ax + hy + gz) + (c'a'' - c''a')(hx + by + fz)$
$+ (a'b'' - a''b')(gx + fy + cz).$

The polar of the intersection of two straight lines with regard to a conic.

Ex. 11. Two ternary quadratics and a linear form have a quadratic covariant.

Ex. 12. Obtain and interpret geometrically a linear covariant of the quaternary quadratic and three linear forms

$$ax^2 + by^2 + cz^2 + dw^2 + 2fyz + 2gzx + 2hxy + 2pxw + 2qyw + 2rzw,$$
$$a'x + b'y + c'z + d'w,$$
$$a''x + b''y + c''z + d''w,$$
$$a'''x + b'''y + c'''z + d'''w.$$

11. **Hessians are covariants.** To prove that the *Hessian*

$$\begin{vmatrix} \frac{\partial^2 u}{\partial x^2}, & \frac{\partial^2 u}{\partial x \partial y}, & \frac{\partial^2 u}{\partial x \partial z}, & \ldots \\ \frac{\partial^2 u}{\partial x \partial y}, & \frac{\partial^2 u}{\partial y^2}, & \frac{\partial^2 u}{\partial y \partial z}, & \ldots \\ \frac{\partial^2 u}{\partial x \partial z}, & \frac{\partial^2 u}{\partial y \partial z}, & \frac{\partial^2 u}{\partial z^2}, & \ldots \\ \cdot & \cdot & \cdot & \cdot \end{vmatrix}$$

of a quantic u in the variables $x, y, z, \ldots$ is a covariant of u.

A natural but erroneous form of argument must first be guarded against. The Hessian of u is the Jacobian of $\partial u/\partial x$, $\partial u/\partial y$, $\partial u/\partial z$, ... Hence by the last article it is a covariant of the system of quantics $\partial u/\partial x$, $\partial u/\partial y$, $\partial u/\partial z$, ... It would be unjustifiable hence to conclude that it is a covariant of u, for when u is transformed by a linear substitution $\partial u/\partial x$, $\partial u/\partial y$, $\partial u/\partial z$, ... are not transformed into $\partial u/\partial X$, $\partial u/\partial Y$, $\partial u/\partial Z$, ...

A correct method of proving the theorem is the following. Multiply the Hessian written above by the modulus

$$\begin{vmatrix} l, & m, & n, & \dots \\ l', & m', & n', & \dots \\ l'', & m'', & n'', & \dots \\ \cdot & \cdot & \cdot & \cdot \end{vmatrix}, \text{ or } M,$$

of the transforming linear substitution. Using the facts, employed in § 10, that, when the operations are on any function of $x, y, z, \dots$ upon the right, and on its equivalent in terms of $X, Y, Z, \dots$ upon the left,

$$\frac{\partial}{\partial X} = l\frac{\partial}{\partial x} + l'\frac{\partial}{\partial y} + l''\frac{\partial}{\partial z} + \dots,$$

$$\frac{\partial}{\partial Y} = m\frac{\partial}{\partial x} + m'\frac{\partial}{\partial y} + m''\frac{\partial}{\partial z} + \dots,$$

&c., &c.

we see at once that the product may be written

$$\begin{vmatrix} \frac{\partial}{\partial X}\cdot\frac{\partial u}{\partial x}, & \frac{\partial}{\partial Y}\cdot\frac{\partial u}{\partial x}, & \frac{\partial}{\partial Z}\cdot\frac{\partial u}{\partial x}, & \dots \\ \frac{\partial}{\partial X}\cdot\frac{\partial u}{\partial y}, & \frac{\partial}{\partial Y}\cdot\frac{\partial u}{\partial y}, & \frac{\partial}{\partial Z}\cdot\frac{\partial u}{\partial y}, & \dots \\ \frac{\partial}{\partial X}\cdot\frac{\partial u}{\partial z}, & \frac{\partial}{\partial Y}\cdot\frac{\partial u}{\partial z}, & \frac{\partial}{\partial Z}\cdot\frac{\partial u}{\partial z}, & \dots \\ \cdot & \cdot & \cdot & \cdot \end{vmatrix},$$

or, since the order of differentiations in such an operator as

$$\frac{\partial}{\partial X}\cdot\frac{\partial}{\partial x} \equiv \left(l\frac{\partial}{\partial x} + l'\frac{\partial}{\partial y} + l''\frac{\partial}{\partial z} + \dots\right)\frac{\partial}{\partial x}$$

may be interchanged, that it may be written

$$\begin{vmatrix} \frac{\partial}{\partial x}\cdot\frac{\partial u}{\partial X}, & \frac{\partial}{\partial x}\cdot\frac{\partial u}{\partial Y}, & \frac{\partial}{\partial x}\cdot\frac{\partial u}{\partial Z}, & \ldots \\ \frac{\partial}{\partial y}\cdot\frac{\partial u}{\partial X}, & \frac{\partial}{\partial y}\cdot\frac{\partial u}{\partial Y}, & \frac{\partial}{\partial y}\cdot\frac{\partial u}{\partial Z}, & \ldots \\ \frac{\partial}{\partial z}\cdot\frac{\partial u}{\partial X}, & \frac{\partial}{\partial z}\cdot\frac{\partial u}{\partial Y}, & \frac{\partial}{\partial z}\cdot\frac{\partial u}{\partial Z}, & \ldots \\ \cdot & \cdot & \cdot & \cdot \end{vmatrix}.$$

Now multiply again by M, taking this time columns with columns in forming the product. The same equivalences of operators as before tell us that the result is

$$\begin{vmatrix} \frac{\partial^2 u}{\partial X^2}, & \frac{\partial^2 u}{\partial X\,\partial Y}, & \frac{\partial^2 u}{\partial X\,\partial Z}, & \ldots \\ \frac{\partial^2 u}{\partial X\,\partial Y}, & \frac{\partial^2 u}{\partial Y^2}, & \frac{\partial^2 u}{\partial Y\,\partial Z}, & \ldots \\ \frac{\partial^2 u}{\partial X\,\partial Z}, & \frac{\partial^2 u}{\partial Y\,\partial Z}, & \frac{\partial^2 u}{\partial Z^2}, & \ldots \\ \cdot & \cdot & \cdot & \cdot \end{vmatrix}.$$

Thus upon multiplying the Hessian of the untransformed quantic by M^2, the square of the modulus, we have obtained the Hessian of the transformed. The Hessian is then a covariant.

When the quantic u is binary only the Hessian is

$$\frac{\partial^2 u}{\partial x^2}\frac{\partial^2 u}{\partial y^2} - \left(\frac{\partial^2 u}{\partial x\,\partial y}\right)^2.$$

Ex. 13. Apply this result to prove Ex. 8 of § 7.

Ex. 14. If the covariant $(ac-b^2)x^2+(ad-bc)xy+(bd-c^2)y^2$ of the binary cubic $ax^3+3bx^2y+3cxy^2+dy^3$ is broken up into factors $(px+qy)(p'x+q'y)$, and if these factors are taken for X and Y, so that the formulae of linear transformation are

$$x = \frac{q'X-qY}{pq'-p'q}, \quad y = \frac{-p'X+pY}{pq'-p'q},$$

show that the cubic takes the form AX^3+DY^3.

Ex. 15. Hence solve the cubic $ax^3+3bx^2+3cx+d=0$. (Cf. § 200.)

Ex. 16. Find a covariant of degree 2 in the coefficients and order 4 in the variables of the binary quartic $(a, b, c, d, e)(x, y)^4$.

Ans. $(ax^2+2bxy+cy^2)(cx^2+2dxy+ey^2)-(bx^2+2cxy+dy^2)^2$.

Ex. 17. Find a covariant of degree 2 and order 6 of the binary quintic $(a, b, c, d, e, f)(x, y)^5$.

Ex. 18. The Hessian of a binary quartic which has a cubed factor is the fourth power of that factor, multiplied by a function of the coefficients. (*Cayley.*)

Ans. Take the cubed factor for X^3.

12. **Discriminants of Quadratics.** The Hessian of a quantic, proved above to be in general a covariant, is in particular an invariant when it is free from the variables. This is the case when the quantic is a quadratic in any number of variables. We have accordingly the proof of a first generalization of § 7, Ex. 1, namely that the discriminant of any quadratic is an invariant of that quadratic. For the Hessians of the binary, ternary, and quaternary quadratics

$$ax^2 + 2bxy + cy^2,$$

$$ax^2 + by^2 + cz^2 + 2fyz + 2gzx + 2hxy,$$

$$ax^2 + by^2 + cz^2 + dw^2 + 2fyz + 2gzx + 2hxy + 2pxw + 2qyw + 2rzw,$$

are, after rejection of the numerical factors 2^2, 2^3, 2^4,

$$\begin{vmatrix} a, & b \\ b, & c \end{vmatrix}, \quad \begin{vmatrix} a, & h, & g \\ h, & b, & f \\ g, & f, & c \end{vmatrix}, \quad \begin{vmatrix} a, & h, & g, & p \\ h, & b, & f, & q \\ g, & f, & c, & r \\ p, & q, & r, & d \end{vmatrix},$$

and, quite generally, that of the q-ary quadratic

$$\sum_{n=1}^{n=q} a_{nn} x_n^2 + 2 \sum_{m=1}^{m=q-1} \sum_{n=m+1}^{n=q} a_{mn} x_m x_n,$$

is, after rejection of the numerical factor 2^q,

$$\begin{vmatrix} a_{11}, & a_{12}, & a_{13}, & \dots & a_{1q} \\ a_{12}, & a_{22}, & a_{23}, & \dots & a_{2q} \\ a_{13}, & a_{23}, & a_{33}, & \dots & a_{3q} \\ \cdot & \cdot & \cdot & \cdot & \cdot \\ a_{1q}, & a_{2q}, & a_{3q}, & \dots & a_{qq} \end{vmatrix}.$$

Now these are the eliminants of the first partial differential coefficients, each divided by 2, of the various quadratics; i.e. they are the discriminants of the quadratics.

13. Eliminants are invariants. Let the q quantics $u, v, w,\ldots$ in q variables $x, y, z,\ldots$ become $U, V, W,\ldots$ when $x, y, z, \ldots$ are replaced according to the linear scheme

$$\begin{aligned} x &= l\ X + m\ Y + n\ Z + \ldots, \\ y &= l'\ X + m'\ Y + n'\ Z + \ldots, \\ z &= l''X + m''Y + n''Z + \ldots, \\ &\ldots\ldots\ldots\ldots \end{aligned}$$

Let $R(a, b, a',\ldots)$ denote the eliminant or resultant of $u, v, w,\ldots$, and $R(A, B, A',\ldots)$ that of $U, V, W, \ldots$, a and A, b and B, a' and A',... being corresponding coefficients in untransformed and transformed quantics. It is to be proved that $R(a, b, a', \ldots)$ is an invariant of $u, v, w, \ldots$.

We will first show that if $R(A, B, A',\ldots) = 0$, then either $R(a, b, a',\ldots) = 0$ or $M = 0$, and conversely that, if either $R(a, b, a',\ldots) = 0$ or $M = 0$, then $R(A, B, A',\ldots) = 0$.

If $R(A, B, A',\ldots) = 0$, there must be some set of values of $X, Y, Z,\ldots$, not all zero, which make $U = 0$, $V = 0$, $W = 0,\ldots$ simultaneously. The equations of transformation just written give us a corresponding set of values of $x, y, z,\ldots$, which make $u = 0$, $v = 0$, $w = 0,\ldots$ simultaneously. If these values of $x, y, z,\ldots$ are not all zero, it must follow that $R(a, b, a',\ldots) = 0$. On the other hand if all are zero, we must have

$$\begin{vmatrix} l\ , & m\ , & n\ , & \ldots \\ l'\ , & m'\ , & n'\ , & \ldots \\ l'', & m'', & n'', & \ldots \\ \cdot & \cdot & \cdot & \cdot \end{vmatrix} = 0,$$

i.e. $M = 0$.

Again, if $R(a, b, a',\ldots) = 0$, there are values of $x, y, z,\ldots$, not all zero, which make $u = 0$, $v = 0$, $w = 0,\ldots$ simultaneously, and, unless $M = 0$, the equations of transformation determine from these a set of values of $X, Y, Z,\ldots$, not all zero, which make $U = 0$, $V = 0$, $W = 0,\ldots$; so that $R(A, B, A',\ldots) = 0$.

Lastly, if $M = 0$, whether $R(a, b, a',\ldots)$ be zero or not, give to $x, y, z,\ldots$ in the equations of transformation the values $0, 0, 0,\ldots$, which of course make $u = 0$, $v = 0$, $w = 0,\ldots$. Because $M = 0$ the equations are satisfied by values of $X, Y, Z,\ldots$, not all zero; and these make $U = 0$, $V = 0$, $W = 0,\ldots$, so that $R(A, B, A',\ldots) = 0$.

Thus the condition $R(A, B, A',\ldots) = 0$ expresses exactly the same special state of things as do the alternative conditions $M = 0$, $R(a, b, a',\ldots) = 0$.

Hence, assuming, as we shall prove in the next article, that the algebraic function M is not resoluble into simpler algebraic factors, but not assuming the unproved fact that $R(a, b, a',\ldots)$ is not so resoluble,

$$R(A, B, A',\ldots) = \text{power of } M \times F(a, b, a',\ldots),$$

where $F(a, b, a',\ldots)$, if not $R(a, b, a',\ldots)$ or a power of it, is at any rate a product of powers of all the factors of $R(a, b, a',\ldots)$, supposing for safety that it may have simpler factors.

This result is proved for all linear substitutions. It holds then for every particular linear substitution. Now take $l, m', n'',\ldots$ all units and the other coefficients in the scheme all zeros, so that the scheme becomes simply $x = X$, $y = Y$, $z = Z,\ldots$, and $M = 1$, while $A, B, A',\ldots$ are merely $a, b, a',\ldots$: then our general result gives

$$R(a, b, a',\ldots) = F(a, b, a',\ldots),$$

so that $F(a, b, a',\ldots)$ is really the eliminant of $u, v, w,\ldots$ itself.

Consequently the general result is

$$R(A, B, A',\ldots) = \text{power of } M \times R(a, b, a',\ldots),$$

which proves that the eliminant $R(a, b, a',\ldots)$ is an invariant.

We now give the proof that M is irresoluble.

14. The modulus irresoluble into factors. Let us use a double suffix notation, and suppose, if possible, that

$$M \equiv \begin{vmatrix} l_{11}, & l_{12}, & l_{13}, & \ldots \\ l_{21}, & l_{22}, & l_{23}, & \ldots \\ l_{31}, & l_{32}, & l_{33}, & \ldots \\ . & . & . & . \end{vmatrix}$$

can be written as a product of two rational factors $\theta\phi$.

The determinant is of the first degree in every constituent. Thus l_{11} cannot occur in both factors θ, ϕ. Suppose that it occurs in θ.

In the expansion of the determinant no term occurs in which l_{11} is multiplied by any constituent belonging to its row or its column. Thus ϕ can involve no constituent belonging to the first row or the first column. Let l_{rs} be a constituent which does occur in ϕ. By similar reasoning no constituent belonging to the rth row or sth column can occur in θ.

Thus two constituents, l_{r1} and l_{1s}, cannot occur either in θ or in ϕ. But the expansion of the determinant involves every constituent. Our supposition that M can be written as a product of factors $\theta\phi$ is therefore untenable.

15. **All discriminants are invariants.** Of this proposition, already proved for quadratics, a general demonstration will now be given.

If u be a quantic in q variables $x, y, z, \ldots$ we have to prove that its discriminant, i.e. the eliminant of its q first partial derivatives $\partial u/\partial x$, $\partial u/\partial y$, $\partial u/\partial z, \ldots$, is an invariant of u.

The scheme of linear substitution being the usual one, we have, as in § 10,

$$\frac{\partial u}{\partial X} = l\frac{\partial u}{\partial x} + l'\frac{\partial u}{\partial y} + l''\frac{\partial u}{\partial z} + \ldots,$$

$$\frac{\partial u}{\partial Y} = m\frac{\partial u}{\partial x} + m'\frac{\partial u}{\partial y} + m''\frac{\partial u}{\partial z} + \ldots,$$

$$\frac{\partial u}{\partial Z} = n\frac{\partial u}{\partial x} + n'\frac{\partial u}{\partial y} + n''\frac{\partial u}{\partial z} + \ldots,$$

$$\cdot \quad \cdot \quad \cdot \quad \cdot \quad \cdot \quad \cdot \quad \cdot \quad \cdot \quad \cdot \quad \cdot \quad \cdot \quad \cdot \quad \cdot$$

Now, in accordance with the definition, the discriminant $\Delta(A, B, \ldots)$ of the transformed form of u will vanish if and only if $\partial u/\partial X$, $\partial u/\partial Y$, $\partial u/\partial Z, \ldots$ are made simultaneously to vanish by some set of values, not all zero, of $X, Y, Z, \ldots$. But the above equivalences tell us that this will be the case if and only if either (1) $\partial u/\partial x$, $\partial u/\partial y$, $\partial u/\partial z, \ldots$ can be made simultaneously to vanish by values of $x, y, z, \ldots$ not all zero, i.e. if the discriminant $\Delta(a, b, \ldots)$ of the untransformed u vanishes, or (2) if the determinant of the coefficients on the right, i.e. M the modulus of the substitution, vanishes.

It follows therefore, since M is irresoluble, that

$$\Delta(A, B, \ldots) = \text{power of } M \times \Delta'(a, b, \ldots),$$

where $\Delta'(a, b, \ldots)$, if not $\Delta(a, b, \ldots)$ itself or a power of it, is at any rate the product of powers of the factors into which we might allow the possibility of $\Delta(a, b, \ldots)$ breaking up.

Apply however the general result to the case of the particular substitution $x = X$, $y = Y$, $z = Z, \ldots$, for which $M = 1$ and $A = a$, $B = b$, &c. It becomes

$$\Delta(a, b, \ldots) = \Delta'(a, b, \ldots).$$

Thus our general conclusion is that

$$\Delta(A, B, \ldots) = \text{power of } M \times \Delta(a, b, \ldots).$$

Consequently the discriminant $\Delta(a, b, \ldots)$ is an invariant.

16. **Determinant expressions for powers of $lm' - l'm$.** For purposes of direct proofs that large classes of functions in determinant form are invariants and covariants of *binary* quantics, a simple theorem, due to Faà de Bruno, as to a

certain class of determinants, is of great utility. The first three cases of the theorem are

$$\begin{vmatrix} l, & m \\ l', & m' \end{vmatrix} = lm' - l'm,$$

$$\begin{vmatrix} l^2, & lm, & m^2 \\ 2ll', & lm' + l'm, & 2mm' \\ l'^2, & l'm', & m'^2 \end{vmatrix} = (lm' - l'm)^3,$$

$$\begin{vmatrix} l^3, & l^2m, & lm^2, & m^3 \\ 3l^2l', & 2ll'm + l^2m', & 2lmm' + l'm^2, & 3m^2m' \\ 3ll'^2, & l'^2m + 2ll'm', & lm'^2 + 2l'mm', & 3mm'^2 \\ l'^3, & l'^2m', & l'm'^2, & m'^3 \end{vmatrix} = (lm' - l'm)^6;$$

and the general theorem is that the determinant whose first row consists of the constituents

$$l^r,\ l^{r-1}m,\ l^{r-2}m^2, \dots lm^{r-1},\ m^r,$$

and whose other rows are obtained in succession by operating on the constituents of this first row with

$$l'\frac{\partial}{\partial l} + m'\frac{\partial}{\partial m},\quad \frac{1}{1\,.\,2}\left(l'\frac{\partial}{\partial l} + m'\frac{\partial}{\partial m}\right)^2,\ \dots\ \frac{1}{r!}\left(l'\frac{\partial}{\partial l} + m'\frac{\partial}{\partial m}\right)^r,$$

is a power, namely the $\frac{1}{2}r(r+1)$th power, of $lm' - l'm$.

It will be readily seen that we might equally write down first the last row

$$l'^r,\ l'^{r-1}m',\ l'^{r-2}m'^2, \dots l'm'^{r-1},\ m'^r,$$

and obtain the other rows in succession upwards by operations on it with

$$l\frac{\partial}{\partial l'} + m\frac{\partial}{\partial m'},\quad \frac{1}{1\,.\,2}\left(l\frac{l}{\partial l'} + m\frac{\partial}{\partial m'}\right)^2, \dots \frac{1}{r!}\left(l\frac{\partial}{\partial l'} + m\frac{\partial}{\partial m'}\right)^r.$$

For the constituents in the $(s+1)$th column, read downwards, are the coefficients of the various powers of t in the expansion of

$$(l + tl')^{r-s}(m + tm')^s$$

by Taylor's theorem; and the same, read upwards, are the coefficients of powers of τ in the expansion of

$$(\tau l + l')^{r-s}(\tau m + m')^s.$$

We speak below of the two modes of forming the determinant as the first and second ways of writing it down.

The first case of the theorem is immediate. The second is at once proved by adding to the first row $-m/m'$ times the second and m^2/m'^2 times the third: and the third case is easily proved in a similar manner. The general theorem is an easy exercise on the theory of Lagrange's solution of linear partial differential equations, as we proceed to show.

By the ordinary rule for differentiation of products we know that the result of differentiating a determinant of the rth order can be written as a sum of r determinants, each obtained by differentiating the constituents of one row, leaving the constituents of all the other rows unaltered. Now operate on the given determinant, thinking of it as written down in its first way, with $l'\frac{\partial}{\partial l}+m'\frac{\partial}{\partial m}$. The result is a sum of r determinants all of which vanish. For the result of operating on any row except the last is to produce a numerical multiple of the following row, and the result of operating on the last row is to produce a row of zeros. If then D denotes the determinant, we have

$$l'\frac{\partial D}{\partial l}+m'\frac{\partial D}{\partial m}=0.$$

Hence by Lagrange's theory D involves l and m only in the connexion $lm'-l'm$.

Again, think of D as written down in its second way, and operate on it with $l\frac{\partial}{\partial l'}+m\frac{\partial}{\partial m'}$. We obtain in like manner

$$l\frac{\partial D}{\partial l'}+m\frac{\partial D}{\partial m'}=0,$$

so that D involves l' and m' only in the connexion $lm'-l'm$.

Thus D is a function of $lm'-l'm$ only; and, being homogeneous, must consist of a single power of $lm'-l'm$, with a possible numerical factor. But this numerical factor is unity, as we see for instance by taking $l=m'=1$, $l'=m=0$, for which $lm'-l'm$ is unity and D consists of a principal diagonal of units with all other constituents zero.

That the power of $lm'-l'm$ is the $\frac{1}{2}r(r+1)$th follows from the fact that D is of dimensions $r(r+1)$ in l, m, l', m'.

17. As a typical application of this theorem let us prove that

$$\begin{vmatrix} \frac{\partial^4 u}{\partial x^4}, & \frac{\partial^4 u}{\partial x^3\partial y}, & \frac{\partial^4 u}{\partial x^2\partial y^2} \\ \frac{\partial^4 u}{\partial x^3\partial y}, & \frac{\partial^4 u}{\partial x^2\partial y^2}, & \frac{\partial^4 u}{\partial x\partial y^3} \\ \frac{\partial^4 u}{\partial x^2\partial y^2}, & \frac{\partial^4 u}{\partial x\partial y^3}, & \frac{\partial^4 u}{\partial y^4} \end{vmatrix}$$

is a covariant of a binary quantic u, or in particular an invariant if u is a quartic.

We will multiply twice, taking columns with columns, by the determinant expression above for $(lm'-l'm)^3$, i.e. M^3.

The first multiplication produces, since

$$\left(l\frac{\partial}{\partial x}+l'\frac{\partial}{\partial y}\right)^2=\frac{\partial^2}{\partial X^2},\ \left(l\frac{\partial}{\partial x}+l'\frac{\partial}{\partial y}\right)\left(m\frac{\partial}{\partial x}+m'\frac{\partial}{\partial y}\right)=\frac{\partial^2}{\partial X\,\partial Y},$$

$$\left(m\frac{\partial}{\partial x}+m'\frac{\partial}{\partial y}\right)^2=\frac{\partial^2}{\partial Y^2}\cdot$$

$$\begin{vmatrix} \frac{\partial^2}{\partial X^2}\cdot\frac{\partial^2 u}{\partial x^2}, & \frac{\partial^2}{\partial X\,\partial Y}\cdot\frac{\partial^2 u}{\partial x^2}, & \frac{\partial^2}{\partial Y^2}\cdot\frac{\partial^2 u}{\partial x^2} \\ \frac{\partial^2}{\partial X^2}\cdot\frac{\partial^2 u}{\partial x\,\partial y}, & \frac{\partial^2}{\partial X\,\partial Y}\cdot\frac{\partial^2 u}{\partial x\,\partial y}, & \frac{\partial^2}{\partial Y^2}\cdot\frac{\partial^2 u}{\partial x\,\partial y} \\ \frac{\partial^2}{\partial X^2}\cdot\frac{\partial^2 u}{\partial y^2}, & \frac{\partial^2}{\partial X\,\partial Y}\cdot\frac{\partial^2 u}{\partial y^2}, & \frac{\partial^2}{\partial Y^2}\cdot\frac{\partial^2 u}{\partial y^2} \end{vmatrix},$$

and the second multiplication of this, with the order of differentiation in each constituent changed, produces

$$\begin{vmatrix} \frac{\partial^4 u}{\partial X^4}, & \frac{\partial^4 u}{\partial X^3\partial Y}, & \frac{\partial^4 u}{\partial X^2\partial Y^2} \\ \frac{\partial^4 u}{\partial X^3\partial Y}, & \frac{\partial^4 u}{\partial X^2\partial Y^2}, & \frac{\partial^4 u}{\partial X\,\partial Y^3} \\ \frac{\partial^4 u}{\partial X^2\partial Y^2}, & \frac{\partial^4 u}{\partial X\,\partial Y^3}, & \frac{\partial^4 u}{\partial Y^4} \end{vmatrix}.$$

Thus the fact stated is proved.

Ex. 19. Prove that
$$\begin{vmatrix} a, & b, & c \\ b, & c, & d \\ c, & d, & e \end{vmatrix},$$
i.e. $ace+2bcd-ad^2-b^2e-c^3$,

is an invariant of the binary quartic $(a, b, c, d, e)\,(x, y)^4$.

Ans. Factor M^6. This important invariant, usually denoted by J, is called the *Catalecticant* of the quartic.

Ex. 20. Obtain a covariant of the third order and degree of the binary quintic $(a, b, c, d, e, f)\,(x, y)^5$.

Ans. Its so-called *canonizant*

$$\begin{vmatrix} ax+by, & bx+cy, & cx+dy \\ bx+cy, & cx+dy, & dx+ey \\ cx+dy, & dx+ey, & ex+fy \end{vmatrix}.$$

Ex. 21. If u_{rs} denote $\dfrac{\partial^{r+s}u}{\partial x^r\,\partial y^s}$, prove that

$$\begin{vmatrix} u_{60}, & u_{51}, & u_{42}, & u_{33} \\ u_{51}, & u_{42}, & u_{33}, & u_{24} \\ u_{42}, & u_{33}, & u_{24}, & u_{15} \\ u_{33}, & u_{24}, & u_{15}, & u_{06} \end{vmatrix}$$

is a covariant of a binary quantic u of order greater than 6.

Ans. Factor M^{12}.

Ex. 22. Prove that the *catalecticant*

$$\begin{vmatrix} a, & b, & c, & d \\ b, & c, & d, & e \\ c, & d, & e, & f \\ d, & e, & f, & g \end{vmatrix}$$

is an invariant of the binary sextic $(a, b, c, d, e, f, g)\,(x, y)^6$.

Ex. 23. Every binary quantic of even order $2n$ has an invariant, its *catalecticant*, of degree $n+1$.

Ans. Factor $M^{n(n+1)}$.

Ex. 24. Prove that
$$\begin{vmatrix} \dfrac{\partial^2 u}{\partial x^2}, & \dfrac{\partial^2 u}{\partial x\,\partial y}, & \dfrac{\partial^2 u}{\partial y^2} \\ \dfrac{\partial^2 v}{\partial x^2}, & \dfrac{\partial^2 v}{\partial x\,\partial y}, & \dfrac{\partial^2 v}{\partial y^2} \\ \dfrac{\partial^2 w}{\partial x^2}, & \dfrac{\partial^2 w}{\partial x\,\partial y}, & \dfrac{\partial^2 w}{\partial y^2} \end{vmatrix}$$

is a covariant of three binary quantics u, v, w.

Ans. Factor M^3.

Ex. 25. Obtain and geometrically interpret the invariant

$$\begin{vmatrix} a, & b, & c \\ a', & b', & c' \\ a'', & b'', & c'' \end{vmatrix}$$

of three binary quadratics

$$(a, b, c)\,(x, y)^2,\ (a', b', c')\,(x, y)^2,\ (a'', b'', c'')\,(x, y)^2.$$

Ans. Criterion of an involution.

Ex. 26. Prove that
$$\begin{vmatrix} \dfrac{\partial^2 u}{\partial x^2}, & \dfrac{\partial^2 u}{\partial x\,\partial y}, & \dfrac{\partial^2 u}{\partial y^2} \\ \dfrac{\partial^2 v}{\partial x^2}, & \dfrac{\partial^2 v}{\partial x\,\partial y}, & \dfrac{\partial^2 v}{\partial y^2} \\ y^2, & -xy, & x^2 \end{vmatrix}$$

is a covariant of two binary quantics u, v.

Ans. Factor $M^3/M^2 = M$.

Ex. 27. Deduce Ex. 7 of § 7.

Ex. 28. Prove that

$$\begin{vmatrix} \dfrac{\partial^3 u}{\partial x^3}, & \dfrac{\partial^3 u}{\partial x^2 \partial y}, & \dfrac{\partial^3 u}{\partial x \partial y^2} \\ \dfrac{\partial^3 u}{\partial x^2 \partial y}, & \dfrac{\partial^3 u}{\partial x \partial y^2}, & \dfrac{\partial^3 u}{\partial y^3} \\ y^2, & -xy, & x^2 \end{vmatrix}$$

is a covariant of a binary quantic u.

Ans. Factor M^2. Multiply first by the determinant expression for M^3, and then by M in the form

$$\begin{vmatrix} l, & m, & 0 \\ l', & m', & 0 \\ 0, & 0, & 1 \end{vmatrix}.$$

Ex. 29. Prove that

$$\begin{vmatrix} u_{50}, & u_{41}, & u_{32}, & u_{23} \\ u_{41}, & u_{32}, & u_{23}, & u_{14} \\ u_{32}, & u_{23}, & u_{14}, & u_{05} \\ y^3, & -xy^2, & x^2y, & -x^3 \end{vmatrix}$$

is a covariant of a binary quantic u.

Ans. Factor M^6. Multiply first by the determinant expression for M^6, and then by that for M^3.

Ex. 30. Prove that
$$\begin{vmatrix} a, & b, & c, & d \\ b, & c, & d, & e \\ c, & d, & e, & f \\ y^3, & -xy^2, & x^2y, & -x^3 \end{vmatrix}$$
is a covariant of the binary quintic $(a, b, c, d, e, f)(x, y)^5$.

Ex. 31. Prove that this covariant of the quintic is, but for sign, the same as the canonizant (Ex. 20).

Ans. Show that the form of Ex. 30 multiplied by

$$\begin{vmatrix} 1, & 0, & 0, & 0 \\ x, & y, & 0, & 0 \\ 0, & x, & y, & 0 \\ 0, & 0, & x, & y \end{vmatrix}$$

is the form of Ex. 20 multiplied by $-y^3$.

18. **Intermediate invariants and covariants.** From a given invariant or covariant of a quantic can always be derived a series of invariants or covariants, as the case may be, of two or more quantics of the same order in the same variables. The

method may be illustrated by the deduction of the result of Ex. 4 (§ 7) from that of Ex. 1.

By the substitution $x = lX + mY$, $y = l'X + m'Y$ let $ax^2 + 2bxy + cy^2$ and $a'x^2 + 2b'xy + c'y^2$ be transformed into $AX^2 + 2BXY + CY^2$ and $A'X^2 + 2B'XY + C'Y^2$ respectively. Then, whatever constant k be,

$$(a + ka')\,x^2 + 2\,(b + kb')\,xy + (c + kc')\,y^2$$

is transformed into $(A + kA')X^2 + 2\,(B + kB')\,XY + (C + kC')\,Y^2$.

Consequently, by Ex. 1,

$$(A + kA')\,(C + kC') - (B + kB')^2$$
$$= M^2\{(a + ka')\,(c + kc') - (b + kb')^2\};$$

i. e.

$$AC - B^2 + k\,(AC' + A'C - 2\,BB') + k^2\,(A'C' - B'^2)$$
$$= M^2\{ac - b^2 + k\,(ac' + a'c - 2\,bb') + k^2\,(a'c' - b'^2)\}.$$

This is true for all values of k. The multipliers of different powers of k on the two sides must then be separately equal each to each. Accordingly

$$AC - B^2 = M^2\,(ac - b^2),$$
$$AC' + A'C - 2\,BB' = M^2\,(ac' + a'c - 2\,bb'),$$
$$A'C' - B'^2 = M^2\,(a'c' - b'^2).$$

Of these three equalities the first and third are merely expressive of the fact of invariancy from which we started. The second however gives us the additional fact that

$$ac' + a'c - 2\,bb'$$

is an invariant of the quadratics

$$ax^2 + 2bxy + cy^2,\; a'x^2 + 2b'xy + c'y^2$$

jointly. It is said to be the invariant *intermediate* between $ac - b^2$ and $a'c' - b'^2$.

This result is one of great historic interest. With Boole's discovery of it in 1841 the era of systematic investigation in the algebra of invariants began. In his original memoir (*Cambridge Math. Journal*, Vol. III) he showed how to find from any discriminant the intermediate invariants between the discriminants of two quantics of the same kind and order.

For another well-known example of the method reference may be made to the investigation (Salmon's *Conic Sections*, 6th. ed. § 370) of the intermediate invariants Θ, Θ' between the discriminants Δ, Δ' of two conics (ternary quadratics).

19. The method is clearly one of perfectly general application when we are given any invariant or covariant whatever of any quantic whatever. Let P be any invariant or any covariant of a q-ary p-ic in which the coefficients are $a, b, c, \ldots$ and the variables $x, y, z, \ldots$. Consider also another q-ary p-ic,

in the same variables, whose coefficients in the same order are $a', b', c', \ldots$. Put for $a, b, c, \ldots$, in P, $a+ka'$, $b+kb'$, $c+kc', \ldots$, and expand in powers of k. The multiplier of every power of k in the result is an invariant or covariant, as the case may be, of the two q-ary p-ics, and the same function of the constants in the scheme of linear substitution is present as factor in the relation expressive of its invariancy or covariancy as in the relation which expresses the invariancy or covariancy of P. The multiplier of the highest power of k which occurs is P', the result of replacing $a, b, c, \ldots$ by $a', b', c', \ldots$ in P, and the multipliers of other powers of k are invariants, or covariants, *intermediate* between P and P'.

The general form of the invariants or covariants thus derived from P is

$$\frac{1}{r!}\left(a'\frac{\partial}{\partial a}+b'\frac{\partial}{\partial b}+c'\frac{\partial}{\partial c}+\ldots\right)^r P,$$

for this is, by Taylor's theorem, the coefficient of k^r. Or, again, it may be written

$$\frac{1}{(i-r)!}\left(a\frac{\partial}{\partial a'}+b\frac{\partial}{\partial b'}+c\frac{\partial}{\partial c'}+\ldots\right)^{i-r} P',$$

where i is the degree in the coefficients $a, b, c, \ldots$ of P. The values $1, 2, 3, \ldots i-1$ of r give the intermediates between P and P'. The values 0 and i give P and P' respectively. Greater values of r than i are unproductive, for the differential operation $a'\frac{\partial}{\partial a}+b'\frac{\partial}{\partial b}+c'\frac{\partial}{\partial c}+\ldots$ repeated more than i times annihilates P.

In like manner invariants and covariants of systems of more than two quantics of the same order in the same variables are derived from invariants and covariants P of a single quantic of that type. We have only to put in P, for a, $a+k_1a_1+k_2a_2+\ldots$, for b, $b+k_1b_1+k_2b_2+\ldots$, and similarly for $c, d, \ldots$, to expand according to powers and products of powers of $k_1, k_2, \ldots$, and to take the multipliers of these powers and products separately. We thus obtain that, for any positive integral or zero values of $r_1, r_2, r_3, \ldots$ whose sum does not exceed i,

$$\left(a_1\frac{\partial}{\partial a}+b_1\frac{\partial}{\partial b}+\ldots\right)^{r_1}\left(a_2\frac{\partial}{\partial a}+b_2\frac{\partial}{\partial b}+\ldots\right)^{r_2}\left(a_3\frac{\partial}{\partial a}+b_3\frac{\partial}{\partial b}+\ldots\right)^{r_3}\ldots P$$

is an invariant or covariant of the system of q-ary p-ics whose coefficients in the same order are $a, b, c, \ldots$; $a_1, b_1, c_1, \ldots$; $a_2, b_2, c_2, \ldots$; $a_3, b_3, c_3, \ldots$; $\ldots$, according as P is an invariant or covariant of the first q-ary p-ic. The corresponding invariants or covariants $P_1, P_2, \ldots$ of the second, third, &c. q-ary p-ics, as well as their intermediates, and the corresponding invariants or covariants of triads, &c. of q-ary p-ics chosen from among the entire system, are all included.

20. The method admits of a limited application to quantics of different orders in the same variables; namely to the case when the order of one quantic is a multiple of the order of every other quantic of the system. For instance, if two quantics u, v in the same variables are of orders $p'p$, p respectively, and if $a, b, c, \ldots$ are the coefficients in u and $\alpha, \beta, \gamma, \ldots$ the corresponding coefficients in $v^{p'}$, then the functions

$$\left(\alpha \frac{\partial}{\partial a} + \beta \frac{\partial}{\partial b} + \gamma \frac{\partial}{\partial c} + \ldots\right)^r P, \quad (o < r < i+1),$$

where P is any invariant or covariant of u, are invariants or covariants of u and $v^{p'}$, and therefore of u and v.

Ex. 32. From the invariant $ae - 4bd + 3c^2$ of the quartic

$$(a, b, c, d, e)(x, y)^4$$

obtain an invariant of that quartic and the quadratic $(a', b', c')(x, y)^2$ of the first degree in the coefficients of the quartic and of the second in those of the quadratic.

Ans. $a'^2e - 4a'b'd + 2(a'c' + 2b'^2)c - 4b'c'b + c'^2a$. Factor M^4.

Ex. 33. If P is an invariant or covariant of $(a_0, a_1, a_2, \ldots a_p)(x, y)^p$, prove that the functions

$$\left(\xi^p \frac{\partial}{\partial a_0} + \xi^{p-1}\eta \frac{\partial}{\partial a_1} + \xi^{p-2}\eta^2 \frac{\partial}{\partial a_2} + \ldots + \eta^p \frac{\partial}{\partial a_p}\right)^r P,$$

for values of r between 1 and $i-1$ inclusive, where i is the degree of P in $a_0, a_1, a_2, \ldots a_p$, are invariants of the p-ic and the linear form $\xi x + \eta y$ jointly.

The importance of *evectants*, as the functions obtained in this manner from invariants are called, will be seen hereafter.

Ex. 34. From any invariant or covariant of several quantics of the same order in the same variables the operation

$$a' \frac{\partial}{\partial a} + b' \frac{\partial}{\partial b} + c' \frac{\partial}{\partial c} + \ldots,$$

repeated till a vanishing result is obtained, produces a series of invariants or covariants, as the case may be. Here $a, b, c, \ldots$ and $a', b', c', \ldots$ are corresponding coefficients in any two of the quantics.

Ex. 35. The effect of replacing $a', b', c', \ldots$ by $a, b, c \ldots$ in an invariant or covariant of two quantics u, v of the same order in the same variables, where $a, b, c, \ldots$ and $a', b', c', \ldots$ are corresponding coefficients in u and v, is to give an invariant or covariant of u alone, or else a vanishing result.

CHAPTER II

ESSENTIAL QUALITIES OF INVARIANTS.

21. In the present chapter we shall, at the expense of some repetition hereafter, confine our attention to invariants, reserving till the next the analogous consideration of covariants.

Except where otherwise stated, rational integral invariants are alone dealt with, the words 'rational integral' being as a rule omitted.

And first we consider invariants of a single quantic only.

Let us denote constantly by u the quantic under consideration, by p its order in the variables, by q the number of those variables, by small letters $a, b, c, \ldots, x, y, \ldots$ the coefficients and variables in its original form, and by capitals $A, B, C, \ldots, X, Y, \ldots$ the corresponding coefficients and variables in the transformed form to which it is reduced by a linear substitution. Also let us, except where otherwise stated, consider the scheme of linear substitution to be perfectly general as in § 2, and denote by $l, m, \ldots l', m', \ldots$ the assemblage of the coefficients of $X, Y, \ldots$ in the expressions for $x, y, \ldots$. These coefficients we will speak of as the constants of the substitution, or of the transformation.

Taking the identical equality

$$F(A, B, \ldots) = \phi(l, m, \ldots l', m', \ldots)\, F(a, b, \ldots),$$

which expresses that $F(a, b, \ldots)$ is an invariant of u, our immediate aim will be to prove

(1) that $F(a, b, \ldots)$ is necessarily homogeneous, and

(2) that $\phi(l, m, \ldots l', m', \ldots)$ is necessarily a power of the modulus M of the transformation, defined in § 2.

A knowledge of the first fact must precede a proof of the second.

22. **An invariant necessarily homogeneous in the coefficients.** We shall speak of the dimensions of a homogeneous function of the coefficients in these coefficients as its *degree*[1].

[1] I should have preferred to use the older term *order* for this characteristic. But the practice of speaking of a function (in particular of a covariant),

If possible let the invariant $F(a, b, \ldots)$ consist of a sum of parts

$$H_1(a, b, \ldots) + H_2(a, b, \ldots) + H_3(a, b, \ldots) + \ldots$$

of different degrees $i_1, i_2, i_3, \ldots$.

Since $F(a, b, \ldots)$ is an invariant for all possible schemes of linear substitution, it is so of course for a particular scheme. Let us express the fact of invariancy for the scheme of substitution

$$x = \lambda X, y = \lambda Y, z = \lambda Z, \ldots,$$

which, it is to be observed, has only the effect of multiplying the p-ic u by λ^p and replacing $x, y, z, \ldots$ by $X, Y, Z, \ldots$. The coefficients $A, B, C, \ldots$ in the transformed p-ic have then in this case the values $\lambda^p a, \lambda^p b, \lambda^p c, \ldots$. Any homogeneous function of degree i in them is accordingly λ^{ip} times the same function of $a, b, c, \ldots$.

Thus, if $\psi(\lambda)$ is the form taken by $\phi(l, m, \ldots l', m', \ldots)$ for the particular substitution we are using, the identical equality expressive of the invariancy gives us

$$\lambda^{i_1 p} H_1(a, b, \ldots) + \lambda^{i_2 p} H_2(a, b, \ldots) + \lambda^{i_3 p} H_3(a, b, \ldots) + \ldots$$
$$= \psi(\lambda)\{H_1(a, b \ldots) + H_2(a, b, \ldots) + H_3(a, b, \ldots) + \ldots\}.$$

This is an identity, true for all values of $a, b, \ldots$. Consequently the terms of each degree in $a, b, \ldots$ on the left are the same as the corresponding terms in each case on the right. Hence we must have simultaneously

$$\lambda^{i_1 p} = \psi(\lambda), \quad \lambda^{i_2 p} = \psi(\lambda), \quad \&c., \&c.,$$

which are inconsistent if $i_1, i_2, i_3, \ldots$ are different. The supposition was therefore unsound, and the invariant $F(a, b, \ldots)$ is of the same degree i throughout.

The proof holds for irrational invariants.

23. The factor a power of the modulus. The formulae of the general linear substitution

$$\left.\begin{aligned} x &= lX + mY + nZ + \ldots, \\ y &= l'X + m'Y + n'Z + \ldots, \\ z &= l''X + m''Y + n''Z + \ldots, \\ &\cdots\cdots\cdots\cdots, \end{aligned}\right\} \quad \ldots (1)$$

may we know, by solution for $X, Y, Z, \ldots$, be reversed and written

whose dimensions are i in the coefficients and ϖ in the variables, as of *degree* i and *order* ϖ has of late become almost universal. While regretting this, I feel bound to adopt it consistently throughout.

$$\left.\begin{aligned} X &= M^{-1}\left\{\frac{\partial M}{\partial l}x + \frac{\partial M}{\partial l'}y + \frac{\partial M}{\partial l''}z + \dots\right\}, \\ Y &= M^{-1}\left\{\frac{\partial M}{\partial m}x + \frac{\partial M}{\partial m'}y + \frac{\partial M}{\partial m''}z + \dots\right\}, \\ Z &= M^{-1}\left\{\frac{\partial M}{\partial n}x + \frac{\partial M}{\partial n'}y + \frac{\partial M}{\partial n''}z + \dots\right\}, \\ &\cdots\cdots\cdots\cdots\cdots , \end{aligned}\right\} \quad \dots (2)$$

where M denotes the modulus

$$\begin{vmatrix} l, & m, & n, & \dots \\ l', & m', & n', & \dots \\ l'', & m'', & n'', & \dots \\ \cdot & \cdot & \cdot & \cdot \end{vmatrix},$$

and (cf. § 2) must not vanish.

Looking upon the formulae of substitution for $x, y, z, \dots$ in terms of $X, Y, Z, \dots$ as those of the standard substitution, we may speak of the formulae for $X, Y, Z, \dots$ in terms of $x, y, z, \dots$ as those of the reversed substitution. The reversal of the reversed substitution reproduces the standard substitution. The modulus of the reversed substitution is M^{-1}, the reciprocal of the modulus of the standard substitution, as immediately follows from the known fact (cf. Burnside and Panton's *Theory of Equations*, 4th ed. § 146) that the determinant reciprocal to a given determinant of q rows and q columns is its $(q-1)$th power.

Our present object is to prove the factor $\phi(l, m, \dots l', m', \dots)$ in the equality (§ 21) expressive of the fact of invariancy of $F(a, b, \dots)$ to be a power of M. We have seen in the last article that $F(a, b, \dots)$ is homogeneous in $a, b, \dots$, and therefore $F(A, B, \dots)$ homogeneous in $A, B, \dots$. Now $A, B, \dots$ are homogeneous and of degree p in $l, m, \dots l', m', \dots$. For our quantic u is transformed from the form

$$ax^p + pbx^{p-1}y + \dots$$

to the form

$$AX^p + pBX^{p-1}Y + \dots$$

by the scheme (1) in which $x, y, \dots$ are homogeneous and linear in $l, m, \dots l', m', \dots$, so that $x^p, x^{p-1}y, \dots$ are homogeneous and of degree p in $l, m, \dots l', m', \dots$. Thus $F(A, B, \dots)$, being homogeneous, and of degree i say, in its arguments $A, B, \dots$, which are all homogeneous and of degree p in $l, m, \dots l', m', \dots$, is itself homogeneous, and of degree ip, in $l, m, \dots l', m', \dots$. Seeing then that it is equal to

$$\phi(l, m, \dots l', m', \dots)\, F(a, b, \dots),$$

where the second factor $F(a, b, \dots)$ is free from $l, m, \dots l', m', \dots$, we conclude that $\phi(l, m, \dots l', m', \dots)$ is homogeneous and of degree ip in its arguments.

We now use the fact that the effect of the reversed substitution (2) is to bring the q-ary p-ic u back from its second form $AX^p + \dots$ to its first $ax^p + \dots$. The invariant equality

$$F(A, B, \dots) = \phi(l, m, \dots l', m', \dots)\, F(a, b, \dots), \qquad \dots (3)$$

applying as it does to all linear transformations of all q-ary p-ics, must hold when we interchange $a, b, \dots$ and $A, B, \dots$, and replace $l, m, \dots l', m', \dots$ by the corresponding coefficients in the scheme (2). Thus

$$F(a, b, \dots)$$
$$= \phi\left(M^{-1}\frac{\partial M}{\partial l},\ M^{-1}\frac{\partial M}{\partial l'},\ \dots M^{-1}\frac{\partial M}{\partial m},\ M^{-1}\frac{\partial M}{\partial m'}, \dots\right) F(A, B, \dots)$$
$$= M^{-ip}\,\phi\left(\frac{\partial M}{\partial l}, \frac{\partial M}{\partial l'}, \dots \frac{\partial M}{\partial m}, \frac{\partial M}{\partial m'}, \dots\right) F(A, B, \dots), \qquad \dots (4)$$

in virtue of the homogeneity of degree ip possessed by the function ϕ. Accordingly, by combination of (3) and (4), we arrive at the identity

$$\phi(l, m, \dots l', m', \dots)\,\phi\left(\frac{\partial M}{\partial l}, \frac{\partial M}{\partial l'}, \dots \frac{\partial M}{\partial m}, \frac{\partial M}{\partial m'}, \dots\right) = M^{ip} \dots (5)$$

Thus M^{ip} breaks up into two rational integral factors, of which $\phi(l, m, \dots l', m', \dots)$ is one. But (§ 14) M has no factors but unity and itself. Consequently $\phi(l, m, \dots l', m', \dots)$ is a power of M, or a numerical multiple of such a power.

Suppose then that

$$\phi(l, m, \dots l', m', \dots) = kM^r.$$

By (5) it follows that

$$\phi\left(\frac{\partial M}{\partial l}, \frac{\partial M}{\partial l'}, \dots \frac{\partial M}{\partial m}, \frac{\partial M}{\partial m'}, \dots\right) = \frac{1}{k} M^{ip-r}.$$

But $\partial M/\partial l, \partial M/\partial l', \dots \partial M/\partial m, \partial M/\partial m', \dots$ are all of $q-1$ dimensions in $l, m, \dots l', m', \dots$, so that the dimensions in $l, m, \dots l', m', \dots$ of the second ϕ are $q-1$ times those of the first. Hence

$$ip - r = (q-1)\,r, \quad \text{i.e.} \quad r = ip/q.$$

Accordingly the equality expressive of the fact that $F(a, b, \dots)$ is an invariant is of the form

$$F(A, B, \dots) = kM^{ip/q}\,F(a, b, \dots),$$

where k is a numerical constant. That this constant is necessarily unity we see at once by application to the case of the substitution

$$x = X,\ y = Y,\ z = Z, \dots,$$

for which $A, B, \dots$ are the same as $a, b, \dots$, and $M = 1$.

We have proved, then, completely that if $F(a, b, \ldots)$ is an invariant of a q-ary p-ic it is necessarily homogeneous, and that, if its degree is i, the identity expressive of the fact of its invariancy is

$$F(A, B, \ldots) = M^{ip/q} F(a, b, \ldots).$$

The proof holds for irrational invariants, if we raise the two sides of (5), before reasoning from that equivalence, to such a power μ as to make μip, the index of the power of M, an integer.

24. A consequence of the above is that, i being the *degree* in the coefficients of any rational integral invariant, ip/q must necessarily be integral. For the left-hand member $F(A, B, \ldots)$, when expressed in terms of $a, b, \ldots$ and $l, m, \ldots l', m', \ldots$, is rational and integral in $l, m, \ldots l', m', \ldots$ as well as in $a, b, \ldots$. So too must the right-hand member be. Thus $M^{ip/q}$ is rational in $l, m, \ldots l', m', \ldots$. But M is not a power of any rational function, seeing that it has no factors but unity and itself. Hence ip/q is an integer.

The particular form which this conclusion takes when $q = 2$, i.e. for the case of binary quantics, should be at once noticed. It is that i and p cannot both be odd. Hence the theorem:

No binary quantic of odd order can have any invariant of odd degree.

In the next few articles an interpretation will be given to the integer ip/q, first in the case $q = 2$ of binary quantics, and afterwards generally.

It will be seen, in fact, that there is another characteristic which is constant throughout an invariant, and equal to this integer; namely, its *weight*.

25. **Weight.** In the binary p-ic

$$(a_0, a_1, a_2, \ldots a_p)(x, y)^p$$

we have, as is usually done, given to every coefficient a suffix equal to the defect below the order p of the index of the power of x which it multiplies.

This suffix is, it will be remembered, in each case equal to the dimensions, in the roots of the equation in x/y obtained by equating the p-ic to zero, of the symmetric function of the roots which is equal to the ratio of the coefficient in question to the first coefficient a_0. Or, if we choose, as we may, to regard a_0 as merely denoting a number a_0 of abstract units, and so as being of no dimensions in the roots, we may say that the suffix attached to every coefficient exactly measures the dimensions in the roots of that coefficient. The suffix or degree in the roots of a coefficient is designated its *weight*.

The *weight* of any product of coefficients is the sum of the weights of its various factors, i.e. the sum of their suffixes, and measures the dimensions in the roots of the product in question. A repeated factor in a product must be reckoned as many times as it is repeated in estimating the product's weight. Thus, for instance, the product $a_r^\rho a_s^\sigma a_t^\tau \ldots$ is of weight $\rho r + \sigma s + \tau t + \ldots$.

An invariant of degree i of a binary p-ic has been proved to be homogeneous, i.e. to consist of a sum of positive and negative numerical multiples of products of i factors chosen from among $a_0, a_1, a_2, \ldots a_p$, repeated factors being allowed. The theorem now to be established is that all these products have the same weight $\frac{1}{2}ip$.

A function which is thus of one weight throughout is said to be *isobaric*.

26. **An invariant of a binary quantic is isobaric.** Apply to

$$(a_0, a_1, a_2, \ldots a_p)(x, y)^p$$

the particular linear substitution $x = X$, $y = \lambda Y$, of which the modulus is

$$\begin{vmatrix} 1, & 0 \\ 0, & \lambda \end{vmatrix} = \lambda.$$

This transforms the quantic into

$$(a_0, a_1\lambda, a_2\lambda^2, \ldots a_p\lambda^p)(X, Y)^p.$$

Consequently, if $F(a_0, a_1, a_2, \ldots a_p)$ is an invariant of degree i, the identity expressive of the fact, viz.

$$F(A_0, A_1, A_2, \ldots A_p) = M^{\frac{1}{2}ip} F(a_0, a_1, a_2, \ldots a_p),$$

tells us that

$$F(a_0, a_1\lambda, a_2\lambda^2, \ldots a_p\lambda^p) = \lambda^{\frac{1}{2}ip} F(a_0, a_1, a_2, \ldots a_p).$$

The right-hand member here is entirely of degree $\frac{1}{2}ip$ in λ. So therefore must the left be. Now the term on the left corresponding to a term

$$a_r^\rho a_s^\sigma a_t^\tau \ldots \text{ in } F(a_0, a_1, a_2, \ldots a_p)$$

is

$$(a_r\lambda^r)^\rho (a_s\lambda^s)^\sigma (a_t\lambda^t)^\tau \ldots,$$

i.e.

$$a_r^\rho a_s^\sigma a_t^\tau \ldots \lambda^{\rho r + \sigma s + \tau t + \ldots}.$$

Consequently for every such term

$$\rho r + \sigma s + \tau t + \ldots = \tfrac{1}{2}ip.$$

Thus $F(a_0, a_1, a_2, \ldots a_p)$ is isobaric throughout, the constant weight of its terms such as $a_r^\rho a_s^\sigma a_t^\tau \ldots$ being $\frac{1}{2}ip$.

This applies even when the invariant is irrational, for an irrational invariant may be expressed as a sum, not necessarily finite, of terms to which the reasoning may be applied.

Ex. 1. If $p = 2n$ or $2n+1$ there is no term in any invariant of the binary p-ic which has not at least one of $a_0, a_1, a_2, \ldots a_n$ for a factor.

Ex. 2. Every invariant vanishes for a binary p-ic which has a linear factor raised to the rth power if $2r > p$. (*Cayley*.)

Ans. Take the linear factor for Y. It will hereafter (§ 165) be proved, conversely, that if every invariant of a binary p-ic vanishes, the p-ic has a linear factor raised to the power $\frac{1}{2}(p+1)$ or $\frac{1}{2}p+1$, according as p is odd or even.

27. **Weight generalized.** A like method and the analogous conclusion apply in general to a quantic in q variables. Of these variables call one, singled out as the last, ω, and the others $x, y, z, \ldots$.

In our q-ary p-ic let the suffix given to each coefficient be the index of the power of ω which it multiplies. Thus, for instance,

the coefficients of $x^p, y^p, z^p, x^{p-1}y, y^{p-1}z, \ldots$ have the suffix 0,

" $x^{p-1}\omega, y^{p-1}\omega, z^{p-1}\omega, x^{p-2}z\omega, \ldots$ " 1,

" $x^{p-2}\omega^2, y^{p-2}\omega^2, x^{p-3}y\omega^2, y^2z^{p-4}\omega^2, \ldots$ " 2,

. . . .

" $x\omega^{p-1}, y\omega^{p-1}, z\omega^{p-1}, \ldots$ " $p-1$,

and the coefficient of ω^p has the suffix p.

Our definition of *weight* is that every coefficient is of weight measured by its suffix, and that every product of coefficients is of weight measured by the sum of the suffixes of its various factors.

Our ideas of the import of weight according to this definition are made more definite by supposing that the result of equating our q-ary p-ic to zero is a relation in $q-1$ quantities of the same kind, $x/\omega, y/\omega, z/\omega, \ldots$. To be intelligible, and not imply more relations than one, it must be of the same dimensions throughout in that kind of quantity. For this to be the case the coefficients which multiply products of p factors $x, y, z, \ldots$ without ω, those which multiply products of ω and $p-1$ factors $x, y, z, \ldots$, those which multiply ω^2 and $p-2$ factors $x, y, z, \ldots$, and so on, must be of dimensions in that kind of quantity which form an ascending arithmetic progression of common difference unity. If then, as implies no real loss of generality, we choose to regard the first class of coefficients as of no dimensions in the kind of quantity, the dimensions of the other classes will be 1, 2, 3, ... p respectively. In other words, the dimensions of the various coefficients are measured by the suffixes assigned according to the convention from which we started. The idea of such dimensions is then identical with that of weight.

28. **All invariants isobaric.** We can now prove the constancy and equality to ip/q of the weight, defined as above, for all terms of an invariant of a q-ary p-ic.

Transform the quantic by the substitution

$$x = X,\ y = Y,\ z = Z, \dots\ \omega = \lambda\Omega,$$

which leaves every variable unaltered except ω. Its modulus is λ.

The coefficients in the transformed quantic are at once seen to be the same as those in the untransformed, except that those with suffixes 0, 1, 2, 3, ... p are multiplied by $1, \lambda, \lambda^2, \lambda^3, \dots \lambda^p$ respectively. Thus, if $F(a_0, b_0, \dots, a_1, b_1, \dots a_2, b_2, \dots, a_p)$ is an invariant of degree i, we have

$$F(a_0, b_0, \dots, a_1\lambda, b_1\lambda, \dots, a_2\lambda^2, b_2\lambda^2, \dots, a_p\lambda^p)$$
$$= \lambda^{ip/q} F(a_0, b_0, \dots, a_1, b_1, \dots, a_2, b_2, \dots, a_p).$$

Here the left-hand member must be, like the right, a multiple of a single power, the ip/qth, of λ. The index of every power of λ which occurs as multiplying a product in the expanded left, and consequently the weight of every product of coefficients in F, must therefore be constant and equal to ip/q.

This applies even when the invariant is irrational.

Ex. 3. Every term in any invariant of a q-ary p-ic must contain at least one factor with a suffix less than r if $qr > p$.

Ex. 4. No quadratic in more than two variables can have any invariant which does not vanish when the quadratic breaks up into two linear factors.

Ex. 5. Every term in any invariant of a q-ary p-ic must contain at least one factor with a suffix greater than r if $qr < p$.

29. **Absolute invariants.** For integral invariants the degree i, and consequently the weight ip/q, are essentially positive and different from zero. Thus the power of M in the equality expressive of invariancy

$$F(A, B, \dots) = M^{ip/q} F(a, b, \dots)$$

is essentially a positive power. We cannot then discover any integral function of the coefficients of a quantic which is what is called an *absolute invariant*, that is to say a function of the coefficients which is absolutely equal to the same function of the coefficients in the transformed quantic. For an absolute invariant the power of M above would have to be M^0, or the weight ip/q, and consequently the degree i, would have to be zero.

If, however, a quantic has two or more distinct integral invariants, i.e. two invariants which are not powers of the same invariant, it will have one or more absolute fractional invariants. For, if $F_1(a, b, \ldots)$ and $F_2(a, b, \ldots)$ are two invariants of the same degree i of a q-ary p-ic, we have

$$F_1(A, B, \ldots) = M^{ip/q} F_1(a, b, \ldots),$$

and

$$F_2(A, B, \ldots) = M^{ip/q} F_2(a, b, \ldots);$$

so that

$$\frac{F_1(A, B, \ldots)}{F_2(A, B, \ldots)} = \frac{F_1(a, b, \ldots)}{F_2(a, b, \ldots)},$$

which shows that the ratio of F_1 to F_2 is an absolute invariant. Again, if $F_1(a, b, \ldots)$ and $F_2(a, b, \ldots)$ are of different degrees i_1, i_2, let k be the L.C.M. of i_1 and i_2. Then F_1^{k/i_1} and F_2^{k/i_2} are two distinct invariants of the same degree k, and their ratio $F_1^{k/i_1}/F_2^{k/i_2}$ is an absolute invariant.

For instance, we have seen (§ 7, Ex. 5) that

$$I \equiv ae - 4bd + 3c^2$$

is an invariant of the binary quartic $(a, b, c, d, e)(x, y)^4$. Its degree is 2 and its weight 4, which is rightly equal to $2.4/2$. We have also seen (§ 17, Ex. 19) that the same quartic has another invariant

$$J \equiv ace + 2bcd - ad^2 - b^2e - c^3$$

of degree 3 and weight 6. I^3 and J^2 are then both of degree 6 and weight 12, and are distinct from one another. If then I' and J' are the same functions of the coefficients in the quartic obtained from the given quartic by a linear substitution for x and y as I and J are of the coefficients in the given quartic,

$$\frac{I'^3}{J'^2} = \frac{M^{12} I^3}{M^{12} J^2} = \frac{I^3}{J^2},$$

so that I^3J^{-2} is an absolute invariant of the binary quartic.

30. Limit to the number of independent invariants. A binary p-ic has $p-3$ independent absolute invariants, if p exceeds 3, and none if p does not exceed 3. The first part of this statement is one which cannot well be proved at the present stage; but it may be seen as follows that $p-3$ is a superior limit which the number of independent absolute invariants cannot exceed.

Let $(A_0, A_1, A_2, \dots A_p)(X, Y)^p$ be the transformed quantic obtained from $(a_0, a_1, a_2, \dots a_p)(x, y)^p$ by the linear substitution

$$x = lX + mY, \quad y = l'X + m'Y.$$

Its coefficients $A_0, A_1, A_2, \dots A_p$ are at once expressed as $p+1$ functions of $a_0, a_1, a_2, \dots a_p$ and the four letters l, m, l', m'. If p does not exceed 3 it is impossible to eliminate l, m, l', m' and obtain a relation connecting $A_0, A_1, \dots A_p$ with $a_0, a_1, \dots a_p$ alone. If, however, p exceeds 3 it is possible, by elimination of l, m, l', m', to obtain $p-3$ independent relations which must subsist between $A_0, A_1, A_2, \dots A_p$ and $a_0, a_1, a_2, \dots a_p$, but no more. If, as is in fact the case, these $p-3$ relations can be thrown into such a form as to express $p-3$ equalities of functions of $a_0, a_1, a_2, \dots a_p$ to the same functions respectively of $A_0, A_1, A_2, \dots A_p$, those $p-3$ functions are absolute invariants; but there cannot be more than that number which are independent.

It now follows that if p does not exceed 3 there cannot be two independent invariants which are not absolute, and that if p exceeds 3 there cannot be more than $p-2$ which are independent. For, as seen in the preceding article, any two independent invariants determine an absolute invariant, so that two, or more than $p-2$, independent invariants would determine one, or more than $p-3$, independent absolute invariants.

We must not, however, form the erroneous conclusion that, when $p-2$ independent rational integral invariants have been discovered, every other rational integral invariant can be expressed as a *rational integral* function of these $p-2$. The system of $p-2$ invariants is *algebraically* complete, but another may be a function of them, as it must be, without being a rational integral function of them. For binary quantics of the first four orders there are, as a matter of fact, algebraically complete systems, 0, 1, 1, 2 in number, in terms of which all other invariants can be rationally and integrally expressed, but for the fifth, sixth, &c., orders there is no corresponding simplicity. For instance, the binary quintic has 3 $(=p-2)$ independent invariants of degrees 4, 8, 12, and these are the invariants of lowest degrees which it possesses. They form an algebraically complete system. But there is another invariant of the quintic of degree 18. This must be a function of the three first, but it is perfectly clear that it cannot be a rational integral function of them, for the degree 18, which is not divisible by 4, cannot be expressed as a sum of multiples of degrees chosen from 4, 8, 12, which are all divisible by 4. It is found to be the square root of a rational integral function of the three. Because it cannot be expressed rationally and integrally in terms of *irreducible* invariants of lower degrees it is said to be itself *irreducible.*

That the number of irreducible invariants of a binary p-ic is finite for all values of p is a proposition of some difficulty which was first established by Gordan. The number, though finite, is not known to follow any simple law for all values of p. Proofs of the finiteness due to Hilbert will be given in a later chapter.

31. **Invariants of two or more quantics.** So far in this chapter we have been dealing with invariants of a single quantic only. With regard to invariants of a system consisting of two or more quantics in the same variables the methods of §§ 22 to 28 establish with equal ease the following theorems.

(1) In any invariant of r quantics of orders $p_1, p_2, \dots p_r$ in the same q variables, the sum

$$\Sigma(ip) = i_1p_1 + i_2p_2 + \dots + i_rp_r$$

is constant for all terms, $i_1, i_2, \dots i_r$ being the degrees of any term in the coefficients of the various quantics respectively.

This is established as in § 22.

(2) The factor, depending on the constants of the transformation only, by which the invariant has to be multiplied to make it equal to the same function of the coefficients in the transformed quantics, is M^w, where M is the modulus, and

$$w = q^{-1}\Sigma(ip).$$

This is established as in § 23.

(3) The whole weight, i.e. the sum of the r weights in the sets of coefficients of the r quantics, is the same for every term of the invariant, and equal to w the index of the power of M in (2).

This is established as in §§ 26, 28.

It also follows that, for a rational integral invariant, the sum $\Sigma(ip)$ is necessarily divisible by q; for the weight, a sum of integers, must be integral.

32. It will be observed that there is nothing in these conclusions to prevent our contemplating the existence of invariants of two or more quantics, which, though isobaric (i.e. of constant weight throughout), are not homogeneous, either in the sets of coefficients of the various quantics separately, or on the whole. Nothing in the above indicates that $i_1, i_2, \dots i_r$ are constant throughout the invariant, or even that Σi is constant.

To contemplate such non-homogeneous invariants is, however, unnecessary, for the different parts of such an invariant, which are homogeneous on the whole and also separately in the coefficients of every quantic of the system, are separately invariants.

The proof of this may with ease be stated generally. It will perhaps be made all the clearer by considering an example only.

Suppose the fact to have been noticed that

$$\{ab'^3 - 3ba'b'^2 + 3ca'^2b' - db'^3\}^4 + \{(ac-b^2)b'^2 - (ad-bc)a'b' + (bd-c^2)a'^2\}^3$$

is an invariant of the binary cubic and linear forms

$$ax^3 + 3bx^2y + 3cxy^2 + dy^3,$$

$$a'x + b'y,$$

in that, denoting as usual coefficients in the transformed quantics by capitals,

$$\{AB'^3 - \ldots\}^4 + \{(AC-B^2)B'^2 - \ldots\}^3 = M^{12}[\{ab'^3 - \ldots\}^4 + \{(ac-b^2)b'^2 - \ldots\}^3]. \quad \ldots(1)$$

The invariant consists of a part of degree 4 in the coefficients of the cubic and 12 in those of the linear form, and a part of degree 6 in the coefficients of each form.

Now A, B, C, D are of the first degree in a, b, c, d, and A', B' of the first degree in a', b', involving besides, in each case, the constants l, m, l', m' of the transformation only. The left-hand member of (1) contains then, like the right, terms of partial degrees 4, 12, in a, b, c, d and in a', b', and terms of partial degrees 6, 6. Consequently, the equality being an identity holding whatever a, b, c, d, a', b' are, the terms of partial degrees 4, 12 on the left and right must be equal, and also those of partial degrees 6, 6. In other words,

$$\{ab'^3 - 3ba'b'^2 + 3ca'^2b' - da'^3\}^4$$

and $$\{(ac-b^2)b'^2 - (ad-bc)a'b' + (bd-c^2)a'^2\}^3$$

are invariants separately.

A simple quantic has, we know (§ 22), homogeneous invariants only.

33. We lose then no completeness by considering only those invariants of two or more quantics which are homogeneous in the different sets of coefficients separately as fundamental. Non-homogeneous invariants are linear functions of such homogeneous invariants as have the same whole weight. Thus with regard to a complete system of invariants of two or more quantics we have the conclusions:—

(1) That they are homogeneous in the coefficients of every quantic of the system separately, so that also, if $i_1, i_2, \ldots i_r$ are the degrees of any invariant in these sets of coefficients, the whole degree is constant, viz.

$$i = i_1 + i_2 + \ldots + i_r;$$

(2) that they are isobaric *on the whole*, any one being of weight $$w = q^{-1}(i_1 p_1 + i_2 p_2 + \ldots + i_r p_r).$$

(N.B.—There is no reason to expect them to be isobaric in the coefficients of the quantics separately.)

(3) That the factor which has to multiply an invariant to produce the same function of the coefficients in the linearly transformed quantics is M^w.

CHAPTER III

ESSENTIAL QUALITIES OF COVARIANTS.

34. In accordance with the remark in § 4, the consideration of covariants which are rational and integral both in the coefficients and variables is fundamental. By the word 'covariant' we, as a rule, mean 'rational integral covariant.' The conclusions which follow apply for the most part also to covariants which are irrational or fractional, but this will be stated where it is important to observe that it is the case.

It is well in the first place to see that we may confine attention to covariants which are homogeneous in the variables—to covariant quantics, in fact.

35. **A covariant which is not homogeneous in the variables is a sum of other covariants which are homogeneous in them.**

For in the relation

$$f(A, B, \dots, X, Y, \dots) = \phi(l, m, \dots l', m', \dots) f(a, b, \dots, x, y, \dots),$$

which expresses that $f(a, b, \dots, x, y, \dots)$ is a covariant, the terms of order ϖ in $x, y, \dots$ on the right can produce, upon putting $x = lX + mY + \dots$, $y = l'X + m'Y + \dots$, ..., terms of order ϖ only in $X, Y, \dots$; and no other terms on the right can produce terms of order ϖ in $X, Y, \dots$. Consequently, the relation being an identity, these terms must be identical with the terms of order ϖ in $X, Y, \dots$ on the left. In other words, if the covariant f is not homogeneous in $x, y, \dots$, its various parts of different orders in $x, y, \dots$ are separately covariants.

This applies also to irrational and fractional covariants, which by expansion can be expressed as sums of parts, not necessarily finite in number, arranged according to their orders in the variables.

The proof deals equally with covariants of one and covariants of several quantics. In the next few articles for greater clearness covariants of a single quantic are alone first considered.

36. **Homogeneity in the coefficients.** By the *order* of a covariant, now regarded as homogeneous in the variables, is meant its order or degree in those variables. By *degree* is meant, as in the preceding chapter, degree in the coefficients.[1]

[1] See the footnote to § 22.

If possible let the covariant $f(a, b, \dots, x, y, \dots)$, of the same order ϖ throughout, be a sum of parts of different degrees $i_1, i_2, i_3, \dots$. Apply the identity expressive of the covariancy to the case of the particular linear substitution $x = \lambda X$, $y = \lambda Y, \dots$. As in § 22, the coefficients $A, B, \dots$ in the transformed quantic are in this case $\lambda^p a, \lambda^p b, \dots$, while the variables $X, Y, \dots$ in the transformed quantic are $\lambda^{-1}x, \lambda^{-1}y, \dots$. Thus if H_r is the aggregate of those terms in $f(a, b, \dots, x, y, \dots)$ which are of degree i_r, and of order ϖ, the corresponding terms in $f(A, B, \dots, X, Y, \dots)$ are $\lambda^{i_r p - \varpi} H_r$. Hence, by exactly the same argument as in § 22, if $\psi(\lambda)$ is what $\phi(l, m, \dots l', m', \dots)$ becomes for the particular values of $l, m, \dots l', m', \dots$ which we are considering, $\psi(\lambda)$ must be equal separately to $\lambda^{i_1 p - \varpi}, \lambda^{i_2 p - \varpi}, \lambda^{i_3 p - \varpi}, \dots$. The assumption that $i_1, i_2, i_3, \dots$ are different is then untenable.

Thus, while we lose no real generality by requiring a covariant to be of constant order throughout, we are compelled also to require a covariant of a single quantic whose order is the same throughout to be of the same degree throughout.

Were we to prefer to deal with a covariant having parts of different orders $\varpi_1, \varpi_2, \varpi_3, \dots$ as a single covariant, rather than as a sum of covariants of orders $\varpi_1, \varpi_2, \varpi_3, \dots$, our conclusion come to as above would be that the degrees $i_1, i_2, i_3, \dots$ of those parts respectively are connected with their orders by the equalities

$$i_1 p - \varpi_1 = i_2 p - \varpi_2 = i_3 p - \varpi_3 = \dots .$$

These conclusions apply to irrational and fractional covariants.

37. The factor a power of the modulus.

The proof that the factor $\phi(l, m, \dots l', m', \dots)$, in the relation (§ 35) which expresses the fact of covariancy of a covariant, is a power of the modulus M proceeds exactly as in § 23. If ϖ is the order and i the degree of the covariant $f(a, b, \dots x, y, \dots)$, the power is the $(ip - \varpi)/q$th, $ip - \varpi$ being now the degree of the left-hand side $f(A, B, \dots, X, Y, \dots)$ in the constants of transformation $l, m, \dots l', m', \dots$, when it is expressed explicitly in terms of those constants and

$$a, b, \dots, x, y, \dots .$$

Thus, if we adopt the notation $K(a, b, \dots)^i (x, y, \dots)^\varpi$ to denote a covariant of degree i and order ϖ, the fact of its being a covariant is expressed by

$$K(A, B, \dots)^i (X, Y, \dots)^\varpi = M^{(ip - \varpi)/q} K(a, b, \dots)^i (x, y, \dots)^\varpi.$$

All this applies as well to irrational and fractional covariants as to those which are rational and integral.

If the covariant is rational and integral we can at once draw the conclusion, as in § 24, that the index $(ip-\varpi)/q$ cannot be fractional. It is perhaps well, however, to adopt a different order, and by introduction of the idea of *weight* to ascertain first the import of the integer, or zero, to which it is equal.

38. **Weight in the case of a binary quantic.** As in § 25, the weight of a coefficient in the binary p-ic

$$(a_0, a_1, a_2, \dots a_p)(x, y)^p$$

is its suffix. For present purposes we do best to say further that x and y have weights 1 and 0 respectively. This is in accordance with the idea developed in § 25 that weight measures dimensions in a supposititious kind of quantity of which x/y contains x/y units, and in which $a_1/a_0, a_2/a_0, \dots a_p/a_0$, being of $1, 2, \dots p$ dimensions in the values of x/y which make the quantic vanish, are of $1, 2, \dots p$ dimensions respectively.

With this enlarged conception of weight we may see as follows that $K(a_0, a_1, \dots a_p)^i (x, y)^\varpi$, a covariant of the binary p-ic, is of constant weight $\frac{1}{2}(ip+\varpi)$ throughout.

As in § 26, take for scheme of linear substitution the particular one

$$x = X,\ y = \lambda Y,$$

of which the modulus M is λ. If

$$(A_0, A_1, \dots A_p)(X, Y)^p$$

is the transformed quantic, the values of $A_0, A_1, \dots A_p$ are now $a_0, a_1\lambda, \dots a_p\lambda^p$, and, as in § 26, every product of powers of $A_0, A_1, \dots A_p$ is the same product of powers of $a_0, a_1, \dots a_p$ multiplied by λ raised to a power whose index is the weight of the product. Moreover, every product $X^r Y^{\varpi-r}$ of powers of X and Y is equal to $\lambda^{-\varpi+r} x^r y^{\varpi-r}$, i.e. to the corresponding product of powers $x^r y^{\varpi-r}$ multiplied by a power of λ whose index is the weight of the product diminished by ϖ its order. Thus in the identity

$$K(A_0, A_1, \dots A_p)^i (X, Y)^\varpi = \lambda^{\frac{1}{2}(ip-\varpi)} K(a_0, a_1, \dots a_p)^i (x, y)^\varpi,$$

every term on the left is, for this substitution, the corresponding term in $K(a_0, a_1, \dots a_p)^i (x, y)^\varpi$ multiplied by $\lambda^{w-\varpi}$, where w is the weight of the term. The identity then tells us that for every term

$$\lambda^{w-\varpi} = \lambda^{\frac{1}{2}(ip-\varpi)},$$

so that $w = \frac{1}{2}(ip+\varpi)$ for all terms. A covariant is then *isobaric*.

So far this applies to irrational and fractional as well as to rational integral covariants.

39. For rational integral covariants the weight is a sum of positive integers, and is therefore itself a positive integer.

Thus $\frac{1}{2}(ip+\varpi)$ is necessarily a positive integer.

It follows that the index of the power of M in the equality expressive of the covariancy of a rational integral covariant is integral, or zero, for it is

$$\tfrac{1}{2}(ip-\varpi)=\tfrac{1}{2}(ip+\varpi)-\varpi=w-\varpi,$$

i.e. is the excess of one positive integer over another.

Moreover it cannot be a negative integer. For, w being the weight of the covariant, $w-\varpi$ is the weight of the coefficient of x^{ϖ} in the covariant, and this coefficient being a rational integral function of $a_0, a_1, a_2, \dots a_p$, whose weights are zero and positive, cannot have a negative weight.

This assumes however that in a covariant of order ϖ the term in x^{ϖ} must necessarily occur. This is the case. Were it otherwise the covariant would have y for a factor. Now were it possible for $yF(a, b, \dots, x, y)$ to be a covariant we should have, for any linear substitution whatever,

$$YF(A, B, \dots, X, Y)=(lm'-l'm)^{\frac{1}{2}(ip-\varpi)}\,y\,F(a, b, \dots, x, y),$$

which would necessitate that $YF(A, B, \dots, X, Y, \dots)$ have y, i.e. $l'X+m'Y$, for a factor, whatever l', m' be. Now this is an absurdity, for $YF(A, B, \dots, X, Y)$ has only ϖ linear factors.

From the fact that $\frac{1}{2}(ip-\varpi)$ is integral, or zero, we draw at once the conclusion that ip and ϖ must be either both odd or both even. Hence arise the following theorems.

(1) *No binary quantic of even order p can have a covariant of odd order ϖ.*

(2) *No covariant of a binary quantic can be of even degree i (in the coefficients) and of odd order ϖ (in the variables).*

(3) *No covariant of a binary quantic of odd order p can be of odd degree i and even order ϖ.*

In particular, from (1) and (2) no covariant linear in the variables can belong to a binary quantic of even order, or be of even degree in the coefficients.

Ex. 1. Every term in every coefficient of any covariant of a binary p-ic must contain one or more of the first r coefficients $a_0, a_1, \dots a_{r-1}$ of the p-ic as a factor if $2ir>ip+\varpi$.

Ex. 2. Every covariant of degree i and order ϖ must vanish for a binary p-ic which has a linear factor raised to the rth power if $2ir>ip+\varpi$.

Ans. Take the factor for Y.

Ex. 3. Every term in the coefficients of $x^{\varpi}, x^{\varpi-1}y, \dots x^{\varpi-\rho+1}y^{\rho-1}$ in a covariant of order ϖ and degree i of a binary p-ic must contain at least one of $a_0, a_1, a_2, \dots a_{r-1}$ as a factor if $ir-\rho \not< \frac{1}{2}(ip-\varpi)$.

Ex. 4. If the coefficients in a binary p-ic have such values that the p-ic has a linear factor raised to the rth power, a covariant of degree i and order ϖ must have that factor to the ρth power, where $\rho = ir - \frac{1}{2}(ip - \varpi)$. (*Cayley.*)

Ex. 5. If the degree i and order ϖ of a covariant of a binary p-ic are connected by the relation $ip - \varpi = 0$, show that the covariant can only be the ith power of the p-ic, or a numerical multiple of that ith power.

Ans. The coefficient of x^{ϖ}, i.e. x^{ip}, must be a^i, for its weight must be zero. Also by Ex. 4 the ith power of every linear factor of the p-ic must be a factor of the covariant.

Or thus. The ith power of the p-ic is a covariant; and there cannot be another covariant with $a^i x^{ip}$ for its first term, as otherwise by subtraction a covariant with y for a factor could be formed.

Ex. 6. If the coefficient of the highest power of x in a covariant of the general binary p-ic is known, the order ϖ is determinate, and the covariant unique.

40. **Weight in general.** With regard to a quantic in q variables $x, y, z, \ldots, \omega$ the estimation of weight explained in § 27 requires the supplementary idea that $x, y, z, \ldots$, all the variables except the last one ω, have weight unity, while ω is of weight zero. This being so the weight of the q-ary p-ic is p throughout. The examination for weight of a covariant of degree i and order ϖ proceeds exactly as in § 38, by the method of § 28. The conclusion is that the weight w is constant throughout the covariant, being given by $\lambda^{w-\varpi} = \lambda^{(ip-\varpi)/q}$, so that $w = [ip + (q-1)\varpi]/q$.

This applies to covariants which are not rational and integral as well as to those which are. For rational integral covariants we have the further fact that w is a positive integer, and consequently that $w - \varpi = (ip - \varpi)/q$ is an integer or zero. Moreover that it cannot be a negative integer is proved exactly as in § 39, by showing that the terms free from ω in a covariant cannot all be absent.

Ex. 7. If the terms free from ω in a covariant are known, the covariant is unique.

Ans. Otherwise a covariant with ω for a factor could be formed.

Ex. 8. If $\varpi = ip$, so that $w = \varpi$, the coefficients of the terms free from ω in a covariant involve only the coefficients of the terms free from ω in the p-ic.

Ex. 9. In this case of $\varpi = ip$, the terms free from ω in a covariant of a q-ary p-ic constitute a covariant of the $(q-1)$ary p-ic, obtained by replacing ω by zero in that q-ary p-ic.

Ans. Apply a linear substitution which leaves ω unaltered and expresses the other variables $x, y, z, \ldots, \psi$ linearly in terms of $X, Y, Z, \ldots, \Psi$. The terms free from ω are then transformed by a $(q-1)$ary substitution.

Ex. 10. Hence, by passing in succession to $(q-2)$ary, $(q-3)$ary, ... binary p-ics, deduce from § 39, Ex. 5, that a covariant of the q-ary p-ic for which $\varpi = ip$ has for its term in x alone $a^i x^{ip}$, or a numerical multiple of this.

Ex. 11. Hence, by returning in succession from a binary, to a ternary, a quaternary, ... and at length a q-ary, p-ic, show from Ex. 5 and Ex. 7 that a covariant, of a q-ary p-ic, for which $\varpi = ip$, can be only the ith power of that q-ary p-ic, affected at most by a numerical multiplier.

41. **Absolute covariants.** An *absolute* covariant is one which is exactly equal, without any factor which is even a power of M, to the same function of the coefficients and variables in the linearly transformed quantic. Thus, if the function K be an absolute covariant, we must have, in the identity

$$K(A, B, \ldots)^i (X, Y, \ldots)^{\varpi} = M^{(ip-\varpi)/q} K(a, b, \ldots)^i (x, y, \ldots)^{\varpi},$$

$$(ip-\varpi)/q = 0, \quad \text{i.e.} \quad w-\varpi = 0.$$

Now $w-\varpi$ is the weight of those coefficients in the covariant which multiply products of the variables whose weight is ϖ, i.e. products into which the last variable ω does not enter. The only rational integral absolute covariants are then those in which the coefficients of products of the variables into which the last ω does not enter are of zero weight. In particular, for a binary quantic, the coefficient of x^{ϖ} must be a function of zero weight of $a_0, a_1, a_2, \ldots a_p$, and so must be a mere power of a_0, or a numerical multiple of such a power. In § 39, Ex. 5, it has been seen that such a covariant can only be a numerical multiple of a power of the binary quantic of which it is a covariant. And in § 40, Ex. 11, the corresponding fact has been given for quantics in general. Thus powers of quantics are the only rational integral absolute covariants of those quantics. Further light will be thrown on this fact in future chapters.

Fractional absolute covariants may, however, be seen to exist, as were fractional absolute invariants in § 29, whenever there are two or more distinct integral covariants, powers of the same covariant not being regarded as distinct, for each of which $ip-\varpi$ does not vanish. If, for instance, K and K' are two covariants of a q-ary p-ic, whose degrees are i, i' and orders ϖ, ϖ' respectively, and if μ is the least common multiple of the integers $(ip-\varpi)/q$, $(i'p-\varpi')/q$, then the ratio of

$$K^{\mu q/(ip-\varpi)} \text{ to } K'^{\mu q/(i'p-\varpi')}$$

is an absolute covariant.

For example, it will be seen later (§ 45, Ex. 13) that the binary cubic

$$(a, b, c, d)(x, y)^3$$

has, besides its quadratic covariant (§ 7, Ex. 8)

$$(ac-b^2)x^2+(ad-bc)xy+(bd-c^2)y^2,$$

a cubic covariant

$$(a^2d-3\,abc+2b^3)x^3+\dots .$$

For these two covariants $\frac{1}{2}(ip-\varpi)$ has the values 2, 3 respectively. The cube of the first divided by the square of the second is then a fractional absolute covariant.

42. **Limit to the number of independent covariants.** A limit to the possible number of independent covariants and invariants of a binary quantic may be found as follows.

In the equations of linear substitution

$$x=lX+mY, \qquad y=l'X+m'Y,$$

in the expression for the modulus

$$M=lm'-l'm,$$

and in the $p+1$ equations, in the two sets of coefficients and l, m, l', m', which are obtained by expressing the identity of

$$(A_0, A_1, \dots A_p)(X, Y)^p \text{ with } (a_0, a_1, \dots a_p)(x, y)^p,$$

i.e. with $\quad (a_0, a_1, \dots a_p)(lX+mY, l'X+m'Y)^p,$

we have altogether $p+4$ relations connecting the old and new coefficients, the old and new variables, the modulus M, and l, m, l', m'. The elimination of these last four leaves exactly p independent relations as all that can connect only the old and new coefficients and variables and M.

For instance, the first three equations

$$x=lX+mY,\ y=l'X+m'Y,\ M=lm'-l'm,$$

suffice to determine three of l, m, l', m', the last three say, in terms of the fourth l and x, y, X, Y, M, and lead to no relation free from l, m, l', m'. The expressions for m, l', m' inserted in the remaining $p+1$ equations, produce from them $p+1$ equations involving one unknown l, the old and new coefficients and variables, and M. By elimination of l from these, exactly p independent relations in coefficients and variables and M follow.

Now if there were more than p independent covariants, including the quantic itself and invariants, there would be more than p independent relations in coefficients and variables, old and new, and M; viz. the more than p equalities of the several covariants and invariants, multiplied by proper powers of M, to the same functions of the new coefficients and variables. The number p is then a superior limit to the possible number of independent covariants and invariants of a binary p-ic.

As a matter of fact p is not only a superior limit to the number of algebraically independent covariants and invariants, but the exact number of a complete system. The present however is not the stage at which to prove this important fact.

The warning of the latter part of § 30 should be repeated. When p covariants and invariants, algebraically independent of one another, are known, any other covariant or invariant is a function of them. But this does not imply that, when p independent rational integral covariants and invariants are known, all others can be expressed as rational integral functions of them. There may be others that are *irreducible* in the sense of not being expressible as rational integral functions of simpler irreducible covariants and invariants; and except for the values 1 and 2 of p this is in fact the case. Thus for the binary cubic $p = 3$, but, when the three independent covariants and invariants, all covariants in fact, of lowest degrees in the coefficients have been found, there proves to be a fourth, an invariant, which, though of course a function of them, is irreducible in that it cannot be expressed rationally and integrally in terms of them. So too for the binary quartic $p = 4$, but there prove to be five irreducible covariants and invariants. For the quintic, $p = 5$, the facts are even more striking. All covariants and invariants are functions of the five independent ones of lowest degrees. But there prove to be as many as eighteen other covariants and invariants which are irreducible, in that they are not rational integral functions of the five, or of those five and others of as low degrees as themselves among the eighteen.

Remember that in this enumeration, and always, we count a quantic itself as one of its system of covariants.

43. We have here for clearness adopted a different order of reasoning from that applied in § 30 to invariants alone. There we first found a limit to the number of independent absolute invariants, and deduced conclusions as to the number of independent invariants not necessarily absolute. Here the idea of absolute covariants and invariants is made the subsequent one. In all cases there is one absolute covariant, namely the quantic itself. We have also seen (§§ 41, 29) that there is no other rational integral absolute covariant or

invariant. For the *linear* quantic, $p = 1$, there is no other independent covariant or invariant whatever, and consequently no other that is absolute. For higher binary quantics, $p > 1$, there cannot be more than $p - 1$ independent absolute covariants and invariants. Otherwise a complete system of p independent covariants and invariants would be absolute, and consequently all covariants and invariants would be absolute. But for any value of p exceeding unity there is (§ 15) a non-absolute invariant, the discriminant.

44. **Covariants of two or more quantics.** With regard to covariants of two or more quantics in the same variables, the methods of the earlier articles of this chapter yield, in a manner analogous to that of §§ 31 to 33, conclusions of which a summary follows.

Such a covariant is, as in § 35, either homogeneous in the variables or a sum of covariants which are homogeneous in them. Those which are homogeneous in the variables—of the same *order* throughout—form a complete system.

A covariant homogeneous in the variables may or may not be homogeneous in the coefficients of the various quantics severally and collectively. If, however, it be not so homogeneous, it is a sum of covariants every one of which is homogeneous separately in the coefficients of each quantic, and of course therefore in the coefficients of all the quantics collectively. Covariants, then, which are throughout of constant partial *degrees* in the various sets of coefficients, and therefore of constant total *degree* in all the coefficients, form a complete system. This is seen as in § 33.

If $p_1, p_2, \ldots p_r$ are the orders of r q-ary quantics, the factor by which a covariant of order ϖ and partial degrees $i_1, i_2, \ldots i_r$ in their coefficients respectively has to be multiplied to be made equal to the same function of the variables and coefficients in the linearly transformed quantics is

$$M^{(\Sigma \, . \, ip - \varpi)/q},$$

where M is the modulus of the linear substitution, and

$$\Sigma \, . \, ip = i_1 p_1 + i_2 p_2 + \ldots + i_r p_r .$$

The whole *weight* of the covariant is constant throughout, and exceeds the index of this power of M by ϖ, i.e. is

$$\{\Sigma \, . \, ip + (q-1)\varpi\}/q.$$

If the covariant is rational and integral this weight must be a positive integer, and consequently the index

$$w - \varpi = \{\Sigma \, . \, ip - \varpi\}/q$$

is not a fraction. It is, moreover, not negative, being the

weight of those coefficients in the covariant which multiply products of the variables in which the last ω does not occur, which coefficients cannot all be absent, as no covariant can have ω for a factor when the coefficients in the quantics are general.

45. **Covariants productive of other covariants and invariants.** At this point it may be well to prove an important fact, which, stated for the moment without complete generality, is that any invariant or covariant of a covariant of a quantic is an invariant or covariant, as the case may be, of that quantic itself.

Let $(a, b, \ldots)(x, y, \ldots)^p$ be the quantic u, in any number of variables, in its untransformed shape, and let $(A, B, \ldots)(X, Y, \ldots)^p$ be its linearly transformed shape. Also let $(a', b', \ldots)(x, y, \ldots)^\varpi$ be a covariant of u, so that $a', b', \ldots$ are functions, of degree i say, of the coefficients $a, b, \ldots$, and let $A', B', \ldots$ be the same functions respectively of $A, B, \ldots$. We have simultaneously the identities

$$(A, B, \ldots)(X, Y, \ldots)^p = (a, b, \ldots)(x, y, \ldots)^p,$$

$$(A', B', \ldots)(X, Y, \ldots)^\varpi = M^{q^{-1}(ip-\varpi)}(a', b', \ldots)(x, y, \ldots)^\varpi.$$

If then $K(a', b', \ldots)^{i'}(x, y, \ldots)^{\varpi'}$ is a covariant, or invariant in case $\varpi' = 0$, of the covariant $(a', b', \ldots)(x, y, \ldots)^\varpi$, we have

$$K(A', B', \ldots)^{i'}(X, Y, \ldots)^{\varpi'}$$
$$= M^{q^{-1}(i'\varpi-\varpi')} K(M^{q^{-1}(ip-\varpi)}a', M^{q^{-1}(ip-\varpi)}b', \ldots)^{i'}(x, y, \ldots)^{\varpi'},$$

and consequently, in virtue of the homogeneity of the covariant K,

$$K(A', B', \ldots)^{i'}(X, Y, \ldots)^{\varpi'}$$
$$= M^{q^{-1}(i'\varpi-\varpi')+i'q^{-1}(ip-\varpi)} K(a', b', \ldots)^{i'}(x, y, \ldots)^{\varpi'}$$
$$= M^{q^{-1}(i'ip-\varpi')} K(a', b', \ldots)^{i'}(x, y, \ldots)^{\varpi'},$$

which, since $a', b', \ldots$ are functions, of degree i, of $a, b, \ldots$, and $A', B', \ldots$ are the same functions respectively of $A, B, \ldots$, shows that $K(a', b', \ldots)^{i'}(x, y, \ldots)^{\varpi'}$ is a function, of degree $i'i$ and order ϖ', of $a, b, \ldots, x, y, \ldots$ which, when multiplied by the $q^{-1}(i'ip-\varpi')$th power of the modulus M, becomes the same function of $A, B, \ldots, X, Y, \ldots$. It is then a covariant of u, or, in particular if $\varpi' = 0$, an invariant.

It will be at once seen that only brevity of writing has been secured by attending to but one covariant $(a', b', \ldots)(x, y, \ldots)^p$ of but one quantic u. The argument would have been exactly the same if we had been dealing with more given covariants than one of a quantic, or a given covariant or covariants of more quantics than one in the same variables. We may state in fact the general conclusion, to which the method leads us, as follows.

Any covariant, or in particular invariant, of any covariant, or system of covariants, of any quantic, or system of quantics in the same variables, is a covariant, or in particular invariant, of that quantic or system of quantics.

Ex. 12. The binary cubic $(a, b, c, d)(x, y)^3$ has the covariant (§ 7, Ex. 8), its Hessian,

$$(ac-b^2)x^2+(ad-bc)xy+(bd-c^2)y^2,$$

which has the invariant (§ 7, Ex. 1)

$$(ad-bc)^2-4(ac-b^2)(bd-c^2).$$

This then is an invariant of the cubic. It is its discriminant.

Ex. 13. Find a covariant of degree 3 and order 3, the *cubicovariant*, of the binary cubic.

Ans. $(a^2d-3abc+2b^3,\ abd-2ac^2+b^2c,\ -acd+2b^2d-bc^2,$
$-ad^2+3bcd-2c^3)(x, y)^3,$

the Jacobian of the cubic and its Hessian.

Ex. 14. Show that the binary quintic $(a, b, c, d, e, f)(x, y)^5$ has an invariant of the twelfth degree.

Ans. The discriminant of the canonizant. (Cf. § 17, Ex. 20, and Ex. 12 above.)

CHAPTER IV

COGREDIENT AND CONTRAGREDIENT QUANTITIES.

46. BEFORE proceeding to the further definitions and principles on which most of the propositions of this chapter are to rest, we here first investigate a fruitful method, whose connexion with them will be seen later, for the derivation of invariants and covariants of *binary* quantics, and binary quantics only.

The linear transformation of two variables,

$$x = lX + mY, \qquad y = l'X + m'Y, \qquad \ldots (1)$$

leads, as has been seen in § 10, to the equalities of differential operators

$$\left.\begin{aligned} \frac{\partial}{\partial X} &= l\frac{\partial}{\partial x} + l'\frac{\partial}{\partial y}, \\ \frac{\partial}{\partial Y} &= m\frac{\partial}{\partial x} + m'\frac{\partial}{\partial y}, \end{aligned}\right\} \qquad \ldots (2)$$

where on the right the operation is on any function of x and y, and on the left it is on the function of X and Y, which is equivalent to that function of x and y in virtue of (1).

Now the equalities (2) may be written

$$\left.\begin{aligned} (lm'-l'm)\frac{\partial}{\partial y} &= l\frac{\partial}{\partial Y} + m\left(-\frac{\partial}{\partial X}\right), \\ (lm'-l'm)\left(-\frac{\partial}{\partial x}\right) &= l'\frac{\partial}{\partial Y} + m'\left(-\frac{\partial}{\partial X}\right), \end{aligned}\right\} \qquad \ldots (3).$$

Thus, except for the factor $lm'-l'm$, i.e. M, the symbols of operation $\partial/\partial y$, $-\partial/\partial x$ are transformed by the same scheme of linear substitution as are the variables x, y.

Thus if $f(x, y)$ is any homogeneous function, of order ϖ say, of x and y, and if $F(X, Y)$ is what this becomes when the substitutions (1) are made for x and y in it, we have not only

$$F(X, Y) = f(x, y),$$

but also

$$F\left(\frac{\partial}{\partial Y}, -\frac{\partial}{\partial X}\right) = M^{\varpi} f\left(\frac{\partial}{\partial y}, -\frac{\partial}{\partial x}\right),$$

where the operations on the right and left are on any function of x and y, with or without other arguments independent of x and y, and on its equivalent in terms of X and Y obtained from it by means of (1), respectively.

47. Let us now apply this fact to covariants of one or more binary quantics. If $\phi(a, b, \ldots, x, y)$ and $\psi(a, b, \ldots, x, y)$ are any two covariants of the quantic or quantics—either or both of them may be in particular the quantic itself, or one of the quantics—of orders ϖ, ϖ' in x and y, and of weights w, w' respectively, we have (§§ 37, 39)

$$\phi(A, B, \ldots, X, Y) = M^{w-\varpi}\phi(a, b, \ldots, x, y),$$

and $$\psi(A, B, \ldots, X, Y) = M^{w'-\varpi'}\psi(a, b, \ldots, x, y).$$

We have consequently also, by the preceding article,

$$\phi\left(A, B, \ldots, \frac{\partial}{\partial Y}, -\frac{\partial}{\partial X}\right) = M^{w}\phi\left(a, b, \ldots, \frac{\partial}{\partial y}, -\frac{\partial}{\partial x}\right),$$

and $$\psi\left(A, B, \ldots, \frac{\partial}{\partial Y}, -\frac{\partial}{\partial X}\right) = M^{w'}\psi\left(a, b, \ldots, \frac{\partial}{\partial y}, -\frac{\partial}{\partial x}\right);$$

whence it follows that by operating with either one of this last pair on either one of the immediately preceding pair, left on left and right on right, we get a covariant identity.

All the four conclusions are really contained in the one

$$\phi\left(A, B, \ldots, \frac{\partial}{\partial Y}, -\frac{\partial}{\partial X}\right)\psi(A, B, \ldots, X, Y)$$
$$= M^{w+w'-\varpi'}\phi\left(a, b, \ldots, \frac{\partial}{\partial y}, -\frac{\partial}{\partial x}\right)\psi(a, b, \ldots, x, y);$$

for ϕ and ψ may be interchanged, or may be identical.

Thus the result of operating in this way with any covariant, or one of the quantics, on any covariant, or one of the quantics, is a covariant, or invariant, unless it vanishes. It will certainly vanish if ϖ the order of ϕ exceeds ϖ' that of ψ. It will be an invariant, unless it vanishes, if $\varpi = \varpi'$. It will be a covariant, unless it vanishes, if ϖ is less than ϖ'.

The exact powers of M in the above are not essential to the argument. It is of interest, however, to verify that the power in the conclusion is what it should be in accordance with §§ 37, 39. In the operating factor on the right the weight of the coefficient of $(\partial/\partial y)^{\varpi}$ is $w-\varpi$, while in the factor operated on that of the coefficient of $y^{\varpi'}$ is w'. Also the order is $\varpi'-\varpi$. Thus the index of the power of M should be (§ 39)

$$w-\varpi+w'-(\varpi'-\varpi),$$

i.e. $w+w'-\varpi'$, as is the case.

48. **Invariants of the second degree.** One of the most interesting conclusions from the above is that every binary quantic of even order has an invariant of the second degree. For operate on the binary p-ic

$$(a_0, a_1, a_2, \dots a_p)(x, y)^p$$

with the result of putting $\partial/\partial y$, $-\partial/\partial x$ for x, y in itself, i.e. with

$$(a_0, a_1, a_2, \dots a_p)(\partial/\partial y, -\partial/\partial x)^p.$$

We thus get, after division by $p\,!$, that

$$a_0 a_p - p a_1 a_{p-1} + \frac{p(p-1)}{1\,.\,2} a_2 a_{p-2} - \dots$$
$$+ (-1)^{p-1} p a_{p-1} a_1 + (-1)^p a_p a_0$$

is an invariant unless it vanishes.

It vanishes if p is odd, as the first and last, second and last but one, &c., terms in that case cancel. If, however, p is even it does not vanish, but the last term is a repetition of the first, the last but one of the second, and so on till the middle term, which stands alone. Thus, halving, and replacing p by $2n$, we see that if $\binom{2n}{r}$ denotes the number of combinations of $2n$ things r together,

$$a_0 a_{2n} - 2n a_1 a_{2n-1} + \binom{2n}{2} a_2 a_{2n-2} - \binom{2n}{3} a_3 a_{2n-3} + \dots$$
$$+ (-1)^{n-1}\binom{2n}{n-1} a_{n-1} a_{n+1} + (-1)^n \tfrac{1}{2}\binom{2n}{n} a_n^2$$

is an invariant of the binary $2n$-ic

$$(a_0, a_1, a_2, \dots a_{2n})(x, y)^{2n}.$$

In particular the binary quadratic, quartic, sextic, &c.,

$(a, b, c)(x, y)^2$, $(a, b, c, d, e)(x, y)^4$, $(a, b, c, d, e, f, g)(x, y)^6$, &c.

have respectively the invariants of the second degree

$$ac - b^2,$$
$$ae - 4bd + 3c^2,$$
$$ag - 6bf + 15ce - 10d^2,$$
&c.,

of which the first two have been obtained earlier.

49. Two different binary quantics of the same order have in all cases, whether that order be even or odd, an invariant

of the first degree in the coefficients of each quantic, and so of the second degree on the whole. If the two quantics are

$$(a_0, a_1, a_2, \dots a_p)(x, y)^p$$

and
$$(b_0, b_1, b_2, \dots b_p)(x, y)^p,$$

this joint invariant is in fact

$$(a_0, a_1, a_2, \dots a_p)(\partial/\partial y, -\partial/\partial x)^p (b_0, b_1, b_2, \dots b_p)(x, y)^p,$$

which, divided by $p\,!$, is seen to be

$$a_0 b_p - p a_1 b_{p-1} + \frac{p(p-1)}{1.2} a_2 b_{p-2} - \dots$$
$$+ (-1)^{p-1} p a_{p-1} b_1 + (-1)^p a_p b_0.$$

This is called the *lineo-linear* invariant of the two binary p-ics.

Of the result Exx. 2, 4 of § 7 are particular cases.

We notice that the results of the preceding article are correctly given from this one by making the b's the same as the a's, i.e. by making the quantics the same.

We also notice that for an even order p the joint invariant obtained here for two p-ics is the intermediate (§ 19) between the invariants of the second degree of the two p-ics.

These two observations illustrate the fact that we can either pass from invariants of one quantic to those of two of the same kind and order, or from those of two quantics to those of one, but that the information given by two quantics as to one is complete, while that given by one as to two is not so.

Ex. 1. Employ § 47 to find the invariant $ace + 2bcd - ad^2 - b^2e - c^3$ of a binary quartic by aid of the quartic and its Hessian (§ 11, Ex. 16).

Ex. 2. Find the invariant of degree 4, the discriminant, of a binary cubic by operating with the Hessian on itself, or again by operating on the cubic with its cubicovariant (§ 45, Ex. 13).

Ex. 3. Prove that

$$(a, b, c, d)(\partial/\partial y, -\partial/\partial x)^3 . \{(a, b, c, d)(x, y)^3\}^2$$

is -108 times the cubicovariant of the binary cubic.

Ex. 4. The invariants of the second degree

$$ac - b^2,\ ae - 4bd + 3c^2,\ ag - 6bf + 15ce - 10d^2, \dots$$

of binary quantics of even order, are linear functions of determinants chosen from among

$$\left\| \begin{matrix} a, & b, & c, & d, & e, & \dots \\ b, & c, & d, & e, & f, & \dots \end{matrix} \right\|. \quad (\textit{Cayley.})$$

Ex. 5. The lineo-linear invariant of the x- and y- first differential coefficients of a binary quantic u of even order is the invariant of the second degree of u. (*Cayley.*)

(N.B.—The function obtained in the same way from a binary quantic of odd order is not an invariant.)

Ex. 6. Two binary quantics of different orders p, p', $(p>p')$, have a covariant of order $p-p'$ whose coefficients are lineo-linear.

Ans. The result of operating with the second on the first.

Ex. 7. In particular two binary quantics of orders p, $p-1$, have a linear covariant, in the variables, which is also linear in the coefficients of each quantic.

50. Another result of the close resemblance in form between the schemes (1) and (3) of § 46 is obtained by making (3) operate on any binary quantic u. We thus get that, when formulae give x and y linearly in terms of X and Y, the same formulae give $M\partial u/\partial y$ and $-M\partial u/\partial x$ in terms of $\partial u/\partial Y$ and $-\partial u/\partial X$. It follows that if in any covariant of a binary quantic u, homogeneous as usual in the variables, $\partial u/\partial y$ and $-\partial u/\partial x$ are substituted for x and y another covariant of u is obtained. This theorem is Sylvester's, having been overlooked by Boole, who had given the more far-reaching kindred theorem of § 47.

Ex. 8. If in a binary quantic u we replace x and y by $\partial u/\partial y$ and $-\partial u/\partial x$, we obtain the product of u and a covariant. (*Salmon.*)

Ans. That u is a factor we may see as follows. The values of x, y which make $u=0$ make

$$x\frac{\partial u}{\partial x}+y\frac{\partial u}{\partial y}=0,\text{ i.e. make }\frac{\partial u}{\partial y}:-\frac{\partial u}{\partial x}=x:y,$$

so that u, a homogeneous function $f(x, y)$, is a factor of

$$f\left(\frac{\partial u}{\partial y}, -\frac{\partial u}{\partial x}\right).$$

Ex. 9. Hence obtain the cubicovariant of a binary cubic.

51. **Cogredient quantities.** If two equally numerous sets of quantities, $x, y, z, \ldots$ and $x', y', z', \ldots$ are such that, whenever one set $x, y, z, \ldots$ are expressed in terms of new quantities $X, Y, Z, \ldots$ by any scheme of linear substitution, the second set $x', y', z', \ldots$ are expressed in terms of other new quantities $X', Y', Z', \ldots$ by the same scheme of linear substitution, the two sets are said to be sets of *cogredient* quantities.

For instance, the coordinates of two points in a plane, or in space, are cogredient sets of three, or four, quantities.

Again, in § 46 it has been shown that, but for the factor M, $\partial/\partial y$ and $-\partial/\partial x$ are cogredient with x and y.

Once more, if the binary p-ic

$$(a_0, a_1, a_2, \dots a_p)(x, y)^p$$

is regarded as a product of p factors

$$(xy_1 - x_1 y)(xy_2 - x_2 y)\dots(xy_p - x_p y),$$

so that $x_1/y_1, x_2/y_2, \dots x_p/y_p$ are the roots, and $y_1, y_2, \dots y_p$ may in fact be chosen arbitrarily subject to $y_1 y_2 \dots y_p = a_0$, and if the quantic is linearly transformed by taking

$$x = lX + mY, \quad y = l'X + m'Y,$$

into one of which $X_1/Y_1, X_2/Y_2, \dots X_p/Y_p$, say, are the roots, we have

$$\frac{x_1}{y_1} = \frac{lX_1/Y_1 + m}{l'X_1/Y_1 + m'} = \frac{lX_1 + mY_1}{l'X_1 + m'Y_1},$$

so that without impropriety we may take

$$x_1 = lX_1 + mY_1, \quad y_1 = l'X_1 + m'Y_1,$$

and similarly for other suffixes 2, 3, ..., p. We have then, in the language of the present article, x_1, y_1; x_2, y_2; ...; x_p, y_p cogredient with x, y.

52. **Emanants.** Some functions have the covariant property with regard to a quantic or set of quantics, though they involve, not only the coefficients and variables in the quantic or quantics, but also a set or sets of quantities cogredient with those variables. Allowing ourselves some freedom of expression, when no confusion can arise, we may designate such functions covariants. We proceed to the consideration of a very important class of covariants of this kind.

Let u be a p-ic in the q variables $x, y, z, \dots$. The functions

$$\left(x' \frac{\partial}{\partial x} + y' \frac{\partial}{\partial y} + z' \frac{\partial}{\partial z} + \dots\right)^r u,$$

for values of the positive integer r from 1 to p inclusive, are defined as the first, second, ..., pth *emanants* of u. There would be some convenience in defining the rth emanant rather as the above expression multiplied by the numerical factor $(p-r)!/p!$, but there is no real importance in this, as a numerical multiple of a covariant is of course a covariant not distinct from it, and as we have as yet introduced no convention as to the best numerical multiple of a function, found to have the property of an invariant or covariant of any quantic, to denote by a letter and speak of as that invariant or covariant. Moreover, the simplest form is given to general conclusions by use of emanants as written above.

Inconvenient numerical factors in any conclusions with regard to quantics of particular orders can be rejected when the end is reached.

The pth emanant is $p!$ times the quantic u itself with $x, y, z, \ldots$ replaced by $x', y', z', \ldots$. For values of r exceeding p there are no emanants, as $(p+1)$th differential coefficients of u vanish.

That the emanants of u are absolute covariants in the extended sense is readily seen. If we have

$$\begin{aligned} x &= lX + mY + nZ + \ldots, \\ y &= l'X + m'Y + n'Z + \ldots, \\ z &= l''X + m''Y + n''Z + \ldots, \\ &\cdot \quad \cdot \quad \cdot \quad \cdot \quad \cdot \quad \cdot \quad \cdot \quad \cdot \quad \cdot \quad \cdot, \end{aligned}$$

and

$$\begin{aligned} x' &= lX' + mY' + nZ' + \ldots, \\ y' &= l'X' + m'Y' + n'Z' + \ldots, \\ z' &= l''X' + m''Y' + n''Z' + \ldots, \\ &\cdot \quad \cdot \quad \cdot \quad \cdot \quad \cdot \quad \cdot \quad \cdot \quad \cdot \quad \cdot \quad \cdot, \end{aligned}$$

then, since

$$\begin{aligned} \frac{\partial}{\partial X} &= l\frac{\partial}{\partial x} + l'\frac{\partial}{\partial y} + l''\frac{\partial}{\partial z} + \ldots, \\ \frac{\partial}{\partial Y} &= m\frac{\partial}{\partial x} + m'\frac{\partial}{\partial y} + m''\frac{\partial}{\partial z} + \ldots, \\ \frac{\partial}{\partial Z} &= n\frac{\partial}{\partial x} + n'\frac{\partial}{\partial y} + n''\frac{\partial}{\partial z} + \ldots, \\ &\cdot \quad \cdot \quad \cdot \quad \cdot \quad \cdot \quad \cdot \quad \cdot \quad \cdot \quad \cdot \quad \cdot \quad \cdot, \end{aligned}$$

where on the right the operations are upon any function of $x, y, z, \ldots$, with or without $x', y', z', \ldots$, and on the left they are upon the equivalent of that function expressed in terms of $X, Y, Z, \ldots$, with or without $X', Y', Z', \ldots$, we have

$$X'\frac{\partial}{\partial X} + Y'\frac{\partial}{\partial Y} + Z'\frac{\partial}{\partial Z} + \ldots = (lX' + mY' + nZ' + \ldots)\frac{\partial}{\partial x}$$

$$+ (l'X' + m'Y' + n'Z' + \ldots)\frac{\partial}{\partial y} + (l''X' + m''Y' + n''Z' + \ldots)\frac{\partial}{\partial z} + \ldots$$

$$= x'\frac{\partial}{\partial x} + y'\frac{\partial}{\partial y} + z'\frac{\partial}{\partial z} + \ldots.$$

Hence by successive operations on u, any quantic in $x, y, z, \ldots$, or indeed any function of those variables, the operations on the right and left being upon its original and transformed forms respectively,

$$\left(X'\frac{\partial}{\partial X}+Y'\frac{\partial}{\partial Y}+Z'\frac{\partial}{\partial Z}+\ldots\right)u=\left(x'\frac{\partial}{\partial x}+y'\frac{\partial}{\partial y}+z'\frac{\partial}{\partial z}+\ldots\right)u,$$

$$\left(X'\frac{\partial}{\partial X}+Y'\frac{\partial}{\partial Y}+Z'\frac{\partial}{\partial Z}+\ldots\right)^2u=\left(x'\frac{\partial}{\partial x}+y'\frac{\partial}{\partial y}+z'\frac{\partial}{\partial z}+\ldots\right)^2u,$$

$$\cdot \quad \cdot \quad \cdot \quad \cdot \quad \cdot \quad \cdot \quad \cdot \quad \cdot \quad \cdot \quad \cdot$$

$$\left(X'\frac{\partial}{\partial X}+Y'\frac{\partial}{\partial Y}+Z'\frac{\partial}{\partial Z}+\ldots\right)^ru=\left(x'\frac{\partial}{\partial x}+y'\frac{\partial}{\partial y}+z'\frac{\partial}{\partial z}+\ldots\right)^ru,$$

&c., &c.

Thus the emanants are all absolute covariants.

It may be noticed that the emanants may be otherwise expressed. Thus

$$\frac{1}{r!}\left(x'\frac{\partial}{\partial x}+y'\frac{\partial}{\partial y}+z'\frac{\partial}{\partial z}+\ldots\right)^ru$$

$$=\frac{1}{(p-r)!}\left(x\frac{\partial}{\partial x'}+y\frac{\partial}{\partial y'}+z\frac{\partial}{\partial z'}+\ldots\right)^{p-r}u',$$

where u' is what u becomes when in it $x', y', z', \ldots$ are put for $x, y, z, \ldots$. This follows at once from the fact that either side is the coefficient of t^r in the expansion in powers of t of $f(x+tx', y+ty', z+tz', \ldots)$, where $f(x, y, z, \ldots)$ is u.

Ex. 10. Prove that the emanants are absolute covariants by identifying the results of replacing in u

$$x, y, z, \ldots \text{ by } x+tx', y+ty', z+tz', \ldots,$$

and $$X, Y, Z, \ldots \text{ by } X+tX', Y+tY', Z+tZ', \ldots.$$

53. **Geometrical aspect of emanants.** The process of finding emanants is sometimes called the polar process. The student of geometry will notice that the theory of emanants, with regard to ternary and quaternary systems, is that of polar curves and surfaces.

Thus if the ternary p-ic u is taken as representing a curve, when equated to zero, its first emanant equated to zero represents the first polar curve of a point x', y', z' with regard to u, i. e. a certain curve of order $p-1$ which possesses the property, among others, of determining by its intersections with u all the points of contact of tangents from x', y', z'. The second emanant is in like manner the criterion of the second polar curve of x', y', z', i. e. of the first polar curve with regard to the first polar curve; &c., &c.

That the emanants are covariants is the expression of the fact that the various polar curves of a point with regard to a curve are the same, for the same point and the same curve, in whatever system of point-coordinates the curve and point are taken as expressed, and to whatever axes or triangle of reference they are referred.

In like manner, with regard to quaternary quantics, the fact that the emanants are covariants is the fact that the polar surfaces of a point with regard to a surface are the same surfaces whatever be the reference.

54. **Geometry of binary systems.** The occasion is a good one for a geometrical consideration of binary systems. Their geometry may be regarded either as that of ranges of points on a line or of pencils of lines through a point. To begin with we adopt the former aspect.

Let a and b be two fixed points of reference on a straight line, P any point on that line. Let x and y denote λaP and μbP respectively, where λ and μ are constants. Take A and B two new fixed points of reference on the same line, and let X and Y denote $\lambda' AP$ and $\mu' BP$ respectively, where λ', μ' are new constants. Suppose that a divides AB in the ratio $r:s$ and that b divides it in the ratio $\rho:\sigma$. Then

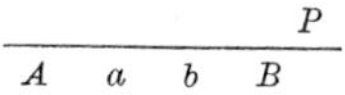

$$(r+s)aP = sAP + rBP, \quad (\rho+\sigma)bP = \sigma AP + \rho BP,$$

so that
$$x = \frac{\lambda}{r+s}\left(\frac{s}{\lambda'}X + \frac{r}{\mu'}Y\right), \quad y = \frac{\mu}{\rho+\sigma}\left(\frac{\sigma}{\lambda'}X + \frac{\rho}{\mu'}Y\right).$$

Now these may be identified with

$$x = lX + mY, \quad y = l'X + m'Y,$$

by proper choice of r/s, r'/s', λ', μ' in terms of l, m, l', m' and λ, μ, provided that $lm' - l'm$ does not vanish.

Thus the most general linear substitution for x and y is equivalent to the change of the reference of points (x, y) to new fixed base points, and the adoption for the new coordinates (X, Y) of new constant multiples of the distances from those new base points.

A binary p-ic represents a range of p points P. (x', y') is an additional point P' on the line of reference. The first, second, &c. emanants are first, second, &c. polar ranges of $p-1$, $p-2$, &c. points on that line. The property of covariancy belonging to the emanants is the expression of the fact that the polar systems of points are systems of points having to the p points and the additional point P' a geometrical relationship quite independent of the reference,

i. e. of the base-points a, b and the multipliers λ, μ. For instance if $p = 2$ the first emanant specifies the harmonic conjugate of P' with regard to the two points u. This can be constructed without any use of the points a, b, or of metrical geometry.

55. Or we may adopt a strictly correlative geometrical representation. We may regard a binary p-ic, equated to zero, as representing p straight lines through an origin, taking the x, y of any line through the origin as given constant multiples of the sines of the angles which that line makes with two fixed lines. We may take as new lines of reference any other pair of lines through the origin, and adopt for the X, Y of the line x, y any new constant multiples of the sines of the angles which it makes with the new lines of reference. The substitution for x, y in terms of X, Y is readily seen to be the most general linear substitution, in virtue of the two degrees of arbitrariness involved in the choice of the new lines of reference, and the two degrees of arbitrariness involved in the choice of the multiples.

A property of covariancy of a function with regard to the p-ic is expressive of the fact that the pencil of lines obtained by equating the covariant function to zero is a fixed pencil of lines, whatever be the lines of reference or the multiples, the p-ic equated to zero being a given pencil of lines. In other words, the relation of the pencils of lines is one of strictly geometrical connexion, of a nature entirely uninfluenced by the geometry of other pencils, such as the pencil to the circular points at infinity. If the cogredient x', y' enter, as is the case with emanants, there is no difference, except that the geometrical connexion of the covariant pencil of lines is with the p-ic pencil and the line (x', y').

It will be noticed that the aspect of the geometry of covariants sketched in § 6 differs from that here developed. There we looked upon a linear substitution as replacing a pencil of lines by a projectively corresponding pencil, retaining the same reference. Here we look upon the substitution as changing the reference, retaining the same pencil. There is a corresponding choice when, as in the last article, we regard the geometry of binary systems as that of ranges of points on a line.

56. **Covariants derived from emanants.** From the emanants of u, themselves, as has been seen, covariants in an extended sense, can be derived covariants of u in the ordinary sense, i. e. covariants free from the quantities x', y', z', ... which

are cogredient with the variables. The basis of this fact is the following theorem.

If any of the emanants of u be expanded and arranged as a quantic in $x', y', z', \dots$, any invariant of that quantic is a covariant of u.

Considered as a quantic in $x', y', z', \dots$, the rth emanant

$$\left(x'\frac{\partial}{\partial x} + y'\frac{\partial}{\partial y} + z'\frac{\partial}{\partial z} + \dots\right)^r u$$

may be written

$$\left(\frac{\partial^r u}{\partial x^r}, \frac{\partial^r u}{\partial x^{r-1}\partial y}, \dots, \frac{\partial^r u}{\partial z^r}, \dots\right)(x', y', z', \dots)^r,$$

its coefficients being all the rth partial derivatives of u, and so functions of $x, y, z, \dots$, for values of r less than p. Its transformed form is, as has been seen in § 52, similar, so that it may be written

$$\left(\frac{\partial^r u}{\partial X^r}, \frac{\partial^r u}{\partial X^{r-1}\partial Y}, \dots, \frac{\partial^r u}{\partial Z^r}, \dots\right)(X', Y', Z', \dots)^r.$$

Now let $F(a, b, \dots, k, \dots)$ be an invariant of the quantic $(a, b, \dots, k, \dots)(x', y', z', \dots)^r$, so that, for some value of μ,

$$F(A, B, \dots, K, \dots) = M^{\mu} F(a, b, \dots, k, \dots),$$

where $(A, B, \dots, K, \dots)(X', Y', Z', \dots)^r$ is the transformed quantic. We conclude that

$$F\left(\frac{\partial^r u}{\partial X^r}, \frac{\partial^r u}{\partial X^{r-1}\partial Y}, \dots, \frac{\partial^r u}{\partial Z^r}, \dots\right)$$
$$= M^{\mu} F\left(\frac{\partial^r u}{\partial x^r}, \frac{\partial^r u}{\partial x^{r-1}\partial y}, \dots, \frac{\partial^r u}{\partial z^r}, \dots\right).$$

But the function F on the left is the same function of the coefficients and variables in the transformed u as the function F on the right is of the coefficients and variables in the untransformed u; for each differential coefficient which occurs on the left is the same function of the new variables and coefficients as the corresponding differential coefficient on the right is of the old ones. Thus

$$F\left(\frac{\partial^r u}{\partial x^r}, \frac{\partial^r u}{\partial x^{r-1}\partial y}, \dots, \frac{\partial^r u}{\partial z^r}, \dots\right)$$

is a function of the coefficients and variables which obeys the definition of covariants.

We see from this theorem that every invariant of a q-ary r-ic gives a covariant of any q-ary quantic of order p higher than r, by taking for the r-ic the rth emanant of the p-ic.

Moreover, the identity expressive of the fact of covariancy, for any covariant thus derived, involves as its factor M^μ exactly the same power of the modulus M as does the identity which expresses the invariancy of the invariant from which it is derived. In other words, the weight of the coefficients of terms free from the last variable ω in the covariant is exactly the weight of the invariant. The degree (in the coefficients) of the covariant is moreover equal to the degree of the invariant.

57. For an example take the second emanant

$$\left(x'\frac{\partial}{\partial x}+y'\frac{\partial}{\partial y}+z'\frac{\partial}{\partial z}+\ldots\right)^2 u.$$

Written as a quantic in $x', y', z', \ldots$ this is

$$\begin{aligned}\frac{\partial^2 u}{\partial x^2}x'^2+2\frac{\partial^2 u}{\partial x\,\partial y}x'y'+2\frac{\partial^2 u}{\partial x\,\partial z}x'z'+\ldots\\ +\frac{\partial^2 u}{\partial y^2}y'^2+2\frac{\partial^2 u}{\partial y\,\partial z}y'z'+\ldots\\ +\frac{\partial^2 u}{\partial z^2}z'^2+\ldots\\ +\ldots,\end{aligned}$$

and of this the discriminant, which is (§ 15) an invariant, is

$$\begin{vmatrix}\frac{\partial^2 u}{\partial x^2}, & \frac{\partial^2 u}{\partial x\,\partial y}, & \frac{\partial^2 u}{\partial x\,\partial z}, & \ldots\\ \frac{\partial^2 u}{\partial x\,\partial y}, & \frac{\partial^2 u}{\partial y^2}, & \frac{\partial^2 u}{\partial y\,\partial z}, & \ldots\\ \frac{\partial^2 u}{\partial x\,\partial z}, & \frac{\partial^2 u}{\partial y\,\partial z}, & \frac{\partial^2 u}{\partial z^2}, & \ldots\\ \cdot & \cdot & \cdot & \cdot\end{vmatrix},$$

the Hessian of u. Another proof that the Hessian is a covariant (§ 11) is thus afforded.

In § 12 we saw that a knowledge that Hessians are covariants told us in particular that discriminants of quadratics are invariants. We now see that the order of reasoning may be reversed. Discriminants are invariants by § 15, and therefore Hessians are covariants.

The geometrical aspect of the fact that the Hessian of a ternary quantic is a covariant may be mentioned. In works on geometry the Hessian of a curve of order p is found as a curve of order $3(p-2)$ which has the property of determining the points of inflexion on the first curve by its intersections with it. The covariant property tells us that the curve found by expressing this fact is the same curve whatever be the system of point coordinates or the triangle of reference, i.e. that we do not, when employing different references, obtain different curves with the one property of determining points of inflexion in common, but identically the same curve. This fact is fundamental in the proof of Plücker's equations.

Ex. 11. Prove that

$$\frac{\partial^4 u}{\partial x^4}\frac{\partial^4 u}{\partial y^4} - 4\frac{\partial^4 u}{\partial x^3\partial y}\frac{\partial^4 u}{\partial x\partial y^3} + 3\left(\frac{\partial^4 u}{\partial x^2\partial y^2}\right)^2$$

is a covariant of a binary quantic u of order exceeding 4.

Ans. Factor M^4. Use § 7, Ex. 5.

Ex. 12. The invariant of the second degree of a binary $2n$-ic gives a covariant of any binary quantic of order exceeding $2n$.

Ex. 13. Deduce the covariant of a binary quantic found in § 17 from the catalecticant of a quartic (§ 49, Ex. 1).

Ex. 14. Write down from Ex. 11 a quadratic covariant of a binary quintic, and a quartic covariant of a binary sextic.

Ex. 15. Every binary quantic of odd order $2n+1$ has a covariant of the second order and second degree.

Ans. The invariant of the second degree (§ 48) of its $2n$th emanant.

Ex. 16. Every binary quantic of odd order $2n+1$ exceeding 3, has at least one linear covariant, obtained by operating on it, as in § 47, with the nth power of its quadro-quadric covariant (Ex. 15). (*Hermite.*)

Ans. For order 3 the result vanishes. For higher orders it does not. To see this let the substitution be adopted which reduces the quadro-quadric covariant to the form kXY, and the quantic to

$$(A_0, A_1, A_2, \dots A_{2n+1})(X, Y)^{2n+1},$$

where $A_0, A_1, A_2, \dots A_{2n+1}$ have consequently to satisfy only

$$A_0A_{2n} - 2nA_1A_{2n-1} + \binom{2n}{2}A_2A_{2n-2} - \dots = 0$$

and

$$A_1A_{2n+1} - 2nA_2A_{2n} + \binom{2n}{2}A_3A_{2n-1} - \dots = 0.$$

The linear covariant derived becomes a numerical multiple of

$$k^2(A_nX + A_{n+1}Y),$$

and $k^2A_n = 0$, $k^2A_{n+1} = 0$ do not follow from the two conditions when $n > 1$.

Ex. 17. For the binary quintic this linear covariant is of degree 5. Show that there is another of degree 7, and, assuming as suggested by § 48 and proved hereafter that a binary quantic of odd order has no invariant of degree 2, that it must be distinct from the former.

Ans. The Jacobian of the quadro-quadric covariant (Ex. 14) and the linear covariant of Ex. 16.

58. Precisely as in § 56 we see that if we take more emanants than one of u, or if we take any emanant or emanants of a covariant of u, or if we take any emanants of two or more quantics $u, v, w, \ldots$ in the same variables, or of covariants of two or more quantics, taking in all of course the same cogredient quantities $x', y', z', \ldots$, and if we arrange them as quantics in $x', y', z', \ldots$, and write down any invariant of the system of quantics in $x', y', z', \ldots$ thus obtained, we have a covariant of u, or of the quantics $u, v, w, \ldots$ jointly.

Ex. 18. From § 9 deduce § 10.

Ex. 19. Employ § 49 to obtain covariants of two binary quantics.

59. **Basis of symbolical representation of covariants and invariants.** For full information as to the system of invariants and covariants of a single quantic, it proves to be important to have recourse to more quantics than one; and not to quantics in one and the same set of variables only, but to quantics in different cogredient sets of variables.

We here consider binary quantics only.

Let x_1, y_1 and x_2, y_2 be two cogredient pairs of variables, so that simultaneously

$$x_1 = lX_1 + mY_1, \qquad x_2 = lX_2 + mY_2,$$
$$y_1 = l'X_1 + m'Y_1, \qquad y_2 = l'X_2 + m'Y_2.$$

We notice that

$$x_1 y_2 - x_2 y_1 = M(X_1 Y_2 - X_2 Y_1),$$

where M is the modulus $lm' - l'm$.

Hence, by § 46,

$$\frac{\partial}{\partial X_1}\frac{\partial}{\partial Y_2} - \frac{\partial}{\partial Y_1}\frac{\partial}{\partial X_2} = M\left(\frac{\partial}{\partial x_1}\frac{\partial}{\partial y_2} - \frac{\partial}{\partial y_1}\frac{\partial}{\partial x_2}\right),$$

so that $\frac{\partial}{\partial x_1}\frac{\partial}{\partial y_2} - \frac{\partial}{\partial y_1}\frac{\partial}{\partial x_2}$ is what may be called an invariant symbol of operation.

Now let u, v be any two binary quantics, and let them be called u_1, v_1 when the variables in them are x_1, y_1, and u_2, v_2 when they are x_2, y_2. Also let U, V; U_1, V_1; U_2, V_2 denote their linearly transformed forms.

We deduce from the above that, for any positive integral value of r,

$$\left(\frac{\partial}{\partial X_1}\frac{\partial}{\partial Y_2}-\frac{\partial}{\partial Y_1}\frac{\partial}{\partial X_2}\right)^r (U_1 V_2) = M^r\left(\frac{\partial}{\partial x_1}\frac{\partial}{\partial y_2}-\frac{\partial}{\partial y_1}\frac{\partial}{\partial x_2}\right)^r (u_1 v_2),$$

i.e. $$\frac{\partial^r U_1}{\partial X_1^{\,r}}\cdot\frac{\partial^r V_2}{\partial Y_2^{\,r}} - r\frac{\partial^r U_1}{\partial X_1^{\,r-1}\partial Y_1}\cdot\frac{\partial^r V_2}{\partial X_2 \partial Y_2^{\,r-1}}+\ldots$$
$$= M^r\left\{\frac{\partial^r u_1}{\partial x_1^{\,r}}\cdot\frac{\partial^r v_2}{\partial y_2^{\,r}} - r\frac{\partial^r u_1}{\partial x_1^{\,r-1}\partial y_1}\cdot\frac{\partial^r v_2}{\partial x_2\partial y_2^{\,r-1}}+\ldots\right\}.$$

In this x_1, y_1 and x_2, y_2 are any cogredient pairs. We may in the expanded result obtained make them the same x, y. Thus

$$\frac{\partial^r U}{\partial X^r}\cdot\frac{\partial^r V}{\partial Y^r} - r\frac{\partial^r U}{\partial X^{r-1}\partial Y}\cdot\frac{\partial^r V}{\partial X\,\partial Y^{r-1}}+\ldots$$
$$= M^r\left\{\frac{\partial^r u}{\partial x^r}\cdot\frac{\partial^r v}{\partial y^r} - r\frac{\partial^r u}{\partial x^{r-1}\partial y}\cdot\frac{\partial^r v}{\partial x\,\partial y^{r-1}}+\ldots\right\}.$$

We accordingly have a system of covariants of two binary quantics u, v. They have already been obtained in § 58, Ex. 19, as the lineo-linear invariants (§ 49) of the rth emanants of u and v. In particular if p is the order both of u and v, the value p of r gives the lineo-linear invariant itself, multiplied by $(p\,!)^2$.

Again, we may in the expanded result make u and v the same quantic, and thus get that

$$\frac{\partial^r u}{\partial x^r}\cdot\frac{\partial^r u}{\partial y^r} - r\frac{\partial^r u}{\partial x^{r-1}\partial y}\cdot\frac{\partial^r u}{\partial x\,\partial y^{r-1}}$$
$$+\frac{r(r-1)}{1\,.\,2}\cdot\frac{\partial^r u}{\partial x^{r-2}\partial y^2}\cdot\frac{\partial^r u}{\partial x^2\partial y^{r-2}}-\ldots$$

is unless it vanishes a covariant, or invariant if $r=p$ the order of u, of factor M^r. For odd values of r the result is nugatory, in that its first and last, its second and last but one, &c. terms cancel against one another. For even values of r the last term repeats the first, the last but one repeats the second, and so on till the middle term which occurs once only.

These covariants of u have already been obtained (§ 57, Ex. 12) as the invariants of the second degree of the emanants of even order of u. For $r=p$, the order of u, we have in particular a numerical multiple of the invariant of the second degree (§ 48) itself.

So far then the method is only another one for determining results already known in other ways. It as yet gives us only the covariants and invariants of u which are of the second degree in the coefficients. Its convenience is that it suggests an expressive symbolization for covariants and invariants, and paves the way to a systematic examination of all forms which can be covariants or invariants.

60. **Hyperdeterminants.** The operator $\frac{\partial}{\partial x_1}\frac{\partial}{\partial y_2}-\frac{\partial}{\partial y_1}\frac{\partial}{\partial x_2}$ is denoted by the brief symbol $\overline{12}$. More briefly still the covariant, or invariant, of u found above by operating r times with this symbol $\overline{12}$ on the product $u_1 u_2$, and removing all suffixes in the expanded result when the operations have been performed, is called the covariant or invariant $\overline{12}^r$ of u.

To get covariants and invariants of the third degree in the coefficients of u we may consider the product of three quantics u_1, v_2, w_3, whose suffixes imply that their variables are three cogredient sets, and operate on the product with

$$\left(\frac{\partial}{\partial x_1}\frac{\partial}{\partial y_2}-\frac{\partial}{\partial y_1}\frac{\partial}{\partial x_2}\right)^r\left(\frac{\partial}{\partial x_2}\frac{\partial}{\partial y_3}-\frac{\partial}{\partial y_2}\frac{\partial}{\partial x_3}\right)^s\left(\frac{\partial}{\partial x_3}\frac{\partial}{\partial y_1}-\frac{\partial}{\partial y_3}\frac{\partial}{\partial x_1}\right)^t,$$

thus getting, for positive integral and zero values of r, s, t, functions seen as in § 59 to have the covariant or invariant property. In the result, after giving to it its fully expanded form, we may replace all three sets of cogredient variables x_1, y_1; x_2, y_2; x_3, y_3 by the same set x, y, and also make u, v and w all the same quantic u. We thus get a system of covariants and invariants of u which may be symbolically written

$$\overline{12}^r \, . \, \overline{23}^s \, . \, \overline{31}^t,$$

for different positive integral and zero values of r, s and t.

These covariants and invariants are all of the third degree in the coefficients. It is easy to see the necessary connexions of r, s, t and p, the order of u, that they may be invariants. Any term in the covariant or invariant is a product of differential coefficients of the three factors $u\ u\ u$, the first being differentiated as many times as the figure 1 occurs in the symbolic product, the second as many times as the figure 2 occurs, and the third as many times as 3 occurs. Now if the expansion is to be an invariant each one must be differentiated p times, where p is the order of u. For an invariant then the conditions are

$$r+s=s+t=t+r=p.$$

For a covariant one at least of $r+s$, $s+t$, $t+r$ must be less than p, and none of them greater than p.

To get covariants and invariants of the fourth degree in like manner we have to operate on products of four quantics. The symbolical form of such covariants and invariants is

$$\overline{12}^{r_{12}}\,\overline{13}^{r_{13}}\,\overline{14}^{r_{14}}\,\overline{23}^{r_{23}}\,\overline{24}^{r_{24}}\,\overline{34}^{r_{34}},$$

and the conditions for an invariant are

$$r_{12}+r_{13}+r_{14}=r_{12}+r_{23}+r_{24}=r_{13}+r_{23}+r_{34}=r_{14}+r_{24}+r_{34}=p.$$

Similarly formed products involving five, six, &c. figures are symbolic expressions for covariants and invariants of the fifth, sixth, &c. degrees, derived from products of five, six, &c. quantics, eventually made the same. For invariants every figure must occur in the same number of symbolical factors, and that number must be the order of the quantic of which they are invariants.

Later (§ 89, Exx. 25–28) it will be seen that all invariants are linear functions with constant coefficients of those which can be written down in this way. The like statement may be made as to covariants.

The method is one by which Cayley made great advances in the systematic exhibition of covariant and invariant forms. (See, for instance, his collected works, Vol. I, pp. 95–112.) To pursue it is outside the limits of the present introductory work. For ways of selecting symbolical expressions which do not give vanishing results for a single quantic (cf. § 89, Ex. 28, and § 131), and for applications to the reduction of systems of covariants and invariants, the student is referred to Cayley's original memoirs, and to Salmon's *Higher Algebra*. The method, which is spoken of as that of 'hyperdeterminants,' did not, in its originator's form, succeed in establishing the finiteness of complete systems of irreducible covariants in general. That triumph was reserved for another symbolical method, having much in common with it, which will be referred to in the following articles.

There is a corresponding theory for ternary and higher quantics, which will not be entered into. The student will have no difficulty in seeing that, acting upon a product of three ternary quantics,

$$\begin{vmatrix} \frac{\partial}{\partial x_1}, & \frac{\partial}{\partial y_1}, & \frac{\partial}{\partial z_1} \\ \frac{\partial}{\partial x_2}, & \frac{\partial}{\partial y_2}, & \frac{\partial}{\partial z_2} \\ \frac{\partial}{\partial x_3}, & \frac{\partial}{\partial y_3}, & \frac{\partial}{\partial z_3} \end{vmatrix},$$

which may be called $\overline{123}$, is an invariant operator.

60 (*bis*). **The German symbolism.** The Cayleyan notation for hyperdeterminants has been very generally replaced by another, which is identified with the names of Aronhold, Clebsch, and Gordan. This is based on a purely symbolical representation of the coefficients in a quantic. A binary quantic $(a_0, a_1, a_2, \dots a_p)(x, y)^p$ is denoted by $(ax+a'y)^p$, looked upon as expanded by the Binomial Theorem. Thus, for $r = 0, 1, 2, \dots p$, $a^r a'^{p-r}$ denotes a_r, while $a^r a'^s$ has no meaning unless $r+s=p$. In order to express products of coefficients in one quantic, we have to introduce a number of pairs a, a'; b, b'; c, c'; ... of symbolic letters, and to say that $(ax+a'y)^p$, $(bx+b'y)^p$, $(cx+c'y)^p$, ... all represent the same quantic, so that $a^r a'^{p-r}$, $b^r b'^{p-r}$, $c^r c'^{p-r}$, ... all mean a_r, and, for instance, $a^r a'^{p-r} b^s b'^{p-s} c^t c'^{p-t}$ is the product $a_r a_s a_t$. We, in fact, deal in the first place with quantics which may be all different, and eventually in interpreting conclusions identify them, or such of them as may be given to be the same.

If, as in § 59, x_1, y_1 and x_2, y_2 are cogredient pairs of variables, which we presently identify, and if $(ax_1+a'y_1)^{p_1}$, $(bx_2+b'y_2)^{p_2}$ denote, in the manner just explained, two binary quantics u_1, u_2 in those pairs respectively—quantics which we may also presently identify if $p_1 = p_2$—it is readily seen that

$$\frac{(p_1-r)!\,(p_2-r)!}{p_1!\,p_2!}\left(\frac{\partial}{\partial x_1}\frac{\partial}{\partial y_2}-\frac{\partial}{\partial x_2}\frac{\partial}{\partial y_1}\right)^r u_1 u_2$$
$$\equiv (ab'-a'b)^r (ax_1+a'y_1)^{p_1-r}(bx_2+b'y_2)^{p_2-r},$$

where the right-hand member, when expanded, consists of terms every one of which is of p_1 dimensions in a and a', and of p_2 in b and b', so that only actual products of coefficients in the two quantics present themselves, in addition to the variables. It is usual, for brevity, to call this right-hand member

$$(ab)^r a_{x_1}^{p_1-r} b_{x_2}^{p_2-r},$$

or, after identification of x_1, y_1 and x_2, y_2,

$$(ab)^r a_x^{p_1-r} b_x^{p_2-r}.$$

When only one quantic is really under consideration this gives the covariant, of degree 2 in the coefficients, $(ab)^r a_x^{p-r} b_x^{p-r}$, where a_x^p and b_x^p both mean the one quantic.

In like manner the hyperdeterminant

$$\overline{12}^r\,.\,\overline{23}^s\,.\,\overline{31}^t\; u_1 u_2 u_3,$$

of partial degrees 1, 1, 1 in the coefficients of u_1, u_2, u_3 is a numerical multiple of

$$(ab)^r (bc)^s (ca)^t a_x^{p_1-r-t} b_x^{p_2-r-s} c_x^{p_3-s-t},$$

where p_1, p_2, p_3 are the orders of u_1, u_2, u_3. If for these quantics the same p-ic is taken, this covariant is

$$(ab)^r (bc)^s (ca)^t a_x^{p-r-t} b_x^{p-r-s} c_x^{p-s-t},$$

and is of degree 3 in the coefficients, as

$$a_{p-\rho} = a^\rho a'^{p-\rho} = b^\rho b'^{p-\rho} = c^\rho c'^{p-\rho},$$

for every ρ which enters into its expansion.

Similarly any hyperdeterminant of a higher degree is, but for a numerical factor which it is best to discard, symbolically expressed by a product of powers of symbolic determinants such as (ab), and of powers of $a_x, b_x, \ldots$, such that the sum of the indices of the factors in which a occurs is p_1, the order of the first quantic $a_x^{p_1}$, the sum of those of factors in which b occurs is p_2, the order of the second quantic $b_x^{p_2}$, and so on. If the orders of the quantics are all equal, and in particular if the various quantics are all the same, so that

$$a_x^p \equiv b_x^p \equiv c_x^p \equiv \ldots,$$

the various sums of indices are all equal to p.

It is impossible for all the hyperdeterminants thus written down to be linearly independent. The study of their interdependence is usually based on the 'Jacobian identity'

$$(bc' - b'c)(ax + a'y) + (ca' - c'a)(bx + b'y) + (ab' - a'b)(cx + c'y) = 0,$$

i. e. $$(bc)\, a_x + (ca)\, b_x + (ab)\, c_x = 0,$$

which clearly, for instance, enables us to express a symbolic product divisible by $(bc)\, a_x$ as a sum of two other symbolic products. Even when we have by use of this identity reduced a system of hyperdeterminants to a smaller system of such as are linearly independent so long as $a^r a'^{p-r}$ and $b^r b'^{p-r}$, for instance, mean coefficients in different p-ics, many will still remain which become identical, connected, or zero when in a final interpretation for the case of one p-ic we have to give to these different products the same meaning.

60 (*ter*). **Operational symbolism.** There is a variation of this Clebschian symbolism which is less entirely artificial. Its symbols are not mere *umbrae* with no meaning in themselves, but denote differential operators. Let us take

$$\theta \equiv a_1 \frac{\partial}{\partial a_0} + a_2 \frac{\partial}{\partial a_1} + \ldots + a_p \frac{\partial}{\partial a_{p-1}},$$

so that $$\theta a_0 = a_1,\ \theta^2 a_0 = a_2, \ldots\ \theta^p a_0 = a_p,$$

and, with $p + t > p$, $$\theta^{p+t} a_0 = 0.$$

We can then write

$$u \equiv (a_0, a_1, a_2, \ldots a_p)(x, y)^p \equiv (x + y\theta)^p a_0.$$

Instead of using one such operator θ, let us introduce a number of the same form, one for each of a series of quantics dealt with in the first place. The rth of the series is thus

$$u_r \equiv (a_0^{(r)}, a_1^{(r)}, \ldots a_{p_r}^{(r)})(x, y)^{p_r} \equiv (x + y\,\theta_r)^{p_r} a_0^{(r)},$$

where
$$\theta_r \equiv a_1^{(r)} \frac{\partial}{\partial a_0^{(r)}} + a_2^{(r)} \frac{\partial}{\partial a_1^{(r)}} + \ldots + a_{p_r}^{(r)} \frac{\partial}{\partial a_{p_r-1}^{(r)}}.$$

Let us say $a_0, b_0, c_0, \ldots$ instead of $a_0^{(1)}, a_0^{(2)}, a_0^{(3)}, \ldots$.

The proof that

$$\frac{(p_1 - r)!\,(p_2 - r)!}{p_1!\,p_2!}\left(\frac{\partial}{\partial x_1}\frac{\partial}{\partial y_2} - \frac{\partial}{\partial x_2}\frac{\partial}{\partial y_1}\right)^r u_1 u_2$$
$$= (\theta_2 - \theta_1)^r (x_1 + y_1\theta_1)^{p_1 - r}(x_2 + y_2\theta_2)^{p_2 - r} a_0 b_0$$

is quite direct; and we can proceed to hyperdeterminants of higher degrees as before.

Identifying the cogredient pairs of variables, and taking the orders p_1, p_2, p_3 equal, we obtain for the numerical multiple of the hyperdeterminant $\overline{12}^r \,.\, \overline{23}^s \,.\, \overline{31}^t$, which has been symbolized above by

$$(ab)^r (bc)^s (ca)^t a_x^{p-r-t} b_x^{p-r-s} c_x^{p-s-t},$$

the somewhat more expressive form

$$(\theta_2 - \theta_1)^r (\theta_3 - \theta_2)^s (\theta_1 - \theta_3)^t$$
$$(x + y\theta_1)^{p-r-t}(x + y\theta_2)^{p-r-s}(x + y\theta_3)^{p-s-t} a_0 b_0 c_0.$$

The expression obtained in this way for any hyperdeterminant covariant of degree i in the coefficients of one binary p-ic may be written

$$\prod_{n=2}^{n=i}\prod_{m=1}^{m=n-1}(\theta_m - \theta_n)^{r_{mn}} . \prod_{n=1}^{n=i}(x + y\theta_n)^{\varpi_n}\; a_0 a_0 a_0 \ldots (i \text{ factors } a_0),$$

where θ_1 and its powers act only on the first factor a_0, θ_2 and its powers only on the second, and so on. The indices r_{mn} and ϖ_n are positive numbers or zeros satisfying the equations

$$r_{12} + r_{13} + \ldots + r_{1i} \;\; + \varpi_1 = p,$$
$$r_{12} + r_{23} + \ldots + r_{2i} \;\; + \varpi_2 = p,$$
$$\cdot \quad \cdot \quad \cdot \quad \cdot \quad \cdot \quad \cdot \quad \cdot \quad \cdot \quad \cdot \quad \cdot \quad \cdot$$
$$r_{1i} + r_{2i} + \ldots + r_{i-1\,i} + \varpi_i = p.$$

The order ϖ of this covariant is $\varpi_1+\varpi_2+\ldots+\varpi_i$; and it is easy to see that its weight is

$$\Sigma r_{mn}+\Sigma\varpi_n = \tfrac{1}{2}(ip-\Sigma\varpi_n)+\Sigma\varpi_n$$
$$= \tfrac{1}{2}(ip+\varpi),$$

as we know must be the case, from Chap. III.

In this notation the Jacobian identity is

$$(\theta_2-\theta_3)(x+y\theta_1)+(\theta_3-\theta_1)(x+y\theta_2)+(\theta_1-\theta_2)(x+y\theta_3)=0.$$

61. **Transvectants.** The invariant or covariant $\overline{12}^r(u\,v)$, or rather this multiplied by $(p-r)!\,(p'-r)!/p!\,p'!$, is called the rth *transvectant* of u and v, in German the rth 'Ueberschiebung von u über v.' The process of forming transvectants of u and v is called *transvection.*

In particular the covariant or invariant $\overline{12}^r$ of u, i.e. the covariant or invariant $\overline{12}^r(u\,u)$, is $\{p!/(p-r)!\}^2$ times the rth transvectant of u and itself.

From two binary quantics u, v, whose orders are p, p', of which $p \not> p'$, are derived $p+1$ transvectants. For, besides the values 1, 2, 3, ... p of r, the value 0 is also admissible. The 0th transvectant of u and v is the product uv. The other transvectants of u and v are the covariants, or covariants and invariant, which are of the first degree in the coefficients of u and also of the first degree in the coefficients of v, and so altogether of the second degree. As has been seen, one is the product uv, and the rest may be found from the first, second, ..., pth emanants of u and of v by writing down the lineo-linear invariants of corresponding pairs of those emanants as in § 49.

The 0th transvectant of u and itself is u^2. The other transvectants of u and itself are the covariants of u of degree 2 in the coefficients, obtained by writing down the invariants of the second degree of the successive emanants of u. The first, third, fifth, &c. transvectants of u and itself vanish.

A transvectant, once found, is dealt with as a new quantic. Transvectants of u and covariants of degree 2, already found as transvectants, are of degree 3; and so on. It is clear that by repetitions of transvection we can obtain covariants of all degrees. At any stage we use an operating symbol, such as $\overline{12}^r$, involving two figures only, which refer to two covariants already found, or to one covariant and u. The use of complicated hyperdeterminant products $\overline{12}^r.\overline{13}^s.\overline{23}^t\ldots$, involving many figures all referring to u or another fundamental quantic, is avoided.

The symbolic method of § 60 (*bis*) has been brought to bear on the theory of transvectants; and it was by use of it that Gordan first obtained a proof of the finiteness of the complete system of irreducible covariants and invariants of any binary quantic or quantics.

With regard to a single binary quantic u, what his researches succeeded in establishing is, that all concomitants (this term including both covariants and invariants) of u which are of the second degree in the coefficients are transvectants of u, u^2 in particular being the 0th transvectant; that all of the third degree in the coefficients are linear functions of transvectants of u and concomitants of the second degree, products of u into u^2 and other concomitants of the second degree being included as 0th transvectants; that all of the fourth degree are transvectants of u and concomitants of the third degree; and so on from degree to degree. Gordan proved that this continued process ceases after a time to give new irreducible concomitants, so that the determination of a complete system of irreducible concomitants for any binary quantic is reduced to the examination for irreducibility of those which are obtained as transvectants up to a certain point.

He also proved finite the complete system of irreducible concomitants of a number of binary quantics. In the case of two quantics u, v the complete system is comprised in the complete system of u, the complete system of v, and a terminating system of transvectants of the one complete system with the other complete system. In the case of three quantics u, v, w, the complete system of concomitants is comprised in the complete system of u, v, the complete system of w, and a terminating system of mutual transvectants of these complete systems; and so on for any number of quantics.

This great theory should be studied in Clebsch's *Theorie der Binären Algebraischen Formen*, in Gordan's *Vorlesungen über Invariantentheorie*, or in Grace and Young's *Algebra of Invariants*. It lies outside the scope of the present treatise.

Ex. 20. The Jacobian of u and v is their first mutual transvectant, a numerical factor discarded.

Ex. 21. The Hessian of a binary quantic u is the second transvectant of u and itself, but for a numerical factor.

Ex. 22. The quadratic invariant (§ 48) of a binary $2n$-ic is half its $2n$th transvectant with itself.

Ex. 23. The lineo-linear invariant (§ 49) of two binary p-ics is their pth mutual transvectant.

Ex. 24. The second transvectant of the cubic $(a, b, c, d)(x, y)^3$ and itself is twice the quadratic covariant

$$(ac-b^2)x^2+(ad-bc)xy+(bd-c^2)y^2.$$

Also the first and third transvectants vanish.

Ex. 25. The first transvectant of the cubic and its second transvectant (Ex. 24) is the cubicovariant (§ 45, Ex. 13)

$$(a^2d-3abc+2b^3)x^3+\ \dots.$$

The second mutual transvectant vanishes.

Ex. 26. The first transvectant of the cubic and its cubicovariant is minus twice the square of the quadratic covariant $(ac-b^2)x^2+\dots$. Their second mutual transvectant vanishes. Their third is minus twice the discriminant

$$a^2d^2-6abcd+4ac^3+4b^3d-3b^2c^2 \equiv (ad-bc)^2-4(ac-b^2)(bd-c^2).$$

Ex. 27. The second transvectant of the quartic $(a, b, c, d, e)(x, y)^4$ and itself is twice the quartic covariant (the Hessian simplified by omitting a numerical factor)

$$(ac-b^2)x^4+2(ad-bc)x^3y+(ae+2bd-3c^2)x^2y^2$$
$$+2(be-cd)xy^3+(ce-d^2)y^4;$$

and the fourth transvectant is twice the invariant

$$I \equiv ae-4bd+3c^2.$$

Ex. 28. The first transvectant of the quartic and the quartic covariant of Ex. 27 is half a sextic covariant beginning with

$$(a^2d-3abc+2b^3)x^6+\dots:$$

the second is one-sixth of the product of I and the quartic: the third vanishes: and the fourth is three times the invariant

$$J \equiv ace+2bcd-ad^2-b^2e-c^3.$$

Ex. 29. The binary quintic $(a, b, c, d, e, f)(x, y)^5$ has a covariant of the second order and the second degree.

Ans. $(ae-4bd+3c^2)x^2+(af-3be+2cd)xy+(bf-4ce+3d^2)y^2$, half the fourth transvectant of the quintic and itself. Cf. § 57, Ex. 15.

Ex. 30. The binary quintic has an invariant of the fourth degree.

Ans. $(af-3be+2cd)^2-4(ae-4bd+3c^2)(bf-4ce+3d^2)$,

found as minus twice the second transvectant of the covariant of Ex. 29 and itself.

Ex. 31. The binary quintic has a linear covariant of degree 5 in the coefficients.

Ans. The fourth transvectant of the quintic and the square of the covariant of Ex. 29. Cf. § 57, Ex. 16.

Ex. 32. Find a covariant of the fourth order and second degree of the binary sextic.

Ans. $\overline{12}^4$.

Ex. 33. Prove that, for each of the values $r = 1, 2, 3, \ldots I(\frac{1}{2}p)$,

$$(\theta_1-\theta_2)^{2r}(x+y\theta_1)^{p-2r}(x+y\theta_2)^{p-2r}\,aa$$

is a covariant of a binary p-ic (the last an invariant if p is even), of degree 2 and order $2p-4r$.

Ex. 34. Prove that, for each of the values $r = 1, 2, 3, \ldots I\left(\frac{p-1}{2}\right)$,

$$(\theta_1-\theta_2)^{2r}(\theta_1-\theta_3)(x+y\theta_1)^{p-2r-1}(x+y\theta_2)^{p-2r}(x+y\theta_3)^{p-1}\,aaa$$

is a covariant of degree 3 and order $3p-4r-2$.

Ex. 35. A ternary quadratic has an invariant of the third degree whose symbol is $\overline{123}^2$; and a ternary quartic one whose symbol is $\overline{123}^4$.

Ex. 36. A q-ary $2n$-ic has an invariant of degree q.

62. **Contragredient quantities.** Two sets of quantities $x, y, z, \ldots; \xi, \eta, \zeta, \ldots$ are said to be *contragredient* when formulae of linear substitution for the first set

$$\begin{aligned} x &= lX + mY + nZ + \ldots, \\ y &= l'X + m'Y + n'Z + \ldots, \\ z &= l''X + m''Y + n''Z + \ldots, \\ &\cdots\cdots\cdots, \end{aligned}$$

are necessarily accompanied by the associated but different formulae of substitution for the second set

$$\begin{aligned} \Xi &= l\xi + l'\eta + l''\zeta + \ldots, \\ \mathrm{H} &= m\xi + m'\eta + m''\zeta + \ldots, \\ \mathrm{Z} &= n\xi + n'\eta + n''\zeta + \ldots, \\ &\cdots\cdots\cdots, \end{aligned}$$

in which latter set it is to be noticed that the new quantities are expressed in terms of the old, and not vice versa. Reversed they are

$$\begin{aligned} \xi &= M^{-1}\{\lambda\Xi + \mu\mathrm{H} + \nu\mathrm{Z} + \ldots\}, \\ \eta &= M^{-1}\{\lambda'\Xi + \mu'\mathrm{H} + \nu'\mathrm{Z} + \ldots\}, \\ \zeta &= M^{-1}\{\lambda''\Xi + \mu''\mathrm{H} + \nu''\mathrm{Z} + \ldots\}, \\ &\cdots\cdots\cdots, \end{aligned}$$

where M is as usual the modulus of the scheme of substitution for $x, y, z, \ldots$, and where $\lambda, \mu, \ldots, \lambda', \mu', \ldots, \ldots$ denote the minors

$$\partial M/\partial l,\ \partial M/\partial m, \ldots,\ \partial M/\partial l',\ \partial M/\partial m', \ldots, \ldots.$$

It is convenient to speak of contragredient quantities as being linearly transformed by schemes of substitution of which one is the *dual* of the other. The name is reasonable, as the duality or reciprocal connexion of the two substitutions is precise, it being possible, and a good simple exercise in determinant algebra, to show that the first substitution stands in precisely the same relation to the second as the second does to the first.

63. **Geometrical contragrediency.** The duality of transformations of contragredient quantities has its counterpart and its application in the method of duality in geometry. Taking ternary systems, we know in fact that if x, y, z and ξ, η, ζ are point- and line-coordinates of associated systems, so that $\xi x+\eta y+\zeta z=0$ is the condition that the point (x, y, z) lie on the line (ξ, η, ζ), or that the line (ξ, η, ζ) pass through the point (x, y, z), as, for instance, is the case when the coordinates of a point are areal and the coordinates of a line the perpendiculars upon it from the vertices of the triangle of reference, then the first scheme of linear substitution of § 62 applied to $x, y, z, \ldots$ reduces this condition to the form

$$\xi(lX+mY+nZ)+\eta(l'X+m'Y+n'Z) \\ +\zeta(l''X+m''Y+n''Z)=0,$$

i.e. $$(l\xi+l'\eta+l''\zeta)X+(m\xi+m'\eta+m''\zeta)Y \\ +(n\xi+n'\eta+n''\zeta)Z=0,$$

which is of the same form,

$$\Xi X+\mathrm{H} Y+\mathrm{Z} Z=0,$$

as before if the formulae of substitution for ξ, η, ζ are those of the second scheme in § 62.

Thus corresponding systems of point- and line-coordinates are transformed to corresponding systems by dual linear substitutions. In other words they are contragredient quantities.

64. Another remark of great importance is that the symbols $\partial/\partial x$, $\partial/\partial y$, $\partial/\partial z, \ldots$ are contragredient with the variables $x, y, z, \ldots$. For when

$$\begin{aligned} x &= lX+mY+nZ+\ldots, \\ y &= l'X+m'Y+n'Z+\ldots, \\ z &= l''X+m''Y+n''Z+\ldots, \\ &\ldots\ldots\ldots\ldots, \end{aligned}$$

we have, as used frequently already,

$$\frac{\partial}{\partial X} = l\frac{\partial}{\partial x} + l'\frac{\partial}{\partial y} + l''\frac{\partial}{\partial z} + \ldots,$$

$$\frac{\partial}{\partial Y} = m\frac{\partial}{\partial x} + m'\frac{\partial}{\partial y} + m''\frac{\partial}{\partial z} + \ldots,$$

$$\frac{\partial}{\partial Z} = n\frac{\partial}{\partial x} + n'\frac{\partial}{\partial y} + n''\frac{\partial}{\partial z} + \ldots,$$

$$\cdots\cdots\cdots\cdots\cdots ;$$

and these accord with the two dual schemes of § 62.

65. From the formulae of § 62 it follows at once that

$$\begin{aligned}\Xi X + \mathrm{H} Y + \mathrm{Z} Z + \ldots &= (lX + mY + nZ + \ldots)\,\xi \\ &\quad + (l'X + m'Y + n'Z + \ldots)\,\eta + (l''X + m''Y + n''Z + \ldots)\,\zeta + \ldots \\ &= \xi x + \eta y + \zeta z + \ldots;\end{aligned}$$

so that $\xi x + \eta y + \zeta z + \ldots$ obeys the absolute invariant law.

We might, in fact, have defined the contragrediency of $x, y, z, \ldots$ and $\xi, \eta, \zeta, \ldots$ by postulating that their corresponding schemes of linear substitution are such as to leave

$$\xi x + \eta y + \zeta z + \ldots$$

unaltered. This has been illustrated by means of the geometrical contragrediency of § 63.

In the case of the contragrediency of § 64 this persistence in form of $\xi x + \eta y + \zeta z + \ldots$ means simply that

$$X\frac{\partial}{\partial X} + Y\frac{\partial}{\partial Y} + Z\frac{\partial}{\partial Z} + \ldots = x\frac{\partial}{\partial x} + y\frac{\partial}{\partial y} + z\frac{\partial}{\partial z} + \ldots,$$

which, when we remember Euler's theorem of homogeneous functions, we see to be only the expression of the fact that a homogeneous function of any order in $x, y, z, \ldots$ becomes upon linear transformation a homogeneous function of the same order in the new variables.

66. **Contravariants and mixed concomitants.** If u, a quantic in $x, y, z, \ldots$, is expressed in terms of new variables $X, Y, Z, \ldots$ by linear transformation, and if $\xi, \eta, \zeta, \ldots$ are quantities contragredient to $x, y, z, \ldots$, and accordingly expressed in terms of new quantities $\Xi, \mathrm{H}, \mathrm{Z}, \ldots$ by the substitution dual to that giving $x, y, z, \ldots$ in terms of $X, Y, Z, \ldots$, there are found to exist functions of $\xi, \eta, \zeta, \ldots$ and of the coefficients in u, which need at most to be multiplied by factors involving only the constants of the transformation, always in fact powers of the modulus, to be made equal to

the same functions of Ξ, H, Z, ... and of the coefficients in the transformed form of u. Such functions are called *contravariants* of u.

There also exist functions possessing the same property, which involve both $x, y, z, \ldots$ and $\xi, \eta, \zeta, \ldots$, as well as the coefficients in u. Such functions are called *mixed concomitants* of u.

There also exist contravariants and mixed concomitants of systems of two or more quantics in the same variables $x, y, z, \ldots$.

Invariants, covariants, contravariants, and mixed concomitants are all spoken of as *concomitants* of the quantic or quantics to which they belong.

In a certain sense $\xi x + \eta y + \zeta z + \ldots$ may be itself spoken of as a mixed concomitant. It has, however, no reference to any particular quantic or quantics, but is a function of persistent form of the two contragredient sets of quantities only. It is the *universal* mixed concomitant of all quantics in $x, y, z, \ldots$ or in $\xi, \eta, \zeta, \ldots$.

In a better sense, contravariants and mixed concomitants of a quantic u in $x, y, z, \ldots$ are regarded as respectively invariants and covariants of the system consisting of u and the linear form $\xi x + \eta y + \zeta z + \ldots$.

Ex. 37. If $\phi(x, y, z, \ldots)$ is a covariant and $\psi(\xi, \eta, \zeta, \ldots)$ a contravariant of u, then

$$\psi\left(\frac{\partial}{\partial x}, \frac{\partial}{\partial y}, \frac{\partial}{\partial z}, \ldots\right)\phi(x, y, z, \ldots)$$

is a covariant or invariant, and

$$\phi\left(\frac{\partial}{\partial \xi}, \frac{\partial}{\partial \eta}, \frac{\partial}{\partial \zeta}, \ldots\right)\psi(\xi, \eta, \zeta, \ldots)$$

is a contravariant or invariant. (*Sylvester.*)

67. **Evectants.** It is from the last-mentioned point of view that contravariants and mixed concomitants of a quantic or quantics are most easily discovered.

The method of § 19 may, in fact, be applied to determine a series of contravariants from any invariant of a quantic u, or a series of mixed concomitants from any covariant. We have only in any invariant or covariant P to put for every coefficient in u the corresponding coefficient in

$$u + k(\xi x + \eta y + \zeta z + \ldots)^p,$$

where p is the order of u, and to take separately the coefficients of $k, k^2, \ldots$ in the expanded result. These separately are (§ 19) invariants or covariants, as the case may be, of u and $(\xi x+\eta y+\zeta z+\dots)^p$, and consequently of u and

$$\xi x+\eta y+\zeta z+\dots.$$

In other words, they are, as the case may be, contravariants or mixed concomitants of u.

The method has, it will be remembered, been already used for binary quantics in § 20, Ex. 33.

If the quantic u be

$$ax^p+pbx^{p-1}y+pb'x^{p-1}z+\dots$$
$$+\frac{p(p-1)}{1.2}cx^{p-2}y^2+\frac{p(p-1)}{1.2}c'x^{p-2}z^2+\dots,$$

where the numerical factors of the various coefficients are the corresponding coefficients in the expansion of the multinomial $(x+y+z+\dots)^p$, the rth of these contravariants or mixed concomitants is

$$\Big(\xi^p\frac{\partial}{\partial a}+\xi^{p-1}\eta\frac{\partial}{\partial b}+\xi^{p-1}\zeta\frac{\partial}{\partial b'}+\dots$$
$$+\xi^{p-2}\eta^2\frac{\partial}{\partial c}+\xi^{p-2}\zeta^2\frac{\partial}{\partial c'}+\dots\Big)^r P.$$

The contravariants obtained from any invariant P of u in this way are called the first, second, ... rth, ... *evectants* of P.

The same method applies for the determination of contravariants and mixed concomitants of two or more quantics in the same variables. The same operator as before

$$\xi^p\frac{\partial}{\partial a}+\xi^{p-1}\eta\frac{\partial}{\partial b}+\xi^{p-1}\zeta\frac{\partial}{\partial b'}+\dots$$
$$+\xi^{p-2}\eta^2\frac{\partial}{\partial c}+\xi^{p-2}\zeta^2\frac{\partial}{\partial c'}+\dots,$$

in which p and $a, b, b', \dots c, c', \dots$ refer to one of the quantics only, suffices to derive series of contravariants and mixed concomitants from invariants and covariants of the system.

The general theory of contravariants is Sylvester's. Evectants are due to Hermite.

Ex. 38. Show that

$$e\xi^4-4d\xi^3\eta+6c\xi^2\eta^2-4b\xi\eta^3+a\eta^4,$$

and

$$(ce-d^2)\xi^4-2(be-cd)\xi^3\eta+(ae+2bd-3c^2)\xi^2\eta^2$$
$$-2(ad-bc)\xi\eta^3+(ac-b^2)\eta^4,$$

are contravariants of the binary quartic $(a, b, c, d, e)(x, y)^4$.

Ans. The first evectants of I and J.

Ex. 39. Find a cubic contravariant of a binary cubic as an evectant of its discriminant.

Ex. 40. Use the method of evectants to show that the left-hand side of the tangential equation

$$(bc-f^2)\xi^2+\dots+2(gh-af)\eta\zeta+\dots=0$$

of the conic

$$u\equiv ax^2+by^2+cz^2+2fyz+2gzx+2hxy=0$$

is a contravariant of u.

Ex. 41. From the invariant

$$\Theta\equiv a'(bc-f^2)+\dots+2f'(gh-af)+\dots$$

of two ternary quadratics obtain a contravariant of

$$ax^2+\dots+2fyz+\dots,\ a'x^2+\dots+2f'yz+\dots$$

in which both sets of coefficients occur.

68. **Contravariants of binary quantics not distinct from covariants.** In the case of binary systems there is a connexion between contragrediency and cogrediency which has nothing analogous to it in the cases of ternary and higher systems.

Let x, y and ξ, η be pairs of contragredient variables, so that with the formulae of linear substitution

$$x=lX+mY, \qquad y=l'X+m'Y \qquad \dots(1)$$

go as companions the formulae

$$\Xi=l\xi+l'\eta, \qquad \mathrm{H}=m\xi+m'\eta. \qquad \dots(2)$$

These latter may be written

$$M\eta=l\mathrm{H}-m\Xi, \qquad -M\xi=l'\mathrm{H}-m'\Xi, \qquad \dots(3)$$

where $M=lm'-l'm$; and these differ only by the presence of the factor M on the left of each from the results of putting $\eta, -\xi, \mathrm{H}, -\Xi$ for x, y, X, Y in (1). This has already been encountered in the particular case of § 46.

In an extended sense, then, we may say that η and $-\xi$ are *cogredient* with x and y. The factor M will not affect the legitimacy of their use as variables cogredient with x and y, so long as only homogeneous functions are dealt with, provided, of course, that we pay proper attention to the alteration of the power of M which occurs as a factor on a side of any equality we are dealing with.

We may equally say that, when x' and y' are cogredient with x and y, then $-y'$ and x' are contragredient with x and y, but for a factor which is immaterial so long as homogeneous functions are dealt with. In particular we may say that

$-y$ and x are, with this reservation, contragredient with x and y.

If, then, in any contravariant of a binary quantic u, or of several binary quantics, we replace ξ and η by $-y$ and x, we obtain a function of x, y and the coefficients of u, or of u and the other quantics, which persists in form but for a factor involving only the constants of transformation, a power of M, after any linear transformation. In other words, we obtain a covariant of u, or of u and the other quantics.

In accordance with what has been said, however, it is clear that the power of M, which occurs as a factor in the relation expressive of the covariancy of the derived covariant, is different from that which occurs in the relation expressive of the contravariancy of the contravariant from which it is obtained.

Ex. 42. Apply this method to § 67, Ex. 38.

Ex. 43. Obtain the cubicovariant (§ 45, Ex. 13) of a binary cubic by means of the first evectant of the discriminant. (Cf. § 67, Ex. 39.)

Ex. 44. Prove that

$$M\left(\xi\frac{\partial}{\partial y}-\eta\frac{\partial}{\partial x}\right)=\Xi\frac{\partial}{\partial Y}-\mathrm{H}\frac{\partial}{\partial X};$$

and hence that $(a_0, a_1, \dots a_p)(x, y)^p$ has a concomitant (in general mixed) containing the term $a_r x^{p-r}\xi^r$, where r is any one of

$$0, 1, 2, \dots p.$$

Ex. 45. If P, of degree i and weight w, is any product, or linear function of products, of coefficients in a binary p-ic, prove that there is a concomitant (in general mixed) containing the term $Px^{ip-w}\xi^w$.

69. Covariants of u are invariants of u and a linear form. It is a proposition closely associated with the remark of the preceding article that all invariants, of a complete system (§ 33), of a binary quantic or quantics u, v, w, ... and the linear form $xy'-x'y$ are, when in them x', y' are replaced by x, y, covariants of the quantic or quantics u, v, w, ...; and that conversely all covariants of u, v, w, ... are, when in them x, y are replaced by x', y', invariants of the system consisting of u, v, w, ... and the linear form $xy'-x'y$.

This is easy to see; for, if x', y' are cogredient with x, y,

$$xy'-x'y=M(XY'-X'Y).$$

Now a complete system of invariants of u, v, w, ... and $xy'-x'y$ involve x', y' homogeneously (§ 33), so that to insert MX, MY for x', y' in an invariant is the same thing as to insert X, Y for them and multiply by a power of M. If, then, in a supposed invariant of $u, v, w, \ldots$ and $xy' - x'y$, we put x, y for x', y', we get a function of the coefficients in $u, v, w, \ldots$ and of x, y which persists in form, but for a power of M as factor, after linear transformation. In other words, we get a covariant of $u, v, w, \ldots$. And conversely, if in any covariant of $u, v, w, \ldots$ we put x', y' for x, y, we get a function of the sets of coefficients in $u, v, w, \ldots$ and $xy' - x'y$ which again persists in form, but for a power of M as factor, after linear transformation. In other words, we get an invariant of $u, v, w, \ldots$ and $xy' - x'y$.

A fact closely related to this, and, indeed, a particular case of the first part of the theorem, is that all invariants of the binary $(p+1)$-ic

$$(xy' - x'y)\,u$$

are, when x', y' are replaced by x, y, covariants of the binary p-ic u.

CHAPTER V

BINARY QUANTICS. INVARIANTS, ETC., AS FUNCTIONS OF DIFFERENCES.

70. In most of the chapters which follow, binary quantics will alone be considered, except where otherwise stated. Special methods may be with advantage adopted for the discovery and examination of their concomitants. Moreover, it will be seen later that from invariants and covariants of binary quantics there is a means of passing to those of a ternary quantic, that, in fact, invariants and covariants of a ternary quantic are a class of invariants and covariants of a system of binary quantics. From ternary quantics there is a like passage to quaternary; and so on. Thus there is more than simplicity of treatment in favour of a close examination of binary quantics alone in the first place.

71. **Convention as to numerical multiples of concomitants.** If I is an invariant, so is μI, where μ is any numerical constant. If K is a covariant, so is μK. The invariants I and μI are not of course regarded as distinct invariants, nor the covariants K, μK as distinct covariants. It will be well now to adopt some convention which will relieve us from any ambiguity as to numerical multipliers when we speak of any invariant or covariant I or K. The following is probably the best convention as to invariants of a single binary quantic

$$(a_0, a_1, a_2, \dots a_p)(x, y)^p.$$

Take the term or terms in the invariant which involve a_0 to the highest power. If there are more such terms than one, suppose that a_r is the next earliest coefficient which occurs in any of them. Choose among them the term or terms which involve a_r to the highest power. If there are more than one of these terms, let a_s be the next earliest coefficient which occurs in any of them, and take that term or those terms among them which involve a_s to the highest power; and so on continually till we get but a single term. Now divide or multiply the invariant by such a numerical quantity as will give this term the coefficient $+1$. The invariant thus prepared is what we nearly always henceforth mean when we speak of the invariant as a precise function.

And as to covariants the convention is similar. Take the coefficient of the term free from y in a covariant which has been found. Among the terms of which this coefficient consists single out one by the same rule as above, and apply to the covariant the numerical factor which will reduce the numerical coefficient of this term to $+1$. By the covariant we henceforth mean the covariant thus numerically prepared.

The rule may be more briefly stated if we call the coefficients in the quantic $a, b, c, d, e, \ldots$ instead of $a_0, a_1, a_2, a_3, a_4, \ldots$. Suppose the factors of every term in the invariant, or in the coefficient of x^{ϖ} in the covariant, written from left to right in alphabetical order. Among all the terms choose the one which comes first in alphabetical order, i. e. the one which would stand first in a dictionary. Make the coefficient of this term $+1$.

Thus, in invariants and covariants of various quantics which we have already met with,

$$ac-b^2,$$
$$(ad-bc)^2-4(ac-b^2)(bd-c^2),$$
$$(a^2d-3abc+2b^3)x^3+\ldots,$$
$$ae-4bd+3c^2,$$
$$ace+2bcd-ad^2-b^2e-c^3,$$

the coefficient $+1$ is given to the terms ac, a^2d^2, a^2dx^3, ae, ace, respectively, by the above rule.

72. Covariancy of the factors of a binary quantic. A method already touched upon in § 51 will be now more fully considered.

Let $x_1/y_1, x_2/y_2, \ldots x_p/y_p$ be the p roots of the general binary p-ic

$$(a_0, a_1, a_2, \ldots a_p)(x, y)^p,$$

i. e. let them be the roots of the equation in x/y obtained by equating the p-ic to zero. Moreover let the denominators $y_1, y_2, \ldots y_p$, which are of course arbitrary, be so chosen that

$$y_1 y_2 \ldots y_p = a_0.$$

Another expression for the p-ic must then be

$$(xy_1-x_1y)(xy_2-x_2y)\ldots(xy_p-x_py).$$

As explained in § 51, we may with propriety say that the pairs $x_1, y_1; x_2, y_2; \ldots; x_p, y_p$ are cogredient with x and y; that every suffixed x and the corresponding suffixed y are particular corresponding values of x and y. Thus, going with the formulae of linear substitution

$$x = lX+mY, \quad y = l'X+m'Y,$$

we have, for every value of r from 1 to p inclusive,

$$x_r = lX_r + mY_r, \quad y_r = l'X_r + m'Y_r,$$

so that

$$xy_r - x_r y = M(XY_r - X_r Y), \qquad \dots (1)$$

and similarly, r and s being two distinct numbers not exceeding p,

$$x_r y_s - x_s y_r = M(X_r Y_s - X_s Y_r). \qquad \dots (2)$$

By means of (1) we have that

$$(xy_1 - x_1 y)(xy_2 - x_2 y) \dots (xy_p - x_p y)$$
$$= M^p (XY_1 - X_1 Y)(XY_2 - X_2 Y) \dots (XY_p - X_p Y)$$

is an equivalent way of writing the identity

$$(a_0, a_1, a_2, \dots a_p)(x, y)^p = (A_0, A_1, A_2, \dots A_p)(X, Y)^p;$$

and we are consequently told that, a_r, any coefficient in the original form of our p-ic, being a function of $x_1, x_2, \dots x_p$ and $y_1, y_2, \dots y_p$, the corresponding coefficient A_r in the transformed form of the p-ic is M^p times that same function of $X_1, X_2, \dots X_p$ and $Y_1, Y_2, \dots Y_p$.

In particular we have

$$M^p Y_1 Y_2 \dots Y_p = A_0.$$

73. Now take H_w any homogeneous function of degree w in the differences such as $x_r y_s - x_s y_r$, and let H'_w be the same function of the corresponding differences $X_r Y_s - X_s Y_r$. By the equalities (2) above we see that

$$H_w = M^w H'_w.$$

Should it then be possible to express H_w as a homogeneous function, of degree i say, of $a_0, a_1, a_2, \dots a_p$, in which case H'_w would be the same function of M^{-p} times the corresponding new coefficients $A_0, A_1, A_2, \dots A_p$, and so, in virtue of the homogeneity, would be M^{-ip} times the same function of $A_0, A_1, A_2, \dots A_p$, that function will be an invariant of the p-ic.

The functions H_w in general cannot be so expressed. We will, however, exhibit a class of functions H_w which can, and shall proceed to show that all invariants are thus given.

Writing $\alpha_1, \alpha_2, \dots \alpha_p$ for $x_1/y_1, x_2/y_2, \dots x_p/y_p$, we know that $a_1/a_0, a_2/a_0, \dots a_p/a_0$ are certain numerical multiples of the elementary symmetric functions $\alpha_1 + \alpha_2 + \dots + \alpha_p$, $\Sigma(\alpha_1 \alpha_2), \dots$, $\alpha_1 \alpha_2 \dots \alpha_p$. We also know that any rational integral symmetric function of $\alpha_1, \alpha_2, \dots \alpha_p$ can be expressed rationally and integrally in terms of these elementary symmetric functions, every one of which involves each of the roots to the first degree. If the symmetric function involves a particular root α_1, and therefore every root, to the ith degree and no higher, the expression for it in terms of the elementary symmetric functions must involve at least one product of i of them, distinct or repeated, and no product of more than i. Such a function then, when multiplied by a_0^i, becomes equal to a rational integral function of $a_0, a_1, \dots a_p$, of degree i in those letters, and without a_0 for a factor. If the symmetric function is throughout of dimensions w in all the roots collectively, the rational integral function is isobaric of weight w. Conversely, a rational integral homogeneous isobaric function of $a_0, a_1, \dots a_p$, of degree i and weight w, and without a_0 for a factor, is equal to a_0^i times a symmetric function of the roots, of total dimensions w in them, and of degree i in every particular root. (See Burnside and Panton's *Theory of Equations*, 4th ed., § 81.)

Now take h_w a product of w differences $x_r y_s - x_s y_r$, repetitions allowed, so constructed that every one of the p suffixes $1, 2, \dots p$ occurs in just i of its factors, and no other suffixes enter. As there are p suffixes, and as two occur in every factor, the number of factors has to be $\frac{1}{2}ip$. Thus $2w = ip$.

From h_w derive $p!$ products, including h_w itself, by permuting in all possible ways the suffixes $1, 2, \dots p$. Take for H_w the sum Σh_w of these $p!$ products. It may vanish identically; if not it is symmetric in respect of all the p suffixes, and we will see that it can be expressed as a rational integral function of $a_0, a_1, \dots a_p$, with degree i and weight w, so that, as explained above, it is an invariant.

Upon dividing Σh_w by $(y_1 y_2 \dots y_p)^i$, i.e. by a_0^i, we obtain a sum, symmetric in the suffixes, of products of w factors like $(x_r y_s - x_s y_r)/y_r y_s$, i.e. like $x_r/y_r - x_s/y_s$, i.e. like $\alpha_r - \alpha_s$. Σh_w is then the product of a_0^i into a sum, symmetric in the roots, of products of w $(= \frac{1}{2}ip)$ differences between roots, each product involving every particular root in just i factors. Accordingly, by the facts about symmetric functions just quoted, it is equal to a rational integral function of $a_0, a_1, \dots a_p$ of degree i and weight w; which is what we had to prove.

[It may be remarked, incidentally, that no proof has so far been given of the fact that the symmetric function of the roots $a_0^{-i}\Sigma h_w$ is actually of degree so great as i in each particular root unless it vanishes identically. Were it of degree less than i, owing to the cancelling on addition of the terms of degree i in the various parts $a_0^{-i}h_w$ of the sum, the invariant Σh_w would have the form $a_0 F(a_0, a_1, \dots a_p)$ with the second factor integral. But no invariant can have this form. To see this apply the transformation $x = X$, $xy_1 - x_1 y = Y$, where the latter is one of the linear factors of our p-ic. We thus obtain a transformed p-ic with first coefficient $A_0 = 0$, so that the invariancy of $a_0 F(a_0, a_1, \dots a_p)$ would necessitate $a_0 F(a_0, a_1, \dots a_p) = 0$.]

74. **Invariants as functions of differences of roots.** It is now clear that, if we take any such product of w differences between roots of a p-ic that every root occurs in just i of its factors, where $ip = 2w$, and if we form a function symmetric in the roots by adding together the $p!$ results of permuting the roots in this product in all possible ways, and multiplying the sum by a_0^i, the expression for this function in terms of $a_0, a_1, \dots a_p$ is an invariant, unless it vanishes identically.

For, upon substituting $y_1 y_2 \dots y_p$ for a_0, and

$$(x_1 y_2 - x_2 y_1)/y_1 y_2, \text{ \&c.,} \quad \text{i.e.} \quad x_1/y_1 - x_2/y_2, \text{ \&c.,}$$

for $\alpha_1 - \alpha_2$, &c., we give the function the form of a sum of products in which y_1^i, &c., cancel in numerator and denominator, i.e. the form of a homogeneous H_w in $x_1 y_2 - x_2 y_1$, &c., alone.

It will be shown that invariants obtained in this way constitute a full system, i.e. that the p-ic has no invariant which is not either a single one such as constructed, or a linear function with numerical coefficients of a number of them of one degree and weight. We must first prove the following theorem:

Every invariant of

$$(a_0, a_1, \dots a_p)(x, y)^p$$

can be expressed as a function of the differences between roots, symmetric in the roots, multiplied by a power of a_0, *with or without a purely numerical factor.*

An invariant of degree i, like any other function of that degree in the coefficients, can, as explained earlier, be expressed as a_0^i times a symmetric function of the roots. We will see that it is unaltered when all the roots are increased or diminished by any the same quantity. This will ensure that the symmetric function of the roots can be expressed in terms of differences only; for it will in particular follow that in an expression for it we can diminish all the roots by one of themselves.

The roots of our p-ic, all diminished by m, are the roots of the p-ic obtained from it by the particular linear transformation $x = X + mY$, $y = Y$, of which the modulus is unity, so that by it every invariant is unaltered. This is what we had to see.

We now ask what functions of the differences between roots, symmetric in the roots, produce invariants of degree i when multiplied by a_0^i?

In the first place i must be exactly the highest degree to which any, and therefore every, root enters into the expanded symmetric function.

Next, the dimensions of the symmetric function in the roots collectively must be $w = \frac{1}{2} ip$ throughout, this being the necessary weight of an invariant of degree i (§ 25).

Now it will be proved in § 89 (corollary), from a more general theorem, that every rational integral function of differences between roots, symmetric in the roots, of dimensions $\frac{1}{2} ip$, and of degree i in every particular root, is a linear function with numerical coefficients of symmetric sums of products of differences, every product in which has the like property of being of dimensions $\frac{1}{2} ip$ and of degree i in every root; i.e. that it can be expressed as a linear function with numerical coefficients of symmetric sums, $a_0{}^i$ times which have been proved to be invariants at the outset of the present article. Hence we draw two conclusions: (1) that all functions of differences such as just described become invariants of degree i upon multiplication by $a_0{}^i$, and (2) that the statement made above, as to the fullness of a system of invariants provided by symmetric sums of products, is correct. Accordingly the facts may be summarized in the following comprehensive theorem:

If we take any such product of w of the differences between roots of a binary p-ic that every root occurs in the same number $\frac{2w}{p}$, or i, of its factors, and if we add together all the results of permuting the p roots in this product, the symmetric sum obtained, made integral in the coefficients by the factor $a_0{}^i$, is an invariant of the p-ic, unless it vanishes; there is no invariant which cannot be expressed, but for a factor $a_0{}^i$, as such a symmetric sum or as a sum of positive or negative numerical multiples of such symmetric sums; and no function of the differences, though symmetric in the roots, which cannot be so expressed, can give an invariant.

Ex. 1. Show that every invariant of a binary p-ic must vanish for the special p-ic $(x+y)^p$; and hence that the sum of the numerical coefficients of the terms of an invariant must vanish.

Ex. 2. If $\alpha, \beta, \gamma, \delta$ are the roots of a binary quartic, show that

$$a_0{}^2 \Sigma \{(\alpha-\beta)^2 (\gamma-\delta)^2\}, \quad \text{i.e.} \quad \Sigma \{(x_1 y_2 - x_2 y_1)^2 (x_3 y_4 - x_4 y_3)^2\}$$

is an invariant.

On the other hand $\Sigma\{(\alpha-\beta)^4 (\gamma-\delta)^2\}$ and $\Sigma\{(\alpha-\beta)^3 (\gamma-\delta)^3\}$, of which the latter vanishes, are not productive of invariants.

Ex. 3. Is either of $a_0^2\,\Sigma\{(\alpha-\beta)(\alpha-\gamma)(\beta-\delta)(\gamma-\epsilon)(\delta-\epsilon)\}$,
and $a_0^4\,\Sigma\{(\alpha-\beta)^2(\alpha-\gamma)^2(\beta-\delta)^2(\gamma-\epsilon)^2(\delta-\epsilon)^2\}$,
an invariant of the quintic of which $\alpha, \beta, \gamma, \delta, \epsilon$ are the roots?

Ans. The second.

75. By 'invariant' in the last article has been meant 'rational integral invariant.' An irrational invariant need not be symmetrical in the roots. A word may be said about one class of irrational invariants—the class of invariants which, though irrational in the coefficients, have rational integral expressions in terms of a_0 and the roots. What has been said applies to these, except that the references to symmetry must be omitted. A product of w differences between roots, such that every root occurs in just i of its factors, where $ip = 2w$, or a linear function of such products for the same i, produces when multiplied by a_0^i an invariant, which is irrational unless the product or linear function of products is symmetrical. For instance

$$a_0\{(\alpha-\beta)(\gamma-\delta)-(\beta-\gamma)(\alpha-\delta)\}$$

is an irrational invariant of the quartic whose roots are $\alpha, \beta, \gamma, \delta$. It is (see § 81, Ex. 4, below) a root of a cubic equation $z^3-36Iz+432J=0$, with rational invariants for coefficients. It is also a rational invariant of the four factors of the quartic. An anharmonic ratio

$$(\alpha-\gamma)(\beta-\delta)/(\alpha-\delta)(\beta-\gamma)$$

of the four factors of the quartic is an important *absolute* irrational invariant of the quartic—an absolute rational invariant of the four factors.

Those functions H_w of § 73 which do not involve the suffixed letters in such a way as to make them invariants of the p-ic, rational or irrational, as well as those which do, are invariants (rational) of the system of p linear forms xy_r-x_ry, $(r=1, 2, \dots p)$. This is easily proved by showing that every $x_ry_s-x_sy_r$ is an invariant of the system (see § 7, Ex. 2). Moreover, every invariant of the p linear forms is an H_w. To prove this is to prove that the $\frac{1}{2}p(p-1)$ invariants $x_ry_s-x_sy_r$, with $o<r<s\leqq p$, constitute the complete system of irreducible invariants of the p forms, in terms of which all other invariants can be rationally and integrally expressed. (See Ex. 22 below, and Chap. XIV.)

76. It is of interest to verify that the relation $H_w=M^wH'_w$, of § 73, applied to a case in which H_w has been shown to be an invariant $I(a_0, a_1, \dots a_p)$ of degree i and weight $w=\frac{1}{2}ip$,

gives the right power of M in the relation expressive of the invariancy of $I(a_0, a_1, \ldots a_p)$.

In § 72 we saw that, for every r, $M^{-p}A_r$ is the same function of $X_1, X_2, \ldots X_p$ and $Y_1, Y_2, \ldots Y_p$ as a_r is of $x_1, x_2, \ldots x_p$ and $y_1, y_2, \ldots y_p$. Hence, having

$$H_w = I(a_0, a_1, \ldots a_p), \text{ homogeneous of degree } i,$$

we have also $$H'_w = M^{-ip} I(A_0, A_1, \ldots A_p).$$

Accordingly $H_w = M^w H'_w$ gives

$$I(A_0, A_1, \ldots A_p) = M^{ip-w} I(a_0, a_1, \ldots a_p)$$
$$= M^w I(a_0, a_1, \ldots a_p),$$

in agreement with §§ 23, 26.

77. **Discriminants.** The product of the squares of the differences between roots of a binary p-ic is a single product, is symmetric, and involves all roots in equal numbers of its factors, viz. every root in $2(p-1)$ factors. It belongs then to the class of symmetric functions which according to § 74 produce invariants. Now $a_0^{2(p-1)}$ times this product is the discriminant, or rather (cf. § 71) is a numerical multiple of the discriminant. We have then a direct proof that the discriminant of any binary quantic is an invariant, as has been otherwise seen earlier (§ 15) for all quantics.

The weight of the discriminant is $p(p-1)$, and its degree is $2(p-1)$. Thus, in accordance with the general theory,

$$w = \tfrac{1}{2} ip.$$

78. **Invariants of quadratics and of cubics.** Binary *quadratics* and *cubics* have no rational integral invariants but their discriminants and powers of those discriminants.

For the *quadratic* this is obvious. For there is only one difference $\alpha \sim \beta$ between two roots α, β, and no function of $\alpha-\beta$ can be of a single weight and symmetric in α and β unless it be an even power of $\alpha-\beta$.

For the *cubic* § 30 tells us that there cannot be two independent invariants. The discriminant, then, being one, it follows that there is no other which is not a function of that discriminant, and consequently, as invariants are of one weight throughout, none that is not simply a numerical multiple of a power of the discriminant.

We may also reason as follows. Let α, β, γ be the roots of the cubic. Any invariant of a full system of degree i must, by § 74, be of the form

$$a_0^i \Sigma \{(\beta-\gamma)^r (\gamma-\alpha)^s (\alpha-\beta)^t\},$$

where $$s+t = t+r = r+s = i,$$

so that $$r = s = t = \tfrac{1}{2} i.$$

Thus i must be even, and there is at most one invariant of degree i, namely

$$a_0^{\,i}\Sigma\{(\beta-\gamma)(\gamma-a)(a-\beta)\}^{\frac{1}{2}i}.$$

If $\frac{1}{2}i$ is even, the product under the Σ is itself symmetric, so that every permutation of a, β, γ in it merely repeats it. Thus there is a single invariant of every degree divisible by 4, namely, the appropriate power of

$$a_0^{\,4}\{(\beta-\gamma)(\gamma-a)(a-\beta)\}^2,$$

i. e. of the discriminant, or of a multiple of the discriminant.

An odd power of $(\beta-\gamma)(\gamma-a)(a-\beta)$ is not, however, symmetric as it stands; for if we interchange β, γ in it we alter its sign. If we make all possible permutations of a, β, γ in it, and add, we do not get a symmetric function, but zero, the terms cancelling in pairs. Thus with $\frac{1}{2}i$ odd there are no invariants.

79. **Discriminants freed from inconvenient numerical factors.** The right numerical multiples of $a_0^{\,2}(a-\beta)^2$ and $a_0^{\,4}\{(\beta-\gamma)(\gamma-a)(a-\beta)\}^2$ to speak of as the discriminants of the binary quadratic and cubic, are decided by the convention of § 71.

By elementary processes of the theory of equations it can be proved, taking for convenience $(a, b, c)(x, y)^2$ and $(a, b, c, d)(x, y)^3$ to be the quadratic and cubic, that for the two cases respectively

$$a^2(a-\beta)^2 = -4(ac-b^2),$$

and $$a^4\{(\beta-\gamma)(\gamma-a)(a-\beta)\}^2$$
$$= -27\{(ad-bc)^2-4(ac-b^2)(bd-c^2)\};$$

and it is to the expressions in brackets on the right that, in accordance with § 71, the name of discriminants is properly given, and not to -4 and -27 times those expressions respectively.

In Cayley's fourth memoir on quantics the corresponding multiple to the -4 and -27 above has been found in the case of the discriminant of any binary quantic. Consider the binary p-ic $(a_0, a_1, a_2, \ldots a_p)(x, y)^p$. The product of the squares of differences between pairs of its roots is of weight $p(p-1)$, being the product of $\frac{1}{2}p(p-1)$ factors of two dimensions in the roots, and consequently, being an invariant, is of degree $2w/p = 2(p-1)$. That this is the degree also follows from the fact that any particular root enters in $p-1$ squared factors, and so to the degree $2(p-1)$; for the degree in the coefficients $a_1, a_2, \dots a_p$ is the degree in any particular root. We have, then, to consider the expression for

$$a_0^{2(p-1)} \Pi (a_r - a_s)^2$$

in terms of the coefficients.

Since $p(p-1)$ is the weight, the term $a_0^{p-1} a_p^{p-1}$, if it actually occurs, is the one term in the discriminant into which a_0 enters to the highest power. This, then, if it occurs, is the term in the discriminant to which the coefficient $+1$ is given in accordance with the convention of § 71. Now the term must occur; for it is the only one which does not vanish for the special p-ic $a_0 x^p + a_p y^p$, and the discriminant of this special p-ic does not vanish, since no two roots of the equation $a_0 z^p + a_p = 0$ are equal when neither a_0 nor a_p vanishes.

Now consider the yet more special p-ic $x^p + y^p$. Its roots are those of $z^p + 1 = 0$, i.e. the p pth roots of -1. Denote these by $\rho_1, \rho_2, \dots \rho_p$. We know that if $\rho_1, \rho_2, \dots \rho_p$ are the roots of $f(z) = 0$, then

$$f'(z) = \frac{f(z)}{z-\rho_1} + \frac{f(z)}{z-\rho_2} + \dots + \frac{f(z)}{z-\rho_p},$$

so that $f'(\rho_1) = \left[\frac{f(z)}{z-\rho_1}\right]_{z=\rho_1} = (\rho_1 - \rho_2)(\rho_1 - \rho_3) \dots (\rho_1 - \rho_p),$

and so for other roots $\rho_2, \rho_3, \dots \rho_p$. It follows, by multiplication of the p right-hand and p left-hand members, that

$$f'(\rho_1) f'(\rho_2) \dots f'(\rho_p) = (-1)^{\frac{1}{2}p(p-1)} \Pi (\rho_r - \rho_s)^2,$$

the sign being as stated because each of the $\frac{1}{2}p(p-1)$ differences $\rho_r \sim \rho_s$ occurs once in the product as $\rho_r - \rho_s$ and once as $\rho_s - \rho_r$. In the present case, then, of the equation $z^p + 1 = 0$,

$$p\rho_1^{p-1} \cdot p\rho_2^{p-1} \cdot \dots p\rho_p^{p-1} = (-1)^{\frac{1}{2}p(p-1)} \Pi (\rho_r - \rho_s)^2,$$

so that $\Pi (\rho_r - \rho_s)^2 = (-1)^{-\frac{1}{2}p(p-1)} p^p (\rho_1 \rho_2, \dots \rho_p)^{p-1}$

$$= (-1)^{-\frac{1}{2}p(p-1)} p^p \{(-1)^p\}^{p-1}$$

$$= (-1)^{\frac{1}{2}p(p-1)} p^p.$$

Now if, for the general p-ic $(a_0, a_1, a_2, \dots a_p)(x, y)^p$,

$$a_0^{2(p-1)} \Pi (a_r - a_s)^2 = k \{a_0^{p-1} a_p^{p-1} + \dots\},$$

we get as a particular case of this

$$\Pi (\rho_r - \rho_s)^2 = k.$$

Consequently $k = (-1)^{\frac{1}{2}p(p-1)} p^p$.

Thus the product $a_0^{2(p-1)} \Pi (a_r - a_s)^2$ for the binary p-ic is properly spoken of, not as the discriminant, but as

$$(-1)^{\frac{1}{2}p(p-1)} p^p$$

times the discriminant.

The multipliers -4, -27 for the cases of the quadratic and cubic accord with this general result.

80. The binary quartic. The binary quartic $(a, b, c, d, e)(x, y)^4$ has not more than two independent invariants (§ 30). Now the discriminant is one (§§ 15, 77). There are, however, two of lower degrees than this. It is preferable to regard them as the two fundamental invariants, and the discriminant as consequently a function of them. The two are the I and J of § 29.

In fact, $$a^2 \Sigma\{(\beta-\gamma)^2 (\alpha-\delta)^2\}$$
and $$a^3 \Sigma\{(\beta-\gamma)(\alpha-\delta)(\gamma-\alpha)^2(\beta-\delta)^2\}$$
are invariants according to the criterion of § 74.

A remark as to the number of terms covered in these and such-like summations will be here in place. We must always bear in mind that for purposes of expression in terms of the coefficients it is symmetry in the roots rather than in the differences which is fundamental; and we most safely take one term for every permutation of $\alpha, \beta, \gamma, \delta$. Thus, since we may take a first root α in four ways, then a second β in three ways, and then a third γ in two ways, we regard each of the above sums as a sum of twenty-four terms, even though these are, in the first, three terms eight times repeated, and, in the second, six terms four times repeated. The student is recommended to give the close attention necessary to convince him of this second fact.

Let the four roots be separated into a triad α, β, γ and the fourth δ, and let $(\beta-\gamma)(\alpha-\delta)$, $(\gamma-\alpha)(\beta-\delta)$, $(\alpha-\beta)(\gamma-\delta)$ be denoted by u, v, w. Then he will see that the first sum is eight times
$$a^2(u^2+v^2+w^2), \qquad \ldots (1)$$
and the second four times
$$a^3\{u(v^2-w^2)+v(w^2-u^2)+w(u^2-v^2)\}, \qquad \ldots (2)$$
which latter may, by elementary algebra, equally be written
$$-a^3\{u^2(v-w)+v^2(w-u)+w^2(u-v)\},$$
or $$a^3(v-w)(w-u)(u-v),$$
or again $$\tfrac{1}{3}a^3\{(v-w)^3+(w-u)^3+(u-v)^3\}.$$

The values of the invariants (1) and (2) in terms of the coefficients may be calculated by the ordinary methods of symmetric functions. (See, for instance, Burnside and Panton's *Theory of Equations*, § 27, Exx. 16, 18.) The results are that
$$a^2(u^2+v^2+w^2) = 24(ae-4bd+3c^2) = 24I$$
and $$a^3\{u(v^2-w^2)+v(w^2-u^2)+w(u^2-v^2)\}$$
$$= -432(ace+2bcd-ad^2-b^2e-c^3) = -432J.$$

This direct process is however unnecessary. For it will be seen in the next chapter that I and J are the only invariants of degrees 2 and 3 which the quartic possesses. The invariants (1) and (2) must then be numerical multiples kI, $k'J$ of I and J respectively. This being granted, that k and k' have the values 24 and -432 respectively may be seen by considering a particular case. Take, for instance, the particular case of the quartic whose roots are ± 1, ± 2.

It will be noticed that in I and J the alphabetically leading terms ae, ace have the coefficient $+1$ according to the convention of § 71.

The proof that all rational integral invariants of the quartic can be rationally and integrally expressed in terms of I and J is reserved till a later chapter.

81. **Discriminant of quartic.** The discriminant, an invariant, must, as explained at the opening of the last article, be a function of I and J. We proceed to see what function.

It is an invariant of degree 6 and weight 12 (§ 77), which vanishes when the quartic has a square factor, and consequently when it has the square factor y^2, i. e. when $a = 0$ and $b = 0$.

Now in this case I and J become $3c^2$ and $-c^3$ respectively. Of these no rational integral function vanishes except

$$(3c^2)^3 - 27(-c^3)^2$$

and functions with this as a factor.

Consequently

$$I^3 - 27J^2 \equiv (ae - 4bd + 3c^2)^3 - 27(ace + 2bcd - ad^2 - b^2e - c^3)^2,$$

whose degree and weight are right, is the discriminant of the quartic.

The coefficient of its alphabetically leading term a^3e^3 is correctly $+1$.

By the general proposition of § 79, the invariant

$$a^6(\alpha-\beta)^2(\alpha-\gamma)^2(\alpha-\delta)^2(\beta-\gamma)^2(\beta-\delta)^2(\gamma-\delta)^2,$$

or, in the notation of the preceding article, $a^6u^2v^2w^2$, which must be a numerical multiple of the discriminant, is equal to

$$4^4(I^3 - 27J^2) = 256(I^3 - 27J^2).$$

Ex. 4. Prove this also by showing that $v-w$, $w-u$, $u-v$ are the roots of the cubic $z^3 - 36a^{-2}Iz + 432a^{-3}J = 0$, and that $27^2u^2v^2w^2$ is the product of the squares of differences between roots of this cubic.

Ex. 5. Obtain the same result by showing that $432^2a^{-6}J^2$ is the product of the squares of differences between roots of the cubic

$$t^3 - 12a^{-2}It - uvw = 0,$$

whose roots are u, v, w.

Ex. 6. The products *au*, *av*, *aw* are irrational invariants of the binary quartic.

Ans. Cf. § 75, or Ex. 4 above.

Ex. 7. The six ratios of u, v, w to one another, which are respectively minus the six anharmonic ratios of the factors of the quartic, are irrational fractional invariants.

Ex. 8. Any anharmonic ratio $(a_1-a_3)(a_2-a_4)/(a_2-a_3)(a_1-a_4)$ of any four factors of a binary p-ic is an irrational invariant of the p-ic.

Ex. 9. All invariants of a binary quartic can be expressed as functions of the discriminant and any single anharmonic ratio $(\alpha-\gamma)(\beta-\delta)/(\alpha-\delta)(\beta-\gamma)$ of the factors.

Ex. 10. All invariants of a binary p-ic are functions of the discriminant and the $p-3$ anharmonic ratios of four factors

$$\frac{(\beta-\alpha)(\gamma-\alpha_4)}{(\gamma-\alpha)(\beta-\alpha_4)},\ \frac{(\beta-\alpha)(\gamma-\alpha_5)}{(\gamma-\alpha)(\beta-\alpha_5)},\ \dots\ \frac{(\beta-\alpha)(\gamma-\alpha_p)}{(\gamma-\alpha)(\beta-\alpha_p)},$$

where α, β, γ are three roots, and α_4, α_5, ... α_p the rest. (*Cayley.*)

Ans. These are $p-2$ independent invariants.

Ex. 11. In a binary quartic for which $I = 0$ the six anharmonic ratios of the four factors are equal in sets of three to the two imaginary cube roots of -1. Geometrically the pencil or range of four elements which the quartic denotes is said to be 'equi-anharmonic.'

Ans. From $u^2+v^2+w^2 = 0$ and $u+v+w = 0$

we have $$\left(\frac{u}{v}\right)^2 + \frac{u}{v} + 1 = 0.\quad \text{Hence, \&c.}$$

Ex. 12. In a binary quartic for which $J = 0$ the six anharmonic ratios are -1, -1, 2, 2, $\frac{1}{2}$, $\frac{1}{2}$; and the pencil or range is harmonic.

82. Covariants as functions of differences. We now proceed to notice briefly the facts as to covariants of a binary quantic which are analogous to, and in reality include, the facts as to invariants dealt with in §§ 72 to 76.

Using the results (1) and (2) of § 72 we can at once write down the analogue of the first statement in § 73; viz. that, if G_w is a homogeneous function of degree w in the two sets of differences whose types are $xy_r - x_ry$ and $x_ry_s - x_sy_r$, where x_1/y_1, x_2/y_2, ... x_p/y_p are the roots of $(a_0, a_1, a_2, \dots a_p)(x, y)^p$, and if G'_w is the same homogeneous function of the corresponding differences $XY_r - X_rY$, &c., and $X_rY_s - X_sY_r$, &c. with reference to the roots of the transformed quantic

$$(A_0, A_1, A_2, \dots A_p)(X, Y)^p,$$

then $$G_w = M^w G'_w.$$

Should it then be possible to express G_w in terms of the variables x, y and the coefficients $a_0, a_1, a_2, \dots a_p$, and G'_w as the same function, divided by a power of the modulus, of X, Y and $A_0, A_1, A_2, \dots A_p$, such a function G_w when so expressed will be a covariant.

Notice that any covariant so obtained must be *homogeneous in the coefficients* $a_0, a_1, a_2, \dots a_p$. For if the expression for G_w be

$$K(a_0, a_1, a_2, \dots a_p;\ x, y),$$

that for G'_w is

$$K(A_0/M^p, A_1/M^p, A_2/M^p, \dots A_p/M^p;\ X, Y);$$

and this must be homogeneous in the fractions with denominator M^p if the equality $G_w = M^w G'_w$ is to take the form

$$K(A_0, A_1, A_2, \dots A_p;\ X, Y) = M^\mu K(a_0, a_1, a_2, \dots a_p;\ x, y).$$

It is to be concluded also that G_w, or K, is *homogeneous in x and y*, i.e. that in every product of differences which is a part of G_w there must occur the same number of differences $xy_r - x_r y$, $xy_s - x_s y, \dots$ of the first type. For, the coefficients $a_0, a_1, a_2, \dots a_p$ being all homogeneous in $x_1, x_2, \dots x_p$, $y_1, y_2, \dots y_p$, the covariant K, or G_w, must be homogeneous in these quantities. Now any term in G_w which is a product of ϖ differences of the type $xy_r - x_r y$ and, consequently, $w - \varpi$ differences of the other type $x_r y_s - x_s y_r$, is of dimensions $\varpi + 2(w - \varpi)$, i.e. $2w - \varpi$, in $x_1, x_2, \dots x_p, y_1, y_2, \dots y_p$. This then having to be constant for all products of which G_w consists, ϖ must be the same for all.

Covariants thus produced are then necessarily of one degree in the coefficients and one order in the variables throughout.

83. Now any covariant of degree i and order ϖ of a binary quantic is necessarily $a_0^i y^\varpi$ times a function of the differences between roots and of the differences between x/y and roots. For it must be unaltered by the linear transformation

$$x = X + mY,\ y = Y$$

of which the modulus is 1; that is to say, it must be unchanged in value when $\frac{x}{y}$ and all the roots are diminished by any the same quantity m, and so in particular when all are diminished by one root.

Those functions of the two sets of differences which, when multiplied by factors $a_0^i y^\varpi$, become covariants are exactly those which, when so multiplied, become functions such as G_w above. We will prove this for rational integral covariants—to which as usual attention is confined—by exhibiting a system of functions of the differences which, upon multiplication by $a_0^i y^\varpi$, become covariants because they become functions G_w, and showing that all other covariants of degree i and order ϖ are sums of positive or negative numerical multiples of these.

We first notice that a function of the differences which yields a rational covariant must involve the roots symmetrically: otherwise it could not be expressed rationally in terms of the coefficients and x, y at all. Also, if ϖ is the order of the covariant yielded, so that y^ϖ is the necessary y-factor to be applied, the function must be of degree ϖ in $\frac{x}{y}$. Once more, if i is the degree of the covariant, so that a_0^i, i.e. $(y_1 y_2 \dots y_p)^i$, is the necessary a_0-factor, every one of the roots $a_1, a_2, \dots a_p$, or $x_1/y_1, x_2/y_2, \dots x_p/y_p$, must be involved to the degree i: if one is, so too are the rest by the symmetry. Further (§ 39) $ip - \varpi$ must be positive or zero, and (§ 38) $\frac{1}{2}(ip+\varpi) = w$ must be the whole weight of the covariant, i.e. the dimensions of the function of differences in $\frac{x}{y}$ and the roots together.

Take then any degree i and order ϖ such that $ip \geqq \varpi$, and $ip+\varpi$ is even $(= 2w)$. Write down a product of w factors, of which $\frac{1}{2}(ip-\varpi)$ are differences $a_r - a_s$, i.e. $(x_r y_s - x_s y_r)/y_r y_s$, between roots, and the remaining ϖ are differences $\frac{x}{y} - a_r$, i.e. $(xy_r - x_r y)/yy_r$, between $\frac{x}{y}$ and roots, so choosing these factors that every root occurs in just i of the whole number w, x/y of course occurring in just ϖ of them. The product is a function G_w over the denominator $(y_1 y_2 \dots y_p)^i y^\varpi$, i.e. $a_0^i y^\varpi$. Multiplying by this denominator we obtain the function G_w, say g_w. Now the product written down is probably not symmetric in the roots. But permute the roots in it in all the $p!$ possible ways, and add the $p!$ results of permutation. Unless the sum vanishes identically we thus get a function symmetric in the roots, which may be expressed as a rational integral function of degree i in $a_1/a_0, a_2/a_0, \dots a_p/a_0$, and of degree ϖ in x/y. The result of multiplying this by $a_0^i y^\varpi$ is a homogeneous rational integral function of degree i in $a_0, a_1, \dots a_p$ and of order ϖ in x, y. It is also a G_w function Σg_w. Accordingly it is a covariant.

Now it will be proved in § 89, Cor. (2), that every rational integral function of $\frac{1}{2}(ip+\varpi) = w$ dimensions in x/y and the roots, which (1) is symmetric in the roots, (2) is a function of the two sets of differences, and (3) involves every root to just the degree i and x/y to just the degree ϖ, i.e. every function of differences which can conceivably yield a rational integral covariant of degree i and order ϖ, is either one of those just constructed, or a sum of positive or negative numerical multiples of several of them with the same i and ϖ. Taking this as known, we thus have that all the functions of differences which could conceivably yield covariants do actually yield them, and that those constructed above as productive of functions Σg_w suffice to form, for any allowable degree and order, a system in terms of which all others of that degree and order can be linearly expressed. We can in fact state the following complete result:

If, choosing numbers i, ϖ such that $ip \geqq \varpi$ and $ip+\varpi$ is even, we take any such product of $\frac{1}{2}(ip-\varpi)$ differences between roots of a binary p-ic, and ϖ differences between x/y and roots, that every root occurs in just i of all the $\frac{1}{2}(ip+\varpi)$ factors, and x/y of course in just ϖ, and add together all the $p!$ results of permuting in it the p roots, the symmetric sum obtained, made integral in the coefficients and in x, y by the factor $a_0{}^i y^\varpi$, is a covariant of the p-ic, unless it vanishes; there is no covariant which cannot be expressed, but for a factor $a_0{}^i y^\varpi$, as such a symmetric sum or as a sum of positive or negative numerical multiples of such symmetric sums; and no function of the two sets of differences, though symmetric in the roots, which cannot be so expressed, can give a covariant.

Ex. 13. All covariants, except powers of the p-ic itself, vanish for the special p-ic $(x+y)^p$.

Ex. 14. The sums of the numerical coefficients of the products of $a_0, a_1, a_2, \ldots a_p$ which occur in $K_0, K_1, K_2, \ldots K_\varpi$ respectively, where $(K_0, K_1, \ldots K_\varpi)(x, y)^\varpi$ is a covariant of $(a_0, a_1, \ldots a_p)(x, y)^p$, all vanish, unless the covariant is merely a power of

$$(a_0, a_1, \ldots a_p)(x, y)^p.$$

Ex. 15. Every term in the summation which gives a covariant Σg_w of a binary p-ic must involve at least one difference between a pair of r chosen roots if $2ir > ip+\varpi$.

Ans. Cf. § 39, Ex. 2.

Ex. 16. Every term in the summation which gives an invariant Σh_w must have this property if $2r > p$.

Ex. 17. Verify as in § 76 that the relation $G_w = M^w G'_w$, applied to a case in which G_w is a covariant of a p-ic, gives correctly $M^{\frac{1}{2}(ip-\varpi)}$ as the factor by which the covariant must be multiplied to be made equal to the covariant of the transformed p-ic.

84. The binary quadratic. This has no covariant distinct from itself and its one invariant, the discriminant.

In fact, if

$$ax^2 + 2bxy + cy^2 \equiv a(x-\alpha y)(x-\beta y),$$

covariants of degree i and order ϖ have, by § 83, to be linear functions of expressions

$$a^i y^\varpi \Sigma\{(a-\beta)^\lambda (x/y-a)^\mu (x/y-\beta)^\nu\},$$

i. e.

$$a^i y^\varpi \{(a-\beta)^\lambda (x/y-a)^\mu (x/y-\beta)^\nu + (\beta-a)^\lambda (x/y-\beta)^\mu (x/y-a)^\nu\},$$

where $$\lambda+\mu = \lambda+\nu = i,$$

and $$\mu+\nu = \varpi,$$

so that $\mu = \nu = \frac{1}{2}\varpi$, and $\lambda = \frac{1}{2}(2i-\varpi)$, are unique.

There is then at most one covariant of this degree and order, namely,

$$a^i\{(a-\beta)^{\frac{1}{2}(2i-\varpi)} + (\beta-a)^{\frac{1}{2}(2i-\varpi)}\}\{(x-ay)(x-\beta y)\}^{\frac{1}{2}\varpi}.$$

For this to be rational, ϖ, and therefore $2i-\varpi$, must be even; and, for it not to vanish, $\frac{1}{2}(2i-\varpi)$ must be even. Accordingly every covariant of degree and order i, ϖ must be a numerical multiple of

$$\{a^2(a-\beta)^2\}^m \{a(x-ay)(x-\beta y)\}^n,$$

where $2n = \varpi$, $2m+n = i$, and m, n are positive numbers or zero.

In other words, all covariants of one order and degree, including invariants, are numerical multiples of products of integral (or zero) powers of the quadratic $ax^2+2bxy+cy^2$ itself and its discriminant $ac-b^2$.

Hence (§§ 35, 36) the quadratic itself and its discriminant form the complete system of irreducible covariants and invariants.

85. **Covariants of the cubic.** If a, β, γ are the roots of the binary cubic

$$ax^3+3bx^2y+3cxy^2+dy^3 \equiv a(x-ay)(x-\beta y)(x-\gamma y),$$

the cubic has two independent covariants, numerical multiples of

$$a^2\Sigma\{(x-ay)^2(\beta-\gamma)^2\}$$

and $$a^3\Sigma\{(x-ay)^2(x-\beta y)(\beta-\gamma)^2(\gamma-a)\},$$

which, writing θ, ϕ, ψ for

$$(x-ay)(\beta-\gamma),\quad (x-\beta y)(\gamma-a),\quad (x-\gamma y)(a-\beta),$$

are respectively twice and once

$$a^2(\theta^2+\phi^2+\psi^2) = a^2 h, \text{ say},$$

and $$a^3\{\theta^2(\phi-\psi)+\phi^2(\psi-\theta)+\psi^2(\theta-\phi)\} = a^3 g, \text{ say}.$$

That the two obey the criteria of § 83, and are consequently covariants, is at once verified. That there cannot be more than two covariants, independent of one another and the cubic itself, is known from § 42. All other covariants, and invariants too, can then be expressed in terms of them and the cubic. The one irreducible invariant, the discriminant (§ 78), is of course not a rational integral function of the three—no rational integral function of them can be free from the variables. We reserve till a later chapter the proof that there is no other irreducible covariant or invariant of the cubic, so that any other covariant or invariant is a rational integral function of the cubic, the two covariants above, and the discriminant.

The expressions for a^2h and a^3g in terms of the coefficients and variables can be obtained by elementary methods of the theory of equations. We know however (cf. § 45, Exx. 12, 13) two covariants of the degrees and orders of a^2h and a^3g, viz.

$$H = (ac-b^2)x^2 + (ad-bc)xy + (bd-c^2)y^2,$$

and $$G = (a^2d - 3abc + 2b^3,\ abd - 2ac^2 + b^2c,\\ -acd + 2b^2d - bc^2,\ -ad^2 + 3bcd - 2c^3)(x, y)^3,$$

and we shall see later (see, for instance, § 114, Ex. 16) that these are the only covariants of the degrees and orders in question. Hence, for some numerical values of k and k', we must have
$$a^2h = kH,$$
and
$$a^3g = k'G.$$
This being known, we can find k and k' by consideration of the values of the covariants in a particular case. Take for instance the cubic x^3-y^3, for which $a, b, c, d, \alpha, \beta, \gamma$ have the values $1, 0, 0, -1, 1, \omega, \omega^2$. The above equalities become

$$18xy = -kxy,$$
$$27(x^3+y^3) = -k'(x^3+y^3),$$

whence the values of k and k' are -18 and -27. Thus
$$a^2h = -18H,$$
and
$$a^3g = -27G.$$

In accordance with the convention of § 71 we speak of H and G, rather than of a^2h and a^3g, as the fundamental covariants.

The close similarity between the forms, in terms of differences, of the covariants of a cubic and the invariants of a quartic will not have escaped notice. It is not accidental, but is a result of the fact, to which attention has been called in § 69, that the invariants of
$$(xy'-x'y)u$$
are, when x' and y' are replaced by x and y, covariants of u.

86. Syzygy among concomitants of cubic. The cubic u, its two covariants H and G, and its discriminant
$$\Delta = (ad-bc)^2 - 4(ac-b^2)(bd-c^2)$$

must, as we have seen, be connected by a relation. To find this relation we may consider the cubic in the form

$$u = ax^3 + dy^3$$

which is not special, but is, as we have seen in § 11, Ex. 14, one to which the general cubic can be reduced by linear substitution. For this form

$$H = adxy,$$
$$G = a^2dx^3 - ad^2y^3 = ad\,(ax^3 - dy^3),$$
$$\Delta = a^2d^2;$$

whence, by elimination of a, d, x, y, the connecting relation is seen to be

$$\Delta u^2 = G^2 + 4H^3,$$

which holds when the general expressions for u, H, G and Δ are substituted.

Ex. 18. Prove the same relation by showing that $\theta^2\phi^2\psi^2$, a determinate numerical multiple of the product Δu^2, is 3^{-6} times the product of the squares of the differences between roots of the equation $z^3 - \frac{3}{2}hz + g = 0$ whose roots are $\phi - \psi$, $\psi - \theta$, $\theta - \phi$, and so a determinate numerical multiple of the discriminant of this cubic.

Ex. 19. If the roots of the cubic equation $u = 0$ are a, β, γ, the roots of $H = 0$ are

$$-\frac{\beta\gamma + \omega\gamma a + \omega^2 a\beta}{a + \omega\beta + \omega^2\gamma}, \quad -\frac{\beta\gamma + \omega^2\gamma a + \omega a\beta}{a + \omega^2\beta + \omega\gamma},$$

and those of $G = 0$ are

$$\frac{2\beta\gamma - \gamma a - a\beta}{\beta + \gamma - 2a}, \quad \frac{2\gamma a - a\beta - \beta\gamma}{\gamma + a - 2\beta}, \quad \frac{2a\beta - \beta\gamma - \gamma a}{a + \beta - 2\gamma}. \quad \text{(Cayley.)}$$

87. **Several binary quantics.** Into a full discussion of the expressions by means of differences of invariants and covariants of systems of more binary quantics than one it is not proposed here to enter; but the facts may be developed by the same methods as have been adopted in this chapter.

It will be found, for instance, with regard to *invariants* of *two* binary quantics, that functions of the roots which produce them must, for rationality, be symmetrical in the roots of each quantic separately, and will in general be functions of three classes of differences, viz. (1) differences between two roots of the first quantic, (2) differences between two roots of the second quantic, and (3) differences between a root of the first and one of the second. In order to produce invariants which are not more properly regarded as sums of simpler invariants, such functions must be homogeneous, not only on the whole, but in each of the three sets of differences singly. Any one of a full system for given partial degrees must, moreover, be a sum of products of differences, in every one of which all roots of the first quantic occur in equal constant numbers of factors, and all roots of the second in equal constant numbers of factors, the numbers not being, however, necessarily or as a rule the same.

88. **Functions of differences.** In § 74 and § 83 assumptions needing justification have been made as to certain classes of functions of differences.

It will be convenient to establish a test as to whether a given function $F(a_1, a_2, \dots a_p)$ can or cannot be expressed in terms of differences $a_r - a_s$ only, each between two of the letters involved.

If it can, then, for every value of h,

$$F(a_1, a_2, \dots a_p) = F(a_1 + h, a_2 + h, \dots a_p + h). \qquad \dots (1)$$

Conversely it can if this is the case; for then, in particular,

$$F(a_1, a_2, \dots a_p) = F(0, a_2 - a_1, \dots a_p - a_1).$$

Now the necessary and sufficient condition for (1) to hold for every value of h is that

$$\left(\frac{\partial}{\partial a_1} + \frac{\partial}{\partial a_2} + \dots + \frac{\partial}{\partial a_p}\right) F(a_1, a_2, \dots a_p) = 0, \qquad \dots (2)$$

where identical vanishing is meant: we are dealing with $a_1, a_2, \dots a_p$ as independent arbitrary quantities, connected by no relation.

To prove this, observe that

$$\frac{d}{dh} F(a_1 + h, a_2 + h, \dots a_p + h)$$
$$\equiv \left(\frac{\partial}{\partial a_1} + \frac{\partial}{\partial a_2} + \dots + \frac{\partial}{\partial a_p}\right) F(a_1 + h, a_2 + h, \dots a_p + h). \quad \dots (3)$$

Here, if $F(a_1 + h, a_2 + h, \dots a_p + h)$ is independent of h, and so equal to $F(a_1, a_2, \dots a_p)$, the left-hand side vanishes, and therefore also the right-hand side, so that (2) holds. Conversely, if (2) is satisfied identically, it is satisfied when we put $a_1 + h, a_2 + h, \dots a_p + h$ for $a_1, a_2, \dots a_p$, so that, by (3), $\frac{d}{dh} F(a_1 + h, a_2 + h, \dots a_p + h) = 0$, and $F(a_1 + h, a_2 + h, \dots a_p + h)$ is independent of h.

The theorem obtained may be stated as follows:

$F(a_1, a_2, \dots a_p)$ *will or will not be a function of differences, according as the differential operator*

$$\partial/\partial a_1 + \partial/\partial a_2 + \dots + \partial/\partial a_p$$

does or does not annihilate it.

88 (*bis*). An expression for a function of differences in terms of differences is not unique. From one expression

which involves a_2-a_1, for instance, we can derive a different one by putting $(a_2-a_3)+(a_3-a_1)$ for a_2-a_1.

Our justification of assumptions made in §§ 74, 83 will rest on a proof of the important fact that, if a rational integral function $F(a_1, a_2, \dots a_p)$, given in its expanded form, is a function of differences, then, among the expressions for it as linear functions of products of differences, there will certainly be one, such that none of the products of differences in it involves any of $a_1, a_2, \dots a_p$ to a higher degree than the expanded $F(a_1, a_2, \dots a_p)$ does.

For instance, $\beta^2-\gamma^2-2\alpha\beta+2\alpha\gamma$ is a function of differences, as $\partial/\partial\alpha+\partial/\partial\beta+\partial/\partial\gamma$ annihilates it. An expression for it in terms of differences is $(\beta-\alpha)^2-(\gamma-\alpha)^2$. But each product of differences here is of degree 2 in α, whereas the expanded function is only of degree 1 in that letter. Another expression for the function is, however, $(\beta-\gamma)(\beta-\alpha)+(\beta-\gamma)(\gamma-\alpha)$, which has no such defect.

In proving the desired theorem we shall need the following lemma:

If $i_1, i_2, \dots i_p$ are the degrees to which $a_1, a_2, \dots a_p$ respectively enter in the expanded expression for any homogeneous function of the differences of total dimensions w, then

$$2w \leqq i_1+i_2+\dots+i_p.$$

Suppose that, on the contrary, we have a function, as described, for which

$$2w > i_1+i_2+\dots+i_p.$$

It cannot be merely $k(a_1-a_2)^w$, for which $2w=\Sigma i$. It might, however, be divisible by some lower power of a_1-a_2; say by $(a_1-a_2)^r$. If so, the removal from it of this factor would diminish each of w, i_1, i_2 by r, leaving $i_3, i_4, \dots i_p$ unchanged; and consequently would leave $2w-\Sigma i$ unaltered.

If, then, there is any function whatever, such as described, for which $2w>\Sigma i$, there is one with the same property which does not vanish when we put a_2 for a_1. Let w and $i_1, i_2, \dots i_p$ refer to this function.

Put in it a_2 for a_1. A function of the differences of $a_2, a_3, \dots a_p$ results. This is homogeneous of w dimensions; and its degrees in $i_2, i_3, \dots i_p$ are certainly not greater respectively than $i_1+i_2, i_3, \dots i_p$. Now, on our supposition,

$$2w > (i_1+i_2)+i_3+\dots+i_p.$$

Consequently for the function of differences of $p-1$ letters which we have derived $2w>\Sigma i$.

By repetition of the same process, we must be able to derive certain functions of differences of $p-2, p-3, \dots 2$ letters with the same property.

But for 2 letters there is no function with the property. All functions of w dimensions of their differences are included in $k(a_{p-1}-a_p)^w$; and for this $2w=\Sigma i$.

Accordingly our supposition is untenable; and we have always $2w \leqq \Sigma i$.

89. **A fundamental theorem.** *If a rational integral function of dimensions w throughout in $a_1, a_2, \ldots a_p$ is a function of their differences, i.e. if it is annihilated by $\Sigma(\partial/\partial a)$, and if in its expanded form in terms of $a_1, a_2, \ldots a_p$ these letters occur to degrees $i_1, i_2, \ldots i_p$ respectively, it can be expressed as a linear function with numerical coefficients of products of w differences (repetitions allowed) in such a way that in none of the products does a_1 occur in more than i_1 factors, or a_2 in more than i_2, or &c., or a_p in more than i_p.*

Let the expanded function be arranged by powers of a_1, and written $$a_1^{i_1}P+a_1^{i_1-1}Q+\ldots+Z. \qquad \ldots (1)$$
Here P is a function of differences of $a_2, a_3, \ldots a_p$. For, as $\partial/\partial a_1+\partial/\partial a_2+\ldots+\partial/\partial a_p$ annihilates the sum, the coefficient of $a_1^{i_1}$ in the result of applying this operation vanishes: in other words, $\partial/\partial a_2+\partial/\partial a_3+\ldots+\partial/\partial a_p$ annihilates P. Moreover P is of $w-i_1$ dimensions, and involves $a_2, a_3, \ldots a_p$ (if at all) to degrees which do not exceed $i_2, i_3, \ldots i_p$ respectively.

We proceed to show that, if the theorem holds for $p-1$ letters, it must hold for p letters. If it holds for $p-1$ letters, P can be arranged as a sum of parts like
$$\lambda(a_2-a_3)^{m_{23}}(a_2-a_4)^{m_{24}}\ldots(a_{p-1}-a_p)^{m_{p-1\,p}},$$
where
$$m_{23}+m_{24}+\ldots+m_{2p} \leqq i_2' = i_2-n_2, \text{ say},$$
$$m_{23}+m_{34}+\ldots+m_{3p} \leqq i_3' = i_3-n_3, \text{ say},$$
$$\cdot \quad \cdot \quad \cdot \quad \cdot \quad \cdot \quad \cdot \quad \cdot \quad \cdot$$
$$m_{2p}+m_{3p}+\ldots+m_{p-1\,p} \leqq i_p' = i_p-n_p, \text{ say}.$$
Addition of these qualities gives
$$2(w-i_1)=i_2+i_3+\ldots+i_p-(n_2+n_3+\ldots+n_p),$$
so that
$$n_2+n_3+\ldots+n_p = i_1+(i_1+i_2+i_3+\ldots+i_p-2w)$$
$$\geqq i_1, \text{ by the lemma.}$$
Hence there exist numbers (or some zero) $\nu_2, \nu_3, \ldots \nu_p$, not greater than $n_2, n_3, \ldots n_p$ respectively, such that
$$\nu_2+\nu_3+\ldots+\nu_p = i_1.$$
Choosing such numbers, write down
$$(a_1-a_2)^{\nu_2}(a_1-a_3)^{\nu_3}\ldots(a_1-a_p)^{\nu_p}$$
$$\times\,\lambda(a_2-a_3)^{m_{23}}(a_2-a_4)^{m_{24}}\ldots(a_{p-1}-a_p)^{m_{p-1\,p}}.$$

This is λ times a product of w differences into which a_1 enters in i_1 factors, and $a_2, a_3, \dots a_p$ enter in numbers of factors not exceeding $i_2, i_3, \dots i_p$ respectively.

We have chosen one of the products as a sum of which P is arranged according to our assumption that the theorem is true for $p-1$. Deal with all the other products of the sum in like manner, and add the results of introducing additional factors as above. The result is a linear function of products such as described in our enunciation, and the highest terms in a_1 which it contains are $a_1^{i_1}P$. By subtraction from (1) we obtain

Given function $-$(linear function of products as described)

$$= a_1^{i_1-1}P' + a_1^{i_1-2}Q' + \dots + Z', \qquad \dots (2)$$

where it may happen that some or all of $P', Q', \dots Z'$ vanish. If they do not it is a function of differences, of w dimensions as before, of degree in a_1 at least one less than the given function, and of degrees in $a_2, a_3, \dots a_p$ not greater than the given function.

Repeat the argument with the diminished degree in a_1 of (2), in place of i_1. And so again and again. After at most i_1 applications of it we obtain

Given function = linear function of products as described $+ Z_r$,

where Z_r, if not zero, is a rational integral function of differences of $a_2, a_3, \dots a_p$, of dimensions w, and of degrees in $a_2, a_3, \dots a_p$ which do not exceed $i_2, i_3, \dots i_p$ respectively, and is consequently, by our assumption, itself a linear function of products as described. Accordingly on this assumption, that the theorem holds for $p-1$ letters, it holds for p.

Now it holds for 2 letters a_{p-1}, a_p, as $(a_{p-1}-a_p)^w$, the only possible function of dimensions w in the one difference, but for a numerical multiple, is of the form described.

The mathematical induction is then at once completed; and the certainty that we can in all cases express a function of differences, as given, in the form of a linear function of products, as described, is established.

COROLLARY. *If the weight and partial degrees of the function satisfy $2w = i_1 + i_2 + \dots + i_p$, the linear function of sums of products must be such that a_1 enters into every product in exactly i_1 factors, a_2 in exactly i_2, and so on.*

Let them enter in $i_1', i_2', \dots i_p'$ factors of one of the products. The number of factors is $w = \frac{1}{2}(i_1 + i_2 + \dots + i_p)$. Each factor contains two letters, so that to write down all the factors requires the writing down of $2w$ letters. But it also requires, on our supposition, the writing down of just i_1' letters a_1, i_2' letters a_2, and so on. Therefore

$$i_1'+i_2'+\ldots+i_p' = 2w = i_1+i_2+\ldots+i_p,$$

i. e. $$(i_1-i_1')+(i_2-i_2')+\ldots+(i_p-i_p') = 0.$$

None of the differences here is negative, by the theorem. Consequently all are zero.

Two particular cases give us needed facts.

(1) Take $i_1 = i_2 = \ldots = i_p = i$, $2w = ip$. Also take the function symmetric in $a_1, a_2, \ldots a_p$. An expression in terms of *symmetric* sums of products as described can be found for it. The expression at first found is probably not symmetric, but from this expression equally valid ones can be found by permuting the p letters in it in all ways; and the sum of all the expressions thus obtained, divided by their number $p\,!$, is equally an expression for it, and is symmetric. Thus a symmetric function of $a_1, a_2, \ldots a_p$, of degree i in each of them, and of dimensions in them all $\frac{1}{2}ip$ throughout, which is a function of their differences, can be expressed as a linear function of symmetric sums of products of those differences in such a way that every product involves every one of $a_1, a_2, \ldots a_p$ in just i factors. This is what we assumed in § 74.

(2) Take $i_1 = i_2 = \ldots = i_{p-1} = i$, $i_p = \varpi$, $2w = i(p-1)+\varpi$. Also take the function symmetric in $a_1, a_2, \ldots a_{p-1}$. From an expression for it as a linear function of products as described can be derived $(p-1)\,!$ expressions for it, including the first one, by permutations of $a_1, a_2, \ldots a_{p-1}$; and the sum of these divided by $(p-1)\,!$ is an expression for it as a linear function of sums, symmetric in $a_1, a_2, \ldots a_{p-1}$, of products as described. Consequently a function of dimensions $\frac{1}{2}\{i(p-1)+\varpi\}$ throughout in $a_1, a_2, \ldots a_{p-1}, a_p$, which (1) is a function of their differences, (2) is symmetric in $a_1, a_2, \ldots a_{p-1}$, and (3) is of degree i in each of these $p-1$ letters and of degree ϖ in the remaining a_p, can be expressed as a linear function of sums, symmetric in $a_1, a_2, \ldots a_{p-1}$, of products of differences of the p letters, in such a way that in every product a_p occurs in just ϖ factors, while every one of $a_1, a_2, \ldots a_{p-1}$ occurs in just i factors. This, with $p+1$ for p, and x/y for a_{p+1}, is what we assumed in § 83.

Ex. 20. Observing that any rational integral function of the coefficients of p linear forms

$$xy_1-x_1y,\ xy_2-x_2y,\ \ldots\ xy_p-x_py,$$

or $$y_1(x-a_1y),\ y_2(x-a_2y),\ \ldots\ y_p(x-a_py),$$

which is homogeneous in the two coefficients of every one, must be of the form

$$y_1^{i_1} y_2^{i_2} \dots y_p^{i_p} \; F(a_1, a_2, \dots a_p),$$

prove, by use of a particular linear transformation, that if the function is an invariant of the forms, we must have for every value of h

$$F(a_1, a_2, \dots a_p) = F(a_1+h, a_2+h, \dots a_p+h).$$

Ex. 21. Observing that, if the function of the coefficients has not any one of $x_1, y_1, x_2, y_2, \dots x_p, y_p$ for a factor, then $i_1, i_2, \dots i_p$ must be exactly the degrees to which $a_1, a_2, \dots a_p$ respectively occur in the expanded form of $F(a_1, a_2, \dots a_p)$, show that, if the function is an invariant of degrees $i_1, i_2, \dots i_p$ in the coefficients of the forms separately, and consequently (§ 31) of total weight

$$w = \tfrac{1}{2}(i_1 + i_2 + \dots + i_p),$$

then $F(a_1, a_2, \dots a_p)$ must be capable of expression as a linear function of products of w differences, in every one of which $a_1, a_2, \dots a_p$ occur in just $i_1, i_2, \dots i_p$ factors respectively.

Ex. 22. Hence show that every rational integral invariant of p linear forms $xy_1 - x_1 y, xy_2 - x_2 y, \dots xy_p - x_p y$ is a rational integral function of one or more of the $\tfrac{1}{2}p(p-1)$ invariants

$$x_r y_s - x_s y_r \; (0 < r < s \leqq p),$$

so that, as each of these is irreducible, the $\tfrac{1}{2}p(p-1)$ together constitute the complete system of irreducible invariants of the p linear forms.

Ex. 23. Every covariant, of partial degrees $i_1, i_2, \dots i_p$ and order ϖ, of the p linear forms can be expressed as $y_1^{i_1} y_2^{i_2} \dots y_p^{i_p} y^{\varpi}$ times a linear function of products of differences like $a_r - a_s$ and products like $\frac{x}{y} - a_r$, in such a way that in every product $a_1, a_2, \dots a_p, \frac{x}{y}$ occur in exactly $i_1, i_2, \dots i_p, \varpi$ factors respectively.

Ex. 24. The determinants $x_r y_s - x_s y_r$, and the p forms themselves, constitute the complete system of irreducible invariants and covariants of the p linear forms $xy_1 - x_1 y, xy_2 - x_2 y, \dots xy_p - x_p y$.

Ex. 25. Observing that $(a_0, a_1, \dots a_p)(x, y)^p \equiv (x + y\theta)^p a_0$, where θ denotes the operator $a_1 \partial/\partial a_0 + a_2 \partial/\partial a_1 + \dots + a_p \partial/\partial a_{p-1}$, show that the transformation of modulus unity $x = X + hY$, $y = Y$ gives it the form $\{X + Y(\theta + h)\}^p a_0$. Expand this, noticing that

$$\theta a_0 = a_1, \; \theta^2 a_0 = a_2, \dots \theta^p a_0 = a_p.$$

Ex. 26. Observing that every function of partial degrees 1, 1, ... 1 in the coefficients of the i quantics

$$(x + y\theta_1)^{p_1} a_0^{(1)}, \; (x + y\theta_2)^{p_2} a_0^{(2)}, \dots (x + y\theta_i)^{p_i} a_0^{(i)},$$

which involves the last coefficient in each, may be written in the form $F(\theta_1, \theta_2, \dots \theta_i)\, a_0^{(1)} a_0^{(2)} \dots a_0^{(i)}$, where F is a rational integral function of degrees p_1 in θ_1, p_2 in θ_2, and so on, show that, if the function is an invariant of the i quantics, $F(\theta_1, \theta_2, \dots \theta_i)$ must be unaltered when we put in it $\theta_1+h, \theta_2+h, \dots \theta_i+h$ for $\theta_1, \theta_2, \dots \theta_i$.

Ex. 27. Observing that if the function is isobaric F must be homogeneous in $\theta_1, \theta_2, \dots \theta_i$, and remembering that if it is an invariant of the quantics we must have $2w=p_1+p_2+\dots+p_i$ (§ 31), prove that every invariant of partial degrees 1, 1, ... 1 of the i quantics is a linear function of 'hyperdeterminant' invariants

$$(\theta_1-\theta_2)^{m_{12}}(\theta_1-\theta_3)^{m_{13}}\dots(\theta_{i-1}-\theta_i)^{m_{i-1\,i}}a_0^{(1)}a_0^{(2)}\dots a_0^{(i)},$$

where θ_1 occurs in just p_1 factors of the product of differences, θ_2 in just p_2, and so on.

Ex. 28. Remembering that from any invariant of degree i of one p-ic, an invariant of i p-ics, of degree 1 in the coefficients of each, may be formed by the method of § 19, and that from this invariant of i p-ics we may return to the original invariant of one p-ic by identifying the i sets of coefficients, prove that every invariant of one p-ic can be expressed as a linear function of 'hyperdeterminant' invariants

$$(\theta_1-\theta_2)^{m_{12}}(\theta_1-\theta_3)^{m_{13}}\dots(\theta_{i-1}-\theta_i)^{m_{i-1\,i}}a_0a_0a_0\dots(i \text{ factors}),$$

where now $\theta_1, \theta_2, \dots \theta_i$ all mean the θ of Ex. 25, but the first and its repetitions operate only on the first factor in $a_0a_0a_0\dots$, the second on the second, and so on. Here $\theta_1, \theta_2, \dots \theta_i$ all occur in just p factors.

Also prove that those of the hyperdeterminants which give invariants, i.e. which do not vanish, are those for which

$$\Sigma.(\theta_1-\theta_2)^{m_{12}}(\theta_1-\theta_3)^{m_{13}}\dots(\theta_{i-1}-\theta_i)^{m_{i-1\,i}}$$

does not vanish identically, the summation covering all permutations of $\theta_1, \theta_2, \dots \theta_i$.

Ex. 29. There is a one to one correspondence between invariants of degree i of a binary p-ic and invariants of degree p of a binary i-ic. (*Hermite.*)

Ex. 30. There is a one to one correspondence between invariants of partial degrees 1, 1, ... 1 of a binary p_1-ic, p_2-ic, ... and p_i-ic and invariants of partial degrees $p_1, p_2, \dots p_i$ of i linear forms.

CHAPTER VI

BINARY QUANTICS CONTINUED. ANNIHILATORS. SEMINVARIANTS.

90. **Annihilators of invariants.** For the calculation of invariants it is a matter of great importance that I any invariant of $(a_0, a_1, a_2, \ldots a_p)(x, y)^p$ must satisfy the two differential equations

$$a_0 \frac{\partial I}{\partial a_1} + 2a_1 \frac{\partial I}{\partial a_2} + 3a_2 \frac{\partial I}{\partial a_3} + \ldots + pa_{p-1} \frac{\partial I}{\partial a_p} = 0,$$

$$pa_1 \frac{\partial I}{\partial a_0} + (p-1)a_2 \frac{\partial I}{\partial a_1} + (p-2)a_3 \frac{\partial I}{\partial a_2} + \ldots + a_p \frac{\partial I}{\partial a_{p-1}} = 0.$$

Professor Sylvester, to whom and to Cayley the theory is due, though the idea had also presented itself to Aronhold, expresses this fact by saying that any invariant I has two *annihilators*, called Ω and O, viz.

$$\Omega \equiv a_0 \frac{\partial}{\partial a_1} + 2a_1 \frac{\partial}{\partial a_2} + 3a_2 \frac{\partial}{\partial a_3} + \ldots + pa_{p-1} \frac{\partial}{\partial a_p},$$

$$O \equiv pa_1 \frac{\partial}{\partial a_0} + (p-1)a_2 \frac{\partial}{\partial a_1} + (p-2)a_3 \frac{\partial}{\partial a_2} + \ldots + a_p \frac{\partial}{\partial a_{p-1}}.$$

The language is a convenient one for expressing that $\Omega I = 0$, and $OI = 0$ identically.

We proceed to prove these facts of annihilation.

91. **The annihilator Ω.** The property of having Ω for an annihilator is one that invariants possess in common with other functions of the coefficients which, when expressed in terms of a_0 and the roots, involve only differences of these latter.

This may be proved by seeing, as we shall later, that the operation with Ω on a function of the coefficients is equivalent to the operation with

$$-\left(\frac{\partial}{\partial \alpha_1} + \frac{\partial}{\partial \alpha_2} + \ldots + \frac{\partial}{\partial \alpha_p}\right)$$

on the equal function of a_0 and the roots $\alpha_1, \alpha_2, \ldots \alpha_p$. We here adopt a different method.

Functions of the coefficients which are equivalent to functions of a_0 and differences between roots are, as we have seen, equal to the same functions of the altered coefficients when the quantic is transformed by the substitution of $X+mY$ and Y for x and y, that is to say, when the roots are diminished by the same (positive or negative) quantity m. Now, this being so for all values of m, let m be taken as very small, so that its square and higher powers may be neglected in comparison with any finite multiple of itself. The quantic

$$a_0x^p + pa_1x^{p-1}y + \frac{p(p-1)}{1.2}a_2x^{p-2}y^2 + \ldots + a_py^p$$

becomes in this case, after the substitution,

$$a_0X^p + p(a_1+ma_0)X^{p-1}Y + \frac{p(p-1)}{1.2}(a_2+2ma_1)X^{p-2}Y^2 + \ldots$$
$$+ (a_p + pma_{p-1})Y^p,$$

so that the new coefficients are the old ones altered by the increments

$$\delta a_0 = 0,\ \delta a_1 = ma_0,\ \delta a_2 = 2ma_1, \ldots,\ \delta a_p = pma_{p-1}.$$

Now I our supposed invariant, or other function of a_0 and the differences between roots, becomes, by Taylor's theorem

$$I + \left(\delta a_0 \frac{\partial}{\partial a_0} + \delta a_1 \frac{\partial}{\partial a_1} + \delta a_2 \frac{\partial}{\partial a_2} + \ldots + \delta a_p \frac{\partial}{\partial a_p}\right) I,$$

in which quadratic, &c. terms in the δa's, i.e. in m, are omitted as vanishing in comparison with the increment retained. Thus a necessary result of I being unaltered is that

$$\left(\delta a_0 \frac{\partial}{\partial a_0} + \delta a_1 \frac{\partial}{\partial a_1} + \delta a_2 \frac{\partial}{\partial a_2} + \ldots + \delta a_p \frac{\partial}{\partial a_p}\right) I = 0,$$

i.e. that $$m\left(a_0 \frac{\partial}{\partial a_1} + 2a_1 \frac{\partial}{\partial a_2} + \ldots + pa_{p-1} \frac{\partial}{\partial a_p}\right) I = 0,$$

i.e. that $$\Omega I = 0.$$

92. It will be well to give another proof of this, both because of the convenient symbolical form of results to which it will lead, and in order to convince ourselves that $\Omega I = 0$ is a sufficient condition to ensure that I is a function equal to the same function of the coefficients in the quantic obtained by putting $X+mY$, Y for x and y in the given quantic, whatever constant m be, as well as a necessary consequence if this persistence is a fact.

If

$$(A_0, A_1, A_2, \ldots A_p)(X, Y)^p \equiv (a_0, a_1, a_2, \ldots a_p)(X + mY, Y)^p,$$

where m is not now necessarily very small, the expressions for the new coefficients are easily seen to be, by use of Taylor's theorem for the expansion of a function of $X/Y + m$ in powers of X/Y,

$$A_0 = a_0,$$
$$A_1 = a_1 + a_0 m,$$
$$A_2 = a_2 + 2a_1 m + a_0 m^2,$$
$$\cdot \quad \cdot \quad \cdot \quad \cdot \quad \cdot \quad \cdot \quad \cdot \quad \cdot$$
$$A_p = a_p + pa_{p-1}m + \frac{p(p-1)}{1.2}a_{p-2}m^2 + \ldots + a_0 m^p,$$

where we notice that

$$\frac{dA_0}{dm} = 0, \frac{dA_1}{dm} = A_0, \frac{dA_2}{dm} = 2A_1, \frac{dA_3}{dm} = 3A_2, \ldots, \frac{dA_p}{dm} = pA_{p-1}.$$

We draw the conclusion that, if $F(A_0, A_1, A_2, \ldots A_p)$ is any function of the new coefficients,

$$\frac{d}{dm}F(A_0, A_1, A_2, \ldots A_p)$$

$$= \frac{\partial F}{\partial A_0} \cdot \frac{dA_0}{dm} + \frac{\partial F}{\partial A_1} \cdot \frac{dA_1}{dm} + \frac{\partial F}{\partial A_2} \cdot \frac{dA_2}{dm} + \ldots + \frac{\partial F}{\partial A_p} \cdot \frac{dA_p}{dm}$$

$$= A_0 \frac{\partial F}{\partial A_1} + 2A_1 \frac{\partial F}{\partial A_2} + 3A_2 \frac{\partial F}{\partial A_3} + \ldots + pA_{p-1}\frac{\partial F}{\partial A_p}.$$

Now for $\frac{d}{dm}F(A_0, A_1, A_2, \ldots A_p)$ to vanish, whatever m be, is the necessary and sufficient condition that

$$F(A_0, A_1, A_2, \ldots A_p)$$

be independent of m, and so equal to $F(a_0, a_1, a_2, \ldots a_p)$ which is its value when $m = 0$. Thus the condition, both sufficient and necessary, that

$$F(A_0, A_1, A_2, \ldots A_p) = F(a_0, a_1, a_2, \ldots a_p)$$

is $\left(A_0 \frac{\partial}{\partial A_1} + 2A_1 \frac{\partial}{\partial A_2} + 3A_2 \frac{\partial}{\partial A_3} + \ldots + pA_{p-1}\frac{\partial}{\partial A_p}\right)$

$$F(A_0, A_1, A_2, \ldots A_p) = 0,$$

or, replacing capital by small letters,

$$\Omega F(a_0, a_1, a_2, \ldots a_p) = 0.$$

93. We can by this method prove that, if F is any rational integral function,

$$F(A_0, A_1, A_2, \dots A_p) = \left(1 + m\Omega + \frac{m^2}{1 \cdot 2}\Omega^2 + \frac{m^3}{1 \cdot 2 \cdot 3}\Omega^3 + \dots\right) F(a_0, a_1, a_2, \dots a_p),$$

which may be written symbolically

$$= e^{m\Omega} F(a_0, a_1, a_2, \dots a_p).$$

In fact we have, by Maclaurin's theorem,

$$\phi(m') = \phi(0) + m'\left[\frac{d\phi}{dm}\right]_0 + \frac{m'^2}{1 \cdot 2}\left[\frac{d^2\phi}{dm^2}\right]_0 + \dots$$

$$= \left[e^{m'\frac{d}{dm}}\phi(m)\right]_{m=0}.$$

Now $F(A_0, A_1, A_2, \dots A_p)$ is a function of m. Hence, if A'_r denotes the result of replacing m by m' in A_r, we have by the preceding article

$$F(A'_0, A'_1, A'_2, \dots A'_p)$$

$$= \left[e^{m'\left(A_0\frac{\partial}{\partial A_1} + 2A_1\frac{\partial}{\partial A_2} + \dots + pA_{p-1}\frac{\partial}{\partial A_p}\right)} F(A_0, A_1, A_2, \dots A_p)\right]_{m=0},$$

$$= e^{m'\Omega} F(a_0, a_1, a_2, \dots a_p).$$

This is proved, subject to considerations of convergency, for any function F. When F is a rational integral function no question of convergency arises. For we notice that F, ΩF, $\Omega^2 F, \dots$ are of weights regularly diminishing by unity, so that presently we get to a term $\Omega^w F$ of zero weight, i.e. a function of a_0, and beyond this point $\Omega^{w+1}F$, $\Omega^{w+2}F$, &c. all vanish. The symbolic series practically consists therefore of only a finite number of terms.

We have thus another proof that, if a function I persists in form after the substitution of $X + mY$, Y for x and y when m is infinitesimal, it does equally when m is finite. For if $\Omega I = 0$, the condition of § 91, then also $\Omega^2 I = \Omega\Omega I = 0$, $\Omega^3 I = 0$, &c., &c.

Of course the student will recognize that $\Omega^2 I$ denotes the full expression for the result of operating with Ω on ΩI, viz.

$$a_0^2\frac{\partial^2 I}{\partial a_1^2} + 4a_0a_1\frac{\partial^2 I}{\partial a_1\,\partial a_2} + 6a_0a_2\frac{\partial^2 I}{\partial a_1\,\partial a_3} + \dots + 4a_1^2\frac{\partial^2 I}{\partial a_2^2} + \dots$$

$$+ 1 \cdot 2a_0\frac{\partial I}{\partial a_2} + 2 \cdot 3a_1\frac{\partial I}{\partial a_3} + 3 \cdot 4a_2\frac{\partial I}{\partial a_4} + \dots,$$

and not merely the first line of this expression; and so for $\Omega^3 I$, $\Omega^4 I$, &c.

94. **The annihilator** O. We have still to see that, if I is an invariant, the second operator O of § 90 annihilates I, as well as the first Ω.

This property invariants have in common with other functions of the coefficients which persist in form after the substitution

$$x = X, \quad y = l'X + Y,$$

i. e. in common with all functions of the coefficients which can be expressed in terms of a_p and the differences between reciprocals of roots. The substitution is in fact one which transforms the quantic into another in which a_p is unaltered and the reciprocals of the roots differ by l' from the reciprocals of the original roots.

The proof is exactly as before, the present substitution dealing with y and x exactly as that of the preceding articles has dealt with x and y, and consequently dealing with the quantic read backwards from its end $a_p y^p$, exactly as the former substitution dealt with it read forwards from its beginning $a_0 x^p$. It will be noticed that O exactly corresponds to Ω in this reversed reading.

We have then that $OF = 0$ is the necessary and sufficient condition for F to persist in form when for x and y we make such substitutions as X, $l'X + Y$.

95. **Symmetry of an invariant. Skew invariants.** If in an invariant a_0 and a_p, a_1 and a_{p-1}, a_2 and a_{p-2}, &c. are interchanged, the invariant is unaltered if its weight is even, and changed only in sign if its weight is odd.

For the substitution $x = Y$, $y = X$ has for its modulus -1. Now the effect of it is to interchange a_0 and a_p, a_1 and a_{p-1}, a_2 and a_{p-2}, &c. in the quantic. Consequently, if

$$F(a_0, a_1, a_2, \dots a_p)$$

is an invariant, we have (§§ 23, 26, 76)

$$F(a_p, a_{p-1}, a_{p-2}, \dots a_0) = (-1)^w F(a_0, a_1, a_2, \dots a_p).$$

We see then that there is an essential difference in character between invariants of even and invariants of odd weight. Those of odd weight are, because of this change of sign, known as *skew* invariants.

Skew invariants do not exist for the quadratic cubic and quartic, and it came as a surprise upon mathematicians when Hermite discovered the first skew invariant of a higher quantic; viz. that of degree 18 and weight 45 of the quintic.

Invariants of odd weight cannot, it is clear, be rational integral functions of invariants of even weight. Thus when a binary quantic has one or more skew invariants one at least of them must be irreducible.

96. One result of the symmetry to which attention has just been called is that, when we have found a function of the coefficients which has Ω for an annihilator, it is unnecessary to test directly whether it is also annihilated by O, in order to ascertain whether it is or is not an invariant. If it is altered in more than sign when the first coefficient and last in the quantic, the second and last but one, &c. are interchanged in pairs, it is not an invariant. If on the other hand it is not so altered in more than sign it must be annihilated by O as well as by Ω, for the interchanges in Ω produce O.

We must prove, however, that any function which is of one order and one weight throughout, and which is annihilated both by Ω and by O, is an invariant.

97. **A homogeneous isobaric function annihilated by Ω and by O is necessarily an invariant.**

Consider in succession the substitutions

$$x = \lambda x', \ y = \mu y', \qquad \dots (1)$$

$$x' = X' + tY', \ y' = Y', \qquad \dots (2)$$

$$X' = X, \ Y' = \tau X + Y. \qquad \dots (3)$$

The result of the succession is that of the performance of the substitutions

$$\left.\begin{aligned} x &= \lambda(1+t\tau)X + \lambda tY, \\ y &= \mu\tau X + \mu Y. \end{aligned}\right\} \qquad \dots (4)$$

Now these are the most general formulae of linear substitution; for, λ, μ, t, τ being arbitrary, so are the coefficients

$$\lambda(1+t\tau), \ \lambda t, \ \mu\tau, \ \mu,$$

as is clear by taking them in reversed order. The modulus of the resultant substitution (4) is $\lambda\mu$.

Let the original form of a p-ic be

$$(a_0, a_1, a_2, \dots a_p)(x, y)^p,$$

and let the forms it successively takes be

$$(a_0', a_1', a_2', \dots a_p')(x', y')^p,$$

$$(A_0', A_1', A_2', \dots A_p')(X', Y')^p,$$

$$(A_0, A_1, A_2, \dots A_p)(X, Y)^p.$$

Take $F(a_0, a_1, a_2, \dots a_p)$ a homogeneous isobaric function, of degree i and weight w, which is annihilated by Ω and by O.

We have first that, for values of r from 0 to p inclusive,

$$a_r' = \lambda^{p-r}\mu^r a_r,$$

where the index of the power of μ is the weight of a_r, and that of the power of λ is the excess of p over that weight. Accordingly, because F is homogeneous and isobaric,

$$F(a_0', a_1', a_2', \dots a_p') = \lambda^{ip-w}\mu^w F(a_0, a_1, a_2, \dots a_p).$$

Again, because Ω annihilates F, F persists in form after the substitution (2). Therefore

$$F(A_0', A_1', A_2', \dots A_p') = F(a_0', a_1', a_2', \dots a_p').$$

Once more, because O annihilates F,

$$F(A_0, A_1, A_2, \dots A_p) = F(A_0', A_1', A_2', \dots A_p').$$

We see then, taking these three facts together, that

$$F(A_0, A_1, A_2, \dots A_p) = \lambda^{ip-w}\mu^w F(a_0, a_1, a_2, \dots a_p). \quad \dots (5)$$

In other words, we see that F is a function of the coefficients, which needs only to be multiplied by a factor involving only the constants in the general scheme of linear substitution (4) to be made equal to the same function of the coefficients in the quantic into which the given quantic is transformed by that substitution. By the definition, then, F is an invariant.

Moreover the fact (§ 26) that $w = \frac{1}{2}ip$ follows. For, by § 23, the factor $\lambda^{ip-w}\mu^w$ in (5) must be a power of the modulus, i.e. of $\lambda\mu$. Thus the indices of λ^{ip-w} and μ^w must be equal. Therefore $w = \frac{1}{2}ip$.

Another interesting proof that, when Ω and O both annihilate a homogeneous isobaric function F, the weight and degree of F must be connected with p by the relation $ip - 2w = 0$, will be afforded when we have seen in the next chapter that

$$(\Omega O - O\Omega)F = (ip - 2w)F.$$

For the left-hand member vanishes when $\Omega F = 0$ and $OF = 0$. So then must the right-hand member.

98. A good proof in small compass of all the fundamental properties of invariants of a binary quantic is afforded by a method which will also be useful for other purposes.

We notice that, if

$$u = (a_0, a_1, a_2, \dots a_p)(x, y)^p,$$

then
$$\Omega u = y\frac{\partial}{\partial x}u, \quad \Omega^2 u = \left(y\frac{\partial}{\partial x}\right)^2 u, \dots$$

and, generally,
$$\Omega^r u = \left(y\frac{\partial}{\partial x}\right)^r u.$$

Consequently

$$e^{t\Omega}(a_0, a_1, a_2, \dots a_p)(x, y)^p = e^{ty\frac{\partial}{\partial x}}(a_0, a_1, a_2, \dots a_p)(x, y)^p$$
$$= (a_0, a_1, a_2, \dots a_p)(x + ty, y)^p,$$

by Taylor's theorem.

Similarly

$$Ou = x\frac{\partial}{\partial y}u, \quad O^2 u = \left(x\frac{\partial}{\partial y}\right)^2 u, \ldots$$

and, generally, $$O^r u = \left(x\frac{\partial}{\partial y}\right)^r u;$$

and therefore

$$e^{\tau O}(a_0, a_1, a_2, \ldots a_p)(x, y)^p = e^{\tau x\frac{\partial}{\partial y}}(a_0, a_1, a_2, \ldots a_p)(x, y)^p$$
$$= (a_0, a_1, a_2, \ldots a_p)(x, \tau x + y)^p.$$

Hence, performing one operation after the other,

$$e^{t\Omega}e^{\tau O}(a_0, a_1, a_2, \ldots a_p)(x, y)^p$$
$$= (a_0, a_1, a_2, \ldots a_p)(x + t(\tau x + y), \tau x + y)^p,$$

and, putting λx, μy, for x, y,

$$e^{t\Omega}e^{\tau O}(a_0, a_1, a_2, \ldots a_p)(\lambda x, \mu y)^p$$
$$= (a_0, a_1, a_2, \ldots a_p)((1 + t\tau)\lambda x + t\mu y, \tau\lambda x + \mu y)^p,$$

i.e., taking

$$(1 + t\tau)\lambda = l, \quad t\mu = m, \quad \tau\lambda = l', \quad \mu = m',$$

so that

$$\mu = m', \quad t = \frac{m}{m'}, \quad \tau = \frac{l'm'}{lm' - l'm}, \quad \lambda = \frac{lm' - l'm}{m'},$$

$$(a_0, a_1, a_2, \ldots a_p)(lx + my, l'x + m'y)^p$$
$$= e^{\frac{m}{m'}\Omega} e^{\frac{l'm'}{lm' - l'm}O}(a_0, a_1, a_2, \ldots a_p)\left(\frac{lm' - l'm}{m'}x, m'y\right)^p.$$

Thus the most general linear substitution of $lx + my$, $l'x + m'y$ for x and y is effected by a substitution of the form λx, μy followed by a complex differential operation.

This is an identity. If then the expanded left be

$$(A_0, A_1, A_2, \ldots A_p)(x, y)^p,$$

we have for all values of r from 0 to p inclusive

$$A_r = e^{\frac{m}{m'}\Omega} e^{\frac{l'm'}{lm' - l'm}O}\left(\frac{lm' - l'm}{m'}\right)^{p-r} m'^r a_r$$

$$= (lm' - l'm)^{p-r} m'^{2r-p} e^{\frac{m}{m'}\Omega} e^{\frac{l'm'}{lm' - l'm}O} a_r,$$

so that we have a formula for every new coefficient.

We can readily pass to products of coefficients. For, if P, Q are two functions of the coefficients,

$$e^{kO}PQ = e^{k(O_1 + O_2)}PQ,$$

where O_1 and O_2 both mean the same as O, but the former and its repetitions act on P only, and the latter and its repetitions on Q only,

$$= e^{kO_1} e^{kO_2} PQ$$
$$= e^{kO_1} P \,.\, e^{kO_2} Q$$
$$= e^{kO} P \,.\, e^{kO} Q;$$

and, in like manner,

$$e^{k'\Omega} e^{kO} PQ = e^{k'\Omega}(e^{kO} P \,.\, e^{kO} Q)$$
$$= e^{k'\Omega} e^{kO} P \,.\, e^{k'\Omega} e^{kO} Q.$$

Hence, if $F(a_0, a_1, a_2, \dots a_p)$ is a product, or a sum of multiples of products of the same degree i and weight w, of coefficients chosen from among $a_0, a_1, a_2, \dots a_p$,

$$F(A_0, A_1, A_2, \dots A_p)$$
$$= (lm' - l'm)^{ip-w} m'^{2w-ip} e^{\frac{m}{m'}\Omega} e^{\frac{l'm'}{lm'-l'm}O} F(a_0, a_1, a_2, \dots a_p),$$

so that any rational integral homogeneous isobaric function of the new coefficients A is obtained from the same function of the old coefficients a by a complex differential operation and a multiplication.

By reversing the order of the Ω and O operations we obtain in like manner a second expression for $F(A_0, A_1, A_2, \dots A_p)$; viz.

$$F(A_0, A_1, A_2, \dots A_p)$$
$$= (lm' - l'm)^{w} l^{ip-2w} e^{\frac{l'}{l}O} e^{\frac{lm}{lm'-l'm}\Omega} F(a_0, a_1, a_2, \dots a_p).$$

99. All the fundamental facts as to invariants flow hence. These are that an invariant is annihilated by Ω and by O, that its degree and weight are connected with p, the order of the quantic, by the relation $ip - 2w = 0$, and that the factor in the equality expressive of its invariancy is the wth power of the modulus $lm' - l'm$.

To see this, suppose that $F(a_0, a_1, a_2, \dots a_p)$, a homogeneous isobaric function, is an invariant, so that

$$F(A_0, A_1, A_2, \dots A_p) = \phi(l, m, l', m') F(a_0, a_1, a_2, \dots a_p),$$

where the form of ϕ is at present unknown. We have three expressions for $F(A_0, A_1, A_2, \dots A_p)$, which we can identify, and obtain

$$(lm' - l'm)^{ip-w} m'^{2w-ip} e^{\frac{m}{m'}\Omega} e^{\frac{l'm'}{lm'-l'm}O} F(a_0, a_1, a_2, \dots a_p)$$
$$= \phi(l, m, l', m') F(a_0, a_1, a_2, \dots a_p)$$
$$= (lm' - l'm)^{w} l^{ip-2w} e^{\frac{l'}{l}O} e^{\frac{lm}{lm'-l'm}\Omega} F(a_0, a_1, a_2, \dots a_p).$$

In the first equality put $l' = 0$. It becomes

$$l^{ip-w} m'^{w} e^{\frac{m}{m'}\Omega} F(a_0, a_1, a_2, \dots a_p)$$
$$= \phi(l, m, 0, m') F(a_0, a_1, a_2, \dots a_p).$$

Now ΩF is of lower weight than F, and $\Omega^2 F$, $\Omega^3 F$, &c. of lower weights still. The terms of different weights on the two sides must be separately equal. Hence

$$\Omega F = 0, \quad \Omega^2 F = 0, \text{ \&c.}$$

Again, put $m = 0$. We obtain in like manner

$$l^{ip-w} m'^{w} e^{\frac{l'}{l} O} F(a_0, a_1, a_2, \dots a_p)$$
$$= \phi(l, 0, l', m') F(a_0, a_1, a_2, \dots a_p);$$

whence, by considering terms of different weights, since operation with O increases weight,

$$OF = 0, \quad O^2 F = 0, \text{ \&c.}$$

Thus the facts that an invariant is annihilated by Ω and by O are obtained. This being so, the general equalities become

$$(lm' - l'm)^{ip-w} m'^{2w-ip} F = \phi(l, m, l', m') F = (lm' - l'm)^{w} l^{ip-2w} F,$$

in which l, m' and $lm' - l'm$ are independent. The equality of the first and third expressions requires that the indices of m'^{2w-ip} and l^{ip-2w} vanish, and that the indices of $(lm' - l'm)^{ip-w}$ and $(lm' - l'm)^{w}$ be equal. These are all satisfied if and only if $ip - 2w = 0$.

Lastly, using this fact, the value of $\phi(l, m, l', m')$ is $(lm' - l'm)^{w}$.

100. A similar analysis will lead us to a theorem of great importance which we shall use hereafter.

By the early part of § 98 we have, putting $-\tau^{-1}$ for t,

$$e^{-\tau^{-1}\Omega} e^{\tau O} (a_0, a_1, a_2, \dots a_p)(x, y)^p$$
$$= (a_0, a_1, a_2, \dots a_p)(-\tau^{-1} y, \tau x + y)^p$$
$$= e^{-\tau O} (a_0, a_1, a_2, \dots a_p)(-\tau^{-1} y, \tau x)^p$$
$$= e^{-\tau O} (a_p, a_{p-1}, a_{p-2}, \dots a_0)(\tau x, -\tau^{-1} y)^p;$$

whence, equating the coefficients of $x^{p-r} y^r$ on the two sides

$$e^{-\tau^{-1}\Omega} e^{\tau O} a_r = (-1)^r \tau^{p-2r} e^{-\tau O} a_{p-r},$$

for every value of r from 0 to p inclusive.

We may hence pass to products, and linear functions of products, of coefficients $a_0, a_1, a_2, \dots a_p$ as in § 98, and obtain that, if $F(a_0, a_1, a_2, \ldots a_p)$ is any rational integral homogeneous isobaric function of degree i and weight w,

$$e^{-\tau^{-1}\Omega} e^{\tau O} F(a_0, a_1, a_2, \ldots a_p)$$
$$= (-1)^w \tau^{ip-2w} e^{-\tau O} F(a_p, a_{p-1}, a_{p-2}, \ldots a_0),$$

i.e.

$$\left(1 - \tau^{-1}\Omega + \tau^{-2}\frac{\Omega^2}{1\,.\,2} - \ldots\right)\left(1 + \tau O + \tau^2 \frac{O^2}{1\,.\,2} + \ldots\right) F(a_0, a_1, a_2, \ldots a_p)$$

$$= (-1)^w \tau^{ip-2w}\left(1 - \tau O + \tau^2 \frac{O^2}{1\,.\,2} - \ldots\right) F(a_p, a_{p-1}, a_{p-2}, \ldots a_0).$$

Now equate terms free from τ on the two sides, as we may do since the equality is identical, holding for all values of τ. The conclusion is that

$$\left(1 - \frac{\Omega O}{1^2} + \frac{\Omega^2 O^2}{1^2\,.\,2^2} - \frac{\Omega^3 O^3}{1^2\,.\,2^2\,.\,3^2} + \ldots\right) F(a_0, a_1, a_2, \ldots a_p)$$

$$= 0, \text{ if } ip - 2w > 0,$$

but $= (-1)^w F(a_p, a_{p-1}, a_{p-2}, \ldots a_0)$, if $ip - 2w = 0$,

and $= (-1)^{ip-w} \dfrac{O^{2w-ip}}{(2w-ip)!} F(a_p, a_{p-1}, a_{p-2}, \ldots a_0)$, if $ip - 2w < 0$.

The first part of the conclusion is the one to which we wish to draw particular attention. It tells us that, if $ip - 2w > 0$,

$$F(a_0, a_1, a_2, \ldots a_p)$$
$$= \Omega\left\{\frac{O}{1^2} - \frac{\Omega O^2}{1^2\,.\,2^2} + \frac{\Omega^2 O^3}{1^2\,.\,2^2\,.\,3^2} - \ldots\right\} F(a_0, a_1, a_2, \ldots a_p),$$

i.e. that any rational integral homogeneous isobaric function, for which $ip > 2w$, can be obtained by operation with Ω on another rational integral homogeneous isobaric function.

101. **Formation of invariants by aid of Ω.** We return to invariants. A rational integral invariant of the binary p-ic is, we have seen, a rational integral homogeneous isobaric function, whose degree and weight are connected with p by the relation $ip = 2w$, and which is annihilated by Ω. These two requirements are necessary, and we shall see in § 112 that they suffice. They lead to the following method of formation of all invariants of given degree i.

Write down all those products of i factors chosen from among $a_0, a_1, a_2, \ldots a_p$, repeated factors being allowed, which are such that the sum of the suffixes in every one is $\frac{1}{2}ip$, and take the sum of arbitrary multiples of those products. Operate on the sum with Ω, and express that the result vanishes. This will give a number of equations in the arbitrary multipliers, since the multiplier of every distinct product of suffixed a's in the result of operating must vanish separately. If the number of the arbitrary multipliers is not greater than the number of independent equations to be satisfied, values of them different from zero cannot be found to accord with the requirements, and there is no invariant of degree i. If the number of independent equations is one less than the number of arbitrary multipliers, the ratios of these can be chosen in one way to satisfy them, and there is one invariant. If the number of independent equations is more than one less than the number of multipliers the equations can be satisfied in more than one way. In fact, if the excess of the one number over the other is r, r of the multipliers may be left arbitrary, and the equations can still be satisfied by proper choice of the rest. We thus get an invariant

$$\lambda_1 I_1 + \lambda_2 I_2 + \dots + \lambda_r I_r,$$

where $\lambda_1, \lambda_2, \dots \lambda_r$ are arbitrary. This is expressed by saying that there are r linearly independent invariants $I_1, I_2, \dots I_r$ of degree i.

It will be proved later, by means of the last article, that all the equations for determining the multipliers are independent, so that the number of linearly independent invariants of degree i is the excess of the number of products of $a_0, a_1, a_2, \dots a_p$, of degree i and weight $\frac{1}{2}ip$, over the number of products which occur in the results of operating with Ω on these products, i.e. over the number of products of degree i and weight $\frac{1}{2}ip-1$. By deferring the proof we shall avoid repetition, as the theorem is a case of a more general one which will be required later.

Notice that the number of products of degree i and weight w is the number of ways in which the number w can be formed by the addition of i or fewer numbers, none exceeding p. This number of partitions of w is usually denoted by $(w;\ i, p)$. Thus the number of linearly independent invariants of degree i is

$$(\tfrac{1}{2}ip;\ i, p) - (\tfrac{1}{2}ip - 1;\ i, p).$$

102. As an example of this method let us prove the statement made in § 80, that I and J are the only invariants of degrees 2 and 3 respectively of the binary quartic.

Here $p = 4$. Take first $i = 2$. Then $w = \frac{1}{2}.2.4 = 4$. Now the only partitions of 4 into two or fewer parts, none exceeding 4, are $0+4$, $1+3$, $2+2$. The only possible terms in an invariant of degree 2 are, then, a_0a_4, a_1a_3, $a_2{}^2$; or ae, bd, c^2 say. Now suppose that $ae + \lambda bd + \mu c^2$ is an invariant. The result of operating on it with Ω, i. e. with

$$a\partial/\partial b + 2b\partial/\partial c + 3c\partial/\partial d + 4d\partial/\partial e,$$

is $$ad(4+\lambda) + bc(3\lambda + 4\mu);$$

for which to vanish we must have $4+\lambda = 0$ and $3\lambda + 4\mu = 0$,

i. e. $$\lambda = -4, \mu = 3.$$

Thus $$I \equiv ae - 4bd + 3c^2$$

is the only invariant of degree 2, any other being merely a numerical multiple of it.

Again, take $i = 3$, so that $w = \frac{1}{2}.3.4 = 6$. The only partitions of 6 to be dealt with are

$$0+2+4,\ 0+3+3,\ 1+1+4,\ 1+2+3,\ 2+2+2.$$

The necessary form is then

$$ace + \lambda ad^2 + \mu b^2 e + \nu bcd + \rho c^3,$$

and Ω operating on this produces

$$abe\left|\begin{matrix}2\\+2\mu\end{matrix}\right| + acd\left|\begin{matrix}4\\+6\lambda\\+\nu\end{matrix}\right| + b^2d\left|\begin{matrix}4\mu\\+2\nu\end{matrix}\right| + bc^2\left|\begin{matrix}3\nu\\+6\rho\end{matrix}\right|,$$

for which to vanish we must have

$$2+2\mu = 0,\ 4+6\lambda+\nu = 0,\ 4\mu + 2\nu = 0,\ 3\nu + 6\rho = 0,$$

i. e. $$\mu = -1,\ \nu = 2,\ \lambda = -1,\ \rho = -1.$$

Thus $$J \equiv ace + 2bcd - ad^2 - b^2e - c^3$$

is the only invariant of degree 3 which the quartic possesses.

Ex. 1. Show that a binary p-ic has no invariant of the second degree if p is odd, and only one, that of § 48, if p is even.

Ex. 2. Show that no binary quantic has an invariant of the first degree.

Ex. 3. Show that a binary cubic has one invariant, its discriminant, of the fourth degree.

Ex. 4. Show that $a_0^2a_3 - 3a_0a_1a_2 + 2a_1^3$ is annihilated by Ω, for any value of p not less than 3. Is it an invariant for any value of p?

Ans. No.

103. **Invariants of several binary quantics.** The methods of the earlier part of this chapter apply, *mutatis mutandis*, to a system of binary quantics. The facts led to are as follows.

Let

$$(a_0, a_1, a_2, \ldots a_{p_1})(x, y)^{p_1},$$
$$(b_0, b_1, b_2, \ldots b_{p_2})(x, y)^{p_2},$$
$$(c_0, c_1, c_2, \ldots c_{p_3})(x, y)^{p_3},$$
$$\cdots\cdots\cdots$$

be a system of binary quantics in x, y. Take the operators

$$\left(a_0\frac{\partial}{\partial a_1}+2a_1\frac{\partial}{\partial a_2}+\ldots+p_1a_{p_1-1}\frac{\partial}{\partial a_{p_1}}\right)$$
$$+\left(b_0\frac{\partial}{\partial b_1}+2b_1\frac{\partial}{\partial b_2}+\ldots+p_2b_{p_2-1}\frac{\partial}{\partial b_{p_2}}\right)$$
$$+\left(c_0\frac{\partial}{\partial c_1}+2c_1\frac{\partial}{\partial c_2}+\ldots+p_3c_{p_3-1}\frac{\partial}{\partial c_{p_3}}\right)+\ldots\equiv\Sigma\Omega,\text{ say,}$$

and $$\left(p_1a_1\frac{\partial}{\partial a_0}+\overline{p_1-1}\,a_2\frac{\partial}{\partial a_1}+\ldots+a_{p_1}\frac{\partial}{\partial a_{p_1-1}}\right)$$
$$+\left(p_2b_1\frac{\partial}{\partial b_0}+\overline{p_2-1}\,b_2\frac{\partial}{\partial b_1}+\ldots+b_{p_2}\frac{\partial}{\partial b_{p_2-1}}\right)$$
$$+\left(p_3c_1\frac{\partial}{\partial c_0}+\overline{p_3-1}\,c_2\frac{\partial}{\partial c_1}+\ldots+c_{p_3}\frac{\partial}{\partial c_{p_3-1}}\right)+\ldots$$
$$\equiv\Sigma O,\text{ say.}$$

Then any invariant of the system is annihilated by $\Sigma\Omega$ and by ΣO. Also, conversely, any rational integral function of the different sets of coefficients which is homogeneous in each set, of partial degrees $i_1, i_2, i_3, \ldots$ say, and of the same total weight w throughout in the sets jointly, and which has both $\Sigma\Omega$ and ΣO for annihilators, is an invariant of the system. Moreover, the possession of these two annihilators necessitates that the several partial degrees and the total weight must be connected with one another and the orders of the quantics by the relation

$$i_1p_1+i_2p_2+i_3p_3+\ldots=2w.$$

Also, as in § 95, an invariant is unaltered if its weight is even, or altered only in sign if its weight is odd, when we interchange a_0 and a_{p_1}, a_1 and $a_{p_1-1}, \ldots$, b_0 and b_{p_2}, b_1 and $b_{p_2-1}, \ldots$, c_0 and c_{p_3}, c_1 and $c_{p_3-1}, \ldots, \ldots$. Thus, since these interchanges make $\Sigma\Omega$ into ΣO, and vice versa, we need not, when we have found a function which $\Sigma\Omega$ annihilates, test by direct operation whether it is also annihilated by ΣO before being sure whether it is an invariant. It is or not according as it has or has not the above symmetry.

Ex. 5. Find the invariant of partial degrees 1, 1, and consequently of weight 2, of the two quadratics

$$(a_0, a_1, a_2)(x, y)^2,\ (b_0, b_1, b_2)(x, y)^2.$$

Ans. Its form must be $\lambda a_0b_2+\mu a_1b_1+\nu a_2b_0$. Now $\Sigma\Omega$ on this produces $(2\lambda+\mu)a_0b_1+(\mu+2\nu)a_1b_0$. Thus $\mu=-2\lambda=-2\nu$. The one invariant is then that of § 7, Ex. 4, $\lambda(a_0b_2-2a_1b_1+a_2b_0)$.

Ex. 6. Show more generally that the invariant of § 49 is the only lineo-linear invariant of two binary p-ics.

Ex. 7. Show that the quartic and quadratic

$$(a_0, a_1, \dots a_4)(x, y)^4, \ (b_0, b_1, b_2)(x, y)^2$$

have no lineo-linear invariant.

Ans. The weight would have to be $\frac{1}{2}(4+2) = 3$. The only possible form is then $\lambda a_1 b_2 + \mu a_2 b_1 + \nu a_3 b_0$; and $\Sigma\Omega$ on this produces

$$\lambda a_0 b_2 + (2\lambda + 2\mu) a_1 b_1 + (\mu + 3\nu) a_2 b_0;$$

for which to vanish would require $\lambda = 0$, $\mu = 0$, $\nu = 0$.

Ex. 8. No two binary quantics of different orders can have a lineo-linear invariant.

Ex. 9. Find the only invariant of partial degrees 2, 1 of a linear form and a quadratic.

Ans. The invariant of § 7, Ex. 3.

Ex. 10. Find an invariant of partial degrees 1, 2 of a quadratic and cubic.

Ans. $a_0(b_1 b_3 - b_2^2) - a_1(b_0 b_3 - b_1 b_2) + a_2(b_0 b_2 - b_1^2)$.

Ex. 11. Find an invariant of partial degrees 1, 1, 1 of three quadratics.

Ans. That of § 17, Ex. 25.

104. **Annihilators of covariants.** In § 69 it has been seen that the covariants of a binary quantic u are identical with the results of replacing x' and y' by x and y in the invariants of u and the linear form $xy' - x'y$.

Now invariants of these two quantics have, by the preceding article, the two annihilators

$$\Omega - y'\frac{\partial}{\partial x'}, \quad O - x'\frac{\partial}{\partial y'}.$$

It follows that covariants of u have the annihilators

$$\Omega - y\frac{\partial}{\partial x}, \quad O - x\frac{\partial}{\partial y}.$$

It seems best, however, to prove this fact and investigate its consequences *ab initio*, as was done in the matter of invariants.

105. Let $F(a_0, a_1, a_2, \dots a_p; x, y)$ be a covariant of $(a_0, a_1, a_2, \dots a_p)(x, y)^p$; and let the quantic be transformed into

$$(A_0, A_1, A_2, \dots A_p)(X, Y)^p$$

by the substitution

$$x = X + mY, \quad y = Y,$$

whose modulus is unity. We seek first the necessary and sufficient condition that we may have

$$F(A_0, A_1, A_2, \ldots A_p; X, Y) = F(a_0, a_1, a_2, \ldots a_p; x, y),$$

which will be the case when F is a covariant, though not then only.

If $A_0, A_1, A_2, \ldots A_p$ are expressed in terms of m and $a_0, a_1, a_2, \ldots a_p$, we have, as in § 92,

$$\frac{dA_0}{dm} = 0, \quad \frac{dA_1}{dm} = A_0, \quad \frac{dA_2}{dm} = 2A_1, \ldots, \quad \frac{dA_p}{dm} = pA_{p-1}.$$

Also the expressions for X and Y in terms of m and x and y are

$$X = x - my, \quad Y = y,$$

so that $\quad dX/dm = -y = -Y, \quad dY/dm = 0.$

Consequently

$$\frac{d}{dm} F(A_0, A_1, A_2, \ldots A_p; X, Y)$$

$$= \frac{\partial F}{\partial A_0}\cdot\frac{dA_0}{dm} + \frac{\partial F}{\partial A_1}\cdot\frac{dA_1}{dm} + \ldots + \frac{\partial F}{\partial A_p}\cdot\frac{dA_p}{dm} + \frac{\partial F}{\partial X}\cdot\frac{dX}{dm} + \frac{\partial F}{\partial Y}\cdot\frac{dY}{dm}$$

$$= A_0\frac{\partial F}{\partial A_1} + 2A_1\frac{\partial F}{\partial A_2} + \ldots + pA_{p-1}\frac{\partial F}{\partial A_p} - Y\frac{\partial F}{\partial X}.$$

Now the vanishing of the left-hand member here is the necessary and sufficient condition for

$$F(A_0, A_1, A_2, \ldots A_p; X, Y)$$

to be a function of $a_0, a_1, a_2, \ldots a_p; x, y$ which is free from m, and consequently equal to $F(a_0, a_1, a_2, \ldots a_p; x, y)$, its value when $m = 0$. The vanishing of the right-hand member must then express the same thing. Thus the necessary and sufficient condition required is that

$$\left(A_0\frac{\partial}{\partial A_1} + 2A_1\frac{\partial}{\partial A_2} + 3A_2\frac{\partial}{\partial A_3} + \ldots + pA_{p-1}\frac{\partial}{\partial A_p} - Y\frac{\partial}{\partial X}\right) F(A_0, A_1, A_2, \ldots A_p; X, Y) = 0,$$

or, replacing capital by small letters, that

$$(\Omega - y\partial/\partial x)\, F(a_0, a_1, a_2, \ldots a_p; x, y) = 0.$$

We have also, as in § 93, that even when this condition is not satisfied

$$F(A_0, A_1, A_2, \ldots A_p; X, Y) = e^{m\left(\Omega - y\frac{\partial}{\partial x}\right)} F(a_0, a_1, a_2, \ldots a_p; x, y).$$

Thus we have the means of writing down the result of applying the transformation of this article to any function of the coefficients and variables.

We might also have adopted the method of § 91.

106. In precisely the same way, the necessary and sufficient condition for the persistence in form of F after transformation by the substitution

$$x = X,\ y = l'X + Y,$$

is
$$(O - x\,\partial/\partial y)\,F(a_0, a_1, a_2, \dots a_p;\ x, y) = 0,$$
where O is the second operator of § 90.

Any covariant has, then, the two annihilators

$$\Omega - y\,\partial/\partial x, \quad O - x\,\partial/\partial y.$$

107. **Symmetry of a covariant.** Again, as in § 95, we see that there is a symmetry in any covariant. The simultaneous interchange of x and y, of a_0 and a_p, a_1 and a_{p-1}, &c. in its expression must, since the interchange means a substitution of modulus -1, have the effect only of multiplying it by $(-1)^{\frac{1}{2}(ip-\varpi)}$, where i is its degree and ϖ its order. Now $\frac{1}{2}(ip+\varpi)$ is the weight of the covariant (Chap. III), and $\frac{1}{2}(ip-\varpi)$ consequently the weight of the coefficient of x^{ϖ} in it. Thus a covariant is unaltered, or altered only in sign, by these interchanges, according as the weight of its leading coefficient is even or odd.

Hence for covariants one of the two conditions of § 106 is necessitated by the other and symmetry. The reasoning is as in § 96.

108. **Sufficiency of the two conditions of annihilation.** We can also prove the converse of § 106 for homogeneous isobaric functions. Stated at length, the fact is that any rational integral function F of $a_0, a_1, a_2, \dots a_p$ and x, y, which is homogeneous, of degree i, in the coefficients, homogeneous, of order ϖ, in x, y, and isobaric on the whole, reckoning a_0, a_1, $a_2, \dots a_p$, x, y as of weights 0, 1, 2, ... p, 1, 0, and which has both $\Omega - y\,\partial/\partial x$ and $O - x\,\partial/\partial y$ for annihilators, is a covariant.

The proof, which proceeds exactly as in § 97, need not be repeated at length. The only variation is that in passing from
$$(a_0, a_1, a_2, \dots a_p)\,(x, y)^p$$
to
$$(a_0', a_1', a_2', \dots a_p')\,(x', y')^p,$$
we have, as well as $\quad a_r' = \lambda^{p-r}\mu^r a_r,$

also $\quad x' = \lambda^{-1}x,\ y' = \mu^{-1}y,$

so that $\quad x'^s y'^{\varpi-s} = \lambda^{-s}\mu^{s-\varpi}x^s y^{\varpi-s},$

where the index of the power of λ is minus the weight of the product $x^s y^{\varpi-s}$, and that of the power of μ is the weight of the product diminished by ϖ. Also the weight of the function of $a_0, a_1, a_2, \dots a_p$ which multiplies $x^s y^{\varpi-s}$ in the function F

which we are considering is $w-s$, where w is the weight of F. Thus, in place of the

$$F(a_0', a_1', a_2', \dots a_p') = \lambda^{ip-w}\mu^w F(a_0, a_1, a_2, \dots a_p)$$

of § 97, what we now have is, since for every s

$$\lambda^{ip-(w-s)}\mu^{w-s} \,.\, \lambda^{-s}\mu^{s-\varpi} = \lambda^{ip-w}\mu^{w-\varpi},$$

$$F(a_0', a_1', a_2', \dots a_p'; x', y') = \lambda^{ip-w}\mu^{w-\varpi} F(a_0, a_1, a_2, \dots a_p; x, y).$$

This difference of the factor will not affect the argument. The supplementary conclusion, from the fact (§ 37) that when we have proved F to be a covariant we know that the factor must be a power of the modulus, is in this case

$$ip-w = w-\varpi = \tfrac{1}{2}(ip-\varpi),$$

so that

$$ip+\varpi = 2w,$$

which accords with Chapter III.

109. **A covariant completely given by an end term.** We are now in a position to find the covariants of a given degree and order by a method like that of § 101. A further theorem of great importance will, however, much facilitate the process. It is due to M. Roberts.

Let a covariant of order ϖ of a binary p-ic be arranged as a quantic in x and y. We may write it

$$C_0x^\varpi + \varpi C_1x^{\varpi-1}y + \frac{\varpi(\varpi-1)}{1\,.\,2}C_2x^{\varpi-2}y^2 + \dots$$
$$+ \varpi C_{\varpi-1}xy^{\varpi-1} + C_\varpi y^\varpi,$$

where $C_0, C_1, C_2, \dots C_\varpi$ are all of degree i in $a_0, a_1, a_2, \dots a_p$, and are of weights respectively

$$\tfrac{1}{2}(ip-\varpi),\ \tfrac{1}{2}(ip-\varpi)+1,\ \tfrac{1}{2}(ip-\varpi)+2, \dots\ \tfrac{1}{2}(ip+\varpi).$$

This is annihilated by $\Omega - y\,\partial/\partial x$. We must then have

$$\Omega C_0 . x^\varpi + \varpi(\Omega C_1 - C_0)x^{\varpi-1}y + \frac{\varpi(\varpi-1)}{1\,.\,2}(\Omega C_2 - 2C_1)x^{\varpi-2}y^2 + \dots$$
$$+ \varpi(\Omega C_{\varpi-1} - \overline{\varpi-1}\,C_{\varpi-2})\,xy^{\varpi-1} + (\Omega C_\varpi - \varpi C_{\varpi-1})y^\varpi = 0,$$

for all values of x and y. The various coefficients of x^ϖ, $x^{\varpi-1}y, \dots$ must therefore vanish separately. In other words,

$$\begin{aligned} \Omega C_0 &= 0, \\ \Omega C_1 &= C_0, \\ \Omega C_2 &= 2C_1, \\ &\cdot\quad\cdot\quad\cdot\quad\cdot \\ \Omega C_{\varpi-1} &= (\varpi-1)\,C_{\varpi-2}, \\ \Omega C_\varpi &= \varpi C_{\varpi-1}. \end{aligned}$$

We have then the two most interesting conclusions which follow:

(1) C_0, the leading coefficient in the covariant, is annihilated by Ω, the first of the two annihilators of invariants. For this reason it is called a semi-invariant or *seminvariant.*

(2) When C_ϖ, the last coefficient in a covariant, is known, all the other coefficients are determined from it by mere operations with Ω, i.e. by differentiations only. In fact, we see that

$$C_r = \frac{1}{\varpi(\varpi-1)(\varpi-2)\dots(r+1)}\Omega^{\varpi-r}C_\varpi;$$

and that the whole covariant is

$$\frac{\Omega^\varpi C_\varpi}{\varpi!}x^\varpi + \frac{\Omega^{\varpi-1}C_\varpi}{(\varpi-1)!}x^{\varpi-1}y + \frac{\Omega^{\varpi-2}C_\varpi}{(\varpi-2)!}x^{\varpi-2}y^2 + \dots$$
$$+ \Omega C_\varpi x y^{\varpi-1} + C_\varpi y^\varpi,$$

which, since $\Omega^{\varpi+1}C_\varpi$, $\Omega^{\varpi+2}C_\varpi$, &c., vanish, the first of them being only $\varpi!\,\Omega C_0$ which is zero by the first equality above, may briefly be written

$$y^\varpi e^{\frac{x}{y}\Omega}C_\varpi.$$

For this reason C_ϖ, which is (§ 107) merely the result of interchanging a_0 and a_p, a_1 and a_{p-1}, &c. in $(-1)^{\frac{1}{2}(ip-\varpi)}C_0$, has been called the *source* of the covariant. In the next article we shall see that the same name might equally and for a like reason be given to C_0 itself.

110. Express, in fact, precisely as in the preceding article, that the covariant is annihilated by $O - x\,\partial/\partial y$. The conclusions are that

$$OC_0 = \varpi C_1$$
$$OC_1 = (\varpi-1)C_2$$
$$OC_2 = (\varpi-2)C_3$$
$$\cdot\quad\cdot\quad\cdot\quad\cdot\quad\cdot\quad\cdot\quad\cdot$$
$$OC_{\varpi-1} = C_\varpi,$$
$$OC_\varpi = 0.$$

Thus (1) C_ϖ is annihilated by O the second annihilator of invariants, and may be called an *anti-seminvariant*; and (2) for every value of the number r from 1 to ϖ inclusive

$$C_r = \frac{1}{\varpi(\varpi-1)(\varpi-2)\dots(\varpi-r+1)}O^rC_0,$$

so that the covariant is

$$C_0x^\varpi + OC_0x^{\varpi-1}y + \frac{O^2C_0}{1.2}x^{\varpi-2}y^2 + \dots + \frac{O^\varpi C_0}{\varpi!}y^\varpi,$$

or, as it may be written,

$$x^{\varpi} e^{\frac{y}{x}O} C_0,$$

for $O^{\varpi+1}C_0$, $O^{\varpi+2}C_0, \ldots$ vanish since $OC_{\varpi} = 0$.

Thus, when we have the seminvariant C_0 which is the leading coefficient of a covariant, all the coefficients in the covariant can be obtained from it by mere operations with O, i.e. by differentiations.

In fact, given any coefficient in a covariant, all the coefficients can be found. Successive operations with Ω give the coefficients on the one side of it, and successive operations with O give those on the other.

111. **Seminvariants.** We may define a *seminvariant* as *any* homogeneous isobaric function of the coefficients $a_0, a_1, a_2, \ldots a_p$ which is annihilated by Ω. We now confine attention, however, to seminvariants which are rational and integral.

Looking back at §§ 91, 92 we see that the half invariant property which seminvariants possess is that of being absolutely invariantic for such linear substitutions as

$$x = X + mY, \qquad y = Y.$$

(From § 97 we gather that they are really invariantic for the somewhat more general substitution

$$x = lX + mY, \qquad y = m'Y,$$

though the factor for any one is in this case not as a rule a power of the modulus.)

Consequently, when expressed in terms of a_0 and the roots of the quantic, a seminvariant can involve only differences of these latter. If of degree i, and not divisible by a_0, it is a product of $a_0^{\,i}$ and a function of the differences which involves each particular root to the i-th degree, since the ratios of a_1, a_2, a_3, &c., to a_0 are all of the first degree in every root. Conversely, any rational integral symmetric function of the roots, which can be expressed in terms of their differences only, becomes a rational integral seminvariant when multiplied by such a power of a_0 that it can be expressed integrally in terms of the coefficients. The least power of a_0 which suffices is the i-th, where i is the degree of the symmetric function in any particular root.

We may now see that in the two preceding articles C_0 may be any rational integral seminvariant; that is to say, that any rational integral seminvariant whatever may be taken as the leading coefficient of a covariant, and determines that covariant uniquely.

Take any rational integral seminvariant S of degree i, without a_0 for a factor, and write it as $a_0{}^i$ multiplied into a symmetric function of the roots $\alpha_1, \alpha_2, \dots \alpha_p$. This symmetric function is a function of the differences $\alpha_r - \alpha_s$, is of degree i in each root, and (§ 89) can be expressed as a linear function of products of the differences in such a way that no root occurs in more than i factors of any product. Now, having thus expressed it, write $(\alpha_r - \alpha_s)/(x - \alpha_r y)(x - \alpha_s y)$ for every difference $\alpha_r - \alpha_s$. In this fraction α_r occurs once in the numerator and once in the denominator, and so does α_s.

Clear the function obtained of fractions by multiplying by the lowest necessary power, the i-th, of

$$(x - \alpha_1 y)(x - \alpha_2 y) \dots (x - \alpha_p y).$$

In this multiplier $\alpha_1, \alpha_2, \dots \alpha_p$ occur in equal numbers i of factors.

The result, when expressed in terms of x, y and coefficients only, will be a covariant whose leading coefficient C_0 is the seminvariant S. That the leading coefficient is S is clear from the method of construction. That the whole expression is a covariant follows from the fact (§ 83) that it is a power of a_0 multiplied into a function of differences $x - \alpha y$ and differences $\alpha_r - \alpha_s$, which is symmetrical in the roots, homogeneous in both kinds of differences, and such that all roots α occur in equal numbers of factors in any product, and in the same number in all products.

The covariant is unique; for § 110 shows that a leading coefficient C_0 determines a covariant uniquely, giving ϖ as the least number for which $O^{\varpi+1}C_0 = 0$, and giving $C_1, C_2, \dots C_\varpi$ by a succession of operations with O on C_0. Note, however, that the order ϖ depends on the value of p. For quantics of different orders p, the same seminvariant will lead covariants of different orders ϖ. We had above, in forming the covariant from its seminvariant leader by means of the roots, to divide terms by products of order $2w'$, where w' is the weight of the seminvariant, and to multiply through by a product of order ip. Altogether the covariant obtained is of order $ip - 2w'$, which accords with the known fact that $w' = \frac{1}{2}(ip - \varpi)$.

A seminvariant with a power of a_0, $a_0{}^j$ say, for a factor is of the form $a_0{}^j S$, where S is a seminvariant to which the reasoning above applies. The unique covariant which it leads is the product of the covariant led by S and the j-th power of the p-ic.

Another proof, making no explicit use of the roots, of the important theorem of the present article will be given in the next chapter. (Cf. § 126, Ex. 6.)

112. We now see that the problem of finding covariants by aid of annihilators is reduced to the much simpler one of finding seminvariants. We have found, suppose, a seminvariant of degree i and weight w. Take it for C_0 in § 110. The leading term in the corresponding covariant of the binary p-ic is $C_0 x^{ip-2w}$ as above, when a_0 is a factor of C_0 as well as in other cases, where w is the weight of C_0 and not that of the covariant; and the full expression of the covariant is, by § 110,

$$x^{ip-2w} e^{\frac{y}{x}O} C_0.$$

That the order $ip-2w$ of the covariant cannot be negative, C_0 being a rational integral seminvariant, is clear. For the procedure of the last article determined a covariant of essentially non-negative order in x and y from the seminvariant with which it started. Thus there are no rational integral seminvariants for which $ip-2w$ is negative. Should $ip-2w$ be zero the seminvariant is an invariant. For the covariant derived from it is of zero order as above and consequently an invariant, and is in fact the seminvariant itself. It must clearly be borne in mind, however, that we are dealing only with rational integral seminvariants. The argument does not apply, for instance, to the fractional seminvariant $a^{-1}(a^2d-3abc+2b^3)$. Here, for the cubic, $ip-2w=0$, but nevertheless the function is not an invariant of the cubic. O does not annihilate it.

We may, in fact, state succinctly the conclusions arrived at earlier as to invariants of a binary p-ic. If Ω and O annihilate a function it is an invariant, and $ip-2w=0$ (§ 97). If Ω annihilates a function for which $ip-2w=0$, O must also annihilate it, so that it is an invariant, *provided it is rational and integral*, but not necessarily if it is fractional.

113. **Determination of seminvariants.** The determination of the linearly independent seminvariants of degree i and weight w of a binary p-ic proceeds as in § 101. If $ip<2w$ there are none, as above. If $ip \nless 2w$, write down all the products of weight w of i constituents chosen from among $a_0, a_1, a_2, \dots a_p$, repetitions of factors allowed, and add together arbitrary multiples of these. The number of such products is $(w; i, p)$, this symbol denoting, as in § 101, the number of different partitions of the number w into i or fewer numbers, none exceeding p. Operate on this sum with Ω, thus obtaining a sum of multiples of the $(w-1; i, p)$ products of degree i and weight $w-1$. It will be proved in the next chapter that the $(w-1; i, p)$ coefficients of these products are linearly independent linear functions of the $(w; i, p)$ arbitrary mul-

tipliers of the $(w; i, p)$ products. They have to vanish. Their vanishing gives $(w-1; i, p)$ relations which have to be satisfied by the $(w; i, p)$ multipliers. If then $(w; i, p)$ exceeds $(w-1; i, p)$ we can satisfy them and leave

$$(w; i, p)-(w-1; i, p)$$

of the multipliers still arbitrary. Suppose that this excess is r. We have as the most general seminvariant of the type under consideration a sum of the form

$$\lambda_1 S_1 + \lambda_2 S_2 + \ldots + \lambda_r S_r$$

where $\lambda_1, \lambda_2, \ldots \lambda_r$ are arbitrary, and $S_1, S_2 \ldots S_r$ are known linear functions of the products of type w, i. We express this by saying that there are r linearly independent seminvariants

$$S_1, S_2, \ldots S_r$$

of this type belonging to the p-ic.

114. **Seminvariants of the second degree.** As an example let us discover all the seminvariants of degree 2 of a binary p-ic. The condition $ip \not< 2w$ is for this case $w \not> p$. Two cases will arise.

(1) For an even weight w, not exceeding p, the general form to be assumed is

$$a_0 a_w + \lambda_1 a_1 a_{w-1} + \lambda_2 a_2 a_{w-2} + \ldots + \lambda_{\frac{1}{2}w} a^2_{\frac{1}{2}w}.$$

Expressing that Ω annihilates this, we obtain the conditions

$$w + \lambda_1 = 0, \quad (w-1)\lambda_1 + 2\lambda_2 = 0,$$

$$(w-2)\lambda_2 + 3\lambda_3 = 0, \ldots \quad (\tfrac{1}{2}w+1)\lambda_{\frac{1}{2}w-1} + w\lambda_{\frac{1}{2}w} = 0,$$

the coefficient w in the last of these being double what it would be according to the law of all the other second terms. Solving these for the λ's we have a unique seminvariant of weight w, viz.

$$a_0 a_w - w a_1 a_{w-1} + \frac{w(w-1)}{1\,.\,2} a_2 a_{w-2} - \ldots$$

$$+ (-1)^{\frac{1}{2}w} \frac{w(w-1)\ldots(\frac{1}{2}w+1)}{2\,(\frac{1}{2}w)!} a^2_{\frac{1}{2}w},$$

where the law of coefficients is that of the expansion of $(1+z)^w$ up to its middle coefficient, which one alone is halved.

For every even weight not exceeding p there is then a single seminvariant of degree 2. In particular, of course, it is an invariant for a weight equal to p if p is even.

(2) For an odd weight w, not exceeding p, the form to be assumed is

$$a_0 a_w + \lambda_1 a_1 a_{w-1} + \lambda_2 a_2 a_{w-2} + \ldots + \lambda_{\frac{1}{2}(w-1)} a_{\frac{1}{2}(w-1)} a_{\frac{1}{2}(w+1)},$$

and the conditions obtained from the annihilation by Ω are

$$w+\lambda_1=0,\quad (w-1)\lambda_1+2\lambda_2=0,\quad (w-2)\lambda_2+3\lambda_3=0,\ldots$$
$$\tfrac{1}{2}(w+3)\lambda_{\frac{1}{2}(w-3)}+\tfrac{1}{2}(w-1)\lambda_{\frac{1}{2}(w-1)}=0,\quad \tfrac{1}{2}(w+1)\lambda_{\frac{1}{2}(w-1)}=0,$$

of which the last tells us that $\lambda_{\frac{1}{2}(w-1)}$ vanishes, and the rest, taken in order backwards, tells us that all the other λ's vanish.

For no odd weight, then, is there a seminvariant of degree 2.

Accordingly the complete list of seminvariants of degree 2 is

$$a_0^2,$$
$$a_0a_2-a_1^2,$$
$$a_0a_4-4a_1a_3+3a_2^2,$$
$$a_0a_6-6a_1a_5+15a_2a_4-10a_3^2,$$
$$a_0a_8-8a_1a_7+28a_2a_6-56a_3a_5+35a_4^2,$$
&c., &c.,

the list terminating with the weight p or $p-1$ according as p is even or odd. In the former case the last of the list is an invariant.

The orders of the corresponding covariants are $2p$, $2p-4$, $2p-8,\ldots$. They are the covariants of § 57, Ex. 12, together with the invariant, if p be even, of § 48. In other words, they are the transvectants (§ 61) of the p-ic and itself. Thus we have the theorem that a binary quantic u has no covariants of the second degree in the coefficients besides the 0th, second, fourth, sixth, &c., transvectants of u and itself. The 0th, led by $a_0^2x^{2p}$, is u^2.

In the second symbolical notation of § 60 (*bis*) the seminvariants of degree 2 are denoted by $\frac{1}{2}(\theta_1-\theta_2)^{2r}aa$, with $r=0, 1, 2, \ldots I(\frac{1}{2}p)$. (Cf. § 61, Ex. 33.)

Ex. 12. Use § 110 to write down in full the covariants of degree 2.

$$a_0^2x^{10}+\ldots,\ (a_0a_2-a_1^2)x^6+\ldots,\ (a_0a_4-4a_1a_3+3a_2^2)x^2+\ldots$$

of the binary quintic.

Ans. For the last see § 61, Ex. 29.

Ex. 13. A binary quantic of order not less than 4 has one and only one seminvariant of degree 3 and weight 6.

Ans. $a_0a_2a_4+2a_1a_2a_3-a_0a_3^2-a_1^2a_4-a_2^3.$

Ex. 14. Hence obtain the single covariant of degree 3 and order 3 of the quintic.

Ans.
$$\begin{aligned}&(ace+2bcd-ad^2-b^2e-c^3)x^3\\&+(acf-ade-b^2f+bce+bd^2-c^2d)x^2y\\&+(adf-bcf-ae^2+bde+c^2e-cd^2)xy^2\\&+(bdf+2cde-c^2f-be^2-d^3)y^3.\end{aligned}$$

Ex. 15. Show that a binary quantic of order not less than 3 has one and only one seminvariant of degree 3 and weight 3.

Ans. $a_0^2 a_3 - 3a_0 a_1 a_2 + 2a_1^3$.

Ex. 16. Hence, and from what has been obtained above, prove the statement of § 85 that H and G are the only covariants of a binary cubic whose degrees are 2, 3 and orders 2, 3 respectively.

Ex. 17. Show that a binary quartic, or binary quantic of higher order, has two and only two linearly independent seminvariants of degree 4 and weight 4.

Ans. $\lambda a^2 (ae - 4bd + 3c^2) + \mu (ac - b^2)^2$,

which may also be written

$$\lambda (a^3 e - 4a^2 bd + 6ab^2 c - 3b^4) + \mu' (ac - b^2)^2.$$

Ex. 18. Find the sum σ_4 of the six fourth powers of differences between the roots of the quartic $(a, b, c, d, e)(x, 1)^4$.

Ans. $a^4 \sigma_4 = 720 (ac - b^2)^2 - 16 (a^3 e - 4a^2 bd + 6ab^2 c - 3b^4)$.

Determine λ and μ' in the second form above by taking two particular quartics, e. g. $x^2(x^2-1)$ and x^4-1, in both of which $b=0$, and in one of which $e=0$ and in the other $c=0$.

Ex. 19. Show that a binary quintic has two and only two linearly independent seminvariants of degree 5 and weight 5.

Ans. $\lambda (a^4 f - 5a^3 be + 10a^2 b^2 d - 10ab^3 c + 4b^5)$
$$+ \mu (ac - b^2)(a^2 d - 3abc + 2b^3).$$

Ex. 20. The sum of the numerical coefficients in any seminvariant which is not a mere power of a_0 vanishes.

Ex. 21. If $(C_0, C_1, C_2, \ldots C_\varpi)(x, y)^\varpi$ is a covariant of

$$(a_0, a_1, a_2, \ldots a_p)(x, y)^p$$

prove from § 109 that $a_0 C_1 - a_1 C_0$ is a seminvariant. (*M. Roberts.*)

Ex. 22. By application of this result to the first linear covariant (§ 57, Ex. 17) of a binary quintic, prove that the quintic has a covariant of degree 6 and order 4, and an invariant of degree 18, the catalecticant of this covariant.

115. **Seminvariants and covariants of several binary quantics.** Referring to § 103 for the notation, we define a seminvariant of a system of quantics in the same variables x, y as a function of the several sets of coefficients—in general a rational integral function—which is homogeneous in each set separately, and isobaric on the whole, though not necessarily in the sets separately, and which has $\Sigma\Omega$ for an annihilator.

The methods which have preceded are applicable to covariants and seminvariants of systems of quantics. It is left to the student to convince himself, as in § 104 or §§ 105, 106, that every covariant of the system is annihilated by $\Sigma\Omega - y\partial/\partial x$ and $\Sigma O - x\partial/\partial y$, and, as in § 108, that conversely a function which is homogeneous in the variables and in every set of coefficients separately, and isobaric on the whole, is a covariant if these operators annihilate it. He will also see, as in § 107, that if x and y, a_0 and a_{p_1}, a_1 and a_{p_1-1}, ..., b_0 and b_{p_2}, b_1 and b_{p_2-1}, ..., c_0 and c_{p_3}, c_1 and c_{p_3-1}, ..., ... are interchanged in a covariant the effect is only to multiply the covariant by $(-1)^{\frac{1}{2}(\Sigma . ip-\varpi)}$, where the index is the total weight of the leading coefficient, that of x^{ϖ}. That this leading coefficient C_0 is a seminvariant, i.e. is annihilated by $\Sigma\Omega$, he will see as in § 109, and that all other coefficients can be derived from it by operations with ΣO he will see as in § 110. In fact, the covariant may be written either as

$$x^{\varpi} e^{\frac{y}{x}\Sigma O} C_0, \quad \text{or as} \quad y^{\varpi} e^{\frac{x}{y}\Sigma\Omega} C_{\varpi}.$$

Once more, as in § 111, he will see that any rational integral seminvariant whatever may be taken as the leading coefficient C_0, and determines ϖ, the order, and the full expression for the covariant uniquely. The order ϖ, the partial degrees $i_1, i_2, i_3, \ldots$ in the coefficients of the p_1-ic, the p_2-ic, the p_3-ic, &c., and the weight w of the seminvariant are seen to be connected by the relation

$$i_1 p_1 + i_2 p_2 + i_3 p_3 + \ldots - \varpi = 2w.$$

Thus there is no seminvariant for which $\Sigma . ip - 2w$ is negative. If $\Sigma . ip - 2w = 0$ the derived covariant and the seminvariant are identical. The seminvariant is in fact an invariant, and is annihilated by ΣO.

The method of §§ 98–100 also applies; and the results of § 100 hold, when we put $\Sigma\Omega$, ΣO, $\Sigma . ip - 2w$ in place of Ω, O, $ip - 2w$ respectively, for operations on functions of any or all of the sets of coefficients.

All the linearly independent seminvariants of given weight w and partial degrees $i_1, i_2, i_3, \ldots$ are found, as in § 113, by writing down the most general rational integral function of the type in question and determining the multipliers in it so that it may be annihilated by $\Sigma\Omega$.

Ex. 23. Find a seminvariant of weight 2 and partial degrees, 1, 1, of the quadratic and cubic $(a_0, a_1, a_2)(x, y)^2$, $(b_0, b_1, b_2, b_3)(x, y)^3$, and show that the covariant to which it leads is linear.

Ans. The covariant is

$$(a_0 b_2 - 2a_1 b_1 + a_2 b_0)x + (a_0 b_3 - 2a_1 b_2 + a_2 b_1)y.$$

Ex. 24. Find a linear covariant of partial degrees 2, 1 of the quadratic and cubic.

Ans. $(a_0^2 b_3 - 3a_0 a_1 b_2 + a_0 a_2 b_1 + 2a_1^2 b_1 - a_1 a_2 b_0)x$
$$-(a_2^2 b_0 - 3a_1 a_2 b_1 + a_0 a_2 b_2 + 2a_1^2 b_2 - a_0 a_1 b_3)y.$$

Ex. 25. Remembering that a cubic has a cubicovariant (§ 45, Ex. 13) deduce two other linear covariants of a quadratic and cubic.

Ex. 26. Two different binary quantics of orders p and p' have a single lineo-linear seminvariant of every weight not exceeding the smaller of p, p', and none of higher weight than this.

Ans. $a_0 b_w - w a_1 b_{w-1} + \dfrac{w(w-1)}{1.2} a_2 b_{w-2} + \ldots + (-1)^w a_w b_0.$

Ex. 27. The covariants led by these seminvariants are the mutual transvectants (§§ 59, 61) of the two quantics. Hence the mutual transvectants of u and v are the only covariants of u and v which are lineo-linear in the coefficients.

ADDITIONAL EXAMPLES.

Ex. 28. Prove that $I = 0, J = 0$, where I and J are the invariants of the quartic $u \equiv (a, b, c, d, e)(x, y)^4$ are two results which can be obtained by elimination of x between

$$\frac{\partial^2 u}{\partial x^2} = 0, \quad \frac{\partial^2 u}{\partial x\, \partial y} = 0, \quad \frac{\partial^2 u}{\partial y^2} = 0. \quad (\textit{Cayley.})$$

Ex. 29. If $\alpha, \beta, \gamma, \delta$, the roots of $(a, b, c, d, e)(x, y)^4$, are taken in pairs α, β; γ, δ in any way, the substitution

$$x = (\gamma\delta - \alpha\beta)X - \{\alpha\beta(\gamma+\delta) - \gamma\delta(\alpha+\beta)\}\, Y,$$
$$y = (\gamma+\delta-\alpha-\beta)X - (\gamma\delta - \alpha\beta)\, Y,$$

transforms the quartic into the same quartic $(a, b, c, d, e)(X, Y)^4$ multiplied by a function of the roots.

Ans. Consider the quartic in its factorized form.

Ex. 30. If $x - \alpha y$ is any one of the factors of $(a, b, c, d, e)(x, y)^4$, prove that the transformation $y = -X$, $x - \alpha y = Y$ can be followed by another linear transformation of modulus unity so as to give the quartic the form $(4x'^3 - g_2 x' y'^2 - g_3 y'^3)y'$, and that g_2, g_3 are the invariants I, J.

Hence show that any invariant $F(a, b, c, d, e)$ of the quartic is equal to $F(0, 1, 0, -\frac{1}{4}I, -J)$, so that there are no irreducible invariants but I, J.

Ex. 31. If in any covariant of $(a_0, a_1, a_2, \ldots a_p)(x, y)^p$ we put

$$a_0 x + a_1 y,\ a_1 x + a_2 y,\ a_2 x + a_3 y,\ \ldots\ a_p x + a_{p+1} y$$

for $a_0, a_1, a_2, \ldots a_p$ respectively, we deduce the covariant with the same leading coefficient of

$$(a_0, a_1, a_2, \ldots a_p, a_{p+1})(x, y)^{p+1}. \quad (\textit{Cayley.})$$

Ans. Symmetrical and annihilated by $\Omega_{p+1} - y\,\partial/\partial x$.

Ex. 32. To substitute $(a_0, a_1, a_2)(x, y)^2$, $(a_1, a_2, a_3)(x, y)^2$, ... for $a_0, a_1, a_2, \ldots$ is to repeat the same process twice, and to deduce a covariant of $(a_0, a_1, a_2, \ldots a_p, a_{p+1}, a_{p+2})(x, y)^{p+2}$. (*Cayley.*)

Ex. 33. In any seminvariant or invariant of $(a_0, a_1, a_2, \ldots a_p)(x, y)^p$ put $k, k-1, k-2, \ldots, k-p$ for $a_0, a_1, a_2, \ldots a_p$, and equate to the result of putting $k, -1$ for a_0, a_1 in the one term, if there be any, which involves a_0, a_1 only, or to zero if there be none (i. e. if $w > i$). The result is an identity for all values of k.

Ans. Follows from the equality of seminvariants of

$$k(x+y)^p - p(x+y)^{p-1}y \text{ and } kX^p - pX^{p-1}Y.$$

Ex. 34. Hence by giving k the values 0, 1, 2, ... in succession obtain facts with regard to the numerical coefficients of terms free from a_0, terms free from a_1, terms free from a_2, ... in any seminvariant or invariant.

Ex. 35. In this way determine the seminvariants of degree 3 and weight 3, and of degree 2 and weight 4.

Ex. 36. In the same way determine the terms free from b in the discriminant of the cubic $(a, b, c, d)(x, y)^3$, and deduce the full expression for the discriminant, by considering the transformation of the cubic to a form without a second term.

Ex. 37. By consideration of the special binary quantic

$$k(x+y)^p - \frac{p(p-1)}{1.2}(x+y)^{p-2}y^2,$$

prove that if in any seminvariant or invariant $a_0, a_1, a_2, a_3, a_4, \ldots$ are replaced by $k, k, k-1, k-3, k-6, \ldots$, where 1, 3, 6, 10, 15, ... are the figurate numbers of the third order, the result is equal to that of replacing a_0 and a_2 by k and -1 in the one term which involves a_0 and a_2 only, or to zero if there be no such term.

Ex. 38. Generally, if in any seminvariant or invariant of a binary p-ic we replace $a_0, a_1, \ldots a_{r-1}$ all by k, and $a_r, a_{r+1}, \ldots a_p$ by k diminished respectively by the first, second, ... $(p-r+1)$th figurate numbers of the $(r+1)$th order, the result is equal to that of replacing a_0 and a_r by k and -1 in the one term which involves a_0 and a_r only, or to zero if there be no such term.

Ex. 39. If $F(a_0, a_1, a_2, \ldots a_p)$ is a rational integral homogeneous isobaric function, of the coefficients in $(a_0, a_1, a_2, \ldots a_p)(x, y)^p$, for which $ip - 2w = 0$, prove that

$$\left(2 - \frac{\Omega O}{1^2} + \frac{\Omega^2 O^2}{1^2.2^2} - \frac{\Omega^3 O^3}{1^2.2^2.3^2} + \ldots\right)$$
$$\{F(a_0, a_1, a_2, \ldots a_p) - (-1)^w F(a_p, a_{p-1}, a_{p-2}, \ldots a_0)\} = 0.$$

Ans. Use § 100.

Ex. 40. In the same case prove that

$$F(a_0, a_1, a_2, \dots a_p) - (-1)^w F(a_p, a_{p-1}, a_{p-2}, \dots a_0)$$

is of the form $\Omega G(a_0, a_1, a_2, \dots a_p)$, where G is a rational integral homogeneous isobaric function.

Ex. 41. Prove that the method of § 19 applies to seminvariants, irrespective of the orders of quantics to which they belong, so that from covariants with like seminvariant leaders of two quantics of different orders intermediate covariants follow.

Ex. 42. If J is the Jacobian $(ab'-a'b)x^{p+p'-2}+\dots$ of two binary quantics u, u', and if H and H' are their Hessians

$$(ac-b^2)x^{2p-4}+\dots,\ (a'c'-b'^2)x^{2p'-4}+\dots,$$

and H'' the intermediate covariant

$$(ac'+a'c-2bb')x^{p+p'-4}+\dots$$

between H and H', prove that

$$J^2 = -u^2H'+uu'H''-u'^2H. \quad (\textit{Faà de Bruno.})$$

Ans. It suffices to prove the relation among the seminvariant leaders.

Ex. 43. Any factor of a seminvariant is a seminvariant. (*Sylvester.*)

Ans. If $\Omega P^n = 0$ then $P^{n-1}\Omega P = 0$, i.e. $\Omega P = 0$. If $\Omega . PQ = 0$, then $\Omega P/\Omega Q = -P/Q$, whence, if Q and P have no common factor, $\Omega P = 0$, $\Omega Q = 0$.

Ex. 44. If $A = PB+QC$, where A is a seminvariant, and B, C invariants with no common factor, then there is a relation

$$A = P'B+Q'C$$

in which P' and Q' are seminvariants.

Ans. $B\Omega P+C\Omega Q = 0$. $\therefore \Omega P = -CK$, $\Omega Q = BK$. There is an $\Omega^{-1}K$ by § 100; and

$$P = -C\Omega^{-1}K+P',\ Q = B\Omega^{-1}K+Q'.$$

Ex. 45. If $\phi(a, b, c, d, e, f, g, \dots)$ is a seminvariant, then

$$\phi(0, a, 2b, 3c, 4d, 5e, 6f, \dots),\ \phi(0, 0, a, 3b, 6c, 10d, 15e, \dots),$$
$$\phi(0, 0, 0, a, 4b, 10c, 20d, \dots), \dots$$

are other seminvariants, the series of numbers being figurate. (*Sylvester.*)

Ex. 46. Any $(\theta_1-\theta_2)^{m_{12}}(\theta_1-\theta_3)^{m_{13}}\dots(\theta_{i-1}-\theta_i)^{m_{i-1\,i}}\,a_0^{(1)}a_0^{(2)}\dots a_0^{(i)}$ which does not involve θ_1 in more than p_1 factors, or θ_2 in more than p_2, or &c., is a seminvariant of a p_1-ic, a p_2-ic, ... and a p_i-ic; and all seminvariants of partial degrees (1, 1, ... 1) of the i quantics are linear functions of these seminvariants. (Cf. §§ 60 (*bis*), 89.)

Ex. 47. There is a one to one correspondence between seminvariants of weight w and partial degrees (1, 1, ... 1) of a p_1-ic, a p_2-ic, ..., and a p_i-ic and seminvariants of weight w and partial degrees $(p_1, p_2, \dots p_i)$ of i linear forms.

Ex. 48. Any non-vanishing

$$(\theta_1-\theta_2)^{m_{12}}(\theta_1-\theta_3)^{m_{13}}\dots(\theta_{i-1}-\theta_i)^{m_{i-1i}}\, aaa \dots (i \text{ factors}),$$

where $\theta_1, \theta_2, \dots \theta_i$ mean the same but operate respectively only on the first, second, &c. factors in $aaa \dots$, is a seminvariant of a p-ic provided none of $\theta_1, \theta_2, \dots \theta_i$ occur in more than p factors; and all seminvariants of degree i of the p-ic are linear functions of these seminvariants.

Ex. 49. There is a one to one correspondence between seminvariants of weight w and degree i of a p-ic, and seminvariants of weight w and degree p of an i-ic.

Ex. 50. If a, b are two roots of $u \equiv (a_0, a_1, \dots a_p)(x, 1)^p = 0$, and A, B the two corresponding roots of its linear transformation

$$U \equiv (a_0, a_1, \dots a_p)(lX+m, l'X+m')^p = 0,$$

prove that

$$\int_a^b u^{-\frac{2}{p}}\,dx = (lm'-l'm)\int_A^B U^{-\frac{2}{p}}\,dX.$$

Ex. 51. If

$$u \equiv (a, b, c, d, e)(x, 1)^4 \equiv a\,(x-a)(x-\beta)(x-\gamma)(x-\delta),$$

and

$$4z^3 - Iz - J \equiv 4(z-\beta')(z-\gamma')(z-\delta'),$$

prove that

$$\int_\theta^\phi u^{-\frac{1}{2}}\,dx = \pm\int_{\theta'}^{\phi'}(4z^3-Iz-J)^{-\frac{1}{2}}\,dz,$$

where θ, ϕ are any two of a, β, γ, δ, and θ', ϕ' the two of $\infty, \beta', \gamma', \delta'$ which correspond to them in Ex. 30. The values of β', γ', δ' are $\frac{1}{12}\,a\,\{(a+\beta)(\gamma+\delta)-2(a\beta+\gamma\delta)\}$, &c.

Ex. 52. A binary quartic has a quartic covariant H, and a sextic covariant G, which is one-eighth of the Jacobian of u and H; and it will be shown later that these are connected with u and its invariants by the syzygy $G^2 = -4H^3 + IHu^2 - Ju^3$. Prove (taking 1 for y) that

$$u^{-\frac{1}{2}}\,dx = \pm\tfrac{1}{2}(4v^3 - Iv - J)^{-\frac{1}{2}}\,dv,$$

where $v = -H/u$.

CHAPTER VII

FURTHER THEORY OF THE OPERATORS Ω AND O. RECIPROCITY.

116. FOR brevity we henceforth use, with Sylvester, a single word to denote a function of the p quantities $a_0, a_1, a_2, \ldots a_p$ which is rational and integral and of the same degree and the same weight throughout. The name adopted for such a function is a *gradient* in $a_0, a_1, a_2, \ldots a_p$.

So, too, by a *gradient* in more sets of quantities $a_0, a_1, \ldots a_{p_1}$; $b_0, b_1, \ldots b_{p_2}$; $c_0, c_1, \ldots c_{p_3}$; ... than one we mean a rational integral function of some or all of the quantities which is of constant degrees throughout in the sets of quantities separately, and of constant weight throughout in the sets collectively.

For the present we deal with gradients in one set $a_0, a_1, a_2, \ldots a_p$ only. It is in accordance with what has preceded to denote in general the *degree* of a gradient by i and its *weight* by w.

We need not always have in view that $a_0, a_1, a_2, \ldots a_p$ are the coefficients in a binary p-ic, but may specify that a gradient involves a_p, but no element with a greater suffix than p, by describing it as of *extent* p.

For instance,

$$a_0 a_5 + \lambda a_1 a_4 + \mu a_2 a_3,$$

and

$$a_0 a_2 a_4 + \lambda a_1 a_2 a_3 + \mu a_0 a_3^2 + \nu a_1^2 a_4 + \varpi a_2^3,$$

where the coefficients $\lambda, \mu, \nu, \varpi$ are arbitrary but independent of $a_0, a_1, a_2, a_3, a_4, a_5$, are gradients of degrees 2, 3, weights 5, 6, and extents 5, 4 respectively.

117. **Expressions of homogeneity and isobarism.** Any gradient whatever, of given degree and weight, satisfies two linear differential equations.

Take $G_{w, i, p}$ a gradient of weight w, degree i, and extent p. One of the two differential equations is Euler's equation which expresses its homogeneity, of degree i, viz.

$$\left(a_0 \frac{\partial}{\partial a_0} + a_1 \frac{\partial}{\partial a_1} + a_2 \frac{\partial}{\partial a_2} + \ldots + a_p \frac{\partial}{\partial a_p}\right) G_{w, i, p} = i G_{w, i, p}.$$

The other expresses that it is isobaric, of constant weight w throughout. It is

$$\left(a_1 \frac{\partial}{\partial a_1} + 2a_2 \frac{\partial}{\partial a_2} + \ldots + pa_p \frac{\partial}{\partial a_p}\right) G_{w, i, p} = wG_{w, i, p}.$$

This also follows from Euler's theorem of homogeneous functions, for constancy of weight has been seen to be the same thing as homogeneity in magnitudes which are roots of $(a_0, a_1, a_2, \ldots a_p)(x, y)^p$, in which $a_0, a_1, a_2, \ldots a_p$ are homogeneous and of dimensions $0, 1, 2, \ldots p$ respectively. It is, however, at once clear when we notice that, if $a_r^\rho a_s^\sigma a_t^\tau \ldots$ is any term in $G_{w, i, p}$, then

$$\begin{aligned}\left(a_1 \frac{\partial}{\partial a_1} + 2a_2 \frac{\partial}{\partial a_2} + \ldots + pa_p \frac{\partial}{\partial a_p}\right) . \, a_r^\rho a_s^\sigma a_t^\tau \ldots \\ = (\rho r + \sigma s + \tau t + \ldots) a_r^\rho a_s^\sigma a_t^\tau \ldots \\ = w a_r^\rho a_s^\sigma a_t^\tau \ldots.\end{aligned}$$

118. **Seminvariants as particular gradients.** Referring to § 111 we see that, according to the definition there given, those gradients $G_{w, i, p}$, of type w, i, p, whose arbitrary coefficients are so chosen that they satisfy the third linear differential equation

$$\Omega G_{w, i, p} = 0,$$

where $\Omega \equiv a_0 \frac{\partial}{\partial a_1} + 2a_1 \frac{\partial}{\partial a_2} + 3a_2 \frac{\partial}{\partial a_3} + \ldots + pa_{p-1} \frac{\partial}{\partial a_p}$,

are the seminvariants of the p-ic

$$(a_0, a_1, a_2, \ldots a_p)(x, y)^p,$$

and are equally seminvariants, though not all the seminvariants, of the $(p+q)$-ic

$$(a_0, a_1, a_2, \ldots a_p, a_{p+1}, \ldots a_{p+q})(x, y)^{p+q},$$

where q is any positive integer.

It has already been shown, and will be otherwise exhibited presently, that gradients which are seminvariants exist only when their weights, degrees, and extents are such as to make $ip - 2w \nless 0$. It has also been seen that a gradient which is a seminvariant of type w, i, p is the coefficient of the highest power of x, i. e. x^{ip-2w}, in a covariant of

$$(a_0, a_1, a_2, \ldots a_p)(x, y)^p,$$

and, more generally, the coefficient of the highest power $x^{i(p+q)-2w}$ of x in a covariant of the quantic of higher order

$$(a_0, a_1, a_2, \ldots a_p, a_{p+1}, \ldots a_{p+q})(x, y)^{p+q}.$$

Thus, for instance, $a_0^2 a_3 - 3a_0 a_1 a_2 + 2a_1^3$, a gradient annihilated by Ω, for which $w = 3$, $i = 3$, $p = 3$, $ip - 2w = 3$ is a seminvariant of $(a_0, a_1, a_2, \dots a_{3+q})(x, y)^{3+q}$, where q is zero or any positive integer, and is the leading coefficient of covariants

$$(a_0^2 a_3 - 3a_0 a_1 a_2 + 2a_1^3)x^3 + \dots$$
$$(a_0^2 a_3 - 3a_0 a_1 a_2 + 2a_1^3)x^6 + \dots$$
$$(a_0^2 a_3 - 3a_0 a_1 a_2 + 2a_1^3)x^9 + \dots$$
&c., &c.,

of the cubic $(a_0, a_1, a_2, a_3)(x, y)^3$,
the quartic $(a_0, a_1, a_2, a_3, a_4)(x, y)^4$,
the quintic $(a_0, a_1, a_2, a_3, a_4, a_5)(x, y)^5$,
&c., &c., respectively.

It has also been seen (§ 112) that a gradient $G_{w,i,p}$, of type w, i, p, which satisfies

$$\Omega G_{w,i,p} = 0,$$

and is such that $ip - 2w = 0$, has the further property of satisfying the fourth linear differential equation

$$O G_{w,i,p} = 0,$$

where $$O \equiv pa_1 \frac{\partial}{\partial a_0} + (p-1)a_2 \frac{\partial}{\partial a_1} + \dots + a_p \frac{\partial}{\partial a_{p-1}},$$

so that it is an *invariant* of the p-ic

$$(a_0, a_1, a_2, \dots a_p)(x, y)^p,$$

while still only a seminvariant of the higher binary quantics

$$(a_0, a_1, a_2, \dots a_p, a_{p+1}, \dots a_{p+q})(x, y)^{p+q}.$$

Thus, for instance,

$$a_0 a_4 - 4a_1 a_3 + 3a_2^2,$$

for which $w = 4$, $i = 2$, $p = 4$, $ip - 2w = 0$, is an invariant of the quartic

$$(a_0, a_1, a_2, a_3, a_4)(x, y)^4,$$

and a seminvariant of the quintic, sextic, &c.,

$$(a_0, a_1, \dots a_4, a_5)(x, y)^5,$$
$$(a_0, a_1, \dots a_4, a_5, a_6)(x, y)^6,$$
&c.,

being the leading coefficient in covariants

$$(a_0 a_4 - 4a_1 a_3 + 3a_2^2)x^2 + \dots,$$
$$(a_0 a_4 - 4a_1 a_3 + 3a_2^2)x^4 + \dots,$$
&c.,

of the quintic, sextic, &c., respectively.

We need not then dissociate invariants from seminvariants in searching for them by means of the annihilator Ω. A seminvariant found will be in particular an invariant for the binary p-ic, in case the *excess* (to use another word of Sylvester's) $ip-2w$ vanishes. It has already been established, and will again appear, that there is no rational integral invariant of a binary p-ic which is not thus given.

119. **A seminvariant of extent p involves all of $a_0, a_1, a_2, \ldots a_p$.** Suppose if possible that a_r, where $r < p$, is absent from a seminvariant S of extent p. We may write the fact

$$\Omega S = 0$$

in the form

$$(r+1)\, a_r \frac{\partial}{\partial a_{r+1}} S + \left\{ a_0 \frac{\partial}{\partial a_1} + 2a_1 \frac{\partial}{\partial a_2} + \ldots + r a_{r-1} \frac{\partial}{\partial a_r} \right.$$
$$\left. + (r+2)\, a_{r+1} \frac{\partial}{\partial a_{r+2}} + \ldots + p a_{p-1} \frac{\partial}{\partial a_p} \right\} S = 0.$$

Now, on our supposition, all of the left-hand side but

$$(r+1)\, a_r \frac{\partial}{\partial a_{r+1}} S$$

is free from a_r. But the sum vanishes. Therefore

$$a_r \frac{\partial}{\partial a_{r+1}} S$$

is free from a_r. Therefore $\frac{\partial}{\partial a_{r+1}} S = 0$, i.e. S is free from a_{r+1}.

A seminvariant free from a_r is thus free from a_{r+1}, and therefore from a_{r+2}, from a_{r+3}, &c. Finally it is free from a_p.

Our supposition that a seminvariant of extent p exists which does not contain all of $a_0, a_1, a_2, \ldots a_p$ is consequently untenable.

120. **An invariant of a binary p-ic involves all the coefficients.** Being a seminvariant, it must by the preceding article involve all of $a_0, a_1, a_2, \ldots a_r$ if it extend as far as a_r. Also being an anti-seminvariant, annihilated by O, it must by the same reasoning involve all of $a_p, a_{p-1}, a_{p-2}, \ldots a_0$, since, reckoning extent from a_p back to a_0, it extends to a_0.

121. **Repeated operations with Ω and O.** We proceed to pay attention to the results of operating with Ω or with O, once or any number of times in succession, on any gradient whatever.

The operator $\Omega \equiv a_0 \frac{\partial}{\partial a_1} + 2a_1 \frac{\partial}{\partial a_2} + \ldots + p a_{p-1} \frac{\partial}{\partial a_p}$

acting on any gradient $G_{w,i,p}$ produces another gradient. The degree of the produced gradient is i, that of $G_{w,i,p}$. Its weight is $w-1$, where w is the weight of $G_{w,i,p}$. Its extent is either the extent of $G_{w,i,p}$ or less. These facts are clear when we remark that any term of Ω, $ra_{r-1}\,\partial/\partial a_r$ for instance, operating on a term involving a_r in $G_{w,i,p}$, on $a_r^{\rho} a_s^{\sigma} a_t^{\tau} \ldots$ for instance, has the effect of replacing that term by another,

$$\rho r a_{r-1} a_r^{\rho-1} a_s^{\sigma} a_t^{\tau} \ldots,$$

of the same degree and weight one less, one suffix being diminished by unity and none increased.

Thus if G is a gradient of weight w, degree i, and extent *not exceeding* p, ΩG is a gradient of weight $w-1$, degree i, and extent *not exceeding* p.

Consequently $\Omega^2 G = \Omega\,.\,\Omega G$ is a gradient of weight $w-2$, degree i, and extent not exceeding p.

And generally, by r repetitions of the Ω process, $\Omega^r G$ is a gradient of weight $w-r$, degree i, and extent not exceeding p.

This Ω process cannot be repeated indefinitely without leading to a vanishing result. For a gradient of negative weight is an impossibility, the weight of a gradient being a sum of numbers chosen from among $0, 1, 2, \ldots p$. Thus when we take $w+1$ for r, if not sooner, we must have

$$\Omega^{w+1} G = 0,$$

and consequently also $\quad \Omega^{w+2} G = 0, \;\; \Omega^{w+3} G = 0,$ &c.

122. We may reason in a similar way with regard to the operator

$$O \equiv pa_1 \frac{\partial}{\partial a_0} + (p-1)\,a_2 \frac{\partial}{\partial a_1} + \ldots + a_p \frac{\partial}{\partial a_{p-1}}.$$

Operation with this produces from a gradient of extent p or less another gradient of the same degree, of weight greater by one, and of extent not greater than p. The term *extent* is here used in the sense of the definition (§ 116). That the extent cannot be raised beyond p by operation with O results from the fact that O itself is taken as involving no letter a_r with a suffix (extent) greater than p. Thus, G being of weight w, degree i, and extent not exceeding p,

$$O^r G$$

is a gradient of weight $w+r$, degree i, and extent not exceeding p.

Here, again, the succession of gradients produced is not indefinitely continued. For the greatest possible weight of a product of i constituents of weights chosen from among 0, 1, 2, 3, ... p is ip, that of a^i_p. Consequently

$$O^{ip-w}G$$

can be nothing more than a (non-vanishing or vanishing) multiple of a^i_p, and therefore

$$O^{ip-w+1}G=0, \quad O^{ip-w+2}G=0, \text{ \&c.}$$

We may also consider the results of successive operations with both of Ω and O in any order on a gradient. The conclusion, drawn readily from the above, is that, G being any gradient of weight w, degree i, and extent p or less,

$$\Omega^{m_1}O^{n_1}\Omega^{m_2}O^{n_2}\Omega^{m_3}O^{n_3}\ldots G,$$

where $m_1, m_2, m_3, \ldots, n_1, n_2, n_3, \ldots$ are positive numbers, is, unless it vanishes, a gradient of weight

$$w-m_1-m_2-m_3-\ldots+n_1+n_2+n_3+\ldots,$$

of degree i, and of extent not exceeding p.

123. The alternant of Ω and O. The operators Ω, O are linear: but this is not the case with the operators Ω^2, O^2, ΩO, $O\Omega$, &c. Thus, for instance,

$$\Omega^2 \equiv \left(a_0\frac{\partial}{\partial a_1}+2a_1\frac{\partial}{\partial a_2}+\ldots+pa_{p-1}\frac{\partial}{\partial a_p}\right)^2$$

$$\equiv 1\,.\,2\,a_0\frac{\partial}{\partial a_2}+2\,.\,3\,a_1\frac{\partial}{\partial a_3}+\ldots+(p-1)\,pa_{p-2}\frac{\partial}{\partial a_p}$$

$$+\left\{a_0^2\frac{\partial^2}{\partial a_1^2}+4\,a_0a_1\frac{\partial^2}{\partial a_1\,\partial a_2}+4\,a_1^2\frac{\partial^2}{\partial a_2^2}+\ldots\right\}.$$

Moreover the operators Ω, O are not commutative; i.e. the compound operators ΩO and $O\Omega$ are not identical in meaning. Thus while

$$\Omega O \equiv \left(a_0\frac{\partial}{\partial a_1}+2a_1\frac{\partial}{\partial a_2}+\ldots+pa_{p-1}\frac{\partial}{\partial a_p}\right)$$

$$\left(pa_1\frac{\partial}{\partial a_0}+\overline{p-1}\,a_2\frac{\partial}{\partial a_1}+\ldots+a_p\frac{\partial}{\partial a_{p-1}}\right)$$

$$\equiv 1\,.\,p\,a_0\frac{\partial}{\partial a_0}+2\,(p-1)\,a_1\frac{\partial}{\partial a_1}+3\,(p-2)\,a_2\frac{\partial}{\partial a_2}+\ldots$$

$$+p\,.\,1\,a_{p-1}\frac{\partial}{\partial a_{p-1}}$$

$$+\text{ terms involving }\frac{\partial^2}{\partial a_0\,\partial a_1},\ \frac{\partial^2}{\partial a_1^2},\ldots,\ \frac{\partial^2}{\partial a_{p-1}\,\partial a_p},$$

$$O\Omega \equiv p\,.\,1\,a_1\frac{\partial}{\partial a_1} + (p-1)\,2\,a_2\frac{\partial}{\partial a_2} + (p-2)\,3\,a_3\frac{\partial}{\partial a_3} + \dots + 1\,.\,pa_p\frac{\partial}{\partial a_p}$$

$$+ \text{ the same terms in } \frac{\partial^2}{\partial a_0\,\partial a_1}, \dots \text{ as in } \Omega O.$$

We thus see, however, that the two compound operators differ only in their linear parts. The non-linear parts of both are just the algebraical product of Ω and O. This leads us to consider the difference $\Omega O - O\Omega$ of the two compound operators, the *alternant*, as it is called, of Ω and O. It is always a fact that the alternant $\theta\phi - \phi\theta$ of two linear operators θ and ϕ is a linear operator. In the present case

$$\begin{aligned}\Omega O - O\Omega &\equiv pa_0\frac{\partial}{\partial a_0} + \{2(p-1) - 1\,.\,p\}\,a_1\frac{\partial}{\partial a_1} \\ &\quad + \{3(p-2) - 2(p-1)\}\,a_2\frac{\partial}{\partial a_2} + \dots \\ &\quad + \{p\,.\,1 - (p-1)\,2\}\,a_{p-1}\frac{\partial}{\partial a_{p-1}} - pa_p\frac{\partial}{\partial a_p} \\ &\equiv pa_0\frac{\partial}{\partial a_0} + (p-2)\,a_1\frac{\partial}{\partial a_1} + (p-4)\,a_2\frac{\partial}{\partial a_2} + \dots \\ &\quad - (p-2)\,a_{p-1}\frac{\partial}{\partial a_{p-1}} - pa_p\frac{\partial}{\partial a_p} \\ &\equiv p\left\{a_0\frac{\partial}{\partial a_0} + a_1\frac{\partial}{\partial a_1} + a_2\frac{\partial}{\partial a_2} + \dots + a_p\frac{\partial}{\partial a_p}\right\} \\ &\quad - 2\left\{a_1\frac{\partial}{\partial a_1} + 2a_2\frac{\partial}{\partial a_2} + \dots + pa_p\frac{\partial}{\partial a_p}\right\}.\end{aligned}$$

Now let the operation be on G, a gradient of degree i and weight w. G satisfies the two linear differential equations of § 117, which express its homogeneity and isobarism. Using the two equations, we see that what we are led to is

$$\begin{aligned}(\Omega O - O\Omega)\,G &= p\,.\,i\,G - 2\,.\,w\,G \\ &= (ip - 2w)\,G.\end{aligned}$$

124. An important application of this result has already been mentioned in § 97. Let the gradient G be an invariant I of $(a_0, a_1, a_2, \dots a_p)\,(x, y)^p$, so that $\Omega I = 0$ and $OI = 0$, and therefore $O\Omega I = 0$ and $\Omega O I = 0$. We have the consequence that $(ip - 2w)\,I = 0$, i.e. that the degree and weight of an invariant of a binary p-ic are connected with p by the relation

$$ip - 2w = 0.$$

As another application let the gradient G be a seminvariant S. Then $\Omega S = 0$, and therefore $O\,\Omega S = 0$, so that

$$\Omega O S = (ip - 2w)\,S,$$

which tells us that the result of operating first with O and then with Ω on a seminvariant of extent not exceeding p is to reproduce that seminvariant multiplied by a numerical factor.

This is in accord with the conclusions of §§ 109, 110.

125. **Alternant of Ω and O^r.** Important information is to be gathered from the alternants of Ω and $O^2, O^3, \ldots$ which, though not linear, have simple equivalents when the functions on which they operate are gradients.

It is assumed throughout this article and in what follows, except where otherwise stated, that the operation is on a gradient G of weight w, degree i, and extent not exceeding p. For brevity the G is not as a rule written.

The 'excess' $ip - 2w$, in which p is always the suffix of the highest element which occurs in Ω and O, and may, it must be remembered, be greater than the extent of G, is, also for brevity, denoted by η.

Thus instead of writing

$$(\Omega O - O\,\Omega)\,G = (ip - 2w)\,G,$$

we write merely
$$\Omega O - O\,\Omega = \eta. \qquad \ldots(1)$$

Now notice that

$$\Omega O^2 - O^2\Omega = (\Omega O - O\,\Omega)\,O + O\,(\Omega O - O\,\Omega),$$

and also observe that, G which is operated on being of weight w and degree i, OG is by § 122 of weight $w+1$ and degree i, so that the excess for OG, corresponding to η for G, is $ip - 2(w+1) = \eta - 2$. Thus

$$\begin{aligned}\Omega O^2 - O^2\Omega &= (\eta - 2)\,O + O\,\eta \\ &= 2\,(\eta - 1)\,O,\end{aligned} \qquad \ldots(2)$$

since η, being numerical, is commutative with O.

Again

$$\begin{aligned}\Omega O^3 - O^3\Omega &= (\Omega O - O\,\Omega)\,O^2 + O\,(\Omega O - O\,\Omega)\,O + O^2\,(\Omega O - O\,\Omega) \\ &= (\eta - 4)\,O^2 + O\,(\eta - 2)\,O + O^2\eta,\end{aligned}$$

the excess for O^2G being $ip - 2\,(w+2)$, i. e. $\eta - 4$,

$$= 3\,(\eta - 2)\,O^2. \qquad \ldots(3)$$

In like manner we notice generally that the excess for $O^r G$ is $ip-2(w+r)$, i.e. $\eta - 2r$, and that generally

$$\begin{aligned}\Omega O^r - O^r \Omega &= (\Omega O - O\Omega) O^{r-1} + O(\Omega O - O\Omega) O^{r-2} \\ &\quad + O^2 (\Omega O - O\Omega) O^{r-3} + \ldots + O^{r-1}(\Omega O - O\Omega) \\ &= [\eta - 2(r-1)] O^{r-1} + O[\eta - 2(r-2)] O^{r-2} \\ &\quad + O^2 [\eta - 2(r-3)] O^{r-3} + \ldots + O^{r-1}\eta \\ &= \{r\eta - 2[1+2+3+\ldots+(r-1)]\} O^{r-1} \\ &= r(\eta - r + 1) O^{r-1}. \qquad \ldots (R)\end{aligned}$$

Ex. 1. Deduce that

$$O\Omega^r - \Omega^r O = r(-\eta - r + 1)\Omega^{r-1}.$$

Ex. 2. Prove that

$$\begin{aligned}\Omega^r O^r &= \Omega^{r-1} O^{r-1} \{O\Omega + r(\eta - r + 1)\} \\ &= (O\Omega + 1 \,.\, \eta)[O\Omega + 2(\eta-1)][O\Omega + 3(\eta - 2)] \\ &\qquad \ldots [O\Omega + r(\eta - r + 1)] \\ &= \Omega O(\Omega O + \eta - 2)[\Omega O + 2(\eta - 3)] \ldots [\Omega O + (r-1)(\eta - r)].\end{aligned}$$

Ex. 3. In like manner

$$\begin{aligned}O^r \Omega^r &= (\Omega O - 1 \,.\, \eta)[\Omega O - 2(\eta+1)][\Omega O - 3(\eta+2)] \\ &\qquad \ldots [\Omega O - r(\eta + r - 1)] \\ &= O\Omega(O\Omega - \eta - 2)[O\Omega - 2(\eta+3)] \ldots [O\Omega - (r-1)(\eta + r)].\end{aligned}$$

Ex. 4. Prove that

$$\Omega^r O^r \,.\, \Omega^s O^s = \Omega^s O^s \,.\, \Omega^r O^r,$$
$$O^r \Omega^r \,.\, O^s \Omega^s = O^s \Omega^s \,.\, O^r \Omega^r,$$
$$\Omega^r O^r \,.\, O^s \Omega^s = O^s \Omega^s \,.\, \Omega^r O^r.$$

Ex. 5. Prove by mathematical induction that

$$\begin{aligned}O^r \Omega^s &= \Omega^s O^r - (\eta - r + s) rs \Omega^{s-1} O^{r-1} \\ &\quad + \frac{(\eta - r + s)(\eta - r + s + 1)}{1 \,.\, 2} r(r-1) s(s-1) \Omega^{s-2} O^{r-2} - \ldots\end{aligned}$$

(*Hilbert.*)

126. **The excess non-negative for a seminvariant.** Use of the results of the preceding article gives a proof (Sylvester's) of the fact (§ 112) that for no seminvariant can the 'excess' $ip - 2w$ be negative. Since, if S is a seminvariant of extent p or less, $\Omega S = 0$, the results give

$$\begin{aligned}\Omega O \,.\, S &= \eta S, \\ \Omega O^2 \,.\, S &= 2(\eta - 1) O S, \\ \Omega O^3 \,.\, S &= 3(\eta - 2) O^2 S, \\ &\cdots \\ \Omega O^r \,.\, S &= r(\eta - r + 1) O^{r-1} S, \\ &\text{\&c., \&c.}\end{aligned}$$

If η, or $ip-2w$, is negative, the coefficients on the right in these equalities form a numerically increasing series of negative numbers. None of them can vanish. Now (§ 122) there must be a number r, equal to or less than $ip-w+1$, for which and all greater numbers $O^r S = 0$, and consequently $\Omega O^r S = 0$. The rth of the above equalities gives then

$$0 = r(\eta - r + 1) O^{r-1} S,$$

and therefore $O^{r-1}S = 0$. This necessitates $\Omega O^{r-1} S = 0$, and this again, by the $(r-1)$th equality, that

$$0 = (r-1)(\eta - r + 2) O^{r-2} S,$$

i. e. $O^{r-2}S = 0$. Proceeding thus backwards step by step, we eventually find from the first equality that $0 = \eta S$, i. e. that $S = 0$, since η is negative and not zero. In other words, the supposition that there is a seminvariant S for which η is negative is untenable.

We repeat that the η which it is here proved cannot be negative is $ip-2w$ where p is the greatest suffix occurring in Ω and O. The extent p' of a seminvariant of

$$(a_0, a_1, a_2, \dots a_p)(x, y)^p,$$

if not p itself, is less than p. In this latter case the seminvariant is also one of $(a_0, a_1, a_2, \dots a_{p'})(x, y)^{p'}$, and we might have taken p' as our p in the above reasoning. Thus, if p' is the extent of a seminvariant of weight w and degree i, $ip'-2w$ cannot be negative.

Ex. 6. Use the results of this and the preceding article to prove the theorem of § 111, that any seminvariant S, of extent not exceeding p, leads a covariant of order η of $(a_0, a_1, a_2, \dots a_p)(x, y)^p$, i.e. that $x^\eta e^{\frac{y}{x}O} S$ is not fractional in x, and is annihilated by $\Omega - y\partial/\partial x$.

Ans. $\Omega O^{\eta+1} S = 0$. Therefore $O^{\eta+1}S$, whose excess is negative, $= 0$. The coefficients in the result of operating with $\Omega - y\partial/\partial x$ are of the form $(r!)^{-1}\{\Omega O^r - r(\eta - r + 1) O^{r-1}\} S$, i.e. of the form $(r!)^{-1} O^r \Omega S$, which vanishes.

127. It is clear that the above reasoning, which shows that there is no seminvariant with a negative η, has no application to the cases of η zero and η positive. In these cases one of the series of multipliers $\eta, \eta-1, \eta-2, \eta-3, \dots$ on the right of the equalities of the last article vanishes. Thus from the fact that $O^{\eta+1}S = 0$ it does not follow that $O^\eta S = 0$. It is the factor $\eta - \eta$ on the right of the critical equality which vanishes, and not the other factor $O^\eta S$.

For a positive or vanishing η, a number

$$(w\,;\, i, p) - (w-1\,;\, i, p)$$

has been found in §§ 113, 101 which cannot exceed the number of linearly independent seminvariants (or invariants) of weight w, degree i, and extent p or less. It is now to be proved that the number is exact.

This famous theorem, stated by Cayley and much used, remained long without proof, and was even doubted. The first demonstration of it was given by Sylvester, by means of the results of § 125. The method to be here given is different from his, but is based upon the same results, though, as we shall see, an alternative basis is the theorem of § 100.

128. **Exactness of Cayley's number of linearly independent seminvariants of given type.** Let G be any gradient whatever of degree i, weight w, and extent not exceeding p. Let η be $ip-2w$ the *excess* for G. For ΩG, $\Omega^2 G$, $\Omega^3 G$, &c. the excesses are $\eta+2$, $\eta+4$, $\eta+6$, &c.

Take the operative equalities (1) to (R) of § 125, and operate, not always on G, but on G in the first case, on ΩG in the second, on $\Omega^2 G$ in the third, and so on, so that η has to be replaced by η, $\eta+2$, $\eta+4$, $\eta+6, \ldots$ in the successive cases. We obtain

$$\Omega O G - O\Omega G = \eta G,$$
$$\Omega O^2 \Omega G - O^2\Omega^2 G = 2(\eta+1) O\Omega G,$$
$$\Omega O^3 \Omega^2 G - O^3\Omega^3 G = 3(\eta+2) O^2\Omega^2 G,$$
$$\cdots\cdots\cdots\cdots$$
$$\Omega O^r \Omega^{r-1} G - O^r\Omega^r G = r(\eta+r-1) O^{r-1}\Omega^{r-1} G,$$
&c., &c.

Multiply the first of these by $\frac{1}{\eta}$, the second by $-\frac{1}{2.\eta(\eta+1)}$ the third by $\frac{1}{2.3.\eta(\eta+1)(\eta+2)}, \ldots$, the rth by

$$(-1)^{r-1}\frac{1}{2.3\ldots r.\eta(\eta+1)\ldots(\eta+r-1)},$$

&c., and add. We thus obtain

$$\Omega O\left\{\frac{1}{1.\eta} - \frac{1}{1.2.\eta(\eta+1)}O\Omega + \frac{1}{1.2.3.\eta(\eta+1)(\eta+2)}O^2\Omega^2 - \ldots\right\}G = G,$$

since for a great value of r the residual multiple of $O^r\Omega^r G$ does not exist, for $\Omega^{w+1}G$ vanishes, and therefore $O^r\Omega^r G$ vanishes if r is $w+1$ or more.

Consequently, if η is positive, the result of operating on the gradient

$$O\left\{\frac{1}{1.\eta} - \frac{1}{1.2.\eta(\eta+1)}O\Omega + \frac{1}{1.2.3.\eta(\eta+1)(\eta+2)}O^2\Omega^2 - \ldots\right\}G$$

with Ω is to produce G.

The gradient is a finite one, for though the operative series is regarded as continuing to infinity it produces really only a finite number of terms, since $O^r\Omega^r G$ vanishes when r exceeds w if not earlier.

We have thus proved that any gradient whatever, of weight w, degree i, and extent p or less, for which $\eta = ip - 2w$ is positive, can be obtained by operating with Ω on some gradient or other of weight $w+1$, degree i, and extent p or less. The same was otherwise proved in § 100.

Now for w write $w-1$. It follows that every gradient of weight $w-1$, degree i, and extent p or less, can be obtained by operation with Ω on some gradient of weight w, degree i, and extent p or less, provided that $ip-2(w-1)$ is positive, i.e. that $ip-2w \not< -1$.

This tells us that if we write down the most general gradient G' of weight and degree w, i, and of extent p or less, where $ip-2w \not< -1$, and operate on it with Ω, the result must be the most general gradient of weight and degree $w-1$, i, and of extent p or less. For the arbitrary coefficients in the first gradient may be so chosen that the derived gradient may be any one of type $w-1, i, p$ or less, and so in particular may be any single product of its type we choose.

Consequently the coefficients in the derived gradient $\Omega G'$ are all linearly independent.

Now, in the notation of §§ 101, 113, G' contains

$$(w\,;\,i, p)$$

terms, and $\Omega G'$ contains

$$(w-1\,;\,i, p)$$

terms. For G' to be a seminvariant the condition is $\Omega G' = 0$, i.e. the coefficients of these $(w-1\,;\,i, p)$ terms have separately to vanish. They are all independent, by the above, if $ip-2w \not< -1$, and are linear functions of the $(w\,;\,i, p)$ arbitrary coefficients in G'. Their vanishing determines $(w-1\,;\,i, p)$ of the coefficients in G' in terms of the rest. In other words, exactly

$$(w\,;\,i, p) - (w-1\,;\,i, p)$$

are left arbitrary. This, then, is the exact number of linearly independent seminvariants of weight w, degree i, and extent not greater than p.

(If $\eta < -1$ for G', the general gradient of type w, i, p, it has not been proved, and is not generally true, that $\Omega G'$ is the most general gradient of type $w-1, i, p$. The general gradient of this type will as a rule contain more terms than occur in $\Omega G'$. But $\Omega G'$ contains as many linearly independent coefficients as G' does. Otherwise we could write down a particular G' satisfying $\Omega G' = 0$, which we cannot do when $\eta < 0$.)

Ex. 7. Use § 125, Ex. 3 to obtain another proof that every G for which $\eta > 0$ is an $\Omega G'$.

Ans. $O^{w+1}\Omega^{w+1}G = O^{w+1}.0 = 0$. Hence, by a transposition in the first equality,

$$1.\eta.2(\eta+1)\ldots(w+1)(\eta+w)G = \Omega O\{\ldots\}.$$

Ex. 8. Use the same example to prove that, if $\eta \nless -1$ for G,

$$[O\Omega-\eta-2][O\Omega-2(\eta+3)]\ldots[O\Omega-w(\eta+w+1)]G$$

is annihilated by Ω, so that it is a seminvariant or zero; and that if it is zero, as must in particular be the case when $\eta = -1$, G must be of the form $O\Omega G'$.

Ans. Remember that O cannot annihilate a gradient for which $\eta > 0$.

Ex. 9. It may be proved by aid of § 125, Ex. 5 that, when the operation is on a gradient for which $\eta = ip-2w > 0$, the operator of § 100,

$$1-\frac{\Omega O}{1^2}+\frac{\Omega^2 O^2}{1^2.2^2}-\frac{\Omega^3 O^3}{1^2.2^2.3^2}+\ldots,$$

and that of the present article,

$$1-\frac{\Omega O}{1.\eta}+\frac{\Omega O^2\Omega}{1.2.\eta(\eta+1)}-\frac{\Omega O^3\Omega^2}{1.2.3.\eta(\eta+1)(\eta+2)}+\ldots,$$

are identical. (*Proc. Lond. Math. Soc.* Vol. XXIV. p. 23.)

Ex. 10. If G is a gradient for which η is *negative* prove that

$$\left(1-\frac{O\Omega}{1^2}+\frac{O^2\Omega^2}{1^2.2^2}-\frac{O^3\Omega^3}{1^2.2^2.3^2}+\ldots\right)G = 0,$$

and

$$\left(1+\frac{O\Omega}{1.\eta}+\frac{O\Omega^2 O}{1.2.\eta(\eta-1)}+\frac{O\Omega^3 O^2}{1.2.3.\eta(\eta-1)(\eta-2)}+\ldots\right)G = 0.$$

128 (*bis*). **Separation of gradients into seminvariant and other parts.** We can by direct differential operation express the general gradient of type w, i, p as a sum of parts all of which are coefficients in covariants of a p-ic, and thus confirm and amplify the above conclusions.

From §§ 109, 110 we see that if $C_r x^{\varpi-r} y^r$ is any term in a covariant of order ϖ, so that $\varpi - 2r$ is the η for C_r, then

$$\{\Omega O - (r+1)(\varpi - r)\} C_r = 0,$$

i.e.
$$\{\Omega O - (r+1)(\eta + r)\} C_r = 0.$$

The proof that this condition is sufficient as well as necessary is a good exercise on what has preceded. By § 125, Ex. 3, the condition necessitates $O^{r+1}\Omega^{r+1}C_r = 0$. Now O does not annihilate any gradient for which $\eta > 0$. It follows that, if $\eta \not< -1$ for C_r, $\Omega^{r+1}C_r = 0$. Therefore $\Omega^r C_r$ is a seminvariant, unless it vanishes. But it does not vanish, seeing that $O^r \Omega^r C_r$ does not, but is, by Ex. 3 again and the given condition,

$$\{(r+1)(\eta+r) - 1 . \eta\} \{(r+1)(\eta+r) - 2(\eta+1)\} \ldots \{(r+1)(\eta+r) - r(\eta+r-1)\} C_r,$$

i.e. $\quad r(\eta+r+1) . (r-1)(\eta+r+2) \ldots 1(\eta+2r) C_r$.

Thus $\Omega^r C_r$ is a seminvariant, and, by § 110, $O^r \Omega^r C_r$ and therefore C_r is a numerical multiple of the coefficient of $x^{\eta+r}y^r$ in the covariant which it leads.

Now consider the most general gradient G of type w, i, p, and take as usual $\eta = ip - 2w$. Let this be zero or positive. Gradients included in G figure as

(1) seminvariant coefficients of x^η in covariants of order η,
(2) coefficients of $x^{\eta+1}y$ in covariants of order $\eta + 2$,
(3) coefficients of $x^{\eta+2}y^2$ in covariants of order $\eta + 4$,
&c., &c.
$(w+1)$ the coefficient of $x^{\eta+w}y^w$ in the one covariant of order $\eta + 2w = ip$, i.e. in the ith power of the p-ic.

By the above these included gradients, respectively, satisfy and are determined by the differential equations

$$(1) \quad \{\Omega O - 1 . \eta\} G_1 = 0,$$
$$(2) \quad \{\Omega O - 2(\eta+1)\} G_2 = 0,$$
$$(3) \quad \{\Omega O - 3(\eta+2)\} G_3 = 0,$$
$$\cdots\cdots\cdots$$
$$(w+1) \quad \{\Omega O - (w+1)(\eta+w)\} G_{w+1} = 0.$$

We will see that the general G can be written as a sum of $w+1$ parts satisfying these equations respectively.

If $a_1, a_2, \ldots a_n$ are known constants, we are told by the elementary theory of partial fractions that an identity among products of $n-1$ factors exists of the form

$$1 = \left\{\frac{A_1}{t-a_1} + \frac{A_2}{t-a_2} + \ldots + \frac{A_n}{t-a_n}\right\}(t-a_1)(t-a_2)\ldots(t-a_n),$$

where $A_1, A_2, \ldots A_n$ are constants. In fact, for $r = 1, 2, \ldots n$,

$$A_r = \{(a_r - a_1)(a_r - a_2)\ldots(a_r - a_{r-1}) . (a_r - a_{r+1}) \ldots (a_r - a_n)\}^{-1}.$$

Here for t we may if we like write a symbol of operation instead of one of quantity, and deduce an identity with meaning, provided the operating factors are commutative. Hence

$$G = \left\{ \frac{A_1}{\Omega O - 1 \,.\, \eta} + \frac{A_2}{\Omega O - 2(\eta+1)} + \ldots + \frac{A_{w+1}}{\Omega O - (w+1)(\eta+w)} \right\}$$
$$\{\Omega O - 1 \,.\, \eta\}\{\Omega O - 2(\eta+1)\} \ldots \{\Omega O - (w+1)(\eta+w)\}\, G,$$

for easily written down numerical values of $A_1, A_2, \ldots A_{w+1}$.

Now, putting $w+1$ for r in § 125, Ex. 3, and remembering that $\Omega^{w+1} G = 0$ (§ 121), we have

$$\{\Omega O - 1 \,.\, \eta\}\{\Omega O - 2(\eta+1)\} \ldots \{\Omega O - (w+1)(\eta+w)\}\, G = 0,$$

the factors in the operator on G being commutative.

We have then succeeded, by operating with products of w out of the $w+1$ factors, in obtaining an identity

$$G = \sum_{1}^{w+1} G_r,$$

where G_1 is annihilated by $\Omega O - 1 \,.\, \eta$, G_2 by $\Omega O - 2(\eta+1)$, and so on.

Thus we have expressed the general G, with η zero or positive, as a sum of seminvariants G_1 and other coefficients in covariants. (We might also take $\eta = -1$; but in this case there can of course be no seminvariants of the type.)

If, instead of the general G on the left, we take only the general G_r, which is annihilated by $\Omega O - r(\eta + r - 1)$, everything on the right vanishes except G_r. Thus in the general $G = \Sigma G_r$ every G_r is general.

Accordingly the general gradient G of type w, i, p, with η not negative, has been expressed by direct operation as the sum of (1) the general seminvariant G_1 of the type, (2) the general second coefficient G_2 in a covariant led by a seminvariant ΩG_2 of type $w-1, i, p$, (3) the general third coefficient G_3 in a covariant led by a seminvariant $\Omega^2 G_3$ of type $w-2, i, p$, and so on, and lastly $(w+1)$ the $(w+1)$th coefficient in the only covariant led by a seminvariant of type $0, i, p$, i.e. in the ith power of the p-ic.

A conclusion as to enumeration from the fact that the number of arbitraries on the left of the identity $G = \Sigma G_r$ must be the same as on the right, is that $(w;\, i, p)$, the number of arbitrary multipliers in the general G, is equal to the sum of the numbers of linearly independent seminvariants of degree i, extent p or less, and weights $w, w-1, w-2, \ldots 0$ respectively. In like manner the sum for weights $w-1, w-2, \ldots 0$ is $(w-1;\, i, p)$. By subtraction, the number of degree i, extent

p or less, and weight w, is $(w;\, i,\, p)-(w-1;\, i,\, p)$, as was proved in the last article.

Having obtained the most general seminvariant G_1 of type w, i, p, which, upon giving to A_1 its value and writing $O\Omega+\eta$ for ΩO, may be written

$$\left\{1-\frac{O\Omega}{\eta+2}\right\}\left\{1-\frac{O\Omega}{2(\eta+3)}\right\}\cdots\left\{1-\frac{O\Omega}{w(\eta+w+1)}\right\}G,$$

where G is the general gradient of the type, we have also (§ 110) the most general covariant of degree i and order η of a p-ic, namely,

$$x^{\eta}e^{\frac{y}{x}O}G_1.$$

More generally, for $r=0, 1, 2, \ldots w$, we have that the most general covariant of degree i and order $\eta+2r$ is

$$x^{\eta+2r}e^{\frac{y}{x}O}\Omega^r G_{r+1},$$

where

$$G_{r+1}=A_{r+1}\{\Omega O-1\,.\,\eta\}\{\Omega O-2(\eta+1)\}\ldots\{\Omega O-r(\eta+r-1)\}$$
$$.\,\{\Omega O-(r+2)(\eta+r+1)\}\ldots\{\Omega O-(w+1)(\eta+w)\}\,G.$$

Ex. 11. All covariants containing coefficients for which $\eta=0$ are of even order. Exhibit them; and in particular exhibit all invariants.

Ex. 12. All covariants containing coefficients for which $\eta=1$ or -1 are of odd order, and only exist for quantics of odd order. Exhibit them; and in particular exhibit all linear covariants.

Ex. 13. If by ϕ is meant any given differential operator

$$\phi\,(\partial/\partial x,\ \partial/\partial y,\ \partial/\partial z, \ldots),$$

not necessarily with constant coefficients, if $F(t)$ denotes

$$(t-a_1)(t-a_2)\ldots(t-a_n),$$

and if $f(x, y, z, \ldots)$ is any given function of the independent variables, express any solution u of the differential equation $F(\phi)\,u=f(x, y, z, \ldots)$ in the form $u_1+u_2+\ldots+u_n$, where, for every s from 1 to n, u_s is a solution of the differential equation

$$F'(a_s)(\phi-a_s)\,u_s=f(x, y, z, \ldots).$$

Every such $u_1+u_2+\ldots+u_n$ satisfies the equation. Prove this.

Ex. 14. Use § 125, Ex. 2 to express the general G for which $ip-2w=-\eta'$ is negative as a sum of coefficients in covariants of orders $\eta', \eta'+2, \ldots ip$.

129. **Arithmetical conclusions.** Some arithmetical conclusions of interest with regard to numbers of partitions may be drawn from results at which we have arrived.

Since the most general gradient of type $w-1, i, p$ can when $ip-2w \nless -1$ be derived by operation with Ω from the most general gradient of type w, i, p, the former cannot contain more arbitraries than the latter, i.e. more terms than the latter. Hence if $ip-2w \nless -1$

$$(w; i, p) \nless (w-1; i, p).$$

Again, we have shown in § 126 and elsewhere that if $ip-2w<0$ there is no seminvariant, and in § 128 that if $ip-2w \nless -1$ there are exactly $(w; i, p)-(w-1; i, p)$ seminvariants. The case $ip-2w=-1$ is included in both categories. The conclusion from this case of $ip-2w=-1$, i.e. of $w=\frac{1}{2}(ip+1)$, where i and p must clearly both be odd, is that if i and p are any odd numbers

$$(\tfrac{1}{2}[ip+1]; i, p) = (\tfrac{1}{2}[ip-1]; i, p).$$

This is only a particular case of the fact that, for any w not exceeding ip, whatever numbers i and p may be,

$$(w; i, p) = (ip-w; i, p),$$

which is immediately seen by noticing that the products of weight w and those of weight $ip-w$ are conjugate in pairs. If, in fact, $a_0^{\alpha_0} a_1^{\alpha_1} \dots a_p^{\alpha_p}$ is one of the first type, the conjugate one of the second type is $a_p^{\alpha_0} a_{p-1}^{\alpha_1} \dots a_0^{\alpha_p}$.

130. **Reciprocal partitions.** The number $(w; i, p)$ is, it will be remembered, the number of ways in which the number w may be written as a sum of i or fewer numbers, none exceeding p. It is an important fact that this number is also the number of ways in which w may be written as a sum of p or fewer numbers, none exceeding i; in other words, that

$$(w; i, p) = (w; p, i).$$

The following proof is due to Ferrers. Another will present itself in the next chapter.

Let any partition of w into i or fewer parts, none exceeding p, be the partition into $n_1+n_2+n_3+\dots+n_i$, where no part is greater than p nor than the preceding part, and where one or more at the end may be zero. Write down n_1 dots in a row. Next write n_2 dots under the first n_2 of these dots in a second row. Then write in a third row n_3 dots under the first n_3 of the n_2 dots: and so on, till in all $n_1+n_2+n_3+\dots+n_i=w$ dots have been written. We have thus visibly arranged a partition of w into i or fewer parts, none exceeding p.

Now read the arrangement by columns instead of rows. We have in the first column a number, m_1, of dots not greater than i. In the second column we have, say, m_2 dots where $m_2 \ngtr m_1$ and so $\ngtr i$. In the third we have m_3 dots where $m_3 \ngtr m_2$ and therefore $\ngtr i$: and so on. Finally, in the pth column we have either no dot or a number m_p of dots not greater than any previous m, and so not greater than i. We have thus visibly arranged a partition of w into

$$m_1 + m_2 + m_3 + \ldots + m_p$$

a sum of p or fewer numbers, none greater than i.

Thus to every one of the $(w\,;\,i,\,p)$ partitions we have a conjugate one of the $(w\,;\,p,\,i)$ partitions. Similarly, considering columns first and then rows, to every one of the $(w\,;\,p,\,i)$ partitions there is a conjugate one of the $(w\,;\,i,\,p)$ partitions. And no two of the one set of partitions have the same conjugate in the other set, for a definite arrangement in the one way is also definite in the other. Consequently the numbers $(w\,;\,i,\,p)$ and $(w\,;\,p,\,i)$ are equal.

131. **Hermite's law of reciprocity.** Hence we obtain a famous and most prolific theorem due to Hermite.

Since $$(w\,;i,\,p) = (w\,;p,\,i)$$

for all numbers w, it follows that

$$(w\,;i,p) - (w-1\,;\,i,\,p) = (w\,;p,i) - (w-1\,;\,p,\,i).$$

Accordingly:—*The number of rational integral seminvariants of weight w, degree i, and extent not exceeding p, is equal to the number of rational integral seminvariants of weight w, degree p, and extent not exceeding i.*

In particular take $ip = 2w$. We are told that:—*The number of invariants (i.e. linearly independent rational integral invariants) of degree i of a binary p-ic is equal to the number of invariants of degree p of a binary i-ic.*

Again, take $ip - 2w > 0$, and denote $ip - 2w$ by ϖ. Then, since when i, p, w are known ϖ is known, we may enunciate:—*The number of covariants of degree i (in the coefficients) and order ϖ (in the variables) of a binary p-ic is equal to the number of covariants of degree p and order ϖ of a binary i-ic.*

Another way of arriving at this law of reciprocity has already been noticed in Examples. There is clearly a one to one correspondence between root-expressions

$$a_0^{\,p}\,\Sigma\,(\alpha_1-\alpha_2)^{n_{12}}\,(\alpha_1-\alpha_3)^{n_{13}}\,(\alpha_2-\alpha_3)^{n_{23}}\ldots(\alpha_{i-1}-\alpha_i)^{n_{i-1\,i}},$$

where $n_{12} + n_{13} + n_{23} + \ldots = w$ and no α occurs in more than p factors of a product, for seminvariants of degree p and weight w which lead covariants of order $\varpi = ip - 2w$ of an i-ic with $\alpha_1, \alpha_2, \ldots \alpha_i$ for roots, and symbolical expressions

$$(\theta_1-\theta_2)^{n_{12}}\,(\theta_1-\theta_3)^{n_{13}}\,(\theta_2-\theta_3)^{n_{23}}\ldots(\theta_{i-1}-\theta_i)^{n_{i-1\,i}}$$
$$a_0 a_0 a_0 \ldots (i \text{ factors}),$$

with the sum of the n's as before and no θ occurring in more than p factors, for hyperdeterminant seminvariants of degree i and weight w which lead covariants of order ϖ of a p-ic. Also, the systems of root-expressions and of hyperdeterminants have both been seen to be complete for providing all seminvariants of given degree and weight by their linear combinations. That those sums of α-products which vanish identically, instead of producing seminvariants of the i-ic, correspond to those θ-products which produce zero, instead of seminvariants of the p-ic, follows from the fact that in the expansion of one of the latter every term $k\,\theta_1^q\theta_2^r\ldots\theta_i^t$ must be accompanied by another $-k\theta_\alpha^q\theta_\beta^r\ldots\theta_\kappa^t$, where $\alpha, \beta, \ldots \kappa$ are $1, 2, \ldots i$ in a different order.

Ex. 15. A binary $4n$-ic has one invariant of degree 3, and a binary quantic whose order is not a multiple of 4 has none. (*Cayley.*)

Ans. Since all invariants of a cubic are powers of the discriminant whose degree is 4.

Ex. 16. The Cayleyan hyperdeterminant symbol of this invariant is $\overline{12}^{2n}\,\overline{23}^{2n}\,\overline{31}^{2n}$. Prove that, if u, v, w all denote the quantic, the invariant may be written

$$\overline{12}^{2n-1}\,\overline{23}^{2n-1}\,\overline{31}^{2n-1}\begin{vmatrix} \dfrac{\partial^2 u}{\partial x^2} & \dfrac{\partial^2 u}{\partial x\,\partial y} & \dfrac{\partial^2 u}{\partial y^2} \\ \dfrac{\partial^2 v}{\partial x^2} & \dfrac{\partial^2 v}{\partial x\,\partial y} & \dfrac{\partial^2 v}{\partial y^2} \\ \dfrac{\partial^2 w}{\partial x^2} & \dfrac{\partial^2 w}{\partial x\,\partial y} & \dfrac{\partial^2 w}{\partial y^2} \end{vmatrix},$$

where u, v, w are not to be made identical till all the operations are performed; and hence that the invariant is a linear function of the determinants

$$\begin{Vmatrix} a_0, & a_1, & a_2, & a_3, & \ldots, & a_{4n-2} \\ a_1, & a_2, & a_3, & a_4, & \ldots, & a_{4n-1} \\ a_2, & a_3, & a_4, & a_5, & \ldots, & a_{4n} \end{Vmatrix}. \quad (\textit{Cayley.})$$

Ex. 17. A binary p-ic has as many invariants of degree 4 as there are ways of choosing positive integral or zero values of m and n to satisfy $2m+3n=p$. (*Cayley.*)

Ans. Assume the knowledge that I and J are the only irreducible invariants of the quartic.

Ex. 18. A binary p-ic has a single or no p-ic covariant of the second degree in the coefficients according as p is or is not a multiple of 4. (*Cayley.*)

Ans. Since covariants of equal order and degree of a quadratic must have the form $(ac-b^2)^n\,(ax^2+2bxy+cy^2)^{2n}$.

Ex. 19. The one invariant (Ex. 15) of degree 3 of a $4n$-ic is the lineo-linear invariant of the $4n$-ic and the covariant of Ex. 18. (*Cayley.*)

Ex. 20. A binary p-ic has as many covariants of degree 2 in the coefficients as there are solutions of $2m+n=p$ in positive integers (and zeros); and $2n$ is the order of any such covariant in the variables. (*Hermite.*)

Ex. 21. A binary quantic of odd order has a covariant of the second order and the second degree. (*Hermite.*)

Ex. 22. A binary quantic of order $4n+2$, where n is any number, has a covariant of the second order and third degree. (*Hermite.*)

Ans. Use Ex. 21 for the case of the cubic.

Ex. 23. By the two preceding examples binary quantics whose orders are of the forms $4n+1$, $4n+2$, $4n+3$ have quadratic covariants. Use the facts that a quintic has a quadratic covariant of degree 8, the Jacobian of the cubic covariant of § 17, Ex. 20 and the linear covariant of § 57, Exx. 16, 17, and an invariant of degree 4 (§ 61, Ex. 30) to complete the proof that every binary quantic except the quartic has a quadratic covariant whose degree in the coefficients does not exceed 5. (*Hermite.*)

Ex. 24. No covariant or invariant of the second degree in the coefficients can have an odd weight. In particular, no invariant of the second degree can be skew.

Ex. 25. No invariant of the third degree can be skew.

Ex. 26. A binary quantic of any odd order greater than 3 has a linear covariant of degree 5. (*Hermite.*)

Ans. Use the fact that a quintic has linear covariants of degrees 5 and 7 (§ 57, Ex. 17) and an invariant of degree 4 (§ 61, Ex. 30).

132. **Gradients in more sets than one.** Just as we have dealt with gradients in one set of quantities $a_0, a_1, a_2, \dots a_p$ in the present chapter, we may deal with gradients in more sets than one $a_0, a_1, a_2, \dots a_{p_1}; b_0, b_1, b_2, \dots b_{p_2}; c_0, c_1, c_2, \dots c_{p_3}; \dots$. We have merely throughout to insert $\Sigma\Omega$, ΣO, and

$$i_1p_1+i_2p_2+i_3p_3+\dots-2w$$

for Ω, O, and $ip-2w$. As in § 119 a seminvariant which involves one letter of any set involves all the previous letters of that set. As in § 120 an invariant of the quantics whose coefficients are the sets involves all the coefficients of any one if it involves one of them. As in § 125

$$\Sigma\Omega\,(\Sigma O)^r-(\Sigma O)^r\,\Sigma\Omega = r\,(\eta-r+1)\,(\Sigma O)^{r-1},$$

where

$$\eta = \Sigma\,(ip)-2w.$$

As in § 126 there can be no seminvariant for which $\Sigma(ip)-2w$ is negative. As in § 128 any gradient for which $\Sigma(ip)-2w$ is positive can be written as the result of operating with $\Sigma\Omega$ on another gradient, and hence if $\Sigma(ip)-2w \nless -1$ the exact number of linearly independent seminvariants of weight w and partial degrees $i_1, i_2, i_3, \ldots$ is

$(w;\ i_1, p_1;\ i_2, p_2;\ i_3, p_3, \ldots)-(w-1;\ i_1, p_1;\ i_2, p_2;\ i_3, p_3;\ldots)$, where $(w;\ i_1, p_1;\ i_2, p_2;\ i_3, p_3;\ldots)$ denotes the number of ways in which w may be written as the sum of i_1 or fewer numbers not greater than p_1, of i_2 or fewer not greater than p_2, of i_3 or fewer not greater than p_3, &c. Finally we have arithmetical conclusions corresponding to those of § 129.

The generalization of § 130 is also immediate. It will readily be seen, by considering as many Ferrers' diagrams as there are sets of a's, b's, c's, &c., containing altogether w dots, that in

$$(w;\ i_1, p_1;\ i_2, p_2;\ i_3, p_3;\ldots)$$

i_1 and p_1, or i_2 and p_2, or i_3 and $p_3, \ldots$, or more than one or all of these pairs, may be interchanged without altering the number of partitions. Hence a generalization of the law of reciprocity is easy.

Ex. 27. The number of covariants of any degree i and of order p of a binary p-ic, i. e. of invariants of partial degrees i, p of a p-ic and a linear form, is equal to the number of invariants of partial degrees i, 1 of two binary p-ics.

Ex. 28. Prove that

$(w; i_1, p_1; i_2, p_2; i_3, p_3; \ldots)=\Sigma\Sigma\Sigma\ldots(v_1; i_1, p_1)(v_2; i_2, p_2)(v_3; i_3, p_3)\ldots$, where the summations indicate that to $v_1, v_2, v_3, \ldots$ are to be given all positive integral and zero values which make

$$v_1+v_2+v_3+\ldots=w. \quad (\textit{Franklin.})$$

CHAPTER VIII

GENERATING FUNCTIONS.

133. UNFORTUNATELY no practically convenient algebraical formula[1] is known which gives in all cases the number of partitions denoted by $(w; i, p)$, i.e. the number of ways in which the number w may be formed by adding together i or fewer numbers, every one of which is one of $1, 2, 3, \ldots, p$, or, which is the same thing, by adding i parts every one of which is one of $0, 1, 2, 3, \ldots, p$. For tabulation of such numbers of partitions recourse must be had to a method known as that of *Generating Functions.*

The origin of the theory of numbers of partitions is due to Euler. The theory in its application to invariants, &c., was first studied by Cayley with a view to, and in, his second memoir on quantics (*Collected Works*, Vol. II). The subsequent writings on the subject are very numerous. Cayley himself, Sylvester, Franklin, MacMahon and Hammond as well as others have by means of it obtained results of great precision.

The investigation of the number $(w; i, p)-(w-1; i, p)$ of linearly independent or 'asyzygetic' seminvariants of given weight, degree, and extent by means of generating functions is only a preliminary object of the researches. The ulterior aims are the discovery of the number and types of the *irreducible* concomitants of a binary quantic, and of the relations or syzygies which connect those irreducible concomitants.

The subject being a vast one only an introduction to it can be given here. We consider only quantics of the first few orders. In passing from order to order the complexity of the investigations necessary enormously increases.

134. **Generating function for** $(w; i, p)$. By a *Generating Function* we mean a function of one or more variables which, when it is expanded in powers of that variable, or powers and products of powers of those variables, has for the general coefficient of a power or product of powers the number of an assigned class which is determined by the index of that power,

[1] For a formula due to Brioschi see Faà de Bruno's *Formes Binaires*, § 89.

or the indices of those powers. It may be that only a limited range of the coefficients is relevant. For instance, the expansion may be an infinite one, but the class of numbers a finite one given by the coefficients of a limited range of terms, the indices of other terms being parameters irrelevant to the matter we have in hand.

We proceed to see that a generating function can be formed whose expansion is

$$(0\,;\,i, p)+(1\,;\,i, p)z+(2\,;\,i, p)z^2+\dots$$
$$+(w\,;\,i, p)z^w+\dots+(ip\,;\,i, p)z^{ip},$$

and which accordingly, when i and p are known, gives the number of partitions $(w\,;\,i,\,p)$ as the coefficient of z^w in its developement.

It is at once clear that, by definition of $(w\,;\,i,\,p)$, this number of partitions is the number of ways in which positive integral, or vanishing, values of $r_0, r_1, r_2, \dots r_p$ can be found which satisfy the two equations

$$r_0+r_1+r_2+\dots+r_p\ \ =i,$$
$$r_1+2r_2+\dots+pr_p=w.$$

Now this number is the coefficient of $z^w x^i$ in the product

$$(1+x+x^2+\dots+x^{r_0}+\dots)\,(1+zx+z^2x^2+\dots+z^{r_1}x^{r_1}+\dots)$$
$$(1+z^2x+z^4x^2+\dots+z^{2r_2}x^{r_2}+\dots)\dots$$
$$(1+z^px+z^{2p}x^2+\dots+z^{pr_p}x^{r_p}+\dots),$$

where the series forming any factor may if we please be extended to infinity. This product may be written

$$\{(1-x)\,(1-zx)\,(1-z^2x)\dots(1-z^px)\}^{-1}.$$

It can also be multiplied out and arranged according to ascending powers of x. Suppose that, thus arranged, it is

$$u_0+u_1x+u_2x^2+\dots+u_ix^i+\dots;$$

then $u_0=1$, and $u_1, u_2, \dots u_i, \dots$ are functions of z. In fact,

$$u_i=(0\,;\,i, p)+(1\,;\,i, p)z+(2\,;\,i, p)z^2+\dots$$
$$+(w\,;\,i, p)z^w+\dots+(ip\,;\,i, p)z^{ip}.$$

Notice that $(0\,;\,i,\,p)$ denotes 1. This is reasonable, for there is one partition of zero into i parts not exceeding p, namely, into i zeros. $a_0{}^i$ is the one corresponding term when we are thinking of gradients. In particular, by convention, we may think of $(0\,;\,0,\,p)$ as denoting 1.

Now in

$$1+u_1x+u_2x^2+\dots+u_ix^i+\dots$$
$$=\{(1-x)\,(1-zx)\,(1-z^2x)\dots(1-z^px)\}^{-1},$$

put zx for x, getting

$$1+u_1zx+u_2z^2x^2+\dots+u_iz^ix^i+\dots$$
$$=\{(1-zx)(1-z^2x)(1-z^3x)\dots(1-z^{p+1}x)\}^{-1},$$
$$=\frac{1-x}{1-z^{p+1}x}\{1+u_1x+u_2x^2+\dots+u_ix^i+\dots\}.$$

Here multiply through by $1-z^{p+1}x$, and equate the coefficients of x^i, the equality being identical. We obtain

$$u_iz^i-u_{i-1}z^{p+i}=u_i-u_{i-1},$$

so that $u_i=u_{i-1}\dfrac{1-z^{p+i}}{1-z^i}$

$$=u_{i-2}\frac{1-z^{p+i-1}}{1-z^{i-1}}\cdot\frac{1-z^{p+i}}{1-z^i}$$
$$=\dots\dots\dots\dots$$
$$=u_0\frac{1-z^{p+1}}{1-z}\cdot\frac{1-z^{p+2}}{1-z^2}\cdot\dots\frac{1-z^{p+i-1}}{1-z^{i-1}}\cdot\frac{1-z^{p+i}}{1-z^i}$$
$$=\frac{(1-z^{p+1})(1-z^{p+2})\dots(1-z^{p+i})}{(1-z)(1-z^2)\dots(1-z^i)}.$$

Consequently $(w;i,p)$ is the coefficient of z^w in the expansion of this function in ascending powers of z. Notice that it is incidentally proved that this expansion is a terminating one of degree ip, i.e. that the numerator of the generating function u_i is divisible by the denominator whatever numbers i and p may be.

Notice also that u_i is exactly z^{ip} times the result of replacing in it z by z^{-1}. Coefficients equidistant from the beginning and the end in the developement are then equal. We have thus a proof of one of the facts of § 129, i.e. that

$$(ip-w;i,p)=(w;i,p).$$

135. **Generating function for number of seminvariants of given type.** It is easy to deduce a generating function in which the coefficient of z^w is the difference of numbers of partitions $(w;i,p)-(w-1;i,p)$. This difference is the number of those linearly independent seminvariants of

$$(a_0, a_1, a_2, \dots a_p)(x,y)^p$$

whose weight and degree are w and i, if $ip>2w$, and the number of invariants of the type if $ip=2w$. For values of w, such that $ip-2w<0$, or rather <-1, we are not really concerned with the difference in connexion with seminvariants.

Since

$$u_i = (0\,;\, i,\, p) + (1\,;\, i,\, p)z + (2\,;\, i,\, p)z^2 + \ldots$$
$$+ (w\,;\, i,\, p)z^w + \ldots + (ip\,;\, i,\, p)z^{ip},$$

the value of $(w\,;\, i,\, p) - (w-1\,;\, i,\, p)$, for values of w from 1 to ip inclusive, is the coefficient of z^w in $(1-z)u_i$, i.e. in the developement of

$$\frac{(1-z^{p+1})(1-z^{p+2})(1-z^{p+3})\ldots(1-z^{p+i})}{(1-z^2)(1-z^3)\ldots(1-z^i)}.$$

This developement is a terminating one of degree $ip+1$.

Notice that from the last remark of the preceding article the middle coefficient in the developement, when there could be one, i.e. when ip is odd, vanishes; and that coefficients equidistant from the beginning and end are equal but of opposite signs. Now (§ 129) we know that when $ip - 2w \not< -1$, i.e. when $w \not> \frac{1}{2}(ip+1)$, the difference $(w\,;\, i,\, p) - (w-1\,;\, i,\, p)$ is never negative. The developement of the generating function consists then of a series of terms with positive coefficients followed by a series with the same coefficients taken negatively in reversed order.

A word as to the first coefficient $(0\,;\, i,\, p) = 1$, which is not presented as a difference. It is correctly the number of seminvariants of degree i and zero weight. The one is $a_0{}^i$. We may if we like regard it as a difference $(0\,;\, i,\, p) - (-1\,;\, i,\, p)$ like the rest. For $(-1\,;\, i,\, p)$ is of course zero.

136. **Reciprocity.** The generating function of § 134 may, upon multiplication of numerator and denominator by

$$(1-z)(1-z^2)\ldots(1-z^p),$$

be written

$$\frac{(1-z)(1-z^2)(1-z^3)\ldots(1-z^{p+i})}{(1-z)(1-z^2)\ldots(1-z^p)\,.\,(1-z)(1-z^2)\ldots(1-z^i)},$$

which is unaltered by interchange of i and p. It may, in fact, be written

$$\frac{(1-z^{i+1})(1-z^{i+2})\ldots(1-z^{i+p})}{(1-z)(1-z^2)\ldots(1-z^p)}.$$

The coefficient of z^w in its expansion is then $(w\,;\, p,\, i)$ for exactly the same reason that it is $(w\,;\, i,\, p)$. Thus we have another proof of the theorem of § 130 that

$$(w\,;\, i,\, p) = (w\,;\, p,\, i),$$

and of Hermite's law of reciprocity (§ 131).

The generating function of § 135 may also be written

$$\frac{(1-z^{i+1})(1-z^{i+2})(1-z^{i+3})\dots(1-z^{i+p})}{(1-z^2)(1-z^3)\dots(1-z^p)}.$$

Ex. 1. Prove by aid of generating functions that

$$(w\,;\,i,\,p)-(w\,;\,i-1,\,p)=(w-i\,;\,i,\,p-1).$$

Ex. 2. Prove that

$$(w\,;\,i,\,p)=(w\,;\,0,\,p-1)+(w-1\,;\,1,\,p-1)+(w-2\,;\,2,\,p-1)+\dots+(w-i\,;\,i,\,p-1).$$

Ex. 3. Prove that

$$(w\,;\,i,\,p)-(w-1\,;\,i-1,\,p)=(w\,;\,0,\,p-2)+(w-2\,;\,1,\,p-2)+\dots+(w-2i\,;\,i,\,p-2);$$

and that

$$(w\,;\,i,\,w)-(w-i\,;\,i,\,w-1)=\sum_{n=0}^{n\to\infty}(w-2n\,;\,i-2,\,n).$$

137. **The whole number of seminvariants and invariants of given degree.** The whole number of linearly independent seminvariants of degree i, including invariants if there be any, which a binary p-ic possesses, may be found as follows.

We have seen (§§ 112, 126) that there are none for which $ip-2w$ is negative. Thus the greatest weight of any is $\frac{1}{2}ip$ or $\frac{1}{2}(ip-1)$, according as i and p are not or are both odd. Call this maximum weight W.

The number of seminvariants (or invariants if W be $\frac{1}{2}ip$) of weight W is

$$(W\,;\,i,\,p)-(W-1\,;\,i,\,p);$$

the number (all seminvariants necessarily) of weight $W-1$ is

$$(W-1\,;\,i,\,p)-(W-2\,;\,i,\,p);$$

the number of weight $W-2$ is

$$(W-2\,;\,i,\,p)-(W-3\,;\,i,\,p);$$

and so on. Finally the number of weight zero is unity or

$$(0\,;\,i,\,p).$$

Upon addition, we have for the whole number required

$$(W\,;\,i,\,p),$$

and, restoring to W its value, obtain the two following results.

(1) Unless i and p are both odd, the whole number of linearly independent seminvariants and invariants (i. e. of

covariants and invariants) of degree i in the coefficients of the binary p-ic is

$$(\tfrac{1}{2}ip\ ;\ i,\ p),$$

and these consist of

$$(\tfrac{1}{2}ip\ ;\ i,\ p)-(\tfrac{1}{2}ip-1\ ;\ i,\ p)$$

invariants, and

$$(\tfrac{1}{2}ip-1\ ;\ i,\ p)$$

seminvariants (covariants).

(2) If i and p are both odd the whole number of linearly independent seminvariants, i.e. of covariants, of degree i in the coefficients is

$$\{\tfrac{1}{2}(ip-1)\ ;\ i,\ p\},$$

none of them being invariants.

By § 134 the whole number of degree i is thus seen to be the coefficient of $z^{\frac{1}{2}ip}$ or $z^{\frac{1}{2}(ip-1)}$, as the case may be, in the developement of

$$\frac{(1-z^{p+1})(1-z^{p+2})\ldots(1-z^{p+i})}{(1-z)(1-z^2)\ldots(1-z^i)},$$

or its equivalent

$$\frac{(1-z^{i+1})(1-z^{i+2})\ldots(1-z^{i+p})}{(1-z)(1-z^2)\ldots(1-z^p)}.$$

In both cases the covariants (and invariants) have been actually exhibited in § 128 (*bis*).

We can now illustrate by a few simple cases the way in which generating functions give information as to the number and nature of *irreducible* concomitants.

138. **Has a linear form invariants or covariants?** For the linear form $ax+by$, $p=1$. The whole number of linearly independent seminvariants (including invariants) of degree i is by the preceding article

$$\text{co. } z^W \text{ in developement of } (1-z^{i+1})/(1-z),$$

where $W=\tfrac{1}{2}i$ or $\tfrac{1}{2}(i-1)$ according as i is even or odd,

$$= \text{co. } z^W \text{ in } 1+z+z^2+\ldots+z^i$$
$$= 1.$$

Thus of each degree there is a single seminvariant. What it is is clear. For degree 1 it is a, and for degree i it is a^i. It is a seminvariant and not an invariant, for $ip-2w=i>0$. The covariant which it leads is $(ax+by)^i$, the i-th power of the linear form itself.

Thus a linear form has no invariant, and its only covariants are powers of itself.

139. **Irreducible concomitants of a quadratic.** For the quadratic $ax^2+2bxy+cy^2$, $p=2$. Here $W=\frac{1}{2}.2i=i$. The whole number of linearly independent seminvariants and invariants of degree i is then

$$\text{co. } z^i \text{ in developement of } \frac{(1-z^{i+1})(1-z^{i+2})}{(1-z)(1-z^2)}$$

$$= \quad ,, \quad ,, \quad (1-z)^{-1}(1-z^2)^{-1}$$

$$= \quad ,, \quad ,, \quad (1+z+z^2+z^3+\ldots)(1+z^2+z^4+z^6+\ldots)$$

$$= \text{co. } z^i \text{ in } 1+z+2z^2+2z^3+3z^4+3z^5+\ldots.$$

There is, then, one of degree 1, viz. a; and there are two of degree 2, viz. the square a^2 of the one of degree 1 and another distinct from it, which we know otherwise to be the discriminant $ac-b^2$. Of any higher degree i we see, by considering the product $(1+z+z^2+z^3+\ldots)(1+z^2+z^4+z^6+\ldots)$, that there are just as many as there are ways of making up the number i as a sum of multiples, including zero multiples, of 1 and 2; and these are of course the products of powers of the two independent ones a, $ac-b^2$ of degrees 1, 2. For instance, if $r+2s$ is one of the partitions of i in question, $a^r(ac-b^2)^s$ is a seminvariant of degree i. All seminvariants of the quadratic are then rationally and integrally expressible in terms of the two a and $ac-b^2$, without the necessity of introducing any other. The binary quadratic has therefore no irreducible seminvariant besides a and $ac-b^2$.

The second of these is an invariant. The first leads the quadratic $ax^2+2bxy+cy^2$ itself. Consequently the complete system of irreducible concomitants of the binary quadratic consists of the quadratic itself and its discriminant. (Cf. § 84.)

Had we been looking for the irreducible *invariants* only we might have taken the generating function of § 135. For the quadratic the weight of an invariant of degree i is $\frac{1}{2}2i=i$. Thus the number of invariants of degree i

$$= \text{co. } z^i \text{ in developement of } (1-z^{i+1})(1-z^{i+2})/(1-z^2)$$

$$= \quad ,, \quad ,, \quad (1-z^2)^{-1}$$

$$= \text{co. } z^i \text{ in } 1+z^2+z^4+z^6+\ldots.$$

There is then no invariant of any odd degree, and a single one of every even degree. Thus there is one, the discriminant $ac-b^2$, of the second degree, and no other which is irreducible, all others being powers of this. (Cf. § 78.)

140. **Invariants of a cubic.** Take $p=3$, the case of the binary cubic $(a, b, c, d)(x, y)^3$; and first consider the question of *invariants* only.

An invariant of degree i is of weight $\frac{3i}{2}$. For there to be one then i must be even.

The number of degree i is, by § 135,

$$\text{co. } z^{\frac{3}{2}i} \text{ in developement of } \frac{(1-z^{i+1})(1-z^{i+2})(1-z^{i+3})}{(1-z^2)(1-z^3)}$$

$$= \quad \text{,,} \qquad \text{,,} \qquad \frac{1-z^i(z+z^2+z^3)}{(1-z^2)(1-z^3)}$$

$$= \quad \text{,,} \qquad \text{,,} \qquad \frac{1}{(1-z^2)(1-z^3)}-\frac{z^{i+1}}{(1-z)(1-z^2)}$$

$$= \quad \text{,,} \qquad \text{,,} \qquad \frac{1}{(1-z^2)(1-z^3)}$$

$$-\text{ co. } z^{\frac{1}{2}i} \text{ in developement of } \frac{z}{(1-z)(1-z^2)}$$

$$= \text{co. } z^{\frac{3}{2}i} \text{ in developement of } \frac{1}{(1-z^2)(1-z^3)}-\frac{z^3}{(1-z^3)(1-z^6)}$$

$$= \text{co. } z^{3i} \qquad \text{,,} \qquad \frac{1}{(1-z^4)(1-z^6)}-\frac{z^6}{(1-z^6)(1-z^{12})}$$

$$= \quad \text{,,} \qquad \text{,,} \qquad \frac{1+z^4+z^8-z^6}{(1-z^6)(1-z^{12})}$$

$$= \quad \text{,,} \qquad \text{,,} \qquad \frac{1-z^6}{(1-z^6)(1-z^{12})},$$

since the terms z^4 and z^8 in the numerator cannot when multiplied by powers of z^6 and z^{12} produce terms of form z^{3i},

$$= \text{co. } z^{3i} \text{ in developement of } \frac{1}{1-z^{12}}$$

$$= \text{co. } z^{i} \qquad \text{,,} \qquad \frac{1}{1-z^4}$$

$$= \text{co. } z^i \text{ in } 1+z^4+z^8+z^{12}+\ldots.$$

Thus for a degree not divisible by 4 there is no invariant; and for a degree divisible by 4 there is a single one, which must accordingly be a power of the one of degree 4, i.e. the discriminant $(ad-bc)^2-4(ac-b^2)(bd-c^2)$. This then is the only irreducible invariant of the cubic. (Cf. § 78.)

141. **Irreducible concomitants and syzygy for a cubic.** We seek now the complete system of *seminvariants* and invariants of the cubic.

Here, by § 137, the number that are linearly independent of degree i is the coefficient of $z^{\frac{3}{2}i}$ or $z^{\frac{3}{2}i-\frac{1}{2}}$, according as i is even or odd, in the developement of

$$\frac{(1-z^{i+1})(1-z^{i+2})(1-z^{i+3})}{(1-z)(1-z^2)(1-z^3)}.$$

The two cases may be combined by saying that it is the coefficient of $z^{\frac{3}{2}i}$ in the developement of

$$(1+z^{\frac{1}{2}})\frac{(1-z^{i+1})(1-z^{i+2})(1-z^{i+3})}{(1-z)(1-z^2)(1-z^3)},$$

i. e. in that of
$$\frac{1-z^i(z+z^2+z^3)}{(1-z^{\frac{1}{2}})(1-z^2)(1-z^3)}$$

$$= \text{co. } z^{\frac{3}{2}i} \text{ in developement of } \frac{1}{(1-z^{\frac{1}{2}})(1-z^2)(1-z^3)}$$

$$- \text{co. } z^{\frac{1}{2}i} \text{ in developement of } \frac{z}{(1-z^{\frac{1}{2}})(1-z)(1-z^2)}$$

$$= \text{co. } z^{\frac{3}{2}i} \text{ in developement of } \frac{1}{(1-z^{\frac{1}{2}})(1-z^2)(1-z^3)} - \frac{z^3}{(1-z^{\frac{3}{2}})(1-z^3)(1-z^6)}$$

$$= \text{co. } z^{3i} \quad ,, \quad \frac{1}{(1-z)(1-z^4)(1-z^6)} - \frac{z^6}{(1-z^3)(1-z^6)(1-z^{12})}$$

$$= \quad ,, \quad ,, \quad \frac{(1+z+z^2)(1+z^4+z^8)-z^6}{(1-z^3)(1-z^6)(1-z^{12})}$$

$$= \quad ,, \quad ,, \quad \frac{1+z^9}{(1-z^3)(1-z^6)(1-z^{12})},$$

in the numerator of which all powers of z with indices not divisible by 3 have been omitted as incapable of producing z^{3i} when multiplied into powers of z arising from the denominator, where all indices are multiples of 3,

$$= \text{co. } z^i \text{ in developement of } \frac{1+z^3}{(1-z)(1-z^2)(1-z^4)}$$

$$= \text{co. } z^i \text{ in developement of } \frac{1-z^6}{(1-z)(1-z^2)(1-z^3)(1-z^4)}$$

$$= \quad ,, \qquad ,, \qquad \frac{(1-z^6)(1+z+z^2+\ldots)}{(1+z^2+z^4+\ldots)(1+z^3+z^6+\ldots)(1+z^4+z^8+\ldots)},$$

of which the first few terms are

$$1+z+2z^2+3z^3+5z^4+6z^5+8z^6+\ldots.$$

We have then the following conclusions, gathered from the form before multiplying out.

(1) There is one seminvariant of degree 1, arising from the factor $(1-z)^{-1}$ in the reduced generating function. This is the seminvariant a.

(2) Besides the square of this there is another seminvariant of degree 2, arising from the factor $(1-z^2)^{-1}$. This is $ac-b^2$, the seminvariant which leads the covariant which in § 86 has been called H. Denote it by H'.

(3) Besides a^3 and $a(ac-b^2)$ there is another of degree 3. This is $a^2d-3abc+2b^3$, the leader of the covariant which in § 86 we have called G. Denote it by G'. This arises from the factor $(1-z^3)^{-1}$.

(4) Besides the four seminvariants of degree 4 which can be formed by compounding a, H' and G' rationally, there is an additional one arising from the factor $(1-z^4)^{-1}$. This is the discriminant $(ad-bc)^2-4(ac-b^2)(bd-c^2)$ which we have called Δ. It is an invariant.

(5) There is no other irreducible seminvariant. For all the factors of the denominator of the prepared generating function are now exhausted, and there are no positive terms in the numerator except 1; and this tells us that there is nothing which in the developement can increase the coefficient of z^i, whatever i be, beyond the number of ways in which i can be made up of sums of multiples of 1, 2, 3, 4 the indices of the z, z^2, z^3, z^4 in the denominator.

There are then four, and only four, irreducible seminvariants, including the one invariant Δ. All of degree higher than 4 can be expressed rationally and integrally in terms of these four a, H', G', Δ.

(6) But there is one fact more, given by the existence of the negative term $-z^6$ in the numerator of the reduced generating function. The four a, H', G', Δ, though irreducible are not independent. A relation, or 'syzygy' as it is called, connects them. And this syzygy is of the sixth degree. The presence of the $-z^6$ reduces the coefficient of z^6 in the developement from 9, which would be its value were the numerator 1 only, to 8. The number of linearly independent

seminvariants of degree 6 is then one less than the number of products of degree 6 of powers of a, H', G' and Δ. These products are consequently connected by a linear relation which reduces the most general linear function of them to one with 8 arbitrary coefficients instead of 9. The products are

$$a^6,\ a^4H',\ a^3G',\ a^2H'^2,\ a^2\Delta,\ aH'G',\ H'^3,\ H'\Delta,\ G'^2.$$

The syzygy which connects them must of course connect a number of them which are of the same weight. Now their weights are

$$0,\ 2,\ 3,\ 4,\ 6,\ 5,\ 6,\ 8,\ 6,$$

the only three which are the same being those of $a^2\Delta$, H'^3 and G'^2. The syzygy then connects these. It is found to be

$$a^2\Delta = G'^2 + 4H'^3,$$

which is of course the same relation as the

$$u^2\Delta = G^2 + 4H^3$$

of § 86. For a, H', G' are the seminvariants which lead the covariants u, H, G; and a syzygy connecting the seminvariant leaders of covariants connects also the covariants led, as otherwise by means of the syzygy we could form a covariant whose seminvariant leader vanishes, i.e. a covariant with y for a factor, which is impossible.

The complete system of irreducible concomitants of a binary cubic consists then of itself, its quadratic and cubic covariants H and G, and its discriminant Δ. The four are connected by a syzygy of the sixth degree in the coefficients, and, it may be noticed, of the sixth order in the variables.

142. **Irreducible invariants of the quartic.** For the case $p = 4$, that of the quartic, we at present confine attention to the investigation of the number of irreducible *invariants*.

Since here $\frac{1}{2}ip = 2i$, the number of linearly independent invariants of degree i is, by § 135,

co. z^{2i} in developement of

$$\frac{(1-z^{i+1})(1-z^{i+2})(1-z^{i+3})(1-z^{i+4})}{(1-z^2)(1-z^3)(1-z^4)}$$

$$= \text{co. } z^{2i} \text{ in developement of } \frac{1}{(1-z^2)(1-z^3)(1-z^4)} - \frac{z^{i+1}}{(1-z^2)(1-z^3)(1-z)}$$

$$= \quad \text{,,} \qquad \text{,,} \qquad \frac{1}{(1-z^2)(1-z^3)(1-z^4)}$$

$$- \text{co. } z^{i} \text{ in developement of } \frac{z}{(1-z)(1-z^2)(1-z^3)}$$

$$= \text{co. } z^{2i} \text{ in developement of } \frac{1}{(1-z^2)(1-z^3)(1-z^4)} - \frac{z^2}{(1-z^2)(1-z^4)(1-z^6)}$$

$$= \quad ,, \qquad ,, \qquad \frac{1+z^3-z^2}{(1-z^2)(1-z^4)(1-z^6)}$$

$$= \quad ,, \qquad ,, \qquad \frac{1-z^2}{(1-z^2)(1-z^4)(1-z^6)},$$

for z^3 in the numerator can be a factor only of odd powers in the developement,

$$= \text{co. } z^{2i} \text{ in developement of } \frac{1}{(1-z^4)(1-z^6)}$$

$$= \text{co. } z^{i} \qquad ,, \qquad \frac{1}{(1-z^2)(1-z^3)}.$$

Hence there are two, and only two, irreducible invariants, one of degree 2 and one of degree 3, since there are just as many linearly independent invariants of any higher degree as there are combinations of that degree of these two. The two are (§ 80)

$$I \equiv ae - 4bd + 3c^2,$$
$$J \equiv ace + 2bcd - ad^2 - b^2e - c^3.$$

There is no invariant of higher degree which cannot be expressed rationally and integrally in terms of them.

143. Invariants of the quintic and sextic. The application of these methods has been continued a good many stages further. The labour and ingenuity required increase considerably as we advance.

For the case of the quintic, $p = 5$, the result is that the number of linearly independent invariants of degree i is the coefficient of z^i in the developement of

$$\frac{1-z^{36}}{(1-z^4)(1-z^8)(1-z^{12})(1-z^{18})}.$$

There are then *four* irreducible invariants of the quintic, of degrees 4, 8, 12, 18. They are not, however, independent, as the presence of $-z^{36}$ in the numerator implies. This presence diminishes the number of linearly independent invariants of degree 36 to one below the number of ways of making up 36 by means of repetitions of 4, 8, 12, 18. In other words, there is a 'syzygy,' of degree 36 in a, b, c, d, e, f, the coefficients of the quintic, which connects the irreducible invariants of degrees 4, 8, 12, 18. This syzygy will be exhibited in a later chapter. It expresses the square of I_{18} in terms of I_4, I_8, and I_{12}.

For the sextic the number of linearly independent invariants of degree i is the coefficient of z^i in the developement of

$$\frac{1-z^{30}}{(1-z^2)(1-z^4)(1-z^6)(1-z^{10})(1-z^{15})}.$$

There are *five* irreducible invariants, of degrees 2, 4, 6, 10, 15; and these are connected by a syzygy of degree 30, which expresses the square of I_{15} rationally and integrally in terms of I_2, I_4, I_6, and I_{10}.

For the full investigation of these facts reference should be made to Cayley's second memoir on quantics.

144. **Generating function for concomitants of given degree and order.** A new departure in the use of generating functions dates from Cayley's ninth memoir on quantics (*Collected Works*, Vol. VII). The earlier use of them had not succeeded in exhibiting complete systems of irreducible covariants for higher quantics than the quartic, and indeed mistaken inferences from it had indicated the erroneous conclusion that there were not complete systems of finite number. That there were had meanwhile been conclusively established by Gordan's method of transvectants. The two theories have now been completely reconciled, and verify one another's conclusions. The error arose from considering all syzygies independent, whereas there are syzygies of the second order connecting syzygies, for values of p exceeding 4.

Let us return to § 134, where it was shown that the number of linearly independent partitions of w into i or fewer parts, none exceeding p, is the coefficient of $z^w \xi^i$ (notice that we have changed the notation) in the developement of

$$\frac{1}{(1-\xi)(1-z\xi)(1-z^2\xi)\dots(1-z^p\xi)}$$

in positive powers of ξ, and therefore of z; and consequently that the number of linearly independent seminvariants of weight w and degree i of a binary p-ic,

i. e. $$(w;\, i, p)-(w-1;\, i, p),$$

is the coefficient of $z^w \xi^i$ in the developement of

$$\frac{1-z}{(1-\xi)(1-z\xi)(1-z^2\xi)\dots(1-z^p\xi)}.$$

Here put x^{-2} for z and ax^p for ξ. The number of the seminvariants is therefore the coefficient of $a^i x^{ip-2w}$ in the developement of

$$\frac{1-x^{-2}}{(1-ax^p)(1-ax^{p-2})(1-ax^{p-4})\dots(1-ax^{-p+4})(1-ax^{-p+2})(1-ax^{-p})}$$

in positive powers of a, and powers of x positive and negative as they present themselves.

Now $ip-2w$ is the order ϖ of that covariant of the p-ic which any seminvariant of weight w and degree i leads. Consequently the number of linearly independent covariants of degree i and order ϖ, where ϖ is essentially non-negative, is the coefficient of $a^i x^\varpi$ in the developement of this last written generating function. In particular, the number of linearly independent *invariants* of degree i is the coefficient of a^i in the part of the developement which is free from x.

For the quadratic, the cubic, and the quartic the generating functions are

$$\frac{1-x^{-2}}{(1-ax^2)(1-a)(1-ax^{-2})},$$

$$\frac{1-x^{-2}}{(1-ax^3)(1-ax)(1-ax^{-1})(1-ax^{-3})},$$

$$\frac{1-x^{-2}}{(1-ax^4)(1-ax^2)(1-a)(1-ax^{-2})(1-ax^{-4})}.$$

145. **Reduced generating functions.** We need only those terms in the developement which involve positive powers of x as well as of a. Now it proves to be possible to separate those parts of the generating function, for a given value of p, which give rise to positive powers of x from those which give negative powers. It will be verified without difficulty that the three last written generating functions, for the cases of the quadratic, the cubic, and the quartic, may respectively be written

$$A(x)-x^{-2}A(x^{-1}),$$
$$B(x)-x^{-2}B(x^{-1}),$$
$$C(x)-x^{-2}C(x^{-1}),$$

where

$$A(x)=\frac{1}{(1-ax^2)(1-a^2)},$$

$$B(x)=\frac{1-a^6x^6}{(1-ax^3)(1-a^2x^2)(1-a^3x^3)(1-a^4)},$$

$$C(x)=\frac{1-a^6x^{12}}{(1-ax^4)(1-a^2)(1-a^2x^4)(1-a^3)(1-a^3x^6)}.$$

Hence the numbers of linearly independent covariants of degree i and order ϖ for the quadratic, cubic, and quartic are respectively the coefficients of $a^i x^\varpi$ in the developements in ascending powers of a of $A(x)$, $B(x)$, and $C(x)$.

From $A(x)$ and $B(x)$ we at once gather the information of §§ 139, 141 with regard to the irreducible concomitants of the quadratic and cubic respectively.

From $C(x)$ we gather in like manner the full information as to the quartic. It has *five* irreducible concomitants whose degrees and orders are given by ax^4, a^2, a^2x^4, a^3, a^3x^6. The first is the quartic itself

$$u \equiv (a, b, c, d, e)(x, y)^4;$$

the second is its invariant of the second degree

$$I \equiv ae - 4bd + 3c^2;$$

the third is its Hessian

$$H \equiv (ac - b^2)x^4 + \ldots \equiv x^4 e^{\frac{y}{x}O}(ac - b^2);$$

the fourth is its invariant of the third degree

$$J \equiv ace + 2bcd - ad^2 - b^2e - c^3;$$

and the fifth is its covariant of degree 3 and order 6

$$G \equiv (a^2d - 3abc + 2b^3)x^6 + \ldots \equiv x^6 e^{\frac{y}{x}O}(a^2d - 3abc + 2b^3).$$

The second term $-a^6x^{12}$ in the numerator tells us that the five are connected by a syzygy of degree 6 and order 12, which reduces the number of linearly independent covariants of this degree and order to one below that of the number of products of the degree and order in question of u, I, H, J, G. This is readily found to be

$$Ju^3 - IHu^2 + G^2 + 4H^3 = 0.$$

As to invariants alone, the terms in $A(x)$, $B(x)$, and $C(x)$ which are free from x are the developements of

$$\frac{1}{1-a^2}, \quad \frac{1}{1-a^4}, \quad \frac{1}{(1-a^2)(1-a^3)};$$

whence the information that the discriminant is the only invariant of a quadratic, and that of §§ 140, 142 for the cubic and quartic, is at once gathered.

146. **Reduced and representative generating functions. The Quintic.** To methods and results for quantics above the fourth order we have only space to allude. Most of the investigations are due to Sylvester who, with the collaboration of Franklin, has obtained for quantics of the first ten and the twelfth orders the numbers and types of complete systems of concomitants, or rather, as he himself points out, the types

and numbers of systems which must, if they err from completeness in the higher cases, err by defect and not by excess; the possibility of there being more arising from the fact that the labour of discovery has been reduced to tractable dimensions by the adoption as a fundamental postulate for all cases of a fact observed for the first six orders, viz. that new syzygies and irreducible concomitants do not exist for the same degree and order. To this postulate Hammond has shown that there is an exception in the case of the septimic, for which the investigations had previously indicated a speciality not occurring in other cases so far as examined.

The first step in the process is general for all cases, and consists in showing that, when, as in § 145, the 'crude' generating function of § 144 is written as the difference of two parts, one of which gives all the terms in the developement which proceed by positive and zero powers of x, and the other those which proceed by negative powers, the former part may be written in the form

$$\frac{C_0 + C_1 x + C_2 x^2 + \dots}{(1-ax^p)(1-ax^{p-2})(1-ax^{p-4})\dots(1-a^k)(1-a^{k'})\dots},$$

where the order of the numerator in x is less than that of the denominator, and where C_0, C_1, C_2, ... are finite rational and integral functions of a. This is called the *reduced* generating function.

The second step is one which has to be performed for the cases of quantics of successive orders separately. The numerator and denominator have to be multiplied by such factors as to reduce the latter to a product of $1-ax^p$ and such factors as

$$1-a^i x^\varpi,\ 1-a^j,$$

where i and ϖ are recognized as the degree and order of an irreducible covariant, and j as the degree of a known irreducible invariant. In all cases examined this has proved to be so possible as to keep the numerator a finite expression.

The reduced generating function thus prepared is called the *representative* generating function. For orders of quantics which have been examined the denominators of the representative generating functions are products of $1-ax^p$ and of factors of the simple forms

$$1-a^2 x^\varpi,\ 1-a^j.$$

For the *quintic* ($p=5$) the numerator of the representative generating function proves to be

$$1 + a^3(x^3+x^5+x^9) + a^4(x^4+x^6) + a^5(x+x^3+x^7-x^{11})$$
$$+ a^6(x^2+x^4) + a^7(x+x^5-x^9) + a^8(x^2+x^4) + a^9(x^3+x^5-x^7)$$
$$+ a^{10}(x^2+x^4-x^{10}) + a^{11}(x+x^3-x^9) + a^{12}(x^2-x^8-x^{10})$$

$$+a^{13}(x-x^7-x^9)+a^{14}(x^4-x^6-x^8)+a^{15}(-x^7-x^9)$$
$$+a^{16}(x^2-x^6-x^{10})+a^{17}(-x^7-x^9)+a^{18}(1-x^4-x^8-x^{10})$$
$$+a^{19}(-x^5-x^7)+a^{20}(-x^2-x^6-x^8)+a^{23}(-x^{11}),$$

and the denominator

$$(1-ax^5)(1-a^2x^2)(1-a^2x^6)(1-a^4)(1-a^8)(1-a^{12}).$$

The third step in the process is one of sifting, or 'tamisage' as it is called. We have certain irreducible concomitants, or say 'ground forms,' to use a common designation, represented in the denominator. The earlier terms, after the first 1, in the numerator are positive, and indicate the existence of other ground forms. Proceed onwards from term to term in the numerator. As long as the degree and order of a term $a^i x^\varpi$ in the numerator cannot be made up as a sum of the degrees and orders of previously occurring terms, we have revealed the existence of as many new ground forms of that degree and order as there are positive units in its coefficient. When we have reached a term whose degree and order can be made up as a sum of degrees and orders of ground forms whose existence has been previously revealed by the numerator, *not* also those represented in the denominator, the excess of the coefficient of that term above the number of ways in which this can be done is the number of ground forms of the degree and order of the term in question, diminished by the number of syzygies of the degree and order which connect ground forms that have previously occurred, in the denominator as well as in the numerator, but increased, as will presently happen, by the number of syzygies of the second order which connect previous syzygies and are of the degree and order in question.

For instance, regarding the representative generating function for the quintic above, the eight terms in the numerator which immediately follow the first have all the coefficient + 1, and the degree-orders of these terms, a^3x^3, a^3x^5, a^3x^9, a^4x^4, a^4x^6, a^5x, a^5x^3, a^5x^7, are such as to make it clear that none of the terms can be written as a product of powers of the preceding terms. They indicate, then, that besides the ground forms of degree-orders (1, 5), (2, 2), (2, 6), (4, 0), (8, 0), (12, 0) given by factors of the denominator, there are others of degree-orders (3, 3), (3, 5), (3, 9), (4, 4), (4, 6), (5, 1), (5, 3), (5, 7).

Again, the coefficient of the next term a^5x^{11} in the numerator is -1. This indicates that there must be one syzygy of degree 5 and order 11 connecting some of the fourteen ground forms of degree-orders less than (5, 11). It is found to connect the products $C_{1,5}C_{4,6}$, $C_{2,2}C_{3,9}$, $C_{2,6}C_{3,5}$, where

$C_{r,s}$ is the ground form of degree r and order s. In particular $C_{1,5}$ is the quintic itself.

As soon as the degree-order (i, ϖ) of each new ground form in succession is found, we may, if we please, alter the form of the representative generating function by multiplying its numerator and denominator by $1-a^i x^\varpi$, and so put that ground form in the same position as those whose representatives were before in the denominator, thus narrowing the further search by means of the numerator. In particular, when we know all the ground forms, we may write the generating function with the product of all their representative factors $1-a^i x^\varpi$, $1-a^j$, &c. in the denominator. The sifting of the numerator is then a process of search for syzygies only. This idea has been developed by Hammond. The $A(x)$, $B(x)$, $C(x)$ of § 145 for the quadratic cubic and quartic are generating functions thus written.

Notice that the terms free from x in the developement of the representative generating function for the quintic above are the terms in the developement of the result of putting $x = 0$ in it, i.e. of

$$\frac{1+a^{18}}{(1-a^4)(1-a^8)(1-a^{12})}.$$

This then is the representative generating function for invariants of the quintic. It leads to the conclusions already stated in § 143.

There prove to be twenty-three ground forms of the quintic, of which four, I_4, I_8, I_{12}, I_{18}, are invariants.

147. A method for extracting representative generating functions for invariants only will now be illustrated by the comparatively simple consideration of the sextic.

Writing z for x^2, we have to extract from

$$\frac{1-z^{-1}}{1-a}(3)(2)(1)(-1)(-2)(-3),$$

where (n) means $\dfrac{1}{1-az^n}$, a part which provides the terms free from z in its expansion.

Since the product $(3)(2)(1)(-1)(-2)(-3)$ is unaltered by writing in it z^{-1} for z and z for z^{-1}, we may replace the multiplying $1-z^{-1}$ by $1-z$, or by $\frac{1}{2}(2-z-z^{-1})$, i.e. $\frac{1}{2}(1-z)(1-z^{-1})$, and have the same terms free from z provided. Hence, noticing that

$$(1-z)(2)(1) = \frac{1}{az}\{(1)-(2)\},$$

and that
$$(3)(-3) = \frac{1}{1-a^2}\{(3)+(-3)-1\},$$

we have to look for the part free from z in the expansion in ascending powers of a of

$$\frac{1}{2a^2(1-a)(1-a^2)}\{(1)-(2)\}\{(-1)-(-2)\}\{(3)+(-3)-1\}.$$

Here we may replace the last factor by $2(3)-1$, since $\{(1)-(2)\}\{(-1)-(-2)\}$ is unaltered by the interchange of z and z^{-1}. Thus we look for the part free from z in

$$\frac{1}{a^2(1-a)(1-a^2)}$$
$$\{(1)(-1)(3)+(2)(-2)(3)-(1)(-2)(3)-(2)(-1)(3)$$
$$-\tfrac{1}{2}(1)(-1)-\tfrac{1}{2}(2)(-2)+\tfrac{1}{2}(1)(-2)+\tfrac{1}{2}(2)(-1)\}.$$

The parts provided by the separate products here can all be obtained by noticing that, if n is positive, the part free from z in a product

$$\frac{1}{1-az^{-n}}\{c_0+c_1z+c_2z^2+\ldots\}$$

is
$$c_0+c_na+c_{2n}a^2+\ldots.$$

Thus, for instance,

$$(1)(-2)(3) = \frac{1}{1-az^{-2}}\cdot\frac{1}{(1-az)(1-az^3)}$$
$$= \frac{1}{1-az^{-2}}\cdot\frac{1+az+az^3+a^2z^4}{(1-a^2z^2)(1-a^2z^6)}$$

produces the same part free from z as it would were the terms $az+az^3$, of odd order, missing from the numerator, i.e. it produces
$$\frac{1+a^4}{(1-a^3)(1-a^5)}.$$

The other products—we have taken the worst—are readily dealt with in the same way; and we thus have, as providing all the terms free from z,

$$\frac{1}{a^2(1-a)(1-a^2)}\left\{\frac{1}{(1-a^2)(1-a^4)}+\frac{1}{(1-a^2)(1-a^5)}\right.$$
$$\left.-\frac{1+a^4}{(1-a^3)(1-a^5)}-\frac{1}{(1-a^3)(1-a^4)}-\frac{1}{1-a^2}+\frac{1}{1-a^3}\right\},$$

which is with little difficulty reduced to

$$\frac{1+a^{15}}{(1-a^2)(1-a^4)(1-a^6)(1-a^{10})},$$

and yields the information as to the sextic included in § 143.

147 (*bis*). Sylvester and Franklin have also exhibited generating functions for the whole number of *seminvariants* of any degree for the quantics they have studied.

Moreover, they have obtained representative generating functions of two or more quantics of low degrees, and studied their indications as to systems of ground forms.

For these researches, and for the full theories above illustrated, reference should be made to the first four volumes of the *American Journal of Mathematics*. A few exercises are here left to the student.

Ex. 4. By § 137 the whole number of seminvariants (including invariants) of degree i of a binary p-ic is $(\frac{1}{2}ip\,;\,i,p)$ or $(\frac{1}{2}ip-\frac{1}{2}\,;\,i,p)$, according as ip is even or odd. Show by the method of § 144 that this number is the coefficient of a^i in the part of the developement of

$$\frac{1+x^{-1}}{(1-ax^p)(1-ax^{p-2})\dots(1-ax^{-p+2})(1-ax^{-p})},$$

in ascending powers of a, which is free from x.

Ex. 5. Prove that the number of linearly independent seminvariants of weight w and partial degrees i, i' of a p-ic and a p'-ic is the coefficient of $z^w\xi^i\xi'^{i'}$ in the expansion of

$$\frac{1-z}{(1-\xi)(1-z\xi)\dots(1-z^p\xi)\,.\,(1-\xi')(1-z\xi')\dots(1-z^{p'}\xi')}.$$

Ex. 6. Show, as in § 144, that the number of covariants of order ϖ and partial degrees i, i' of a p-ic and a p'-ic is the coefficient of $a^ia'^{i'}x^{\varpi}$ in the developement of

$$\frac{1-x^{-2}}{(1-ax^p)(1-ax^{p-2})\dots(1-ax^{-p+2})(1-ax^{-p})\,.\,(1-a'x^{p'})(1-a'x^{p'-2})\dots(1-a'x^{-p'+2})(1-}$$

Ex. 7. Show that for two linear forms the reduced generating function for numbers of concomitants is

$$\frac{1}{(1-ax)(1-a'x)(1-aa')},$$

where a refers to one form and a' to the other.

Ex. 8. Show that for a linear form and a quadratic it is

$$\frac{1+abx}{(1-ax)(1-bx^2)(1-b^2)(1-a^2b)},$$

where a refers to the linear form and b to the quadratic.

Ex. 9. Show that for two quadratics it is

$$\frac{1+bb'x^2}{(1-bx^2)(1-b'x^2)(1-b^2)(1-b'^2)(1-bb')}.$$

Ex. 10. The system of irreducible *invariants* of a cubic and quadratic consists of invariants of partial degrees (4, 0), (0, 2), (2, 1), (2, 3), (4, 3); and the last of these need only occur to the first power in the expression of any invariant.

Ans. G. F.

$$\frac{1+a^4b^3}{(1-a^4)(1-b^2)(1-a^2b)(1-a^2b^3)},$$

found by method of § 147.

Ex. 11. For a quartic and quadratic the representative generating function for invariants is

$$\frac{1+a^3b^3}{(1-a^2)(1-a^3)(1-b^2)(1-ab^2)(1-a^2b^2)}.$$

Interpret this.

Ex. 12. Show that, by writing

$$\frac{1}{1-b^2}\left\{\frac{1}{1-bx^2}+\frac{1}{1-bx^{-2}}-1\right\} \quad \text{for} \quad \frac{1}{(1-bx^2)(1-bx^{-2})}$$

and applying the method of the latter part of § 147, we can obtain the generating function for invariants of a p-ic and quadratic from that for in- and co-variants of a p-ic.

Ex. 13. Obtain the generating function for invariants of a quintic from that for in- and co-variants of a cubic by obtaining as in § 147 the part giving terms free from x in the expansion of

$$\frac{1}{1-a^2}\left\{\frac{1}{1-ax^5}+\frac{1}{1-ax^{-5}}-1\right\}\left\{B(x)-x^{-2}B(x^{-1})\right\}.$$

Ex. 14. If $P(x)$ is the representative generating function for in- and co-variants of a $(p-2)$-ic, that for invariants of a p-ic can be found by obtaining the part giving terms free from x in the expansion of

$$(1-x^2)P(x)/(1-a^2)(1-ax^{-p}).$$

148. **Real generating functions.** From representative generating functions Cayley has passed to what he calls *Real Generating Functions.*

Let us return to § 145. The generating function

$$A(x) \equiv \frac{1}{(1-ax^2)(1-a^2)}$$

for the quadratic has told us that there are two ground forms, the quadratic u and the discriminant $\Delta \equiv ac-b^2$, and that there are just as many concomitants of any type as there are products of that type of powers of u and Δ. This tells us that all concomitants of the quadratic are terms which actually occur in the expansion of

$$\frac{1}{(1-u)(1-\Delta)}.$$

This is the real generating function for the quadratic.

Again, for the cubic, that $B(x)$, which write in the form

$$\frac{1+a^3x^3}{(1-ax^3)(1-a^2x^2)(1-a^4)},$$

is the generating function, has told us that there are as many concomitants of any type as there are such products of u, H, Δ and G of that type as do not involve G to a higher power than the first. And this information is exactly expressed by saying that concomitants of the cubic are linear functions of those products of the four ground forms which occur in the developement of

$$\frac{1+G}{(1-u)(1-H)(1-\Delta)},$$

which is the real generating function of the cubic.

Once more, for the quartic, $C(x)$, or

$$\frac{1+a^3x^6}{(1-ax^4)(1-a^2)(1-a^2x^4)(1-a^3)},$$

tells us in like manner that there is a real generating function

$$\frac{1+G}{(1-u)(1-I)(1-H)(1-J)},$$

such that all concomitants of the quartic are linear functions of terms which actually occur in its developement, i. e. of the products into which G does not enter to a higher power than the first.

For the quintic, and beyond, the form of a real generating function derived from the representative generating function of § 146 is not unique, owing to the number of different ways in which we may replace the many terms in the numerator by products of ground forms. Cayley has shown in his tenth memoir that the most useful form into which a real generating function of the quintic can be thrown is

$$\frac{\Sigma P(1-Q)}{(1-u)(1-C_{2,2})(1-C_{2,6})(1-I_4)(1-I_8)(1-I_{12})},$$

where every P and Q, in the products whose sum is the numerator, are products of ground forms and powers of ground forms chosen from among the complete system of 23 whose forms will be exhibited in a later chapter. All the 23 occur in the numerator and denominator together.

For invariants alone, real generating functions are

(1) for the quadratic $\dfrac{1}{1-\Delta}$;

(2) for the cubic $\dfrac{1}{1-\Delta}$, not the same Δ of course as in (1);

(3) for the quartic $\dfrac{1}{(1-I)(1-J)}$;

(4) for the quintic $\dfrac{1+I_{18}}{(1-I_4)(1-I_8)(1-I_{12})}$;

(5) for the sextic $\dfrac{1+I_{15}}{(1-I_2)(1-I_4)(1-I_6)(1-I_{10})}$.

CHAPTER IX

HILBERT'S PROOFS OF GORDAN'S THEOREM.

149. An irreducible invariant has, it will be remembered, been defined as one which cannot be expressed rationally and integrally in terms of invariants of lower degree than its own belonging to the same quantic or quantics.

Similarly, an irreducible covariant is one which cannot be expressed rationally and integrally in terms of covariants and invariants of degree in the coefficients lower than its own.

In the cases of binary quantics of low orders, it has been seen in the last chapter that the number of irreducible invariants and covariants is limited.

And in § 61 it has been stated that Gordan, using the symbolic method of the German investigators, has proved that a complete system of transvectants is coextensive with a complete system of covariants and invariants, and does not comprise an unending series of irreducible forms; thus showing that any binary quantic, or system of binary quantics, has only a finite number of irreducible covariants and invariants. His original proof has since been modified and simplified. See Grace and Young's *Algebra of Invariants*, Chapter V.

Several quite different simpler proofs of the finiteness of the system of irreducibles are due to Hilbert; and one of these establishes it for ternary and higher as well as for binary quantics. We will first give at length his earlier proof, which deals with binary quantics only.

150. **Diophantine equations.** Some lemmas as to the solutions in positive integers of a system of linear indeterminate, or Diophantine, equations are necessary.

(i) An equation

$$a_1x_1 + a_2x_2 + \dots + a_nx_n = 0,$$

where $a_1, a_2, \dots a_n$ are given positive integers, is not satisfied by any set of positive values of $x_1, x_2, \dots x_n$. In fact, the only values, none negative, which satisfy the equation are $x_1 = x_2 = \dots = x_n = 0$.

(ii) An equation

$$a_1x_1 + a_2x_2 + \ldots + a_nx_n = k,$$

where k, as well as $a_1, a_2, \ldots a_n$, is a positive integer, has, if any, only a finite number of positive integral solutions, zero being counted for the purpose a positive integer. For the whole number of ways in which the number k can be expressed as a sum of n or fewer positive integral parts is finite, and the limitation that the parts be integral multiples of some or all of $a_1, a_2, \ldots a_n$ imposes a further restriction.

(iii) An equation of the form in (i), except that some of the coefficients are positive and some negative integers, is satisfied by an infinite number of positive integral, or some vanishing, values of $x_1, x_2, \ldots x_n$. But of this infinite number of positive integral sets of solutions only a finite number are what may be called *simple* sets, i. e. sets which cannot be obtained by adding together other sets of positive integral solutions.

Let the terms with negative coefficients be transposed to the other side of the equation, so that this may be written

$$a_1x_1 + a_2x_2 + \ldots + a_mx_m = b_{m+1}x_{m+1} + b_{m+2}x_{m+2} + \ldots + b_nx_n,$$

where every a and every b is a positive integer.

That there are positive integral solutions is clear. For instance,

$$x_1 = b_{m+1},\ x_{m+1} = a_1,\ x_2 = x_3 = \ldots = x_m$$
$$= x_{m+2} = x_{m+3} = \ldots = x_n = 0,$$

and $$x_1 = b_{m+2},\ x_{m+2} = a_1,\ x_2 = x_3 = \ldots = x_{m+1}$$
$$= x_{m+3} = x_{m+4} = \ldots = x_n = 0,$$

are sets of solutions. Moreover, we may take for $x_1, x_2, \ldots x_n$ any the same positive integral multiples, or any sums of the same positive integral multiples, of the values of $x_1, x_2, \ldots x_n$ in one or a number, respectively, of these particular sets, and thus obtain another set of solutions. The number of sets is thus infinite. Not all sets are as a rule obtained in this manner, for there will usually be other sets in considerable number, for which some or all of $x_1, x_2, \ldots x_n$ have smaller non-vanishing values, than in sets of solutions comprised in the above aggregate.

We have, however, to establish that the number of *simple* sets of solutions is in all cases finite.

No set of solutions in which $x_1 > b_{m+1}$, and $x_{m+1} > a_1$, where a_1x_1 and $b_{m+1}x_{m+1}$ are any terms on the left and right respectively, can be simple. For any such set of solutions is the sum of the first set of solutions written above and another set.

Thus in a simple set of solutions, if an x on the left, x_1 say, exceed the greatest coefficient on the right, none of the x's on the right can exceed a_1; and if an x on the right, x_{m+1} say, exceed the greatest coefficient on the left, none of the x's on the left can exceed b_{m+1}.

Simple sets of solutions can then occur only in one or both of two overlapping classes, the class in which no x on the right exceeds the greatest coefficient on the left, and the class in which no x on the left exceeds the greatest coefficient on the right.

In the first class we have

$$a_1x_1 + a_2x_2 + \dots + a_mx_m \not> (b_{m+1} + b_{m+2} + \dots + b_n)\, a_1,$$

where a_1 denotes the greatest of $a_1, a_2, \dots a_m$. Now by (ii) the number of sets of positive integral, and vanishing, sets of values of $x_1, x_2, \dots x_m$ for which this is the case, is finite; and each set gives for the determination of $x_{m+1}, x_{m+2}, \dots x_n$ an equation like

$$k = b_{m+1}x_{m+1} + b_{m+2}x_{m+2} + \dots + b_nx_n,$$

of which the number of sets of solutions is, again by (ii), finite.

And quite similarly in the second class there is only a finite number of sets of solutions.

Of these sets some will be simple; but the vast majority, as a rule, not so.

It is, however, completely established that the number of simple sets of solutions, being part of a finite number of sets of solutions, is itself finite.

(iv) If $\alpha_1, \alpha_2, \dots \alpha_n$; $\beta_1, \beta_2, \dots \beta_n$; $\gamma_1, \gamma_2, \dots \gamma_n$; ... are all the simple sets of solutions of the equation in (iii), now proved to be finite in number, all sets of positive integral, including zero, values of $x_1, x_2, \dots x_n$ which satisfy the equation are comprised in the system

$$x_1 = \alpha_1t_1 + \beta_1t_2 + \gamma_1t_3 + \dots,$$
$$x_2 = \alpha_2t_1 + \beta_2t_2 + \gamma_2t_3 + \dots,$$
$$\cdot\quad\cdot\quad\cdot\quad\cdot\quad\cdot\quad\cdot\quad\cdot\quad\cdot\quad\cdot\quad\cdot$$
$$x_n = \alpha_nt_1 + \beta_nt_2 + \gamma_nt_3 + \dots,$$

where $t_1, t_2, t_3, \dots$, a known finite number of letters, have positive integral, including zero, values which may be assigned at will.

For the set $x_1, x_2, \dots x_n$, if not simple, can be expressed as a sum of other sets. These, if not simple, can be expressed as sums of other sets; and so on. Proceeding in this way, we eventually get the set $x_1, x_2, \dots x_n$ expressed as a sum of sums of sums of &c. of sets which can no longer be written as sums of sets, i. e. as a sum of multiples of the simple sets

$$a_1, a_2, \dots a_n;\ \beta_1, \beta_2, \dots \beta_n;\ \gamma_1, \gamma_2, \dots \gamma_n; \dots.$$

(v) What has been proved as to the finite number of simple sets of positive integral and zero solutions of a single Diophantine equation may now be extended to the case of a number of such equations. Suppose that we have r such equations in $x_1, x_2, x_3, \dots x_p$, these variables not all necessarily occurring in every one of the equations. By (iv) the variables $x_1, x_2, \dots x_n$ which occur in the first equation must in virtue of that equation have the forms

$$\begin{array}{l} a_1 t_1 + \beta_1 t_2 + \gamma_1 t_3 + \dots, \\ a_2 t_1 + \beta_2 t_2 + \gamma_2 t_3 + \dots, \\ \cdot\quad \cdot\quad \cdot\quad \cdot\quad \cdot\quad \cdot\quad \cdot \\ a_n t_1 + \beta_n t_2 + \gamma_n t_3 + \dots, \end{array}$$

where $a_1, \beta_1, \gamma_1, \dots, a_2, \beta_2, \gamma_2, \dots, \dots, a_n, \beta_n, \gamma_n, \dots$ have definite positive integral or zero values, and $t_1, t_2, t_3, \dots$ are a finite number of variables to which zero and positive integral values alone are open. Substitute these expressions for $x_1, x_2, \dots x_n$ in the remaining $r-1$ equations. These become $r-1$ equations in $x_{n+1}, x_{n+2}, \dots x_p$ and $t_1, t_2, t_3, \dots$, a finite number of variables whose generality as positive integers or zeros is only limited by the $r-1$ equations.

The first of these $r-1$ equations may now be treated exactly as the first of the r equations was, and substitution may then be made in the remaining $r-2$ equations; and so on continually till we get to a single equation only. To this the results of (iii) and (iv) apply. Thus we find eventually, on successive substitution backwards, that all the p variables $x_1, x_2, \dots x_p$ can have no more general values than are included in

$$\begin{array}{l} x_1 = A_1 \tau_1 + B_1 \tau_2 + C_1 \tau_3 + \dots, \\ x_2 = A_2 \tau_1 + B_2 \tau_2 + C_2 \tau_3 + \dots, \\ \cdot\quad \cdot\quad \cdot\quad \cdot\quad \cdot\quad \cdot\quad \cdot\quad \cdot\quad \cdot \\ x_p = A_p \tau_1 + B_p \tau_2 + C_p \tau_3 + \dots, \end{array}$$

where $A_1, B_1, C_1, \dots, A_2, B_2, C_2, \dots, \dots, A_p, B_p, C_p, \dots$ are definite positive integers, or some of them zeros, and where $\tau_1, \tau_2, \tau_3, \dots$ are a finite number of arbitraries to which any positive integral and zero values can be assigned at will.

In other words, a system of any number r of linear Diophantine equations can, if soluble at all in positive integers, have only a finite number of *simple* sets of solutions

$$A_1, A_2, A_3, \dots;\ B_1, B_2, B_3, \dots;\ C_1, C_2, C_3, \dots;\ \&c.,$$

all other sets of positive integral solutions being sums of multiples of some or all of this finite number of sets.

Ex. 1. The only simple set of solutions, excluding the all zero set, of the equations
$$i = y + z = z + x = x + y$$
is the set
$$x = 1,\ y = 1,\ z = 1,\ i = 2.$$

Ex. 2. The simple sets of solutions, besides the all zero set, of
$$i = x + y + w = y + z + u = z + x + v = u + v + w$$
are those of the table

x,	y,	z,	u,	v,	w,	i
1,	0,	0,	1,	0,	0,	1
0,	1,	0,	0,	1,	0,	1
0,	0,	1,	0,	0,	1,	1

Ans. It is easy to reduce the given set to
$$x = u,\ y = v,\ z = w,\ i = u + v + w.$$

Ex. 3. The only not all vanishing simple sets of solutions of
$$4(x + z + u + v) = 2(2z + 3u + 4v),$$
from which z disappears, leaving the equation $2x = u + 2v$, are given by the table

x,	z,	u,	v
0,	1,	0,	0
1,	0,	0,	1
1,	0,	2,	0

This proves that any product of powers of a_0, a_2, a_3, a_4 for which $4i = 2w$ is a product of powers of $a_2,\ a_0a_4,\ a_0a_3^2$.

151. **Application to invariants of one binary quantic.** Now it has been seen in Chapter V that if $\alpha_1, \alpha_2, \dots \alpha_p$ are the roots of the equation in $x : y$
$$(a_0, a_1, a_2, \dots a_p)(x, y)^p = 0,$$
and if
$$\epsilon = a_0^i (\alpha_1 - \alpha_2)^{n_{12}} (\alpha_1 - \alpha_3)^{n_{13}} (\alpha_2 - \alpha_3)^{n_{23}} \dots$$
is a_0^i times a product of differences between its roots, such that $n_{12}, n_{13}, n_{23}, \dots$ are all positive integers, or some of them zero, and that all roots occur in the same number i of factors where
$$\begin{aligned} i &= n_{12} + n_{13} + \dots + n_{1p}, \\ &= n_{12} + n_{23} + \dots + n_{2p}, \\ &= n_{13} + n_{23} + \dots + n_{3p} \\ &\quad \cdot \quad \cdot \quad \cdot \quad \cdot \quad \cdot \quad \cdot \\ &= n_{1p} + n_{2p} + \dots + n_{p-1,p}, \end{aligned}$$
then
$$\Sigma\epsilon,$$
where the Σ means that the roots are permuted in all possible

ways and the sum taken, is, if it does not vanish identically, an invariant of

$$(a_0, a_1, a_2, \dots a_p)(x, y)^p;$$

and, conversely, that any invariant can be expressed as such a sum $\Sigma\epsilon$, or at any rate as a sum of numerical multiples of such sums for which i is the same though the individual n's may be different.

We have to prove that any such sum $\Sigma\epsilon$ can be expressed rationally and integrally in terms of a finite number of elementary sums of the kind. This will show that any invariant is a rational integral function of a finite number of elementary invariants. It will not show that these elementary invariants are irreducible, but it will that all irreducible invariants occur among them.

It will be observed that the system of equations above in i and $n_{12}, n_{13}, n_{23}, \dots$ is a system of Diophantine equations such as that contemplated in § 150 (v). Bringing to bear on the system the theorem which has been proved, we learn that every such product ϵ as above is a product of powers of a finite number of elemental products $\epsilon_1, \epsilon_2, \epsilon_3, \dots \epsilon_\mu$ which obey the same laws, one elemental product being given by every simple set of solutions of the system of Diophantine equations, so that generally

$$\epsilon = \epsilon_1^{r_1}\epsilon_2^{r_2}\dots\epsilon_\mu^{r_\mu},$$

for some set of positive integral, including zero, values of the indices $r_1, r_2, \dots r_\mu$.

Every invariant is then of the form

$$\Sigma\epsilon_1^{r_1}\epsilon_2^{r_2}\dots\epsilon_\mu^{r_\mu}$$

for some such set of indices, or a linear function of such sums; and no such sum which does not vanish identically can fail to be an invariant.

The student must bear very clearly in mind the exact meaning of the summation denoted by the Σ. The summation is that of the $1.2.3\dots p$ terms, obtained by putting for the roots as they occur in the fully written expression of $\epsilon_1^{r_1}\epsilon_2^{r_2}\dots\epsilon_\mu^{r_\mu}$ the corresponding roots in every one of the $1.2.3\dots p$ permutations of the p roots $\alpha_1, \alpha_2, \alpha_3, \dots \alpha_p$ of the quantic under consideration. The number of terms in the summation is in the first place, and is to be regarded as, the full number $p!$ of these permutations, though among them in any particular case there may be expected to be repetitions or cancellings or both. Other meanings might, but must not, be attached to the Σ. For instance, the meaning might be attached that to each of $\epsilon_1, \epsilon_2, \dots \epsilon_\mu$ separately be given every one of its $p!$ permutational values. We should then get it is true an invariant or an identical zero, but we should have no security that every invariant is thus obtained. An instance of the need for this caution will occur in an example on the quartic to be given presently.

152. We now bring in an idea from the theory of equations which will enable us to complete Hilbert's proof of Gordan's theorem.

Consider ϵ_1, one of the elemental products $\epsilon_1, \epsilon_2, \dots \epsilon_\mu$. It is also one of $p\,!$ similar products of which the rest are obtained from it by permuting the p roots $\alpha_1, \alpha_2, \dots \alpha_p$ in all possible ways. These $p\,!$ products are the roots of an equation

$$\epsilon_1^{p!} + P_1\epsilon_1^{p!-1} + P_2\epsilon_1^{p!-2} + \dots + P_{p!} = 0, \qquad \dots (1)$$

of whose coefficients some will frequently vanish identically. Those which do not will be rational integral invariants. For by Newton's theorem on the sums of powers of roots (Burnside and Panton's *Theory of Equations*, 4th ed., § 77) $P_1, P_2, \dots P_{p!}$ can be expressed rationally and integrally in terms of $s_1, s_2, \dots s_{p!}$, the sums of the first, second, ... $p\,!$ th powers of the $p\,!$ values of ϵ_1 which are the roots of the equation. Now $s_1, s_2, \dots s_{p!}$, or rather such of them as do not vanish identically, are invariants exhibited in a form which is a case of the general form of § 151.

Thus the equation (1) expresses $\epsilon_1^{p!}$ as a linear function of the first $p\,!-1$ powers $\epsilon_1^{p!-1}, \epsilon_1^{p!-2}, \dots \epsilon_1$ of ϵ_1 with an absolute term, the coefficients and absolute term being invariants expressible as rational integral functions of $s_1, s_2, \dots s_{p!}$. If we multiply through by ϵ_1 we obtain an expression for $\epsilon_1^{p!+1}$, which, upon insertion in it of the already obtained expression for $\epsilon_1^{p!}$, becomes a linear function of $\epsilon_1^{p!-1}, \epsilon_1^{p!-2}, \dots \epsilon_1$, whose coefficients and absolute term are rational integral functions of $s_1, s_2, \dots s_{p!}$. Multiply again by ϵ_1, and again replace $\epsilon_1^{p!}$ by the expression for it; and repeat the same process any number of times that may be desired. We thus obtain the fact that, the index r_1 being any number not less than $p\,!$,

$$\epsilon_1^{r_1} = Q_1\epsilon_1^{p!-1} + Q_2\epsilon_1^{p!-2} + \dots + Q_{p!},$$

where $Q_1, Q_2, \dots Q_{p!}$ are invariants capable of expression as rational integral functions of the $p\,!$ invariants and zeros $s_1, s_2, \dots s_{p!}$, i.e. $\Sigma\epsilon_1, \Sigma\epsilon_1^2, \dots \Sigma\epsilon_1^{p!}$.

Proceed now in like manner with ϵ_2, a second of the elemental products $\epsilon_1, \epsilon_2, \dots \epsilon_\mu$. This again is a root of an equation of degree $p\,!$ whose first coefficient is unity and whose other non-vanishing coefficients are invariants expressible rationally and integrally in terms of $p\,!$ sums of which those which do not vanish are invariants, viz.

$\Sigma\epsilon_2, \Sigma\epsilon_2^2, \dots \Sigma\epsilon_2^{p!}$. Consequently, if r_2 is not less than $p!$, we have

$$\epsilon_2^{r_2} = R_1\epsilon_2^{p!-1} + R_2\epsilon_2^{p!-2} + \dots + R_{p!},$$

where $R_1, R_2, \dots R_{p!}$ are invariants expressible as rational integral functions of $\Sigma\epsilon_2, \Sigma\epsilon_2^2, \dots \Sigma\epsilon_2^{p!}$.

In like manner we have like expressions for powers not less than the $p!$ th of $\epsilon_3, \epsilon_4, \dots \epsilon_\mu$, the remaining elemental products of powers of a_0 and differences between roots.

153. The number of irreducible invariants of a binary quantic is finite. We now return to the general expression of § 151

$$\Sigma\epsilon_1^{r_1}\epsilon_2^{r_2}\dots\epsilon_\mu^{r_\mu}.$$

There is, in the first place, only a finite number of these expressions for which none of the exponents $r_1, r_2, \dots r_\mu$ exceeds $p!-1$; viz. $(p!)^\mu - 1$.

Take, however, any one in which one or more of $r_1, r_2, \dots r_\mu$ exceeds $p!-1$, and express such higher rth powers of elemental factors in terms under the Σ by the expressions obtained in the last article in terms of powers less than the $p!$ th. Having done so, multiply out the expression obtained. The result is an identity like

$$\Sigma\epsilon_1^{r_1}\epsilon_2^{r_2}\dots\epsilon_\mu^{r_\mu} = \Sigma\{K_1\epsilon_1^{\rho_1}\epsilon_2^{\rho_2}\dots\epsilon_\mu^{\rho_\mu} + K_2\epsilon_1^{\sigma_1}\epsilon_2^{\sigma_2}\dots\epsilon_\mu^{\sigma_\mu} + \dots\}$$
$$= K_1\Sigma\epsilon_1^{\rho_1}\epsilon_2^{\rho_2}\dots\epsilon_\mu^{\rho_\mu} + K_2\Sigma\epsilon_1^{\sigma_1}\epsilon_2^{\sigma_2}\dots\epsilon_\mu^{\sigma_\mu} + \dots,$$

where none of the indices on the right exceeds $p!-1$, and where $K_1, K_2, \dots$ are rational integral functions of the μ times $p!$ sums

$$\begin{array}{l}\Sigma\epsilon_1, \Sigma\epsilon_1^2, \dots \Sigma\epsilon_1^{p!},\\ \Sigma\epsilon_2, \Sigma\epsilon_2^2, \dots \Sigma\epsilon_2^{p!},\\ \cdot\quad\cdot\quad\cdot\quad\cdot\quad\cdot\quad\cdot\quad\cdot\quad\cdot\\ \Sigma\epsilon_\mu, \Sigma\epsilon_\mu^2, \dots \Sigma\epsilon_\mu^{p!},\end{array}$$

which are all rational integral invariants, and are themselves all included in the form $\Sigma\epsilon_1^{\nu_1}\epsilon_2^{\nu_2}\dots\epsilon_\mu^{\nu_\mu}$ for values of the indices not exceeding $p!$

Thus every sum $\Sigma\epsilon_1^{r_1}\epsilon_2^{r_2}\dots\epsilon_\mu^{r_\mu}$, and therefore (§ 151) every rational integral invariant, is a rational integral function of a finite number of rational integral invariants; viz. of those included in the form

$$\Sigma\epsilon_1^{\nu_1}\epsilon_2^{\nu_2}\dots\epsilon_\mu^{\nu_\mu}$$

for values of the indices none of which exceeds $p!$, and which are indeed all less than $p!$ except that one of them may be equal to $p!$ when all the rest are zero.

It is well to repeat that the summation is to be taken as including $p!$ terms, one corresponding to every permutation of the p roots.

As already pointed out in § 151, it must not be supposed that we have here the exact number of irreducible invariants, of which all other invariants are rational integral functions, or the forms of invariants which are irreducible. The number of the invariants in terms of which all invariants are here shown to be capable of rational integral expression is, for quantics of low orders to which Gordan's method of transvectants and the arithmetical method of the last chapter have been applied, vastly in excess of the necessities. Moreover, no precise number is really assigned at all by the above reasoning; for even when the elemental products $\epsilon_1, \epsilon_2, \dots \epsilon_\mu$ are known for any quantic we have still no information as to how many of the sums $\Sigma\epsilon_1^{\nu_1}\epsilon_2^{\nu_2}\dots\epsilon_\mu^{\nu_\mu}$ vanish identically.

But a finite number of expressions has been definitely specified, all non-vanishing individuals among which are invariants, and in terms of which all other invariants can be rationally and integrally expressed. That some of these only are strictly irreducible invariants, while the rest are rational integral functions of them, does not affect the argument that all invariants are rational integral functions of a finite irreducible system. A selection from a finite system is itself finite.

A modification of Hilbert's method has been proposed by Kempe. He succeeds in using a more readily exhibited system of products of differences in place of the elemental products contemplated in this chapter. See his paper 'On Regular Difference Terms,' *Proc. Lond. Math. Soc.* Vol. XXV. p. 343.

154. **The cubic and quartic.** Little is taught us as to the invariants of quantics of particular orders by exhibiting the method in their particular cases, but for the light thrown on the method itself we exemplify it in the cases of the cubic and quartic.

For the cubic $(a, b, c, d)(x, y)^3$, whose roots are α, β, γ, any invariant is a numerical multiple of

$$\Sigma a^i(\beta-\gamma)^r(\gamma-\alpha)^s(\alpha-\beta)^t,$$

where $i=s+t=t+r=r+s$. Of these equations (§ 150, Ex. 1) the only simple set of solutions is $r=s=t=1, i=2$. Thus the only elemental product is

$$\epsilon = a^2(\beta-\gamma)(\gamma-\alpha)(\alpha-\beta).$$

The 3! permutations of α, β, γ in this give three products each equal to ϵ and three equal to $-\epsilon$. Thus the equation with invariant coefficients satisfied by ϵ is

$$\{\epsilon^2-a^4(\beta-\gamma)^2(\gamma-\alpha)^2(\alpha-\beta)^2\}^3=0.$$

All irreducible invariants are then included among

$$\Sigma\epsilon,\ \Sigma\epsilon^2,\ \Sigma\epsilon^3,\ \Sigma\epsilon^4,\ \Sigma\epsilon^5,\ \Sigma\epsilon^6,$$

of which the first, third and fifth vanish, while the second, fourth and sixth are

$$6\epsilon^2,\ 6\epsilon^4,\ 6\epsilon^6.$$

Of these the second and third are numerical multiples of powers of the first. Thus $6\epsilon^2$, or, say,

$$\epsilon^2 = a^4(\beta-\gamma)^2(\gamma-a)^2(a-\beta)^2,$$

is the only irreducible invariant of the cubic.

For the quartic $(a, b, c, d, e)(x, y)^4$, whose roots are a, β, γ, δ, invariants have the form

$$\Sigma a^i(\beta-\gamma)^r(\gamma-a)^s(a-\beta)^t(a-\delta)^{r'}(\beta-\delta)^{s'}(\gamma-\delta)^{t'},$$

where $i = s+t+r' = t+r+s' = r+s+t' = r'+s'+t'$,

of which the simple sets of solutions are given in § 150, Ex. 2, and tell us that the elemental products are

$$\epsilon_1 = a(\beta-\gamma)(a-\delta),$$
$$\epsilon_2 = a(\gamma-a)(\beta-\delta),$$
$$\epsilon_3 = a(a-\beta)(\gamma-\delta),$$

These are, it will be noticed, as is *not* the case in general for the ϵ's corresponding to higher quantics, of one type, and are the au, av, aw of § 80.

The 4 ! permutational values of ϵ_1 are

$$au,\ av,\ aw,\ -au,\ -av,\ -aw$$

each four times repeated; and the values of ϵ_2 and ϵ_3 are the same in different orders.

The equation with invariant coefficients whose roots are the 24 values of either ϵ_1 or ϵ_2 or ϵ_3 is (§ 81, Ex. 5)

$$\{(\epsilon^3-12I\epsilon+a^3uvw)(\epsilon^3-12I\epsilon-a^3uvw)\}^4 = 0. \quad \ldots(1)$$

The irreducible invariants are included in the finite number like

$$\Sigma\epsilon_1^{\lambda}\epsilon_2^{\mu}\epsilon_3^{\nu},$$

where neither of λ, μ, ν exceeds 24, and where if either one is 24 the other two vanish.

This example, then, affords an instance of the great excess over the number of irreducible invariants of the finite number of invariants among which they are included according to the present investigation. For we know from previous chapters that the only really irreducible invariants are

$$\Sigma\epsilon_1^2 = \Sigma\epsilon_2^2 = \Sigma\epsilon_3^2 = 8a^2(u^2+v^2+w^2)$$

and

$$\Sigma\epsilon_1^2\epsilon_2 = \Sigma\epsilon_2^2\epsilon_3 = \Sigma\epsilon_3^2\epsilon_1 = -\Sigma\epsilon_1\epsilon_2^2 = -\Sigma\epsilon_2\epsilon_3^2 = -\Sigma\epsilon_3\epsilon_1^2$$
$$= 4a^3\{u^2(v-w)+v^2(w-u)+w^2(u-v)\}.$$

It also affords an illustration of the care which must be

taken to attach the right meaning (see § 151) to the summation Σ. If in $\Sigma\epsilon_1^2\epsilon_2$, instead of taking this as meaning the sum of 24 terms obtained by permuting the roots as they occur in $\epsilon_1^2\epsilon_2$ in all possible ways, we had wrongly taken it as meaning that ϵ_1 is to be given its 24 (or its 6 essentially different) values, and ϵ_2 similarly, we should have had a sum of 24^2 (or 6^2) terms which vanishes identically, and should not have obtained the, in fact irreducible, invariant

$$a^3\{u^2(v-w)+v^2(w-u)+w^2(u-v)\}$$

at all. Or, if we had taken it as meaning the sum of the 6.5 terms $\epsilon^2\epsilon'$, where ϵ and ϵ' are two different roots of the equation (1) for ϵ_1 or for ϵ_2, the same failure would have resulted.

155. To secure clearness we have in the last four articles restricted our field of investigation as much as possible, and have confined attention to *invariants*, and to invariants of a single binary quantic only. Neither Gordan's theorem, however, nor Hilbert's line of argument is of such restricted application.

Equal fulness of treatment is unnecessary in the next two articles, which deal respectively with the case of covariants of a single binary quantic and the general case of covariants and invariants of more binary quantics than one.

156. **The number of irreducible covariants and invariants of a binary quantic is finite.** Let us use the word covariant as including invariant as a particular case, and also as including the quantic itself.

Any covariant of the binary p-ic

$$(a_0, a_1, a_2, \dots a_p)(x, y)^p$$

whose roots are $\alpha_1, \alpha_2, \alpha_3, \dots \alpha_p$ is, by Chapter V, of the form

$$\Sigma . a_0^i(x-\alpha_1 y)^{m_1}(x-\alpha_2 y)^{m_2}\dots(x-\alpha_p y)^{m_p} . (\alpha_1-\alpha_2)^{n_{12}}(\alpha_1-\alpha_3)^{n_{13}}(\alpha_2-\alpha_3)^{n_{23}}\dots,$$

where the positive integers, or some of them zeros,

$$m_1, m_2, \dots m_p, n_{12}, n_{13}, n_{23}, \dots$$

satisfy the Diophantine equations

$$\begin{aligned}
\varpi &= m_1+m_2+m_3+\dots+m_p,\\
i &= m_1+n_{12}+n_{13}+\dots+n_{1p}\\
&= m_2+n_{12}+n_{23}+\dots+n_{2p}\\
&= m_3+n_{13}+n_{23}+\dots+n_{3p}\\
&\quad \cdot\quad\cdot\quad\cdot\quad\cdot\quad\cdot\quad\cdot\quad\cdot\\
&= m_p+n_{1p}+n_{2p}+\dots+n_{p-1,p},
\end{aligned}$$

or is a linear function of such sums for the same values of i and ϖ; and all sums of this form are covariants. In particular, those for which the m's are all zero are invariants, and those for which the n's are all zero are powers of the p-ic itself.

Now by § 150 (v) the number of simple sets of solutions of these Diophantine equations for i, ϖ and the m's and n's is finite. Every product, such as that under the Σ above, is then a product of powers of elemental products of the same form and with the same properties.

If these elemental products are called $\eta_1, \eta_2, \ldots \eta_\mu$, then, exactly as in § 152, these severally are roots of equations of degree $p\,!$, in each of which the coefficient of the first term is unity, and the other coefficients are covariants which are rational integral functions, in the first case of $\Sigma\eta_1$, $\Sigma\eta_1^2, \ldots \Sigma\eta_1^{p!}$, in the second case of $\Sigma\eta_2$, $\Sigma\eta_2^2, \ldots \Sigma\eta_2^{p!}$, &c., &c. Hence, as in § 153, all covariants can be expressed rationally and integrally in terms of covariants included in the limited class

$$\Sigma\eta_1^{\nu_1}\eta_2^{\nu_2}\ldots\eta_\mu^{\nu_\mu},$$

where neither of the indices exceeds $p\,!$, and none is in fact so great as $p\,!$ unless all the others vanish.

Remark that, the number of irreducible covariants (including invariants) being finite, the number of irreducible seminvariants (including invariants) is also finite. For, if any covariant is a rational integral function of other covariants, the coefficient of the highest power of x in it is that same rational integral function of those of them which are free from x (i.e. the invariants among them) and the coefficients of the highest powers of x in the rest.

Ex. 4. In the case of the cubic the elemental products are

$$a(x-\alpha y)(x-\beta y)(x-\gamma y),$$

$$a^2(\beta-\gamma)(\gamma-\alpha)(\alpha-\beta),$$

and $\quad a(x-\alpha y)(\beta-\gamma),\ a(x-\beta y)(\gamma-\alpha),\ a(x-\gamma y)(\alpha-\beta).$

157. **Several binary quantics.** The proof that all covariants and invariants of a finite number of binary quantics are rational integral functions of a finite number of covariants and invariants of the system is similar.

For a system of a finite number of binary quantics whose leading coefficients are a_0, a_0', ..., and whose roots are $\alpha_1, \alpha_2, \ldots \alpha_p$ in the case of the first, $\alpha_1', \alpha_2', \ldots \alpha'_{p'}$ in the case of the second, and so on, the general expression for covariants of which all other covariants are linear functions of one degree and order is of the form

$$\Sigma \{ a_0{}^i a_0'{}^{i'} \dots \Pi (x - ay) . \Pi (x - a'y) \dots$$
$$\Pi (a_r - a_s) . \Pi (a_r' - a_s') \dots \Pi (a_r - a_s') \dots \},$$

where $\Pi (x - ay)$ denotes a product of a number of the differences $x - a_1 y$, $x - a_2 y$, ... $x - a_p y$ and their powers, $\Pi (x - a'y)$ a product of a number of the differences $x - a_1'y$, $x - a_2'y$, ... $x - a'_{p'} y$ and their powers, $\Pi (a_r - a_s)$, $\Pi (a_r' - a_s')$, &c., products of numbers of differences between two roots of the first, second, &c., quantics and powers of such differences, and $\Pi (a_r - a_s')$, &c., products of differences and powers of differences between roots belonging to different quantics of the system. Also, in a product under the Σ, all roots $a_1, a_2, \dots a_p$ of the first quantic occur in the same number i of factors, all roots $a_1', a_2', \dots a'_{p'}$ of the second quantic occur in the same number i' of factors, and so on. The summation Σ consists of $p!\, p'! \dots$ terms at most, obtained by permuting the p roots $a_1, a_2, \dots a_p$, the p' roots $a_1', a_2', \dots a'_{p'}$, &c., in all possible ways.

The conditions as to degrees in the various a's, a''s, &c., are expressed by $p + p' + \dots$ linear Diophantine equations in $i, i', \dots$ and the exponents of powers of differences; and ϖ, the order in x, y, is determined by another sum of the exponents. Now the whole system of $p + p' + \dots + 1$ equations in $i, i', \dots, \varpi$ and the exponents has, by § 150 (v), only a finite number of simple sets of solutions. To each simple set of solutions corresponds an elemental product. If these elemental products are $\omega_1, \omega_2, \omega_3, \dots$, the general Σ above is, as before, capable of expression in the form $\Sigma \omega_1{}^{r_1} \omega_2{}^{r_2} \omega_3{}^{r_3} \dots$.

Also, precisely as before, every elemental product ω_1 satisfies an equation of finite degree, in no case exceeding $p!\, p'! \dots$, whose coefficients, after the first which is unity, are rational integral functions of a finite number of sums of powers of ω_1 and the results of permuting among themselves the various roots in ω_1. Hence, as in earlier cases, the sum

$$\Sigma \omega_1{}^{r_1} \omega_2{}^{r_2} \omega_3{}^{r_3} \dots$$

can be expressed rationally and integrally in terms of the finite number of like sums in which $r_1, r_2, r_3, \dots$ do not exceed definite numbers; and these like sums are all rational integral covariants and invariants. All rational integral covariants and invariants of a system of binary quantics are then rational integral functions of a finite number of such concomitants of the system.

In particular, all invariants of the system are rational integral functions of a finite number of invariants. For if an invariant, free from the variables, is a rational integral function of invariants and covariants, we obtain, upon putting the variables equal to zero in the identity of the invariant and the function, an identity in which all the covariants are replaced by zeros while the invariants alone remain.

157 (*bis*). **Hilbert's second proof.** This depends on the following far-reaching theorem:

If σ_n is any system whatever of rational integral functions of n letters $x_1, x_2, \ldots x_n$, then it is possible to choose in the system σ_n a finite number $F_1, F_2, \ldots F_\mu$ of the functions such that every function F of the system is a sum $A_1F_1 + A_2F_2 + \ldots + A_\mu F_\mu$, where $A_1, A_2, \ldots A_\mu$, or such of them as are not constants or zero, are rational integral functions of $x_1, x_2, \ldots x_n$.

We will confine attention to *homogeneous* functions, or say *forms*, in $x_1, x_2, \ldots x_n$; and in so doing shall lose no generality. For, when we have proved the theorem for systems of homogeneous forms in n letters, where n is any number, we may put 1 for x_n, and thus be sure that it holds for not necessarily homogeneous functions of $n-1$ letters, where $n-1$ is any number.

There is no limitation whatever to the nature of the definite laws which the forms F of σ_n are required to obey. It suffices to know that a form written down at will either definitely is or definitely is not an F.

First notice that the theorem holds for a system σ_1 in one variable x_1. The forms included in σ_1 are numerical multiples of powers of x_1, and it suffices to take a single F_1, one of lowest degree.

We will now assume the theorem true for every σ_{n-1} in $x_1, x_2, \ldots x_{n-1}$, and prove it true for every σ_n in $x_1, x_2, \ldots x_n$.

In a chosen σ_n take a form F_1 of lowest (or any) degree r. If it does not possess an $x_n{}^r$ term apply to F_1, and to the entire system, a transformation

$$x_1 = x_1' + \lambda_1 x_n', \; x_2 = x_2' + \lambda_2 x_n', \ldots$$
$$x_{n-1} = x_{n-1}' + \lambda_{n-1} x_n', \; x_n = \lambda_n x_n',$$

with definite numerical values of $\lambda_1, \lambda_2, \ldots \lambda_n$ which are not values of $x_1, x_2, \ldots x_n$ making $F_1 = 0$. F_1 is thus given a term which is a numerical multiple of $x_n'^r$. Now remove accents.

By division every F as now written can be given the form

$$F = PF_1 + Qx_n{}^{r-1} + Rx_n{}^{r-2} + \ldots + Z,$$

where P is a form in the new $x_1, x_2, \ldots x_n$, and $Q, R, \ldots Z$ forms in the new $x_1, x_2, \ldots x_{n-1}$ only.

For all the forms F in σ_n, the Q's constitute a σ_{n-1}. By our assumption there is a finite number $Q_2, Q_3, \dots Q_\alpha$ of these Q's, such that every other Q is a sum

$$A_2Q_2 + A_3Q_3 + \dots + A_\alpha Q_\alpha.$$

Thus, if Q_2 occurs in F_2, Q_3 in F_3, and so on, and $P_2, P_3, \dots$ are the corresponding P's, every F is such that a relation holds like

$$F - PF_1 = A_2(F_2 - P_2F_1) + A_3(F_3 - P_3F_1) + \dots$$
$$+ A_\alpha(F_\alpha - P_\alpha F_1) + R'x_n^{r-2} + S'x_n^{r-3} + \dots + Z',$$

i.e. is of the form

$$F = A_1F_1 + A_2F_2 + \dots + A_\alpha F_\alpha + Rx_n^{r-2} + Sx_n^{r-3} + \dots + Z,$$

where $R, S, \dots Z$ are free from x_n.

Here the R's for different forms F in σ_n constitute a σ_{n-1}. By our assumption there is a finite number of them,

$$R_{\alpha+1}, R_{\alpha+2}, \dots R_\beta,$$

such that every other is a sum

$$A_{\alpha+1}R_{\alpha+1} + A_{\alpha+2}R_{\alpha+2} + \dots + A_\beta R_\beta.$$

Hence, by a repetition of the above argument, every F is a sum

$$F = A_1F_1 + A_2F_2 + \dots + A_\alpha F_\alpha + A_{\alpha+1}F_{\alpha+1} + \dots + A_\beta F_\beta$$
$$+ Sx_n^{r-3} + Tx_n^{r-4} + \dots + Z,$$

with a new $A_1, A_2, \dots A_\alpha$, and $S, T, \dots Z$.

Again the S's here constitute a σ_{n-1}, and we can repeat the same argument; and so on. Presently we find that every F in σ_n is a sum

$$F = A_1F_1 + A_2F_2 + \dots + A_\lambda F_\lambda + Z,$$

where $F_1, F_2, \dots F_\lambda$ are forms in σ_n, and Z is a form in $x_1, x_2, \dots x_{n-1}$ only. The forms Z constitute a σ_{n-1}; and one more repetition of the argument tells us that there is a finite number of forms $F_1, F_2, \dots F_\mu$ in σ_n such that every other form in σ_n is a sum

$$F = A_1F_1 + A_2F_2 + \dots + A_\mu F_\mu.$$

Thus if the theorem is true for every σ_{n-1} it is for every σ_n; and, as we have seen that it is true for every σ_1, the mathematical induction proving its universal truth is provided.

157 (*ter*). Now all invariants I of $(a_0, a_1, \dots a_p)(x, y)^p$ constitute a system σ_{p+1} of forms in $a_0, a_1, \dots a_p$. There is then a finite number of the invariants, $I_1, I_2, \dots I_\mu$, such that every other invariant can be written

$$I = A_1I_1 + A_2I_2 + \dots + A_\mu I_\mu,$$

where $A_1, A_2, \dots A_\mu$ are forms in $a_0, a_1, \dots a_p$, but not necessarily invariants. They are however isobaric, and obey the degree and weight condition $\eta = ip - 2w = 0$ appropriate to invariants, because I and $I_1, I_2, \dots I_p$ are and do.

Now, putting $\eta = 0$ in § 128, Ex. 8, we know that the operator

$$X \equiv \left(1 - \frac{O\Omega}{1.2}\right)\left(1 - \frac{O\Omega}{2.3}\right)\dots\left(1 - \frac{O\Omega}{w(w+1)}\right)$$

produces an invariant from any gradient for which $\eta = 0$ which it does not annihilate. Remembering that I and $I_1, I_2, \dots I_\mu$ are annihilated by Ω and by O, we obtain by operating with it on the identity above

$$I = I_1 XA_1 + I_2 XA_2 + \dots + I_\mu XA_\mu$$
$$= J_1 I_1 + J_2 I_2 + \dots + J_\mu I_\mu,$$

where $J_1, J_2, \dots J_\mu$ are invariants, not all at any rate vanishing.

Thus every invariant I which is not one of $I_1, I_2, \dots I_\mu$ is reducible. It is in fact reducible in terms of $I_1, I_2, \dots I_\mu$. For $J_1, J_2, \dots J_\mu$ may be taken for I and expressed as sums of invariant multiples of $I_1, I_2, \dots I_\mu$; so can the invariants $J_1', J_2', \dots$ which occur as coefficients of $I_1, I_2, \dots I_\mu$ in the expressions for the J's; and so on, till at a last stage degrees have been reduced so low that the multipliers are numerical.

Accordingly there is only a finite system of irreducible invariants, namely the lowest base system for which Hilbert's theorem of § 157 (*bis*) holds.

This proof has been given for the case of one binary p-ic. It however applies equally to invariants of a system of binary quantics. We have only (§ 132) in the operator X to take $\Sigma\Omega$ and ΣO in place of Ω and O.

In particular it applies to the invariants of a system comprising one or more binary quantics and a linear form $y'x - x'y$, i.e. (§ 69) to covariants (including invariants) of the one or more quantics. Thus all covariants and invariants of a binary quantic or system of binary quantics can be rationally and integrally expressed in terms of a finite base system $K_1, K_2, \dots K_\nu$ of covariants and invariants.

The usual completion of the proof of the finiteness of the system of irreducibles for *ternary* and *higher* quantics depends on the following theorem—see Ex. 6 below:

If M is the modulus or determinant of the general scheme of linear transformation (§ 2), *and if* $[M]$ *is the operator deduced from M by replacing in it l, &c., by $\partial/\partial l$, &c., then, if we take any product of coefficients and variables in a* transformed *quantic or quantics, or any linear function of such products with the same order ϖ and degree or degrees, if we express it in terms of the coefficients and variables in the* untransformed *quantic or quantics and the constants l, &c., of* *the transformation, if we now multiply it by a high enough integral power of M to make it integral in l, &c., and then operate on what is obtained with [M] just enough times to obtain a result free from l, &c., this result will be a covariant (or invariant if* $\varpi = 0$*), unless it vanishes.*

The application to invariants is as follows. Having

$$I = A_1 I_1 + A_2 I_2 + \ldots + A_\mu I_\mu,$$

substitute, on both sides, transformed coefficients for untransformed, and go through the above processes. In the end $I, I_1, I_2, \ldots I_\mu$ figure as before the substitution, but for numerical multipliers, while invariants and zeros replace $A_1, A_2, \ldots A_\mu$.

Ex. 5. If the linear transformation $x = lX + \ldots, \ldots$, of determinant M, is the result of a sequence of transformations

$$x = l_1 x_1 + \ldots, \ldots \text{ and } x_1 = l_2 X + \ldots, \ldots,$$

of determinants M_1, M_2, prove that $M = M_1 M_2$ and $[M_2] = M_1 [M]$.

Ex. 6. If G, a function of degree i and order ϖ in the final coefficients and variables, is called $G(l, \ldots)$ when expressed in terms of $l, \ldots$ and the original coefficients and variables, and $G(l_2, \ldots)$ when expressed in terms of $l_2, \ldots$ and the intermediate coefficients and variables, prove that

$$[M]^m \{M^n G(l, \ldots)\} = M_1^{n-m} [M_2]^m \{M_2^n G(l_2, \ldots)\};$$

and hence prove the theorem of invariancy, just stated, for the linear transformation $x = l_1 x_1 + \ldots, \ldots$, which may be general.

157 (iv). **Syzygies and syzygants.** Irreducible invariants (or covariants and invariants) are in general too numerous to be algebraically independent. We can find rational integral algebraic functions of them which vanish identically when expressed in terms of the coefficients (and variables). Such a function is called a *syzygant*, and a relation *syzygant* = 0 is called a *syzygy*.

A syzygant (in invariants, say) multiplied by an invariant is still a syzygant, and so too is a sum of products of syzygants and invariants. A direct application of Hilbert's theorem (§ 157 *bis*) to syzygants, regarded as a class of (non-homogeneous) functions of the finite number of invariants, shows that all syzygants can be expressed as sums of invariant multiples of a finite number of syzygants, i.e that irreducible syzygants are finite in number.

Irreducible syzygants may be connected, as functions of the invariants, by syzygies of the second order. There may also be syzygies of the third order among syzygants of the second order; and so on. But it has been shown that the succession of orders of syzygants must terminate.

CHAPTER X

PROTOMORPHS, ETC.

158. **Recapitulation.** We have seen in Chapter VI that the leading coefficient, that of the highest power of x, in any covariant of

$$u \equiv (a_0, a_1, a_2, \dots a_p)\,(x, y)^p$$

is a seminvariant, i. e. is annihilated by

$$\Omega \equiv a_0 \frac{\partial}{\partial a_1} + 2a_1 \frac{\partial}{\partial a_2} + \dots + pa_{p-1} \frac{\partial}{\partial a_p},$$

and consequently possesses the half invariant property of being invariantic for such linear substitutions as

$$x = X + mY, \quad y = Y.$$

It has also been seen that conversely

$$S\,(a_0, a_1, a_2, \dots a_p),$$

any gradient of extent not exceeding p which is such as to satisfy the differential equation

$$\Omega S = 0,$$

and which is consequently a seminvariant, is the leading coefficient of a covariant whose order ϖ in x, y is given in terms of p and i and w, the degree and weight of S, by the relation

$$\varpi = ip - 2w;$$

in fact, that the covariant in question may be written

$$x^{ip-2w} e^{\frac{y}{x} O}\, S\,(a_0, a_1, a_2, \dots a_p),$$

where $$O \equiv pa_1 \frac{\partial}{\partial a_0} + (p-1)\,a_2 \frac{\partial}{\partial a_1} + \dots + a_p \frac{\partial}{\partial a_{p-1}}.$$

If $\varpi = 0$, the seminvariant is an invariant.

Thus covariants, including invariants as a particular case, and seminvariants, also including invariants as a particular case, are equally numerous, and correspond one to another. If any relation or syzygy connects certain covariants, the same syzygy connects their seminvariant leaders, and vice versa.

Another expression for the same covariant, whose leader is the seminvariant $S(a_0, a_1, a_2, \dots a_p)$, is

$$(-1)^w y^{ip-2w} e^{\frac{x}{y}\Omega} S(a_p, a_{p-1}, a_{p-2}, \dots a_0),$$

where $S(a_p, a_{p-1}, a_{p-2}, \dots a_0)$ is the anti-seminvariant obtained by interchanging a_0 and a_p, a_1 and a_{p-1}, &c. in the seminvariant $S(a_0, a_1, a_2, \dots a_p)$.

159. **Elimination of x between u and its successive derivatives with regard to x.** Two interesting conclusions at once follow from the results of Chapter VI.

Of these the first is that if in any seminvariant

$$S(a_0, a_1, a_2, \dots a_p)$$

of u we replace

a_p by u, i.e. by $(a_0, a_1, a_2, \dots a_p)(x, y)^p$, which call α_p,

a_{p-1} by $\frac{1}{p}\frac{\partial u}{\partial x}$, i.e. by $(a_0, a_1, a_2, \dots a_{p-1})(x, y)^{p-1}$, which call α_{p-1},

. . . .

a_2 by $\frac{1}{p(p-1)\dots 3}\frac{\partial^{p-2}u}{\partial x^{p-2}}$, i.e. by $a_0x^2 + 2a_1xy + a_2y^2$, which call α_2,

a_1 by $\frac{1}{p(p-1)\dots 3.2}\frac{\partial^{p-1}u}{\partial x^{p-1}}$, i.e. by $a_0x + a_1y$, which call α_1,

a_0 by $\frac{1}{p(p-1)\dots 3.2.1}\frac{\partial^p u}{\partial x^p}$, i.e. by a_0, which call α_0,

no x appears in the result, which is merely the seminvariant itself multiplied by y^w, where w is its weight.

The result of substitution is annihilated by

$$\alpha_0\frac{\partial}{\partial \alpha_1} + 2\alpha_1\frac{\partial}{\partial \alpha_2} + 3\alpha_2\frac{\partial}{\partial \alpha_3} + \dots + p\alpha_{p-1}\frac{\partial}{\partial \alpha_p}.$$

Now, writing u_r for $\partial^r u/\partial x^r$, for every value of r from 1 to p inclusive, we see that this is

$$u_p\frac{\partial}{\partial u_{p-1}} + u_{p-1}\frac{\partial}{\partial u_{p-2}} + u_{p-2}\frac{\partial}{\partial u_{p-3}} + \dots + u_1\frac{\partial}{\partial u},$$

which, when it operates on a function of $u, u_1, u_2, \dots u_p$, is merely $\partial/\partial x$. The annihilation tells us then that the result of substitution is free from x. What does not vanish when the substitution is made in a seminvariant is clearly y^w into that seminvariant; for weight is order in x, y in the result, and the form of result independent of x is the form we should get by putting $x = 0$ first and then making the substitutions.

The intimate connexion of the theory of seminvariants with that of elimination between u and its x-derivatives is now apparent. For instance, from § 137 we conclude that, if u is any rational integral function of order p in x, the number of linearly independent rational integral functions of u and its successive derivatives with regard to x, which are of degree i in the coefficients and free from x, is $(\frac{1}{2}ip\,;\,i, p)$ or $(\frac{1}{2}ip-\frac{1}{2}\,;\,i, p)$, according as ip is even or odd. And again, from known facts as to numbers of irreducible seminvariants of binary quantics of the first few orders we obtain that, for the values 1, 2, 3, 4, 5 of p, the numbers of rational integral functions of some or all of a p-ic function of x and its successive derivatives, which are independent of x, and in terms of which all such rational integral functions independent of x can be rationally and integrally expressed, are 1, 2, 4, 5, 23 respectively.

Once more, from § 128 or from § 100, we gather that any rational integral function of u, a p-ic in x, and its derivatives, which is throughout of degree i in u and the derivatives, and in every term of which the sum of the indices r for factors like $\partial^r u/\partial x^r$ is constant and equal to $ip-w$, can be written as the derivative with regard to x of a rational integral function of u and its successive derivatives if $ip-2w>0$.

Ex. 1. Integrate the differential equation

$$u\frac{d^4u}{dx^4}-\frac{du}{dx}\frac{d^3u}{dx^3}+\frac{1}{2}\left(\frac{d^2u}{dx^2}\right)^2=0.$$

Ans. $u=ax^4+4bx^3+6cx^2+4dx+e$, where $ae-4bd+3c^2=0$.

Ex. 2. If $u=ax^3+3bx^2+3cx+d$, express $\int u\left(\frac{d^2u}{dx^2}\right)^4dx$ rationally and integrally in terms of u, $\frac{du}{dx}, \frac{d^2u}{dx^2}, \frac{d^3u}{dx^3}$.

Ans. Here $ip-2w=1$. Assume the most general form and determine the arbitrary coefficients by operating with d/dx.

160. **Covariants obtained by substitution of x-derivatives.** The second important conclusion referred to at the outset of the preceding article appears to be due to Faà de Bruno (*Am. J.* III). It is that if we make the same substitutions as in the preceding article for $a_0, a_1, a_2, \ldots a_p$ in

$$S(a_p, a_{p-1}, a_{p-2}, \ldots a_0),$$

the anti-seminvariant obtained by interchanging a_0 and a_p, a_1 and a_{p-1}, &c., in a seminvariant $S(a_0, a_1, a_2, \ldots a_p)$ of weight w and degree i, the result obtained will be the covariant of which that seminvariant is the leader multiplied by $(-y)^w$.

Noticing that the substitution of α_r for a_r is that of $y^r A'_r$, where A'_r is the A_r of § 92 with x/y put for m, we see by § 93, bearing in mind the isobarism of weight $ip-w$ of

$$S(a_p, a_{p-1}, a_{p-2}, \dots a_0),$$

that the result of the substitution is

$$y^{ip-w} e^{\frac{x}{y}\Omega} S(a_p, a_{p-1}, a_{p-2}, \dots a_0).$$

Now by § 109, since $(-1)^w S(a_p, a_{p-1}, \dots a_0)$ is the last coefficient in the covariant which $S(a_0, a_1, a_2, \dots a_p)$ leads, the covariant going with S is

$$(-1)^w y^{ip-2w} e^{\frac{x}{y}\Omega} S(a_p, a_{p-1}, a_{p-2}, \dots a_0).$$

Of these two expressions the former is $(-y)^w$ times the latter.

Thus from any seminvariant a mere substitution derives the corresponding covariant.

If the seminvariant is an invariant, the substitution has the effect only of multiplying it by $(-1)^w y^{ip-w}$, i.e. by $(-y)^w$, since $ip-2w=0$ for an invariant. This accords with the result of § 159.

161. **A seminvariant is given by certain of its terms.** In the substitution of § 159 put $-a_1/a_0$ for x, and 1 for y, i.e. for $a_0, a_1, a_2, \dots a_p$ substitute

$$a_0' \equiv a_0,$$

$$a_1' \equiv 0,$$

$$a_2' \equiv a_2 - \frac{a_1^2}{a_0},$$

$$a_3' \equiv a_3 - 3\frac{a_1}{a_0}a_2 + 2\frac{a_1^3}{a_0^2},$$

$$a_4' \equiv a_4 - 4\frac{a_1}{a_0}a_3 + 6\frac{a_1^2}{a_0^2}a_2 - 3\frac{a_1^4}{a_0^3},$$

$$\cdot \quad \cdot \quad \cdot \quad \cdot \quad \cdot \quad \cdot \quad \cdot \quad \cdot \quad \cdot \quad \cdot$$

$$a_p' \equiv (a_p, a_{p-1}, a_{p-2}, \dots a_0)\left(1, -\frac{a_1}{a_0}\right)^p.$$

The result of § 159 tells us that

$$S(a_0, a_1, a_2, a_3, \dots a_p) = S(a_0', 0, a_2', a_3', \dots a_p'),$$

where S denotes any seminvariant, or, in particular, invariant.

Thus all rational integral seminvariants are rational integral functions of the p expressions a_0' (i.e. a_0), $a_2', a_3', \dots a_p'$. These expressions are all integral in $a_1, a_2, \dots a_p$, but, after the first, are fractional in a_0. They are seminvariants, fractional after the first, for it is easy to see that they are all annihilated by Ω. This will appear in another light presently.

It follows that if we know the terms free from a_1 in any seminvariant or invariant, we know the whole expression of that seminvariant or invariant. To find this whole expression we have merely to write the values of $a_2', a_3', \ldots a_p'$ instead of $a_2, a_3, \ldots a_p$ in the given terms. We shall see presently that this substitution may be effected by differential operation.

We shall also notice later a means of obtaining the terms free from a_1 in *invariants*.

The search for rational integral seminvariants and invariants may be regarded as the search for rational integral homogeneous isobaric functions of $a_0, a_2', a_3', \ldots a_p'$, which, when the full values of $a_2', a_3', \ldots a_p'$ are substituted in them, are integral in a_0.

Ex. 3. Given $a^2d^2+4ac^3$, the terms free from b in the discriminant of the cubic $(a, b, c, d)(x, y)^3$ (cf. Chap. VI, Ex. 36), obtain the full expression for the discriminant.

Ex. 4. Verify that $a_0a_2'a_4'-a_0a_3'^2-a_2'^3$

$$= a_0a_2a_4+2a_1a_2a_3-a_0a_3^2-a_1^2a_4-a_2^3.$$

Ex. 5. No seminvariant has a_1 for a factor.

Ex. 6. The number of linearly independent seminvariants of type w, i of a p-ic, whose terms free from a_1 are integral, and whose other terms are integral in $a_1, a_2, a_3, \ldots a_p$ though not necessarily in a_0, is

$$(w\,;\, i, p)-(w-1\,;\, i-1, p).$$

Ans. Since $(w-1\,;\, i-1, p)$ is the number of products of type w, i which involve a_1, this difference is the number of products of the type of $a_0, a_2', a_3', \ldots a_p'$.

162. **Coefficients of quantic deprived of its second term are seminvariants.** If we inspect the expressions for

$$a_0', a_2', a_3', \ldots a_p'$$

in the last article, we notice that they are the coefficients of $X^p, X^{p-2}Y^2, X^{p-3}Y^3, \ldots Y^p$ in the result of depriving the p-ic

$$(a_0, a_1, a_2, \ldots a_p)(x, y)^p$$

of its second term by the substitution

$$x = X-\frac{a_1}{a_0}Y, \quad y = Y,$$

of which the modulus is unity.

Now this substitution is one after which a seminvariant as well as an invariant persists in form, for it has the effect of altering all roots by the same addition a_1/a_0, and leaves the leading coefficient a_0 or a_0' unaltered.

We thus see clearly the meaning of the identity of the last article

$$S(a_0, a_1, a_2, a_3, \dots a_p) = S(a_0, 0, a_2', a_3', \dots a_p').$$

We also see clearly the reason of the fact that $a_2', a_3', \dots a_p'$ are themselves (fractional) seminvariants. For the roots of the transformed p-ic are

$$\alpha_1 + a_1/a_0,\ \alpha_2 + a_1/a_0, \dots \alpha_p + a_1/a_0,$$

where $\alpha_1, \alpha_2, \dots \alpha_p$ are the roots of the untransformed p-ic; and

$$\alpha_1 + \frac{a_1}{a_0} = \alpha_1 - \frac{\alpha_1 + \alpha_2 + \dots + \alpha_p}{p}$$

$$= \frac{(\alpha_1 - \alpha_2) + (\alpha_1 - \alpha_3) + \dots + (\alpha_1 - \alpha_p)}{p},$$

so that every root of the transformed is a function of the differences between roots of the untransformed; which necessitates that $a_2'/a_0, a_3'/a_0, \dots a_p'/a_0$, being symmetric functions of the roots of the transformed p-ic, are functions of differences of the roots of the untransformed, of course symmetric in these roots from their rationality. They are then (fractional) seminvariants of the p-ic.

163. **Completion of the theorem of § 42.** Consider the results of making $a_2', a_3', \dots a_p'$ integral by powers of a_0 as factors; and write

$$A_0 = a_0' = a_0,$$
$$A_2 = a_0 a_2' = a_0 a_2 - a_1^2,$$
$$A_3 = a_0^2 a_3' = a_0^2 a_3 - 3a_0 a_1 a_2 + 2a_1^3,$$
$$A_4 = a_0^3 a_4' = a_0^3 a_4 - 4a_0^2 a_1 a_3 + 6a_0 a_1^2 a_2 - 3a_1^4,$$
$$\cdots\cdots\cdots\cdots$$
$$A_p = a_0^{p-1} a_p' = a_0^{p-1} (a_p, a_{p-1}, a_{p-2}, \dots a_0)(1, -a_1/a_0)^p.$$

The degree of every one of these integral expressions is equal to its weight. They are all seminvariants, being annihilated by Ω.

The equality

$$S(a_0, a_1, a_2, a_3, \dots a_p) = S(a_0', 0, a_2', a_3', \dots a_p')$$

may now be written

$$S(a_0, a_1, a_2, a_3, \dots a_p) = S\left(a_0, 0, \frac{A_2}{a_0}, \frac{A_3}{a_0^2}, \dots \frac{A_p}{a_0^{p-1}}\right).$$

Let S be as usual of weight w and degree i. Notice that every non-vanishing argument on the right involves a_0 explicitly to the degree $1-r$, where r is its weight. Every product of i arguments on the right consequently involves a_0 to the power $i-w$, where w is its whole weight. Therefore upon multiplying through by a_0^{w-i} we obtain that

$$a_0^{w-i}S(a_0, a_1, a_2, a_3, \dots a_p) = S(1, 0, A_2, A_3, \dots A_p),$$

which is a rational integral function of $A_2, A_3, \dots A_p$ only.

We have here the completion of the theorem of § 42. It was there proved that a binary p-ic cannot have more than p algebraically independent covariants and invariants including itself, but that if $p-1$ distinct from the p-ic itself and independent of it and one another can be found, then all others must be capable of expression in terms of it and them. We have now proved that there actually are $p-1$ covariants distinct from the p-ic, namely, those whose leading coefficients are the seminvariants $A_2, A_3, \dots A_p$. These are certainly independent of one another and the p-ic; for in the series $a_0, A_2, A_3, \dots A_p$ each involves one of the coefficients $a_0, a_2, a_3, \dots a_p$ which is absent from all those which precede it. We have also shown that the expression for any rational integral seminvariant or invariant $S(a_0, a_1, a_2, \dots a_p)$ in terms of $a_0, A_2, A_3, \dots A_p$ is rational, and is integral in all but the first a_0, which it involves only in the form of the factor a_0^{-w+i}.

The expression of the covariant (or invariant) whose leading coefficient is S in terms of those whose leading coefficients are $a_0, A_2, A_3, \dots A_p$, of which the first is the p-ic itself, follows. The covariant whose leading coefficient is a seminvariant is unique (cf. §§ 111, 112). Now, if u is the p-ic, and K the covariant with leading coefficient $S(a_0, a_1, a_2, \dots a_p)$, the covariant whose leading coefficient is $a_0^{w-i}S(a_0, a_1, a_2, \dots a_p)$ is

$$u^{w-i}K.$$

Also, if $\alpha_2, \alpha_3, \dots \alpha_p$ are the covariants whose leading coefficients are $A_2, A_3, \dots A_p$,

$$S(1, 0, \alpha_2, \alpha_3, \dots \alpha_p)$$

is a covariant. For it is a rational integral function of covariants, and is of constant degree and weight throughout; and therefore is of constant order in x, y, since the degree and weight of A_r the leading coefficient of α_r are both r, and consequently the order $ip-2w$ of α_r is $r(p-2)$ so that the order of any product of α's which occurs is $w(p-2)$ where w is the constant weight. This covariant is the one whose leading coefficient is $S(1, 0, A_2, A_3, \dots A_p)$. Hence the identity of seminvariants

$$a_0^{w-i}S(a_0, a_1, a_2, a_3, \dots a_p) = S(1, 0, A_2, A_3, \dots A_p)$$

necessitates the identity of covariants

$$u^{w-i}K = S(1, 0, \alpha_2, \alpha_3, \dots \alpha_p).$$

In other words, any covariant or invariant can be expressed

as the result of dividing a rational integral function of $a_2, a_3, \dots a_p$ by the power u^{w-i} of u, where w and i are the weight and degree of the leading coefficient of the covariant in question.

In particular, any invariant $I(a_0, a_1, a_2, \dots a_p)$ is equivalent to

$$u^{-\frac{1}{2}i(p-2)} I(1, 0, a_2, a_3, \dots a_p);$$

for, in the case when K is an invariant, $ip = 2w$.

We have here reasoned for cases when $w \nless i$. The student can supply the slight modification of reasoning necessary when $w < i$. In such a case the result is best written

$$K = u^{i-w} S(1, 0, a_2, a_3, \dots a_p);$$

so that any covariant, whose leading coefficient is of smaller weight than degree, has a power of the quantic for a factor.

164. **A complete system of protomorphs is not unique.** The seminvariants $a_0, A_2, A_3, \dots A_p$, or

$$a_0, a_0 a_2', a_0^2 a_3', \dots a_0^{p-1} a_p',$$

do not stand alone among rational integral seminvariants as being a set of p in terms of which all others can be expressed rationally and integrally but for a power of the first, which may be a negative power, as factor.

A system of p seminvariants possessing this property is called a set of *protomorphic seminvariants* or *protomorphs*.

We proceed to see that an allowable system of protomorphs is composed of a_0 and any set of $p-1$ rational integral seminvariants $B_2, B_3, \dots B_p$, which are such that

B_2 is of weight 2 and involves a_2,
B_3 ,, 3 ,, a_3,
. . . .
B_p ,, p ,, a_p;

necessities which require that no coefficient a_r of the quantic occurs in a B with a lower suffix than r, and that a_r occurs in B_r multiplied by a power of a_0 only.

To see this, take any seminvariant, and, if a_p occurs in it, take the expression for B_p,

$$B_p = a_0^\lambda a_p + f(a_0, a_1, a_2, \dots a_{p-1}),$$

which gives

$$a_p = a_0^{-\lambda}\{B_p - f(a_0, a_1, a_2, \dots a_{p-1})\},$$

and substitute in the seminvariant this value for a_p. The seminvariant is then expressed as a rational function of B_p and $a_0, a_1, a_2, \dots a_{p-1}$, integral in all of them but a_0.

Again, for a_{p-1} substitute in like manner in terms of B_{p-1} and $a_0, a_1, a_2, \dots a_{p-2}$; and continue this process as long as possible. We thus obtain an expression for the seminvariant

$$S(a_0, a_1, a_2, \dots a_p) \equiv a_0^{-\mu} F(a_0, a_1, B_2, B_3, \dots B_p).$$

But a_1 cannot, as a matter of fact, enter in F. To see this operate on both sides with Ω, which annihilates S and $a_0, B_2, B_3, \dots B_p$. We obtain

$$0 = a_0^{-\mu} a_0 \frac{\partial}{\partial a_1} F(a_0, a_1, B_2, B_3, \dots B_p) = 0,$$

i.e.

$$\partial F / \partial a_1 = 0,$$

the differentiation being partial with regard to a_1 as it occurs explicitly in F. The conclusion is that it cannot so occur. It is proved then that

$$S(a_0, a_1, a_2, \dots a_p) = a_0^{-\mu} F(a_0, B_2, B_3, \dots B_p),$$

for some rational integral form of F and for some integral or zero value of μ.

Notice the two special conveniences of the protomorphs $A_2, A_3, \dots A_p$ of § 163. One is that the form of F for them is at once written down from the form of S; and the other that F does not involve a_0 explicitly. For these protomorphs weight, extent and degree are all equal. For others weight and extent only.

Protomorphs must not be confused with *irreducible* seminvariants. A complete system of irreducible seminvariants and invariants, proved to exist in the preceding chapter, is a system in terms of which all rational integral seminvariants can be rationally and integrally expressed, without the occurrence of a negative power of a_0 as factor.

165. **Protomorphs of lowest degrees.** The system of protomorphs which has been most used is a system

$$a_0, C_2, C_3, C_4, \dots C_p$$

in which each is of the lowest possible degree.

Those of even weights 2, 4, 6, ... are of the second degree; viz. the system of § 114

$$C_2 \equiv a_0 a_2 - a_1^2 \equiv A_2,$$

$$C_4 \equiv a_0 a_4 - 4a_1 a_3 + 3a_2^2,$$

$$C_6 \equiv a_0 a_6 - 6a_1 a_5 + 15a_2 a_4 - 10a_3^2,$$

. . . .

$$C_{2n} \equiv a_0 a_{2n} - \binom{2n}{1} a_1 a_{2n-1} + \binom{2n}{2} a_2 a_{2n-2} - \dots$$

$$+ (-1)^{n-1} \binom{2n}{n-1} a_{n-1} a_{n+1} + \frac{1}{2}(-1)^n \binom{2n}{n} a_n^2,$$

where $\binom{2n}{r}$ denotes the number of combinations of $2n$ things r together.

Observe that if $a_0, C_2, C_4, \dots C_{2n}$ all vanish, we obtain in succession $a_0 = 0, a_1 = 0, a_2 = 0, \dots a_n = 0$, so that, if $2n$ is the greatest even integer in p the order of a quantic, all invariants of that quantic vanish by § 26, Ex. 1. Hence also (cf. § 26, Ex. 2) all invariants vanish for a binary $(2n+1)$-ic if it and its covariants led by $C_2, C_4, \dots C_{2n}$ have a common factor; and all vanish for a $2n$-ic if it and its covariants led by $C_2, C_4, \dots C_{2n-2}$ have a common factor and if its invariant C_{2n} vanishes. (*Hilbert.*)

Ex. 7. In either of these cases all covariants have the same common factor. (*Hilbert.*)

Ex. 8. Conversely to § 26, Ex. 2, a binary $2n$-ic or $(2n+1)$-ic must have a linear factor raised to the $(n+1)$th power if all its invariants vanish. (*Hilbert.*)

Ans. Let $\varpi_1, \varpi_2, \dots$ be the orders of $G_1, G_2, \dots$ the covariants of a p-ic u which are led by $C_2, C_4, \dots$, and let μ be their L. C. M. If we form the eliminant of u and $k_1 G_1^{\mu/\varpi_1} + k_2 G_2^{\mu/\varpi_2} + \dots$, the coefficients of powers and products of $k_1, k_2, \dots$ in it are invariants (§§ 18, 45); and if these invariants vanish $G_1, G_2, \dots$ have all a factor of u in common, so that, &c.

Ex. 9. In the case of a quintic u, the vanishing of three invariants of degrees 4, 12, 8 determined as the discriminant of $C_4 x^2 + \dots$, the lineo-linear invariant of u^2 and $(C_4 x^2 + \dots)^5$, and the lineo-linear invariant of $(C_4 x^2 + \dots)^3$ and $C_2 x^6 + \dots$, necessitates the vanishing of all invariants.

Ans. The first condition necessitates that $C_4 x^2 + \dots$ is a square y'^2, unless all its coefficients vanish. The second and third then necessitate that u and $C_2 x^6 + \dots$ have y' for a factor, in the first case. In the second case it is easy to see that if, as we may, we take $a = 0$ and $f = 0$, then $b = 0$ and $c = 0$, or $d = 0$ and $e = 0$.

Ex. 10. If $\alpha_1, \alpha_2, \dots \alpha_p$ are the roots of $(a_0, a_1, \dots a_p)(x, y)^p = 0$, prove that the protomorphs $C_2, C_4, C_6, \dots$ are numerical multiples of

$$a_0^2 \Sigma (\alpha_1 - \alpha_2)^2,\ a_0^2 \Sigma (\alpha_1 - \alpha_2)^2 (\alpha_3 - \alpha_4)^2,$$
$$a_0^2 \Sigma (\alpha_1 - \alpha_2)^2 (\alpha_3 - \alpha_4)^2 (\alpha_5 - \alpha_6)^2, \dots$$

respectively; and write down in this notation the covariants which they lead.

Ex. 11. If the roots of a p-ic are all real, the roots of its covariants led by protomorphs of degree 2 are all imaginary. For instance those of the Hessian are imaginary.

Ans. Because a sum of squares of real quantities cannot vanish.

Ex. 12. The covariants led by protomorphs of degree 2 are those of § 61, Ex. 33.

Ex. 13. Prove that any gradient G of degree above 2 in $a_0, a_1, a_2, \dots a_{2n}$ (, a_{2n+1}) which contains no term free from all of $a_1, a_2, \dots a_n$ may be expressed in the form

$$P_0 a_0 + P_1 C_2 + P_2 C_4 + \dots + P_n C_{2n} + Q,$$

where $P_0, P_1, \dots P_n$ are gradients (or zeros), and Q is zero or a gradient free from a_0 in which none of $a_1, a_2, \dots a_n$ occurs to a higher power than the first.

Ans. Arrange the factors of terms in G alphabetically as in § 71. Take any term free from a_0, and let a_r be the first of $a_1, a_2, \dots a_n$ which occurs in it to a power above the first. Substitute in it for a_r^2 its expression in terms of C_{2r} and products. The term is thus replaced by a part with C_{2r} as a factor and terms alphabetically previous to itself. Repeat the process for all these terms except those with C_{2r} or a_0 for a factor; and go on in this way as long as possible. As there is only a finite number of words of i letters in an alphabet of $2n$ or $2n+1$ letters, the procedure must stop; i.e. a time must come when the term of G as re-written involves only multiples of $a_0, C_2, C_4, \dots C_{2n}$ and terms without second or higher powers of any of $a_1, a_2, \dots a_n$.

Ex. 14. Show that if G is of weight w and degree i there can be no residual gradient Q in the expansion above if

$$i \nless n \text{ and } w < 1+2+\dots+n+(i-n)(n+1),$$

i.e.
$$< (n+1)(i-\tfrac{1}{2}n).$$

Ex. 15. If S is a seminvariant which leads a covariant of

$$(a_0, a_1, \dots a_{2n})(x, y)^{2n}, \text{ or of } (a_0, a_1, \dots a_{2n+1})(x, y)^{2n+1},$$

so that, as the case may be, $2in-2w \nless 0$ or $i(2n+1)-2w \nless 0$, then, if m is any number greater than $n(n+1)/\{2(n+1)i-2w\}$ and not less than n/i, gradients (or zeros) $P_0, P_1, \dots P_n$ exist such that

$$S^m = P_0 a_0 + P_1 C_2 + \dots + P_n C_{2n}. \qquad (Hilbert.)$$

165 (*bis*). For odd weights there are (§ 114) no seminvariants of degree 2. For each odd weight there is, however, a protomorph of degree 3. We can find by the method of § 114 seminvariants of degree 3 and the requisite odd weights in succession. C_3, C_5, C_7 are thus uniquely determined, but afterwards there is a choice. For instance $(9; 3, 9)-(8; 3, 9) = 2$, and $(11; 3, 11)-(10; 3, 11) = 2$. We must select one of two for C_9, one of two for C_{11}, and so on.

A definite system $C_3, C_5, C_7, C_9, C_{11}, \dots$ can be obtained by operation with $a_0 O-(ip-2w) a_1$ on $C_2, C_4, C_6, C_8, C_{10}, \dots$ respectively. The results contain terms $a_0^2 a_3, a_0^2 a_5, a_0^2 a_7, \dots$ respectively; and we have only to see that they are all seminvariants. Now if S is a seminvariant, so that $\Omega S = 0$, $\{a_0 O-(ip-2w) a_1\} S$ is another. For

$$\begin{aligned}\Omega \{a_0 O-(ip-2w) a_1\} S &= a_0 \{\Omega O-(ip-2w)\} S,\\ &= a_0 O \Omega S, \text{ by § 125 (1)},\\ &= 0.\end{aligned}$$

We thus obtain the succession of cubic protomorphs

$$C_3 = \frac{1}{p-2}\{a_0 O - 2(p-2)a_1\} C_2$$
$$= a_0^2 a_3 - 3a_0 a_1 a_2 + 2a_1^3 = A_3,$$
$$C_5 = \frac{1}{p-4}\{a_0 O - 2(p-4)a_1\} C_4$$
$$= a_0^2 a_5 - 5a_0 a_1 a_4 + 2a_0 a_2 a_3 + 8a_1^2 a_3 - 6a_1 a_2^2,$$
$$C_7 = \frac{1}{p-6}\{a_0 O - 2(p-6)a_1\} C_6$$
$$= a_0^2 a_7 - 7a_0 a_1 a_6 + 9a_0 a_2 a_5 - 5a_0 a_3 a_4 + 12a_1^2 a_5 + 20a_1 a_3^2 - 30a_1 a_2 a_4,$$

&c., &c.

Ex. 16. If θ denotes $a_1\partial/\partial a_0 + a_2\partial/\partial a_1 + \ldots + a_p\partial/\partial a_{p-1}$, prove that
$\Omega\theta - \theta\Omega = (a_0\partial/\partial a_0 + a_1\partial/\partial a_1 + \ldots + a_p\partial/\partial a_p) - (p+1)a_p\partial/\partial a_p$;
and hence that $a_0\theta - ia_1$ generates seminvariants from seminvariants, and in particular generates a system of cubic protomorphs of weights 3, 5, 7, ... from C_2, C_4, C_6, ... (*Cayley.*)

Ex. 17. If ϕ denotes $a_2\partial/\partial a_1 + 2a_3\partial/\partial a_2 + \ldots + (p-1)a_p\partial/\partial a_{p-1}$, prove that $a_0\phi - 2wa_1$ is an operator with the same efficacy. (*Cayley.*)

Ex. 18. These two operators may, respectively, be written

$$(a_0 a_2 - a_1^2)\frac{\partial}{\partial a_1} + (a_0 a_3 - a_1 a_2)\frac{\partial}{\partial a_2} + \ldots + (a_0 a_p - a_1 a_{p-1})\frac{\partial}{\partial a_{p-1}} - a_1 a_p \frac{\partial}{\partial a_p},$$

$$(a_0 a_2 - 2a_1^2)\frac{\partial}{\partial a_1} + 2(a_0 a_3 - 2a_1 a_2)\frac{\partial}{\partial a_2} + \ldots + (p-1)(a_0 a_p - 2a_1 a_{p-1})\frac{\partial}{\partial a_{p-1}} - 2p\, a_1 a_p \frac{\partial}{\partial a_p}.$$

(*Cayley.*)

166. If $\gamma_2, \gamma_3, \ldots \gamma_p$ are the covariants whose leaders are the protomorphs $C_2, C_3, \ldots C_p$, then the expression for a seminvariant S in terms of them and a_0,

$$S = a_0^{-\mu} F(a_0, C_2, C_3, \ldots C_p),$$

where the function F is rational and integral for a rational integral S, leads to the expression for the covariant K whose leader is S,

$$K = u^{-\mu} F(u, \gamma_2, \gamma_3, \ldots \gamma_p).$$

This follows by the same argument as in § 163. In fact, in general the expression for a seminvariant or invariant in terms of any system of protomorphs leads to exactly the same expression for the corresponding covariant or the invariant in terms of the covariants led by the protomorphs.

167. **Seminvariants as integrals of $\Omega S = 0$.** Another aspect of the reason for the expressibility of any seminvariant or invariant in terms of p independent ones should be noticed. A seminvariant is an integral of the differential equation

$$a_0 \frac{\partial S}{\partial a_1} + 2a_1 \frac{\partial S}{\partial a_2} + 3a_2 \frac{\partial S}{\partial a_3} + \dots + pa_{p-1} \frac{\partial S}{\partial a_p} = 0,$$

which is properly regarded as beginning with a vanishing multiple of $\partial S/\partial a_0$.

Now Lagrange's theory of linear partial differential equations tells us that when we have p independent functions S of $a_0, a_1, a_2, \dots a_p$ which satisfy this equation, any other S which satisfies the equation is a function of those p.

But in §§ 161, 163, 164, 165 we have sets of p independent solutions, viz.

$$a_0,\ a_2',\ a_3',\dots a_p';$$
$$a_0,\ A_2,\ A_3,\dots A_p;$$
$$a_0,\ B_2,\ B_3,\dots B_p;$$
$$a_0,\ C_2,\ C_3,\dots C_p.$$

We thus have it clearly exhibited that any seminvariant or invariant, even though fractional or irrational, is capable of expression in terms of a set of protomorphs.

168. **Protomorphs for systems of quantics.** A seminvariant of the system consisting of two binary quantics

$$(a_0, a_1, a_2, \dots a_p)(x, y)^p,$$
$$(b_0, b_1, b_2, \dots b_{p'})(x, y)^{p'},$$

is (§ 115) a solution of the differential equation

$$\left(a_0 \frac{\partial S}{\partial a_1} + 2a_1 \frac{\partial S}{\partial a_2} + \dots + pa_{p-1} \frac{\partial S}{\partial a_p}\right) + \left(b_0 \frac{\partial S}{\partial b_1} + 2b_1 \frac{\partial S}{\partial b_2} + \dots + p'b_{p'-1} \frac{\partial S}{\partial b_{p'}}\right) = 0,$$

in the $p+p'+2$ variables $a_0, a_1, a_2, \dots a_p; b_0, b_1, b_2, \dots b_{p'}$. We need $p+p'+1$ independent solutions of this equation: and these are afforded by a set of p protomorphs of the p-ic, a set of p' protomorphs of the p'-ic, and the one additional $a_0b_1 - a_1b_0$. All seminvariants of the system can then be expressed in terms of these $p+p'+1$ seminvariants.

Moreover, we can easily prove a theorem due to Clebsch,

that the expression for any rational integral seminvariant of the system can be expressed in terms of $a_0b_1-a_1b_0$ and sets of protomorphs $a_0, B_2, B_3, \ldots B_p; b_0, B_2', B_3', \ldots B'_{p'}$ in a form which is rational, and is integral except as regards a_0 and b_0. As in § 164, we reduce it to the form

$$a_0^{-\mu}b_0^{-\mu'}F(a_0, a_1, B_2, B_3, \ldots B_p; b_0, b_1, B_2', B_3', \ldots B_p'),$$

where F is rational and integral in its arguments. We also, upon expressing the annihilation by $\Sigma\Omega$, obtain that

$$\left(a_0\frac{\partial}{\partial a_1}+b_0\frac{\partial}{\partial b_1}\right)F=0;$$

and this tells us that F involves a_1, b_1 in the connexion $a_0b_1-a_1b_0$ only.

And, quite generally, rational integral seminvariants (including, of course, invariants) of any number of binary quantics are rational functions of sets of protomorphs of those quantics severally, and of the leaders

$$a_0b_1-a_1b_0, \; a_0c_1-a_1c_0, \ldots$$

of the Jacobians of one of the quantics and the rest, and are integral except as to powers of $a_0, b_0, c_0, \ldots$, the leaders of the quantics themselves.

169. **Protomorphs applied to the analysis of irreducible systems. The cubic.** There is a method due to Cayley for finding the complete system of irreducible seminvariants and invariants of a binary quantic, and therefore the system of irreducible covariants and invariants, from a system of protomorphs, which is simple for the cases of the cubic and the quartic.

It is of very little consequence whether we start from the system of protomorphs $a_0, A_2, A_3, \ldots A_p$ of § 163, or the system $a_0, C_2, C_3, \ldots C_p$ of §§ 165, 165 (*bis*). For the cubic these systems are the same, since $A_2 \equiv C_2$ and $A_3 \equiv C_3$.

By § 163 any seminvariant of degree i and weight w of the cubic $(a, b, c, d)(x, y)^3$ is of the form

$$a^{-w+i}F(A_2, A_3),$$

where $F(A_2, A_3)$ is rational and integral.

Here, if $i>w$, the seminvariant is integrally expressed, and has the positive power a^{i-w} of a as a factor. It is then a rational integral function of a, A_2, A_3, and is not irreducible, unless it be only a itself.

If $i=w$ the seminvariant is a rational integral function $F(A_2, A_3)$ of A_2 and A_3, and is not irreducible unless it be either A_2 or A_3 itself.

Any irreducible seminvariant, other than a, A_2, A_3, must then be the result of dividing some rational integral function of A_2 and A_3 by a power of a. Such a function, being divisible by a, must vanish when $a = 0$, i.e. when we put for A_2, A_3 the values

$$A_2' = -b^2, \quad A_3' = 2b^3.$$

Now the one rational integral function of these which vanishes is

$$A_3'^2 + 4A_2'^3.$$

Any other can only vanish in consequence of having this for a factor. We are thus led to form

$$A_3^2 + 4A_2^3 \equiv a^2\{a^2d^2 - 6abcd + 4ac^3 + 4b^3d - 3b^2c^2\}$$
$$\equiv a^2\Delta,$$

and to conclude that Δ is a seminvariant—it is of course the discriminant, a full invariant. It is found as one whose weight exceeds its degree, so that it is not a rational integral function of a, A_2, A_3.

We are also led to conclude that any other seminvariant whose weight exceeds its degree is given by the rejection of an a factor from a function $F(A_2, A_3)$ of which

$$A_3^2 + 4A_2^3 \equiv a^2\Delta$$

is a factor, and consequently that it has Δ for a factor, and is not irreducible, but a rational integral function of a, A_2, A_3, Δ.

Thus all rational integral seminvariants of the cubic are rational integral functions of some or all of a, A_2, A_3, Δ, which alone are irreducible, and are connected by the syzygy

$$A_3^2 + 4A_2^3 = a^2\Delta.$$

These are the results of § 141.

170. **Irreducible system for the quartic.** Consider now the quartic $(a, b, c, d, e)(x, y)^4$; and take the protomorphs of §§ 165, 165 (*bis*),

$$a, \quad C_2 \equiv ac - b^2, \quad C_3 \equiv a^2d - 3abc + 2b^3, \quad C_4 \equiv ae - 4bd + 3c^2,$$

the terms free from a in which are

$$0, \quad C_2' \equiv -b^2, \quad C_3' \equiv 2b^3, \quad C_4' \equiv -4bd + 3c^2.$$

As in the last article we are led to a seminvariant (not now an invariant)

$$D \equiv a^2d^2 - 6abcd + 4ac^3 + 4b^3d - 3b^2c^2,$$

which may, so far as we know at present, turn out to be irreducible, though that it was irreducible in the case of the cubic, for which there were three protomorphs only, affords no reason why it should be now that there are four. The terms free from a in D are

$$D' \equiv 4b^3d - 3b^2c^2.$$

Any seminvariant not a rational integral function of these five will, by § 165, be the result of rejecting a factor which is a power of a from a rational integral function of a, C_2, C_3, C_4; and such a rational integral function may present itself in the form

$$F(a, C_2, C_3, C_4, D),$$

where F is rational and integral in its arguments. The result of putting $a = 0$ in this is

$$F(0, C_2', C_3', C_4', D'),$$

and must vanish identically, since F, expressed in terms of a, b, c, d, e, has a for a factor.

Now a result, distinct from $C_3'^2 + 4C_2'^3 = 0$ which led to D, of eliminating b, c, d from

$$C_2' \equiv -b^2, \quad C_3' \equiv 2b^3, \quad C_4' \equiv -4bd + 3c^2, \quad D' \equiv 4b^3d - 3b^2c^2,$$

is

$$C_2'C_4' - D' = 0,$$

and this leads to

$$\begin{aligned} C_2C_4 - D &\equiv a(ace + 2bcd - ad^2 - b^2e - c^3) \\ &\equiv aJ, \end{aligned}$$

which shows two things: (1) that there is a new seminvariant J, an invariant, in fact, which may prove to be irreducible; and (2) that D is not irreducible, but is equal to $C_2C_4 - aJ$.

We have now further to look for rational integral functions of a, C_2, C_3, C_4, J which have a for a factor, so that the same functions of

$$0, \quad C_2' \equiv -b^2, \quad C_3' \equiv 2b^3, \quad C_4' \equiv -4bd + 3c^2,$$
$$J' \equiv 2bcd - b^2e - c^3$$

vanish identically.

But there are no such new functions. For C_4' involves a letter c which does not occur in C_2' or C_3', so that no relation connects it with them; and J' involves e which does not occur in either C_2', C_3' or C_4', so that it again is independent of the preceding.

Consequently a, C_2, C_3, C_4, J is the complete system of irreducible seminvariants and invariants of the quartic. Of these C_4 is what in previous chapters we have called I. The result is that of § 145.

The one syzygy which connects members of the irreducible system (cf. § 145) is also exhibited. We have, as above,

$$C_3^2 + 4C_2^3 = a^2D, \quad \text{and} \quad C_2C_4 - D = aJ,$$

from which, after elimination of the reducible D, there results

$$a^3J - a^2C_2C_4 + C_3^2 + 4C_2^3 = 0.$$

171. The method is not suited for extended application to higher binary quantics. It may be pursued in dealing with the quintic and the sextic, but the labour is enormous owing to the number of eliminations and the length and complexity of the functions dealt with. Moreover serious theoretical difficulties present themselves, and without guidance by a knowledge of the results to be obtained those results could hardly be thus arrived at with certainty.

One general fact should be mentioned. The protomorphs $a_0, C_2, C_3, C_4, \ldots C_p$ are in all cases irreducible; for every one involves a letter absent from all the preceding, involves it to the first degree only, and is of lowest possible degree for its weight. The same cannot be said of the other system of protomorphs $a_0, A_2, A_3, \ldots A_p$, which after the third are of higher degrees than the lowest possible.

172. **A seminvariant arranged by powers of a_1.** When in a seminvariant, or, in particular, invariant, the terms free from a_1 are known, the whole is known.

This has been proved in § 161. We have only to replace in the given terms $a_2, a_3, \ldots a_p$ by the $a_2', a_3', \ldots a_p'$ of that article.

Any gradient in $a_0, a_2', a_3', \ldots a_p'$ is a seminvariant, but not necessarily an integral seminvariant.

A seminvariant which is integral may be expressed in its integral form, when its terms free from a_1 are known, by aid of differentiations only in virtue of the following.

Let Q_i be the given terms free from a_1, and suppose the whole seminvariant to be

$$S \equiv Q_i + a_1 Q_{i-1} + a_1^2 Q_{i-2} + \ldots + a_1^m Q_{i-m},$$

where $Q_i, Q_{i-1}, Q_{i-2}, \ldots Q_{i-m}$ are all free from a_1, and where m is some number not exceeding i, the degree of S.

If we write

$$\Omega \equiv a_0 \frac{\partial}{\partial a_1} + 2a_1 \frac{\partial}{\partial a_2} + \left(3a_2 \frac{\partial}{\partial a_3} + 4a_3 \frac{\partial}{\partial a_4} + \ldots + pa_{p-1} \frac{\partial}{\partial a_p}\right)$$

$$\equiv a_0 \frac{\partial}{\partial a_1} + 2a_1 \frac{\partial}{\partial a_2} + \omega,$$

where ω does not involve either a_1 or $\partial/\partial a_1$, then

$$\Omega(a_1^\mu Q) = a_1^{\mu-1} \cdot \mu a_0 Q + a_1^\mu \cdot \omega Q + a_1^{\mu+1} \cdot 2\frac{\partial}{\partial a_2} Q.$$

Hence, arranging the seminvariant condition $\Omega S = 0$ by powers of a_1, and expressing that the parts of ΩS with different powers of a_1 for factors must vanish separately, we have the succession of facts

$$\begin{aligned}
a_0 Q_{i-1} + \omega Q_i &= 0,\\
2a_0 Q_{i-2} + \omega Q_{i-1} + 2\frac{\partial}{\partial a_2} Q_i &= 0,\\
3a_0 Q_{i-3} + \omega Q_{i-2} + 2\frac{\partial}{\partial a_2} Q_{i-1} &= 0,\\
\cdots\cdots\cdots&\\
\omega Q_{i-m} + 2\frac{\partial}{\partial a_2} Q_{i-m+1} &= 0,\\
2\frac{\partial}{\partial a_2} Q_{i-m} &= 0,
\end{aligned}$$

of which all but the last two suffice to determine from Q_i the expressions for $Q_{i-1}, Q_{i-2}, \ldots Q_{i-m}$ in succession by operations with ω, i.e. by differentiations.

The last equation tells us that the terms multiplying the highest power of a_1 which occurs in a seminvariant are free from a_2.

Ex. 19. State the corresponding facts with regard to anti-seminvariants, derived from their annihilator O.

173. A simpler method of determining the whole seminvariant S, when its terms Q_i free from a_1 are known, is given as follows.

For any gradient whatever the following is an identity,

$$\Omega\left\{1 - \frac{a_1}{a_0}\Omega + \frac{1}{1.2}\frac{a_1^2}{a_0^2}\Omega^2 - \frac{1}{1.2.3}\frac{a_1^3}{a_0^3}\Omega^3 + \ldots\right\} G = 0,$$

since the left-hand member is

$$\begin{aligned}
&\Omega G\\
&-\frac{a_1}{a_0}\Omega^2 G - \Omega G\\
&+\frac{1}{1.2}\frac{a_1^2}{a_0^2}\Omega^3 G + \frac{a_1}{a_0}\Omega^2 G\\
&-\frac{1}{1.2.3}\frac{a_1^3}{a_0^3}\Omega^4 G - \frac{1}{1.2}\frac{a_1^2}{a_0^2}\Omega^3 G\\
&+\ \cdots\cdots\cdots,
\end{aligned}$$

of which the terms cancel against one another up to a certain point, and after that point vanish.

Now take Q_i for the gradient G. We obtain that

$$\left(1-\frac{a_1}{a_0}\Omega+\frac{1}{1.2}\frac{a_1^2}{a_0^2}\Omega^2-\frac{1}{1.2.3}\frac{a_1^3}{a_0^3}\Omega^3+\ldots\right)Q_i$$

is annihilated by Ω, and is consequently a seminvariant unless it vanishes. But it does not vanish since its terms Q_i free from a_1 do not.

Its form is apparently fractional, but cannot be really so. It must, in fact, be exactly

$$Q_i+a_1Q_{i-1}+a_1^2Q_{i-2}+\ldots+a_1^mQ_{i-m};$$

for otherwise the difference of the two would be divisible by a_1 and annihilated by Ω. Now this is impossible, since no seminvariant can have a_1 for a factor, seminvariants being functions of a_0, $a_2-\frac{a_1^2}{a_0}$, $a_3-3\frac{a_1}{a_0}a_2+2\frac{a_1^3}{a_0^2}$, ..., which are the non-vanishing and independent $a_0, a_2, a_3, \ldots$ when $a_1=0$.

The full expression for a seminvariant is then found by operating on its terms free from a_1 with

$$1-\frac{a_1}{a_0}\Omega+\frac{1}{1.2}\frac{a_1^2}{a_0^2}\Omega^2-\frac{1}{1.2.3}\frac{a_1^3}{a_0^3}\Omega^3+\ldots.$$

Ex. 20. Prove that this operator annihilates any gradient with a_1 for a factor, and produces from any other gradient a seminvariant, not necessarily integral, which is also produced from the terms in it which are free from a_1.

Ex. 21. If G is any gradient, $\Omega(a_1G)$ involves as many arbitraries as G.

174. **Annihilator of terms free from a_1 in invariants.** There does not seem to be a simple general method for finding the terms free from a_1 in integral *seminvariants* of given type. The case is different, however, with regard to *invariants*, which are at once seminvariants and anti-seminvariants. The terms free from a_1 in an invariant have an annihilator, which suffices to determine them. The fact is due to Cayley.

Consider the two annihilators,

$$\Omega=a_0\frac{\partial}{\partial a_1}+2a_1\frac{\partial}{\partial a_2}+3a_2\frac{\partial}{\partial a_3}+\ldots+pa_{p-1}\frac{\partial}{\partial a_p},$$

$$O=pa_1\frac{\partial}{\partial a_0}+(p-1)a_2\frac{\partial}{\partial a_1}+(p-2)a_3\frac{\partial}{\partial a_2}+\ldots+a_p\frac{\partial}{\partial a_{p-1}},$$

of invariants of a binary p-ic. Eliminating $\partial/\partial a_1$ we have

$$a_0 O-(p-1)\,a_2\Omega \equiv a_1\left\{pa_0\frac{\partial}{\partial a_0}-2\,(p-1)\,a_2\frac{\partial}{\partial a_2}\right\}$$

$$+\,a_0\left\{(p-2)\,a_3\frac{\partial}{\partial a_2}+(p-3)\,a_4\frac{\partial}{\partial a_3}+\ldots+a_p\frac{\partial}{\partial a_{p-1}}\right\}$$

$$-(p-1)\,a_2\left\{3a_2\frac{\partial}{\partial a_3}+4a_3\frac{\partial}{\partial a_4}+\ldots+pa_{p-1}\frac{\partial}{\partial a_p}\right\}$$

$$\equiv a_1\phi+\psi,\text{ say,}$$

where ϕ and ψ do not involve a_1 or $\partial/\partial a_1$.

Now let an invariant, arranged by powers of a_1 as in the last two articles, be written

$$I\equiv R_i+a_1R_{i-1}+a_1^2R_{i-2}+\ldots+a_1^mR_{i-m}.$$

We find that, since Ω and O, and therefore $a_0O-(p-1)\,a_2\Omega$, annihilate I,

$$\begin{aligned}\psi R_i &= 0,\\ \psi R_{i-1}+\phi R_i &= 0,\\ \psi R_{i-2}+\phi R_{i-1} &= 0,\\ &\cdots\cdots\\ &\cdots\cdots\\ \phi R_{i-m} &= 0.\end{aligned}$$

Of these the first is the result important for our purpose; but before examining it we notice that the last, viz.

$$\left\{pa_0\frac{\partial}{\partial a_0}-2\,(p-1)\,a_2\frac{\partial}{\partial a_2}\right\}R_{i-m}=0,$$

tells us that, since $\dfrac{\partial}{\partial a_2}R_{i-m}=0$ by § 172, we must also have $\dfrac{\partial}{\partial a_0}R_{i-m}=0$, i.e. that the terms which multiply the highest power of a_1 which occurs in any invariant are free from both a_0 and a_2.

The more important conclusion, gathered from the first of the above equalities, is that the terms free from a_1 in an invariant of a binary p-ic have the annihilator

$$\psi\equiv a_0\left\{(p-2)\,a_3\frac{\partial}{\partial a_2}+(p-3)\,a_4\frac{\partial}{\partial a_3}+\ldots+a_p\frac{\partial}{\partial a_{p-1}}\right\}$$

$$-(p-1)\,a_2\left\{3a_2\frac{\partial}{\partial a_3}+4a_3\frac{\partial}{\partial a_4}+\ldots+pa_{p-1}\frac{\partial}{\partial a_p}\right\}.$$

We need to know conversely that all gradients in $a_0, a_2, a_3, \ldots a_p$, for which $ip = 2w$, and which have ψ for an annihilator, are the terms free from a_1 in invariants. When this is known we can be sure that we have a means, by expressing the annihilation by ψ, of finding those terms in all invariants of a given degree, and thence, in either of the ways of §§ 161, 172, 173, the complete expressions of the invariants.

We shall encounter a proof of this converse proposition in the next chapter (cf. § 186). It amounts to proving that all gradients for which $ip = 2w$ in $a_0, a_2', a_3' \ldots a_p'$, the coefficients in the quantic deprived of its second term as in § 162, which are annihilated by ψ', the result of accenting the letters $a_2, a_3, \ldots a_p$ in ψ, are invariants, i.e. are annihilated by O as well as by Ω, which latter must annihilate them since it annihilates a_0, a_2', a_3', a_p'. Note that no expression fractional in a_0 can be annihilated by O.

It is for the present left to the student to establish the proposition for himself by the sequence of theorems of the following four examples. He will see from Ex. 25 that if G' satisfy $\psi' G' = 0$ it must certainly satisfy $OG' \equiv 0$, provided $ip - 2w = 0$, as is the case.

Ex. 22. Prove that, if by the substitution $x = X + mY$, $y = Y$ the quantic $(a_0, a_1, a_2, \ldots a_p)(x, y)^p$ is transformed into

$$(\mathfrak{a}_0, \mathfrak{a}_1, \mathfrak{a}_2, \ldots \mathfrak{a}_p)(X, Y)^p, \text{ so that (§ 92)}$$

$$\mathfrak{a}_0 = a_0,$$

$$\mathfrak{a}_1 = a_1 + a_0 m,$$

$$\mathfrak{a}_2 = a_2 + 2a_1 m + a_0 m^2, \text{ \&c. \&c.},$$

then

$$\frac{\partial}{\partial a_0} = \frac{\partial}{\partial \mathfrak{a}_0} + m\frac{\partial}{\partial \mathfrak{a}_1} + m^2\frac{\partial}{\partial \mathfrak{a}_2} + \ldots + m^p\frac{\partial}{\partial \mathfrak{a}_p},$$

and, generally,

$$\frac{\partial}{\partial a_r} = \frac{1}{r!}\left\{1.2.3\ldots r\frac{\partial}{\partial \mathfrak{a}_r} + 2.3\ldots(r+1)m\frac{\partial}{\partial \mathfrak{a}_{r+1}} + \ldots \right.$$
$$\left. + (p-r+1)(p-r+2)\ldots pm^{p-r}\frac{\partial}{\partial \mathfrak{a}_p}\right\},$$

the last case of which is

$$\frac{\partial}{\partial a_p} = \frac{\partial}{\partial \mathfrak{a}_p};$$

the operations on the left being all upon a function of $a_0, a_1, a_2, \ldots a_p$, and those on the right all on the function of $\mathfrak{a}_0, \mathfrak{a}_1, \mathfrak{a}_2, \ldots \mathfrak{a}_p$ to which it is equal.

Ex. 23. Hence show that the operators

$$i \equiv a_0 \frac{\partial}{\partial a_0} + a_1 \frac{\partial}{\partial a_1} + \dots + a_p \frac{\partial}{\partial a_p},$$

$$\Omega \equiv a_0 \frac{\partial}{\partial a_1} + 2a_1 \frac{\partial}{\partial a_2} + \dots + pa_{p-1} \frac{\partial}{\partial a_p},$$

$$w - \frac{a_1}{a_0}\Omega \equiv a_1 \frac{\partial}{\partial a_1} + 2a_2 \frac{\partial}{\partial a_2} + \dots + pa_p \frac{\partial}{\partial a_p}$$
$$- \frac{a_1}{a_0}\left\{a_0 \frac{\partial}{\partial a_1} + 2a_1 \frac{\partial}{\partial a_2} + \dots + pa_{p-1} \frac{\partial}{\partial a_p}\right\},$$

$$O - \frac{a_1}{a_0}(ip - 2w) - \frac{a_1^2}{a_0^2}\Omega \equiv pa_1 \frac{\partial}{\partial a_0} + (p-1)a_2 \frac{\partial}{\partial a_1} + \dots + a_p \frac{\partial}{\partial a_{p-1}}$$
$$- \frac{a_1}{a_0}\left\{pa_0 \frac{\partial}{\partial a_0} + (p-2)a_1 \frac{\partial}{\partial a_1} + (p-4)a_2 \frac{\partial}{\partial a_2} + \dots - pa_p \frac{\partial}{\partial a_p}\right\}$$
$$- \frac{a_1^2}{a_0^2}\left\{a_0 \frac{\partial}{\partial a_1} + 2a_1 \frac{\partial}{\partial a_2} + \dots + pa_{p-1} \frac{\partial}{\partial a_p}\right\},$$

transform into operators of like forms.

Ex. 24. Show that the only necessary modification of the above when the operation is on a seminvariant, and when m is the non-constant $-a_1/a_0$, and $a_0, a_1, a_2, \dots a_p$ are consequently the $a_0, 0, a_2', a_3', \dots a_p'$ of § 162, is that the undetermined $\partial/\partial a_1'$ is to be taken as defined by the persistence in form of Ω.

Ex. 25. By this and the fourth of Ex. 23 prove that the effect of operating with ψ', i.e.

$$a_0 \left\{(p-2)a_3' \frac{\partial}{\partial a_2'} + (p-3)a_4' \frac{\partial}{\partial a_3'} + \dots + a_p' \frac{\partial}{\partial a'_{p-1}}\right\}$$
$$-(p-1)a_2'\left\{3a_2' \frac{\partial}{\partial a_3'} + 4a_3' \frac{\partial}{\partial a_4'} + \dots + pa'_{p-1} \frac{\partial}{\partial a_p'}\right\},$$

on a gradient in $a_0, a_2', a_3', \dots a_p'$ is the same as that of operating on the equivalent function of $a_0, a_1, a_2, \dots a_p$ with $a_0 O - a_1(ip - 2w)$, since Ω annihilates it.

175. Taking $p = 5$, i.e. the case of the quintic

$$(a, b, c, d, e, f)(x, y)^5,$$

the annihilator ψ is

$$3ad\,\partial/\partial c + (2ae - 12c^2)\,\partial/\partial d + (af - 16cd)\,\partial/\partial e - 20ce\,\partial/\partial f.$$

An invariant of the quintic of degree i, and consequently of weight $\frac{5}{2}i$, if such exist, can then be found as follows. Write down the most general gradient of the type in a, c, d, e, f. Operate on it with the annihilator ψ, and equate to zero the coefficients of the various terms in the result. If the equations can be satisfied by values of the arbitrary coefficients in the assumed gradient which are not all zero, we obtain as many linearly independent invariants of the type as there are coefficients left arbitrary. If they cannot be so satisfied there is no invariant of the type.

The terms R_i free from b in the invariant are thus found, and the whole expression for the invariant of which R_i is part is by § 173

$$e^{-\beta\Omega} R_i,$$

where, after the operations are performed, β is to be replaced by b/a.

In this way the invariants of degrees 4, 8, 12, 18 of the quintic may, with much labour in the last two cases, be calculated.

For the sextic $(a, b, c, d, e, f, g)(x, y)^6$ the annihilator ψ of terms free from b in invariants is, writing ∂_c, &c., for $\partial/\partial c$, &c.,

$$4ad\partial_c + (3ae - 15c^2)\partial_d + (2af - 20cd)\partial_e + (ag - 25ce)\partial_f - 30cf\partial_g,$$

by means of which the invariants of degrees 2, 4, 6, 10, 15 may be found.

And similarly for higher quantics in succession.

Ex. 26. Integrate by Lagrange's method the differential equation for the case of the cubic

$$\psi G \equiv (ad\partial_c - 6c^2\partial_d) G = 0,$$

and thus show, remembering $3i = 2w$, that an invariant of the cubic is necessarily a power of $a^2d'^2 + 4ac'^3$, where

$$c' = c - \frac{b^2}{a},\ d' = d - \frac{3bc}{a} + \frac{2b^3}{a^2}.$$

Ex. 27. Integrate the differential equation for the case of the quartic

$$\psi G \equiv \{2ad\partial_c + (ae - 9c^2)\partial_d - 12cd\partial_e\} G = 0,$$

and show that invariants of the quartic are functions of the invariants

$$ae' + 3c'^2,\ ac'e' - ad'^2 - c'^3.$$

176. **Seminvariants arranged by powers of their most advanced letter.** The present is a convenient place for a theorem or two not directly connected with the rest of the chapter.

Take a seminvariant S of extent p. We are not necessarily regarding it as a seminvariant of a p-ic in particular. It is equally one of course of any binary quantic of order not less than p, whose first $p+1$ coefficients (after rejection of their binomial factors) are the $a_0, a_1, a_2, \ldots a_p$ involved in S.

Arrange S according to powers of a_p, its most advanced letter, and write it

$$S \equiv a_p^n P_0 + a_p^{n-1} P_1 + a_p^{n-2} P_2 + \ldots + P_n,$$

where suffixes of P's do not of course, as they did in § 172, &c., indicate degree.

Express the annihilation of S by Ω, i.e. by

$$a_0\frac{\partial}{\partial a_1}+2a_1\frac{\partial}{\partial a_2}+\ldots+(p-1)\,a_{p-2}\frac{\partial}{\partial a_{p-1}}+pa_{p-1}\frac{\partial}{\partial a_p}.$$

The terms involving different powers of a_p in ΩS must vanish separately, for the vanishing is identical. Hence

$$\begin{aligned}
&\Omega P_0 &&= 0,\\
&\Omega P_1+npa_{p-1}P_0 &&= 0,\\
&\Omega P_2+(n-1)\,pa_{p-1}P_1 &&= 0,\\
&\ldots\ldots\ldots\ldots\\
&\ldots\ldots\ldots\ldots\\
&\Omega P_n+pa_{p-1}P_{n-1} &&= 0.
\end{aligned}$$

From these identities we draw, among others, the following conclusions.

(1) P_0, the function of $a_0, a_1, a_2, \ldots a_{p-1}$ which is the coefficient of the highest power of a_p, the most advanced letter which occurs, in a seminvariant S, is itself a seminvariant.

(2) When P_n, which consists of the terms free from a_p, the most advanced letter in a seminvariant, is known, the rest of the seminvariant can be found by aid of a succession of operations with Ω and divisions by multiples of a_{p-1}, i.e. by aid of differentiations and elementary algebraical processes only.

Ex. 28. In the case of an invariant, prove that also when the terms free from a_0 are known the whole invariant can be written down by aid of differentiations and elementary algebraical processes only.

Ans. Consider the annihilation by O as we have that by Ω.

177. Seminvariants as seminvariants of seminvariants. Another interesting conclusion which can be drawn from the identities of the preceding article is that any seminvariant of a seminvariant of a binary quantic, regarded as itself a binary quantic in $a_p:1$, where a_p is the most advanced letter involved, is a seminvariant of the original quantic.

If $$f(P_0, P_1, P_2, \ldots P_n)$$
is any function of the P's,

$$\begin{aligned}
\Omega f(P_0, P_1, P_2, \ldots P_n) &= \frac{\partial f}{\partial P_0}\Omega P_0+\frac{\partial f}{\partial P_1}\Omega P_1+\frac{\partial f}{\partial P_2}\Omega P_2+\ldots+\frac{\partial f}{\partial P_n}\Omega P_n\\
&= -pa_{p-1}\left\{nP_0\frac{\partial}{\partial P_1}+(n-1)\,P_1\frac{\partial}{\partial P_2}+\ldots\right.\\
&\qquad\left.+P_{n-1}\frac{\partial}{\partial P_n}\right\}f(P_0, P_1, P_2, \ldots P_n),
\end{aligned}$$

by the identities proved.

Now the seminvariant S of the last article is

$$(P_0, P_1, P_2, \ldots P_n)(a_p, 1)^n,$$

and if we write this

$$(P_0, P_1', P_2', \ldots P_n)(a_p, 1)^n,$$

we have generally

$$P_r = \frac{n(n-1)\ldots(n-r+1)}{r!} P_r'.$$

But, with this change of notation,

$$nP_0 \frac{\partial}{\partial P_1} + (n-1) P_1 \frac{\partial}{\partial P_2} + (n-2) P_2 \frac{\partial}{\partial P_3} + \ldots + P_{n-1} \frac{\partial}{\partial P_n}$$

$$\equiv P_0 \frac{\partial}{\partial P_1'} + 2 P_1' \frac{\partial}{\partial P_2'} + 3 P_2' \frac{\partial}{\partial P_3'} + \ldots + nP'_{n-1} \frac{\partial}{\partial P_n},$$

which is of the form of Ω, and annihilates functions of the P's which are seminvariants of S looked upon as a quantic in $a_p : 1$.

Such seminvariants are then also annihilated by Ω, i.e. they are seminvariants of the quantic whose coefficients are $a_0, a_1, a_2, a_3, \ldots$.

This includes as a very particular case the result (1) of the preceding article.

Ex. 29. Meaning by semi-covariant of $(a_0, a_1, \ldots a_p)(x, y)^p$ a function of the coefficients and variables annihilated by $\Omega - y\partial/\partial x$, prove that any semi-covariant of a seminvariant of a binary quantic regarded as itself a binary quantic in $a_p : 1$, where a_p is its most advanced letter, is a seminvariant of the quantic. (*A. P. Thompson.*)

178. Seminvariants derived by differentiation of seminvariants. One more fact with regard to any seminvariant and its most advanced letter a_p may be mentioned.

We immediately prove the alternant identity

$$\Omega \frac{\partial}{\partial a_p} - \frac{\partial}{\partial a_p} \Omega = 0, \text{ or } = -(p+1) \frac{\partial}{\partial a_{p+1}},$$

according as Ω does not or does extend beyond a_p.

If then S is a seminvariant which does not extend beyond a_p

$$\Omega \,.\, \partial S/\partial a_p = 0,$$

i.e. $\partial S/\partial a_p$ is a seminvariant.

By repetition it follows that $\partial^2 S/\partial a_p^2$, $\partial^3 S/\partial a_p^3, \ldots$ are seminvariants, unless they vanish.

This again includes as a particular case the result (1) of § 176.

If a_r is a letter short of the last a_p which occurs in a seminvariant, we have

$$\frac{\partial}{\partial a_r} S = -\frac{1}{r} \Omega \frac{\partial S}{\partial a_{r-1}}.$$

The theorems of these last articles are partly Cayley's and partly Sylvester's.

179. **Passage from discriminant to discriminant.** To Cayley is due an application of § 176 (2) to the determination of the discriminant of a binary p-ic from that of a binary $(p-1)$-ic. Let us apply it to find the discriminant of a cubic from that of a quadratic.

The discriminant of $(a, b, c, d)(x, y)^3$ is an invariant which, when we put $d = 0$ in it, becomes the discriminant of

$$x(ax^2 + 3bxy + 3cy^2),$$

which is a numerical multiple of the product of the squares of differences between 0, α, β, where α, β are the roots of $ax^2 + 3bxy + 3cy^2$, with the factor a^4 necessitated by its known degree. Now this is a numerical multiple of $a^4(\alpha\beta)^2(\alpha-\beta)^2$, i.e. of

$$c^2(4ac - 3b^2).$$

These then are the terms free from the most advanced coefficient d in the discriminant of the cubic. The other terms are determined from them as an example of § 176.

180. **Operators which generate seminvariants.** Seminvariants and invariants can be derived from gradients which are not seminvariants by operations involving differentiation and elementary algebraical processes only. In fact, *all* seminvariants can be thus obtained. The idea is Hilbert's.

In § 128, Ex. 8, it has been pointed out, and the fact has been used in § 157 (*ter*), that if F is any gradient in some or all of $a_0, a_1, \dots a_p$ for which $\eta = ip - 2w \nless -1$, then

$$\left(1 - \frac{O\Omega}{1(\eta+2)}\right)\left(1 - \frac{O\Omega}{2(\eta+3)}\right)\dots\left(1 - \frac{O\Omega}{w(\eta+w+1)}\right)F \quad \dots (1)$$

is a seminvariant or zero—the latter of course if $\eta = -1$. The fact is so important that other forms of operator equally effective for producing seminvariants from gradients will now be given.

It was proved in § 128 that, if G is any gradient in $a_0, a_1, a_2, \dots a_p$, or some of them, for which $\eta \equiv ip - 2w$ is positive,

$$\left\{1 - \frac{1}{1 \cdot \eta}\Omega O + \frac{1}{1 \cdot 2 \cdot \eta(\eta+1)}\Omega O^2 \Omega \right.$$
$$\left. - \frac{1}{1 \cdot 2 \cdot 3 \cdot \eta(\eta+1)(\eta+2)}\Omega O^3 \Omega^2 + \dots \right\} G = 0,$$

and in § 100 was proved the really equivalent theorem that in the same case

$$\left\{1-\frac{\Omega O}{1^2}+\frac{\Omega^2 O^2}{1^2 . 2^2}-\frac{\Omega^3 O^3}{1^2 . 2^2 . 3^2}+\ldots\right\} G=0.$$

Now for G put ΩF, where F is any gradient of degree i and weight $w+1$ in $a_0, a_1, a_2, \ldots a_p$ or some of them. The two theorems tell us that

$$\Omega\left\{1-\frac{1}{1 . \eta} O \Omega+\frac{1}{1 . 2 . \eta(\eta+1)} O^2 \Omega^2 - \frac{1}{1 . 2 . 3 . \eta(\eta+1)(\eta+2)} O^3 \Omega^3+\ldots\right\} F=0$$

and $$\Omega\left\{1-\frac{O \Omega}{1^2}+\frac{\Omega O^2 \Omega}{1^2 . 2^2}-\frac{\Omega^2 O^3 \Omega}{1^2 . 2^2 . 3^2}+\ldots\right\} F=0.$$

Now write w instead of $w+1$, so that F is any gradient of weight w and degree i in $a_0, a_1, a_2, \ldots a_p$, or some of them, for which $\eta \equiv ip-2w$ is greater than -2, i.e. $\nless -1$. We have to put $\eta+2$ for η, and deduce that

$$\left\{1-\frac{1}{1 .(\eta+2)} O \Omega+\frac{1}{1 . 2 .(\eta+2)(\eta+3)} O^2 \Omega^2 - \frac{1}{1 . 2 . 3 .(\eta+2)(\eta+3)(\eta+4)} O^3 \Omega^3-\ldots\right\} F, \quad \ldots (2)$$

or its equivalent

$$\left\{1-\frac{O \Omega}{1^2}+\frac{\Omega O^2 \Omega}{1^2 . 2^2}-\frac{\Omega^2 O^3 \Omega}{1^2 . 2^2 . 3^2}+\ldots\right\} F, \quad \ldots (3)$$

is annihilated by Ω, so that it is either zero or a seminvariant.

In particular, taking $\eta \equiv ip-2w=0$, so that the expression (2) is

$$\left\{1-\frac{O \Omega}{1 . 2}+\frac{O^2 \Omega^2}{1 . 2^2 . 3}-\frac{O^3 \Omega^3}{1 . 2^2 . 3^2 . 4}+\ldots\right\} F,$$

this, and equally the expression (3), is either zero or an invariant.

If $\eta \equiv ip-2w=-1$ for F, the expression (2) is

$$\left\{1-\frac{O \Omega}{1^2}+\frac{O^2 \Omega^2}{1^2 . 2^2}-\frac{O^3 \Omega^3}{1^2 . 2^2 . 3^2}+\ldots\right\} F,$$

and this, or its equivalent the second expression, is necessarily zero, for there are no seminvariants (cf. § 112) for which $ip-2w=-1$.

It will be noticed that the operator in (3) has the advantage over those in (1) and (2) of not involving η explicitly, though for its effectiveness we must have $\eta \nless -1$. The general conclusion arrived at is that if we write down any gradient or sum of gradients whatever, with arbitrary multipliers, and arbitrary degrees and weights subject to $ip-2w \nless -1$, the result of operating on that sum with

$$1-\frac{O\Omega}{1^2}+\frac{\Omega O^2\Omega}{1^2.2^2}-\frac{\Omega^2O^3\Omega}{1^2.2^2.3^2}+\dots$$

is a sum of seminvariants and invariants, except for cases when it vanishes, as it must in particular for degree-weights subject to $ip-2w=-1$.

It is not hard to show by § 125 that the operators in (1), (2), (3), though in very different forms, are the same.

181. We thus obtain all seminvariants and invariants whatever. To see this it suffices to observe that the result of operating on any seminvariant S is to produce S itself, for $\Omega S=0$, so that $O\Omega S=0$, $\Omega O^2\Omega S=0$, &c.

If, then, we operate on the most general gradient of weight w, degree i, and extent in no term exceeding p, which accordingly contains $(w;\, i,\, p)$ arbitraries, we obtain a result with $(w;\, i,\, p)-(w-1;\, i,\, p)$ arbitraries, which is the most general seminvariant of the type in question. There is always the requirement $ip-2w \nless -1$.

We may distinguish between those gradients of type w, i, p from which either form of operator produces seminvariants, and those which it annihilates. The latter are those gradients F of the type which are of the form OF'. [Note that if $ip-2(ip-w)$, i.e. $2w-ip$, were positive, all gradients F would be of the form OF', by the duality of Ω and O and the fact that when $ip-2w$ is positive all gradients are of the form $\Omega F''$. But we are attending to cases in which $ip-2w \nless -1$, for which, except in the one case where $\nless$ is replaced by $=$, there is no such expression in general possible.]

This we can see as follows. First, if the result of operation vanishes, F is of the form OF', for the expression of the vanishing of (2) may be written

$$F=O\left\{\frac{\Omega}{1.(\eta+2)}-\frac{O\Omega^2}{1.2.(\eta+2)(\eta+3)}+\dots\right\}F,$$

which is of the form in question. Secondly, the operator must annihilate an OF'. For

$$\left\{1-\frac{O\Omega}{1.(\eta+2)}+\frac{O^2\Omega^2}{1.2.(\eta+2)(\eta+3)}-\dots\right\}OF'$$

$$=O\left\{1-\frac{\Omega O}{1.(\eta+2)}+\frac{O\Omega^2 O}{1.2.(\eta+2)(\eta+3)}-\dots\right\}F',$$

$$=O\left\{1-\frac{\Omega O}{1.(\eta+2)}+\frac{\Omega O^2\Omega}{1.2.(\eta+2)(\eta+3)}-\dots\right\}F',$$

since $O\Omega.\Omega O=\Omega O.O\Omega$, $O^2\Omega^2.\Omega O=\Omega O.O^2\Omega^2,\dots$ by § 125, Ex. 4. Now this must vanish, for $\eta+2$ is the η of F' and is positive, so that the expression is O operating on a vanishing result, by the first equality in § 180.

182. To determine seminvariants and invariants by this method we naturally operate on the simplest gradients we can choose, i.e. on single products of letters chosen from among $a_0, a_1, a_2, \dots a_p$. Unfortunately no simple rule presents itself as to what products can and what cannot be written in the form OF', i.e. what products lead to seminvariants or invariants and what to zeroes.

In the next chapter we shall, however, see that when we are not limited to a particular extent p a like method can be employed with perfect definiteness, and we can assign an exact system of products to which there is a one to one correspondence of seminvariants.

Ex. 30. Obtain the invariant $ace+2bcd-ad^2-b^2e-c^3$ of a quartic by operating on a single term of it with

$$1-\frac{O\Omega}{1.2}+\frac{O^2\Omega^2}{1.2^2.3}-\frac{O^3\Omega^3}{1.2^2.3^2.4}+\dots.$$

Ex. 31. If $F=OF'$, where F is of the type w, i, p and $ip-2w \nless -1$, prove that

$$F'=\Omega\left\{\frac{1}{1^2}-\frac{\Omega O}{1^2.2^2}+\frac{\Omega^2 O^2}{1^2.2^2.3^2}-\dots\right\}F.$$

Hence if F' is general of type $w-1$, i, p, so as to involve $(w-1\,;\,i,p)$ arbitrary coefficients, F or OF' must also be a sum of $(w-1\,;\,i,p)$ independent multiples of linearly independent gradients.

182 (*bis*). The above has all been stated for one quantic only. In the case of a system, we have only to replace Ω and O by $\Sigma\Omega$ and ΣO, and to mean $\Sigma(ip)-2w$ by η.

Also covariants of a p-ic are (§ 69) invariants of the p-ic and $xy'-x'y$, with accents removed. Thus, in particular, from a rational integral function of $a_0, a_1, \dots a_p$ and x, y of degree i and order ϖ, and of total weight $\frac{1}{2}(ip+\varpi)$, attaching weights 1, 0 to x and y, the operator

$$1-\frac{O'\Omega'}{1.2}+\frac{O'^2\Omega'^2}{1.2^2.3}-\frac{O'^3\Omega'^3}{1.2^2.3^2.4}+\dots,$$

where $\Omega'\equiv\Omega-y\partial/\partial x$ and $O'\equiv O-x\partial/\partial y$, derives a covariant or zero.

Ex. 32. Show that the covariant produced from Sx^{ϖ}, the first term in a covariant C, by operation with $1-\frac{1}{1.2}O'\Omega'+\dots$ is $\frac{1}{\varpi+1}C$.

Ex. 33. If $K_2, K_4, \dots K_{2n}$ are the covariants of a $2n$-ic or $(2n+1)$-ic u which are led by the quadratic protomorphs $C_2, C_4, \dots C_{2n}$, and if K is any other covariant (*not* invariant), a relation holds of the form

$$K^n=\Gamma_0 u+\Gamma_1 K_2+\Gamma_2 K_4+\dots+\Gamma_n K_{2n},$$

where n is a positive integer, and $\Gamma_0, \Gamma_1, \dots \Gamma_n$ are covariants.

Ans. In Ex. 21, with S the seminvariant leader of K, substitute $u, \frac{1}{p}\frac{\partial u}{\partial y}, \frac{1}{p(p-1)}\frac{\partial^2 u}{\partial y^2}, \dots$ for $a_0, a_1, a_2, \dots$. By § 160 a relation

$$x^{mw}K^m=Q_0 u+Q_1 K_2+Q_2 K_4+\dots+Q_n K_{2n}$$

follows, where such as do not vanish among $Q_0, Q_1, \dots Q_n$ are rational and integral in the coefficients and variables. Multiply by x^{λ}, so choosing λ that $\lambda+mw=\mu(ip-2w)$, with μ an integer, and also by S^{μ}. Then operate as above, getting the result with $m+\mu$ for n.

CHAPTER XI

FURTHER THEORY OF SEMINVARIANTS. THE BINARY QUANTIC OF INFINITE ORDER.

183. **Ω expressed by means of roots.** We commence this chapter by a consideration of the expression of seminvariants by means of the roots of a quantic, and more particularly by means of the sums of like powers of the roots, which might well have been given at a much earlier stage.

It was seen in § 91 that a seminvariant of

$$(a_0, a_1, a_2, \dots a_p)(x, 1)^p,$$

in virtue of its having

$$\Omega \equiv a_0 \frac{\partial}{\partial a_1} + 2a_1 \frac{\partial}{\partial a_2} + \dots + pa_{p-1} \frac{\partial}{\partial a_p} \qquad \dots (1)$$

for an annihilator, is a function of a_0 and the differences between roots. It is accordingly annihilated by

$$\Sigma\left(\frac{\partial}{\partial \alpha}\right) \equiv \frac{\partial}{\partial \alpha_1} + \frac{\partial}{\partial \alpha_2} + \dots + \frac{\partial}{\partial \alpha_p}, \qquad \dots (2)$$

where $\alpha_1, \alpha_2, \dots \alpha_p$ are the roots. In § 88 we have seen that functions of the roots annihilated by (2) are necessarily functions of their differences.

We can see as follows, what is thus suggested, that the effects on any function of the coefficients, which is therefore a function of a_0 and the roots, of the operators (1) and (2) are identical, but for sign.

If

$$f(x) \equiv (a_0, a_1, a_2, \dots a_p)(x, 1)^p \equiv a_0 (x-\alpha_1)(x-\alpha_2)\dots(x-\alpha_p),$$

$$\frac{\partial}{\partial \alpha_1} f(x) \equiv -a_0 (x-\alpha_2)(x-\alpha_3)\dots(x-\alpha_p) \equiv -\frac{f(x)}{x-\alpha_1}.$$

Therefore $$\Sigma\left(\frac{\partial}{\partial \alpha}\right) f(x) \equiv -\Sigma \frac{f(x)}{x-\alpha} \equiv -f'(x).$$

Now in this identity equate coefficients of the same powers of x on the left and right. It follows that

$$\Sigma\left(\frac{\partial}{\partial \alpha}\right) a_0 = 0,$$

$$\Sigma\left(\frac{\partial}{\partial \alpha}\right) a_1 = -a_0,$$

$$\Sigma\left(\frac{\partial}{\partial a}\right)a_2 = -2a_1,$$

$$\cdot \quad \cdot \quad \cdot \quad \cdot \quad \cdot \quad \cdot \quad \cdot$$

$$\Sigma\left(\frac{\partial}{\partial a}\right)a_p = -pa_{p-1}.$$

Consequently, when operating on any function of

$$a_0, a_1, a_2, \dots a_p,$$

$$\Sigma\left(\frac{\partial}{\partial a}\right) \equiv \Sigma\left(\frac{\partial}{\partial a}\right)a_0 \cdot \frac{\partial}{\partial a_0}$$
$$+ \Sigma\left(\frac{\partial}{\partial a}\right)a_1 \cdot \frac{\partial}{\partial a_1} + \dots + \Sigma\left(\frac{\partial}{\partial a}\right)a_p \cdot \frac{\partial}{\partial a_p}$$
$$\equiv -a_0\frac{\partial}{\partial a_1} - 2a_1\frac{\partial}{\partial a_2} - \dots - pa_{p-1}\frac{\partial}{\partial a_p}$$
$$\equiv -\Omega.$$

184. **Ω expressed by means of sums of powers of roots.** Now by Newton's formulae for symmetric functions (Burnside and Panton, 4th ed., § 77), $a_1, a_2, \dots a_p$ can be expressed, rationally and integrally, in terms of a_0 and $s_1, s_2, \dots s_p$, the sums of the first, second, ... pth powers of the roots. Thus any rational integral function of $a_0, a_1, a_2, \dots a_p$ may be expressed as a rational integral function of a_0 and $s_1, s_2, \dots s_p$. Let us find the expression for $\Sigma(\partial/\partial a)$ which is suitable for operating with on functions so expressed.

We have at once $\quad \dfrac{\partial}{\partial a_1}s_r = ra_1^{r-1},$

so that $\quad \Sigma\left(\dfrac{\partial}{\partial a}\right)s_r = rs_{r-1}.$

In particular $\quad \Sigma\left(\dfrac{\partial}{\partial a}\right)s_1 = p = s_0$, say.

Also $\Sigma\left(\dfrac{\partial}{\partial a}\right)a_0 = 0$. Thus, the operation being on a function of a_0 and $s_1, s_2, \dots s_p$,

$$\Sigma\left(\frac{\partial}{\partial a}\right) \equiv \Sigma\left(\frac{\partial}{\partial a}\right)a_0 \cdot \frac{\partial}{\partial a_0} + \Sigma\left(\frac{\partial}{\partial a}\right)s_1 \cdot \frac{\partial}{\partial s_1}$$
$$+ \Sigma\left(\frac{\partial}{\partial a}\right)s_2 \cdot \frac{\partial}{\partial s_2} + \dots + \Sigma\left(\frac{\partial}{\partial a}\right)s_p \cdot \frac{\partial}{\partial s_p}$$
$$\equiv s_0\frac{\partial}{\partial s_1} + 2s_1\frac{\partial}{\partial s_2} + \dots + ps_{p-1}\frac{\partial}{\partial s_p},$$

here $s_0 = p$.

We conclude that

$$\Omega \equiv a_0 \frac{\partial}{\partial a_1} + 2a_1 \frac{\partial}{\partial a_2} + \ldots + pa_{p-1} \frac{\partial}{\partial a_p}$$
$$\equiv -\left\{s_0 \frac{\partial}{\partial s_1} + 2s_1 \frac{\partial}{\partial s_2} + \ldots + ps_{p-1} \frac{\partial}{\partial s_p}\right\},$$

i.e. that the Ω operator is identical in form, but for sign, when expressed in form for operation on a function of a_0 and the s's, as when expressed in form for operation on the equivalent function of $a_0, a_1, a_2, \ldots a_p$. Note however the absence of a_0 from the s-form of Ω.

We gather then that, when a function of $a_0, a_1, a_2, \ldots a_p$ is a seminvariant, so is the same function of s_0, i.e. p, and $s_1, s_2, \ldots s_p$. The latter function when expressed in terms of the a's will of course have a negative power of a_0 as factor, since the s's are functions of the ratios of the a's to a_0.

The idea of this duality appears to be due to M. Roberts.

Ex. 1. If a homogeneous isobaric function of degree i, in the coefficients, and weight w, be called ϕ_1 when expressed in terms of $a_0, a_1, a_2, \ldots a_p$, and ϕ_2 when expressed in terms of a_0 and the roots, ϕ_3 when expressed in terms of a_0 and $s_1, s_2, \ldots s_p$, and ϕ when no particular expression is necessarily implied, prove that

$$i\phi = \left(a_0 \frac{\partial}{\partial a_0} + a_1 \frac{\partial}{\partial a_1} + \ldots + a_p \frac{\partial}{\partial a_p}\right) \phi_1 = a_0 \frac{\partial}{\partial a_0} \phi_2 = a_0 \frac{\partial}{\partial a_0} \phi_3.$$

Ex. 2. With the same notation

$$w\phi = \left(a_1 \frac{\partial}{\partial a_1} + 2a_2 \frac{\partial}{\partial a_2} + \ldots + pa_p \frac{\partial}{\partial a_p}\right) \phi_1 = \Sigma \left(a \frac{\partial}{\partial a}\right) \phi_2$$
$$= \left(s_1 \frac{\partial}{\partial s_1} + 2s_2 \frac{\partial}{\partial s_2} + \ldots + ps_p \frac{\partial}{\partial s_p}\right) \phi_3.$$

Ex. 3. With the same notation

$$\left\{O - ip \frac{a_1}{a_0}\right\} \phi = \left\{\left[pa_1 \frac{\partial}{\partial a_0} + (p-1) a_2 \frac{\partial}{\partial a_1} + \ldots + a_p \frac{\partial}{\partial a_{p-1}}\right]\right.$$
$$\left. - p \frac{a_1}{a_0} \left[a_0 \frac{\partial}{\partial a_0} + a_1 \frac{\partial}{\partial a_1} + \ldots + a_p \frac{\partial}{\partial a_p}\right]\right\} \phi_1$$
$$= \Sigma \left(a^2 \frac{\partial}{\partial a}\right) \phi_2 = \left\{s_2 \frac{\partial}{\partial s_1} + 2s_3 \frac{\partial}{\partial s_2} + \ldots + ps_{p+1} \frac{\partial}{\partial s_p}\right\} \phi_3,$$

which by Ex. 1 may also be written

$$O\phi = \left[pa_1 \frac{\partial}{\partial a_0} + (p-1) a_2 \frac{\partial}{\partial a_1} + \ldots + a_p \frac{\partial}{\partial a_{p-1}}\right] \phi_1$$

$$= \left\{\Sigma\left(a^2 \frac{\partial}{\partial a}\right) - \Sigma(a)\, a_0 \frac{\partial}{\partial a_0}\right\} \phi_2$$

$$= \left\{-s_1 a_0 \frac{\partial}{\partial a_0} + s_2 \frac{\partial}{\partial s_1} + 2 s_3 \frac{\partial}{\partial s_2} + \dots + p s_{p+1} \frac{\partial}{\partial s_p}\right\} \phi_3.$$

Ans. Prove the ϕ_1, ϕ_2 equality by considering that, as in § 183, the effect of $-O$ is that of $\Sigma(\partial/\partial a^{-1})$ on the function expressed in terms of a_p and $a_1, a_2, \dots a_p$.

Ex. 4. By means of the expressions for the operators in terms of a_0 and roots prove the known equivalence of an operator and a multiplier

$$\Omega O - O \Omega = ip - 2w.$$

Ex. 5. By Leibnitz' theorem prove (§ 125, Ex. 1) that

$$\Omega^r O - O \Omega^r \equiv (-1)^r \left\{\left(\Sigma \frac{\partial}{\partial a}\right)^r \left[\Sigma\left(a^2 \frac{\partial}{\partial a}\right) - \Sigma(a)\, a_0 \frac{\partial}{\partial a_0}\right] - \left[\Sigma\left(a^2 \frac{\partial}{\partial a}\right) - \Sigma(a)\, a_0 \frac{\partial}{\partial a_0}\right] \left(\Sigma \frac{\partial}{\partial a}\right)^r\right\}$$

$$= r(ip - 2w + r - 1)\, \Omega^{r-1}.$$

Ex. 6. By means of the equivalence of

$$\Sigma\left(\frac{\partial}{\partial a}\right) \text{ and } s_0 \frac{\partial}{\partial s_1} + 2 s_1 \frac{\partial}{\partial s_2} + \dots + p s_{p-1} \frac{\partial}{\partial s_p},$$

prove that, if $s_{p+1}, s_{p+2}, \dots$ be regarded as functions of $s_1, s_2, \dots s_p$,

$$-\Omega s_{p+r} = \left(s_0 \frac{\partial}{\partial s_1} + 2 s_1 \frac{\partial}{\partial s_2} + \dots + p s_{p-1} \frac{\partial}{\partial s_p}\right) s_{p+r} = (p+r)\, s_{p+r-1}.$$

Ex. 7. By means of Ex. 3 prove that, whether m be less than equal to or greater than p,

$$m s_{m+1} = \left(s_2 \frac{\partial}{\partial s_1} + 2 s_3 \frac{\partial}{\partial s_2} + \dots + p s_{p+1} \frac{\partial}{\partial s_p}\right) s_m = O s_m.$$

Ex. 8. Also, even when m exceeds p,

$$m s_{m-1} = \left(s_0 \frac{\partial}{\partial s_1} + 2 s_1 \frac{\partial}{\partial s_2} + \dots + p s_{p-1} \frac{\partial}{\partial s_p}\right) s_m = -\Omega s_m.$$

185. It must be borne in mind that two distinct things may be meant by the expression of a function of $a_0, a_1, a_2, \dots a_p$ in terms of a_0 and the sums of the powers of the roots. We may mean the expression in terms of a_0 and $s_1, s_2, s_3, \dots s_p$ only. This expression is in all cases unique, and, when the function of $a_0, a_1, a_2, \dots a_p$ is rational and integral and of weight not greater than p, is the only expression. When, however, the weight exceeds p, there will be, as a rule, also other expressions involving $s_{p+1}, s_{p+2}, \dots$ or some of them as well as lower sums. The above articles contemplate the unique

expression obtained from any correct expression by giving in it to $s_{p+1}, s_{p+2}, \ldots$ their values in terms of $s_1, s_2, \ldots s_p$.

We shall have occasion presently to consider the binary quantic of infinite order, in which the series $a_0, a_1, a_2, a_3, \ldots$ of coefficients is unending. In its case the distinction does not arise.

Ex. 9. Prove that, if a homogeneous isobaric function ϕ of $a_0, a_1, a_2, \ldots a_p$ is expressed in any manner in terms of a_0 and $s_1, s_2, \ldots s_p, s_{p+1}, \ldots$, and when so expressed is called ϕ_4,

(1) $\Omega\phi = -\left\{s_0 \frac{\partial}{\partial s_1} + 2 s_1 \frac{\partial}{\partial s_2} + \ldots \text{ to } \infty\right\} \phi_4,$

(2) $i\phi = a_0 \frac{\partial}{\partial a_0} \phi_4,$

(3) $w\phi = \left\{s_1 \frac{\partial}{\partial s_1} + 2 s_2 \frac{\partial}{\partial s_2} + \ldots \text{ to } \infty\right\} \phi_4,$

(4) $\left\{O - ip\frac{a_1}{a_0}\right\} \phi = \left\{s_2 \frac{\partial}{\partial s_1} + 2 s_3 \frac{\partial}{\partial s_2} + \ldots \text{ to } \infty\right\} \phi_4.$

186. **Completion of § 174.** It is interesting to gather, from § 183 and the examples which follow § 184, the following conclusions:

$$-\Omega = \Sigma\left(\frac{\partial}{\partial a}\right),$$

$$w - \frac{a_1}{a_0}\Omega = \Sigma\left\{\left(a + \frac{a_1}{a_0}\right)\frac{\partial}{\partial a}\right\},$$

$$O - \frac{a_1}{a_0}(ip - 2w) - \frac{a_1^2}{a_0^2}\Omega = \Sigma\left\{\left(a + \frac{a_1}{a_0}\right)^2 \frac{\partial}{\partial a}\right\},$$

which, if we put a' for $a + \frac{a_1}{a_0}$ and similarly as to all the roots, i.e. if we transform $(a_0, a_1, a_2, \ldots a_p)(x, 1)^p$ into

$$(a_0, 0, a_2', \ldots a_p')(x + a_1/a_0, 1)^p,$$

a form without its second term, may be written

$$-\Omega = \Sigma\left(\frac{\partial}{\partial a'}\right) \quad = -\Omega',$$

$$w - \frac{a_1}{a_0}\Omega = \Sigma\left(a' \frac{\partial}{\partial a'}\right) = w',$$

$$O - \frac{a_1}{a_0}(ip - 2w) - \frac{a_1^2}{a_0^2}\Omega = \Sigma\left(a'^2 \frac{\partial}{\partial a'}\right) = O',$$

the remainders of the right-hand sides vanishing since $a_1' = 0$.

We must not lose sight here of the tacit assumption made that the function operated on can be expressed in terms of a_0 and a_1+a_1/a_0, a_2+a_1/a_0, ... a_p+a_1/a_0, which we have called a_1', a_2', ... a_p'. The functions which can be so expressed are, we know, seminvariants. The second equation really exhibits the fact anew. The weights w and w' are equal. Consequently that equation gives $\Omega = 0$, i.e. that the function operated on is a seminvariant.

In these equalities Ω', O' and w' (regarded as an operator) are the same operators in $a_0, a_1' (= 0), a_2', \ldots a_p'$ as Ω, O and w are in $a_0, a_1, a_2, \ldots a_p$. They contain the symbol $\partial/\partial a_1'$ whose meaning is not obvious, but is really defined by the first of the equalities.

This symbol may be eliminated by subtracting $(p-1)a_2'$ times Ω' from a_0 times O'. We have, in fact, since $a_2' = a_2 - a_1^2/a_0$,

$$a_0 O' - (p-1)\,a_2'\Omega' = a_0 O - a_1\,(ip-2w) \\ - \{(p-1)\,a_2 - (p-2)\,a_1^2/a_0\}\,\Omega.$$

We may take this in connexion with § 174. The operator on the left is the ψ' of that article. We have, in fact, here before us the materials for the proof of the converse proposition there stated, that every gradient in $a_0, a_2', a_3', \ldots a_p'$ for which $ip-2w = 0$ and which has ψ' for an annihilator is an invariant, i.e. is annihilated by O as well as by Ω, which last must annihilate it as it does any function of $a_0, a_2', a_3', \ldots a_p'$. We remember that the facts of being annihilated by Ω, and being of properly connected degree and weight, were not sufficient to assure us of its invariancy, in default of evidence either that it had O for an annihilator or that it was integral in a_0. We now see that as Ω and ψ' annihilate it, and as the relation $ip = 2w$ holds, the annihilation by $a_0 O$, and therefore by O, follows.

Ex. 10. Prove that $a_0 O - a_1(ip-2w)$ cannot annihilate any function which is fractional in a_0 and for which $ip-2w$ is zero or positive.

Ans. The terms of highest degree in a_0^{-1} in the expression of the annihilation of $Pa_0^{-\mu} + Qa_0^{-(\mu-1)} + \ldots + T$ must vanish. This gives $P = 0$. So $Q = 0$, &c.

Ex. 11. Any gradient in $a_0, a_1, a_2, \ldots a_p$ for which $ip-2w$ is positive and which is annihilated by $a_0 O - a_1(ip-2w)$, is the product of a power of a_0 and a gradient which it annihilates and for which

$$ip-2w = 0.$$

Ex. 12. Hence ψ' only annihilates gradients in $a_0, a_2', a_3', \ldots a_p'$ which are invariants or invariants multiplied by powers of a_0.

187. **Partial differentiation with regard to $s_1, s_2, \dots s_p$.** Let us replace $a_0, pa_1, \frac{p(p-1)}{1.2}a_2, \dots, a_p$ by $c_0, c_1, c_2, \dots, c_p$, and also replace $x:1$ by $1:y$, thus considering the p-ic without binomial coefficients

$$c_0 + c_1 y + c_2 y^2 + \dots + c_p y^p \equiv c_0 (1-\alpha_1 y)(1-\alpha_2 y)\dots(1-\alpha_p y).$$

Taking logarithms we have at once

$$\log(c_0 + c_1 y + c_2 y^2 + \dots + c_p y^p)$$
$$= \log c_0 - s_1 y - s_2 \frac{y^2}{2} - s_3 \frac{y^3}{3} - \dots - s_p \frac{y^p}{p} - s_{p+1}\frac{y^{p+1}}{p+1} - \dots.$$

Now regard $c_1, c_2, \dots c_p$, and also $s_{p+1}, s_{p+2}, \dots$ as functions of c_0 and $s_1, s_2, \dots s_p$. Partial differentiation with regard to s_r, where $r \not< 1$ and $\not> p$, gives us the identity

$$\frac{\partial c_1}{\partial s_r} y + \frac{\partial c_2}{\partial s_r} y^2 + \dots + \frac{\partial c_p}{\partial s_r} y^p = (c_0 + c_1 y + c_2 y^2 + \dots + c_p y^p)$$
$$\left\{ -\frac{y^r}{r} - \frac{\partial s_{p+1}}{\partial s_r}\frac{y^{p+1}}{p+1} - \frac{\partial s_{p+2}}{\partial s_r}\frac{y^{p+2}}{p+2} - \dots \right\}$$

which holds for all values of y. Equating corresponding coefficients on the two sides we have

$$\frac{\partial c_m}{\partial s_r} = 0, \text{ if } m < r, \text{ and}$$

$$\frac{\partial c_m}{\partial s_r} = -\frac{1}{r} c_{m-r}, \text{ if } m \text{ lie between } r \text{ and } p \text{ inclusive.}$$

The other equations, given by the terms in $y^{p+1}, y^{p+2}, \dots$, determine for us $\frac{\partial s_{p+1}}{\partial s_r}, \frac{\partial s_{p+2}}{\partial s_r}, \dots$.

Hence, if the operation upon the right be on a function of $c_0, c_1, c_2, \dots c_p$, and that upon the left on the equivalent of that function in terms of c_0 and $s_1, s_2, \dots s_p$,

$$\frac{\partial}{\partial s_r} = \frac{\partial c_0}{\partial s_r}\cdot\frac{\partial}{\partial c_0} + \frac{\partial c_1}{\partial s_r}\cdot\frac{\partial}{\partial c_1} + \frac{\partial c_2}{\partial s_r}\cdot\frac{\partial}{\partial c_2} + \dots + \frac{\partial c_p}{\partial s_r}\cdot\frac{\partial}{\partial c_p}$$
$$= -\frac{1}{r}\left\{ c_0 \frac{\partial}{\partial c_r} + c_1 \frac{\partial}{\partial c_{r+1}} + \dots + c_{p-r}\frac{\partial}{\partial c_p} \right\}.$$

In particular, taking $r = 1$, we have

$$\frac{\partial}{\partial s_1} = -\left\{ c_0 \frac{\partial}{\partial c_1} + c_1 \frac{\partial}{\partial c_2} + c_2 \frac{\partial}{\partial c_3} + \dots + c_{p-1}\frac{\partial}{\partial c_p} \right\}.$$

Let us now revert to our first notation, replacing

$$c_0, c_1, c_2, \dots c_p \text{ by } a_0, pa_1, \frac{p(p-1)}{1.2} a_2, \dots a_p,$$

so that s_1, &c., are the sums of the powers of the roots of

$$(a_0, a_1, a_2, \dots a_p)(x, 1)^p = 0.$$

The result obtained is that

$$\frac{\partial}{\partial s_1} = -\left\{\frac{1}{p} a_0 \frac{\partial}{\partial a_1} + \frac{2}{p-1} a_1 \frac{\partial}{\partial a_2} + \frac{3}{p-2} a_2 \frac{\partial}{\partial a_3} + \dots + \frac{p}{1} a_{p-1} \frac{\partial}{\partial a_p}\right\}.$$

188. **Ω as an annihilator of non-unitary symmetric functions.** A more instructive conclusion is, however, derived by replacing $c_0, c_1, c_2, \dots c_p$ by $b_0, \frac{b_1}{1!}, \frac{b_2}{2!}, \frac{b_3}{3!}, \dots$, so that the equation of which $s_1, s_2, \dots s_p$ are the first p sums of the powers of the roots is

$$b_0 x^p + \frac{b_1}{1!} x^{p-1} + \frac{b_2}{2!} x^{p-2} + \dots + \frac{b_p}{p!} = 0.$$

With this notation we obtain that

$$-\frac{\partial}{\partial s_1} = b_0 \frac{\partial}{\partial b_1} + 2b_1 \frac{\partial}{\partial b_2} + 3b_2 \frac{\partial}{\partial b_3} + \dots + pb_{p-1} \frac{\partial}{\partial b_p},$$

whose right-hand side is of the well-known form of Ω.

Our conclusion hence is that the seminvariants of

$$a_0 x^p + pa_1 x^{p-1} y + \frac{p(p-1)}{1.2} a_2 x^{p-2} y^2 + \dots + a_p y^p$$

are identical, but for the factor a_0^i where i is the degree in each case, with those symmetric functions of the roots of

$$a_0 x^p + \frac{a_1}{1!} x^{p-1} + \frac{a_2}{2!} x^{p-2} + \dots + \frac{a_p}{p!} = 0$$

which when expressed in terms of $s_1, s_2, \dots s_p$ are free from s_1.

Reference is made to works on the Theory of Equations for the fact that a symmetric function

$$\Sigma . \alpha_1^l \alpha_2^m \alpha_3^n \dots,$$

of which $l+m+n+\dots$ is the weight, and the greatest of $l, m, n, \dots$ is the least number which can be taken for i that upon multiplication by a_0^i it may become integral in the coefficients, may be written as a rational integral function of

$$\begin{array}{l} s_l, s_m, s_n, \dots, \\ s_{l+m}, s_{l+n}, s_{m+n}, \dots, \\ s_{l+m+n}, \dots, \\ \cdot \quad \cdot \quad \cdot \quad \cdot \quad \cdot, \end{array}$$

so that, if none of $l, m, n, \ldots$ is unity, and if the weight $l+m+n+\ldots$ does not exceed p, s_1 does not occur, and a seminvariant is thus obtained.

If, however, either of $l, m, n, \ldots$ is unity no seminvariant is given.

If, even though this be not the case, the weight $l+m+n+\ldots$ exceeds p, then, though the expression in terms of a_0 and $s_1, s_2, s_3, \ldots, s_{l+m+n+\ldots}$ does not involve s_1, the same cannot be said necessarily or as a rule of the expression in terms of a_0 and $s_1, s_2, \ldots s_p$; for s_{p+1}, &c., expressed in terms of $s_1, s_2, \ldots s_p$, are not free from s_1 by § 187.

When p is infinite the case of $l+m+n+\ldots$ exceeding p does not arise. Thus in this limiting case s_1 does occur in the symmetric function $\Sigma . \alpha_1{}^l \alpha_2{}^m \alpha_3{}^n \ldots$ if one or more of $l, m, n, \ldots$ is unity, but does not otherwise.

The seminvariants of $(a_0, a_1, a_2, \ldots)(x, y)^p$, when p is infinite, are then what are called the 'non-unitary' symmetric functions of $\alpha_1, \alpha_2, \alpha_3, \ldots$, where

$$a_0 + \frac{a_1}{1!} y + \frac{a_2}{2!} y^2 + \ldots \text{ to } \infty \equiv a_0 (1-\alpha_1 y)(1-\alpha_2 y)(1-\alpha_3 y) \ldots,$$

each multiplied by $a_0{}^i$, where i is the degree, i.e. is the greatest of the indices $l, m, n, \ldots$ in the typical product of roots summed, or any greater number.

It is from this point of view that MacMahon has discussed the concomitants of the binary quantic of infinite order.

It will of course be remembered that a seminvariant, of a quantic of any order $(a_0, a_1, a_2, \ldots a_p)(x, y)^p$, which is only of extent r, i.e. which involves only $a_0, a_1, a_2, \ldots a_r$, is equally a seminvariant of each of the lower quantics

$$(a_0, a_1, a_2, \ldots a_r)(x, y)^r, (a_0, a_1, a_2, \ldots a_r, a_{r+1})(x, y)^{r+1}, \ldots.$$

Thus, in particular, when we have a seminvariant of a binary quantic of infinite order, we have in it a seminvariant of a binary quantic whose order is the extent of the seminvariant and one of every order higher than this extent. If, in fact,

$$a_0 \frac{\partial}{\partial a_1} + 2a_1 \frac{\partial}{\partial a_2} + 3a_2 \frac{\partial}{\partial a_3} + \ldots \text{ to } \infty$$

annihilates $S(a_0, a_1, a_2, \ldots a_r)$, then equally do

$$a_0 \frac{\partial}{\partial a_1} + 2a_1 \frac{\partial}{\partial a_2} + 3a_2 \frac{\partial}{\partial a_3} + \ldots + ra_{r-1} \frac{\partial}{\partial a_r},$$

$$a_0 \frac{\partial}{\partial a_1} + 2a_1 \frac{\partial}{\partial a_2} + 3a_2 \frac{\partial}{\partial a_3} + \ldots + ra_{r-1} \frac{\partial}{\partial a_r} + (r+1) a_r \frac{\partial}{\partial a_{r+1}}$$

&c., &c.

Ex. 13. Prove that, for any positive integral value of p,

$$(a_0, a_1, a_2, \ldots a_p)(x, 1)^p = \left(a_0 + \frac{a_1}{1}\frac{\partial}{\partial x} + \frac{a_2}{2\,!}\frac{\partial^2}{\partial x^2} + \frac{a_3}{3\,!}\frac{\partial^3}{\partial x^3} + \ldots \text{ to } \infty\right) x^p.$$

Ex. 14. Prove that all the coefficients but that of t in the expansion in powers of t of

$$\log\left(a_0 + \frac{a_1}{1}t + \frac{a_2}{2\,!}t^2 + \frac{a_3}{3\,!}t^3 + \ldots\right) - \log a_0$$

are seminvariants in the letters $a_0, a_1, a_2, a_3, \ldots$, fractional in a_0.

189. **Generating functions. Perpetuants.** Complete tables of symmetric functions have been calculated up to the weight 14: for weights 1 to 10 by Meyer Hirsch (cf. Notes to Salmon's *Higher Algebra*): for weight 11 by Faà de Bruno (cf. his *Formes Binaires*): for weights 12 and 14 by Durfee (*Am. Journal*, Vols. V, IX): and for weight 13 by MacMahon (*Am. Journal*, Vol. VI). Thus a complete set of seminvariants up to weight 14, of which all seminvariants whatever up to that weight are linear functions, is known.

It has been seen (§ 135) that the number of linearly independent seminvariants of weight w degree i and extent p or less is the coefficient of x^w in the developement of

$$\frac{(1-x^{p+1})(1-x^{p+2})\ldots(1-x^{p+i})}{(1-x^2)(1-x^3)\ldots(1-x^i)}.$$

Here make $p=\infty$. It follows that the whole number of linearly independent seminvariants of weight w and degree i of the quantic of infinite order, or of a quantic of order not less than the weight w, is

$$\text{co. } x^w \text{ in developement of } \frac{1}{(1-x^2)(1-x^3)\ldots(1-x^i)}.$$

We may want also the number of linearly independent (or asyzygetic) seminvariants of degree-weight i, w which are asyzygetic with seminvariants of the same weight and lower degrees multiplied by powers of a_0. This number may be found by subtracting from the number of weight w and degree i the number of weight w and degree $i-1$. Thus it is

$$\text{co. } x^w \text{ in developement of } \frac{1}{(1-x^2)(1-x^3)\ldots(1-x^{i-1})(1-x^i)} - \frac{1}{(1-x^2)(1-x^3)\ldots(1-x^{i-1})}$$

$$= \quad ,, \qquad ,, \qquad \frac{x^i}{(1-x^2)(1-x^3)\ldots(1-x^i)}.$$

The same generating function is given by MacMahon's theory of non-unitary symmetric functions. The non-unitary symmetric functions which give such seminvariants are of the form $\Sigma . a_1^l a_2^m a_3^n \ldots$, where one at least of the indices $l, m, n, \ldots$ is i, and where, as in general, none of them is unity or greater than i, and their sum is the weight. Now the type-products of weight w, whose summations give such symmetric functions, are in number equal to the number of ways in which $w-i$ may be made up of $i-1$ or fewer numbers chosen from 2, 3, ... i, i.e. to the coefficient of x^{w-i} in the expansion of the product

$$(1+x^2+x^4+\ldots)(1+x^3+x^6+\ldots)\ldots(1+x^i+x^{2i}+\ldots),$$

i.e. to the coefficient of x^w in x^i times this product, which is the developement of

$$\frac{x^i}{(1-x^2)(1-x^3)\ldots(1-x^i)}.$$

The problem of the enumeration of the irreducible seminvariants of the binary quantic of infinite order admits of solution. Indeed it has been solved by MacMahon by an analysis of non-unitary partitions, and his conclusions have been confirmed symbolically by Stroh, Grace, and others. Irreducible seminvariants of the quantic of infinite order are called *perpetuants*, the name being Sylvester's. A perpetuant is a seminvariant which cannot be expressed rationally and integrally in terms of other perpetuants of lower degree. Of the first degree there is one perpetuant a_0. Of the second degree there is one perpetuant of each even weight, viz. $a_0a_2-a_1^2, a_0a_4-4a_1a_3+3a_2^2, a_0a_6-6a_1a_5+15a_2a_4-10a_3^2, \ldots$. For any higher degree i the number of perpetuants of weight w is the coefficient of x^w in the developement of the generating function

$$\frac{x^{2^{i-1}-1}}{(1-x^2)(1-x^3)\ldots(1-x^i)}.$$

The mistaken idea must not be entertained that when we know the perpetuants of extent p or less, i.e. the irreducible seminvariants of extent p or less of the quantic of infinite order, we know the irreducible seminvariants or ground forms of a p-ic. This is not the case. There may be seminvariants of extent p or less, which are not capable of rational integral expression in terms of lower seminvariants of extent p or less, but which are in terms of seminvariants of lower degree and extents some of which exceed p. One instance which we have met with will suffice to illustrate this. We have found (§ 169) that the seminvariant $(ad-bc)^2-4(ac-b^2)(bd-c^2)$ is irreducible when we are confined to extent 3, being an irreducible invariant of the cubic. But (§ 170) when we proceed to extent 4 it is no longer irreducible, being capable of being written

$$(ac-b^2)(ae-4bd+3c^2)-a(ace+2bcd-ad^2-b^2e-c^3).$$

It is an irreducible invariant of the cubic, but is reducible for quantics of higher order, and so is not a perpetuant.

For a synopsis of Stroh's method of investigation (*Mathematische Annalen*, XXXVI), see Exx. 36 to 43 at the end of the present chapter.

MacMahon has given completeness to his theory by exhibiting a complete (infinite) system in a notation of partitions (*Proc. Lond. Math. Soc.* XXVI). He has also enumerated perpetuants in more sets than one of coefficients $a_0, a_1, a_2, \ldots$ (*Camb. Phil. Soc. Trans.* XIX).

Further light has more recently been thrown on the subject by [1] Grace, Young, P. W. Wood, and the present author, by consideration first of i distinct sets of coefficients, and of perpetuant types linear in every set.

190. **Reciprocity.** By Hermite's law of reciprocity there must be a strictly correlative theory to much of the above in which the ideas of degree and extent are interchanged. It has reference to seminvariants of a p-ic for advanced degrees i, just as the above theory refers to seminvariants of degree i for advanced extents p.

The number of asyzygetic seminvariants of weight w of a p-ic, for which the degree i is very great (or not less than w), is thus the coefficient of x^w in the developement of

$$\frac{1}{(1-x^2)(1-x^3)\ldots(1-x^p)};$$

and the number of these which are really of extent p, so as not to belong to a $(p-1)$-ic equally, is the coefficient of x^w in the developement of

$$\frac{x^p}{(1-x^2)(1-x^3)\ldots(1-x^p)}.$$

These facts may be independently arrived at. By § 163 the seminvariants in question are rational integral functions of $A_2, A_3, \ldots A_p$, i.e. $a_0a_2', a_0^2a_3', \ldots a_0^{p-1}a_p'$, raised to the requisite excess of degree over weight by the power a_0^{i-w} of a_0 as factor.

The theory dual to that of perpetuants has not been shown to be of great importance. For a consideration of it see *Proc. Lond. Math. Soc.*, Ser. 2, IV.

[1] Cf. Grace and Young's *Algebra of Invariants*; Wood, *Proc. Lond. Math. Soc.*, Ser. 2, I, II, III; Elliott, *Quarterly Journal*, XXXVI, *Proc. Lond. Math. Soc.*, Ser. 2, IV.

191. **Power ending products.** It has been noticed in the last article that the

$$(w;\infty, p)-(w-1;\infty, p),$$

i. e. $$(w;w, p)-(w-1;w, p),$$

asyzygetic seminvariants of a p-ic whose weight is w and whose degree is a definite number not less than w have a one to one correspondence with the

$$(w;\infty, p)-(w-1;\infty, p)$$

products of weight w of $a_0, a_2, a_3, \dots a_p$, i. e. with the 'non-unitary' partitions of w.

It is by reciprocity suggested as probable that there is a system of

$$(w;i,\infty)-(w-1;i,\infty)$$

partitions of w into i or fewer parts, i. e. a system of this number of products of weight w of i of $a_0, a_1, a_2, a_3, \dots$, to which there is a one to one correspondence of the

$$(w;i,\infty)-(w-1;i,\infty)$$

asyzygetic seminvariants of weight w and degree i of the p-ic, when p is infinite or not less than w.

It is also suggested that those partitions of w, or those products, are the partitions or products which are exhibited in § 130 by aid of Ferrers' diagrams as the duals to non-unitary partitions or products.

Now if we write down the diagram of a non-unitary product, we see that the absence of a_1 in the product is exhibited by the fact that the first two columns at least in the diagram contain equal numbers of dots.

This tells us that in the dual product the letter of highest suffix which occurs is present to a higher power than the first.

Products of this class are called by MacMahon and Cayley *power ending products* or *power enders*. Let us adopt the notation $a, b, c, \dots$ of alphabetical sequence instead of the notation $a_0, a_1, a_2, \dots$ of numerical sequence. *Power enders* are those products of some of $a, b, c, \dots$ which, when their factors are alphabetically arranged from left to right, end in a higher power than the first. Thus ab^2, abd^3, $c^3, \dots$ are power enders, while a^2b, ab^2d, $c, \dots$ are not. A power of a is not called a power ender.

The whole number of products of weight w of i of $a, b, c, \dots$ is $(w;i,\infty)$, and the whole number of non-power enders is the number of products which can be derived from products of degree i and weight $w-1$ by replacing the last letter in each, once only, by the next more advanced letter, i. e. is $(w-1;i,\infty)$. The number of power enders of the type is then

$$(w;i,\infty)-(w-1;i,\infty).$$

We shall see that there is the expected one to one correspondence of these products with a complete system of $(w\,;\,i,\infty)-(w-1\,;\,i,\infty)$ asyzygetic seminvariants of weight w and degree i; in fact, that the latter complete system may be derived, one from one, by differential operations on the former complete system.

192. **An annihilator of all gradients.** Let us refer back to § 180, and proceed to the limit when p, the order of the quantic there under consideration, or the extent of Ω, is infinite. Remember, too, that though we find it convenient to speak of a quantic of infinite order we deal with gradients of finite weight, involving consequently only a finite series of the letters $a, b, c, d, \ldots$.

We have now

$$\Omega \equiv a\partial_b + 2b\partial_c + 3c\partial_d + \ldots \text{ to } \infty,$$

where ∂_k denotes $\partial/\partial k$. We have also

$$O \equiv pb\partial_a + (p-1)\,c\partial_b + (p-2)\,d\partial_c + \ldots,$$

where p is infinite,

$$\equiv p\{b\partial_a + c\partial_b + d\partial_c + \ldots\} - \{c\partial_b + 2d\partial_c + 3e\partial_d + \ldots\}$$
$$\equiv p\vartheta - \phi, \text{ say,}$$

in which the result of operating with ϕ on a gradient of finite extent vanishes in comparison with that of operating with the infinite $p\vartheta$.

We have also $$\eta = ip - 2w,$$
which is infinite, and consequently always positive, w being finite.

The limiting form for p infinite taken by the operator (2) of § 180 is hence at once seen to be

$$1 - \frac{1}{i}\vartheta\Omega + \frac{1}{i^2}\frac{\vartheta^2\Omega^2}{1\,.\,2} - \frac{1}{i^3}\cdot\frac{\vartheta^3\Omega^3}{1\,.\,2\,.\,3} + \ldots.$$

This then, by § 180, operating on any gradient in $a, b, c, d, \ldots$, and in particular of course on any single product, produces either zero or a seminvariant of the quantic of infinite order, and equally of a quantic of order not less than w, the weight of the gradient.

193. It is really most convincing and easiest to prove this independently, and not deduce it as the limit of something else. The student will have no difficulty in proving by the method of §§ 123, &c., that, G being any gradient of degree i,

$$(\Omega\vartheta - \vartheta\Omega)\,G = iG,$$
$$(\Omega\vartheta^2 - \vartheta^2\Omega)\,\Omega G = 2i\vartheta\Omega G,$$
$$(\Omega\vartheta^3 - \vartheta^3\Omega)\,\Omega^2 G = 3i\vartheta^2\Omega^2 G,$$
&c., &c.,

and by addition of properly chosen multiples of these we obtain the identity

$$\left\{1-\frac{1}{i}\cdot\frac{\Omega\vartheta}{1}+\frac{1}{i^2}\cdot\frac{\Omega\vartheta^2\Omega}{1\,.\,2}-\frac{1}{i^3}\cdot\frac{\Omega\vartheta^3\Omega^2}{1\,.\,2\,.\,3}+\ldots\right\}G=0,$$

in which the series practically terminates, since $\Omega^{w+1}G=0$, so that no doubt arising from questions of convergency presents itself.

This tells us first that any gradient G is of the form ΩF, when we allow the extent of F to be greater than that of G, and Ω to be non-terminating. The limitation imposed by the requirement of $ip-2w$ to be positive in § 128 does not of course arise, p being now infinite.

The result we need follows by putting ΩF, where F is any gradient of degree i, for G. This gives us that

$$\Omega\left\{1-\frac{1}{i}\frac{\vartheta\Omega}{1}+\frac{1}{i^2}\frac{\vartheta^2\Omega^2}{1\,.\,2}-\frac{1}{i^3}\frac{\vartheta^3\Omega^3}{1\,.\,2\,.\,3}+\ldots\right\}F=0,$$

so that, as in the last article,

$$1-\frac{1}{i}\frac{\vartheta\Omega}{1}+\frac{1}{i^2}\frac{\vartheta^2\Omega^2}{1\,.\,2}-\frac{1}{i^3}\frac{\vartheta^3\Omega^3}{1\,.\,2\,.\,3}+\ldots$$

produces from any gradient of degree i a seminvariant or zero.

Ex. 15. Prove in like manner that, with the ϕ of § 192,

$$(\Omega\phi-\phi\Omega)G=2wG,$$
$$(\Omega\phi^2-\phi^2\Omega)\Omega G=2(2w-1)\phi\Omega G,$$
$$(\Omega\phi^3-\phi^3\Omega)\Omega^2G=3(2w-2)\phi^2\Omega^2G,$$

&c. &c.,

and hence that

$$1-\frac{1}{2w-2}\frac{\phi\Omega}{1}+\frac{1}{(2w-2)(2w-3)}\frac{\phi^2\Omega^2}{1\,.\,2}$$
$$-\frac{1}{(2w-2)(2w-3)(2w-4)}\frac{\phi^3\Omega^3}{1\,.\,2\,.\,3}+\ldots,\text{ to }w+1\text{ terms},$$

produces a seminvariant or a zero from every gradient of weight 2 or more.

194. **Two generators of all seminvariants. One to one correspondence of seminvariants and power enders.** Now a gradient F which

$$1-\frac{1}{i}\frac{\vartheta\Omega}{1}+\frac{1}{i^2}\frac{\vartheta^2\Omega^2}{1\,.\,2}-\ldots$$

annihilates is of the form $\vartheta F'$, for the fact of annihilation gives us

$$F=\vartheta\left\{\frac{1}{i}\Omega-\frac{1}{i^2}\frac{\vartheta\Omega^2}{1\,.\,2}+\ldots\right\}F.$$

If then we can be sure that no power ending product can be of the form $\vartheta F'$, we shall be sure that the result of operating on any power ending product is a seminvariant and not a zero.

Now this is the case. Take any gradient F' whatever, and let a_r be the most advanced letter which occurs in it, so that

$$F' = A + a_r B + a_r^2 C + \dots,$$

where $A, B, C, \dots$ are all free from a_r, and $B, C, \dots$ do not all vanish. It follows that

$$\vartheta F' = \left(\dots + a_{r+1}\frac{\partial}{\partial a_r} + \dots\right) F'$$

$$= a_{r+1}\{B + 2a_r C + 3a_r^2 D + \dots\} + \text{terms free from } a_{r+1}.$$

Thus, $B, C, D, \dots$ not all vanishing, $\vartheta F'$ contains necessarily a non-power ending term or terms; namely a term or terms ending in the first power a_{r+1}.

Thus $$1 - \frac{1}{i}\frac{\vartheta\Omega}{1} + \frac{1}{i^2}\frac{\vartheta^2\Omega^2}{1.2} - \dots,$$

which write $$1 - \vartheta\zeta,$$

generates seminvariants from all power enders.

Moreover, from the complete system of

$$(w; i, \infty) - (w-1; i, \infty)$$

power enders of degree i and weight w it generates a complete system of $(w; i, \infty) - (w-1; i, \infty)$ seminvariants of that degree and weight. For, if possible, let the seminvariants

$$S_1 = (1-\vartheta\zeta)P_1,\ S_2 = (1-\vartheta\zeta)P_2,\ S_3 = (1-\vartheta\zeta)P_3, \dots,$$

generated from the complete system of power enders of degree i and weight w, be connected by a linear relation

$$\lambda_1 S_1 + \lambda_2 S_2 + \lambda_3 S_3 + \dots = 0.$$

This would necessitate that

$$\lambda_1(1-\vartheta\zeta)P_1 + \lambda_2(1-\vartheta\zeta)P_2 + \lambda_3(1-\vartheta\zeta)P_3 + \dots = 0,$$

i. e. that $$(1-\vartheta\zeta)(\lambda_1 P_1 + \lambda_2 P_2 + \lambda_3 P_3 + \dots) = 0,$$

or $$\lambda_1 P_1 + \lambda_2 P_2 + \lambda_3 P_3 + \dots = \vartheta . \zeta(\lambda_1 P_1 + \lambda_2 P_2 + \lambda_3 P_3 + \dots),$$

i. e., by the above, that

$$\lambda_1 P_1 + \lambda_2 P_2 + \lambda_3 P_3 + \dots$$

should involve at least one non-power ending product. But it does not.

It is then completely established that there is a one to one correspondence between a complete system of power enders and a complete system of seminvariants, the latter complete system for any degree i being generated from the former by operation with

$$1 - \frac{1}{i}\frac{\vartheta\Omega}{1} + \frac{1}{i^2}\frac{\vartheta^2\Omega^2}{1\,.\,2} - \frac{1}{i^3}\frac{\vartheta^3\Omega^3}{1\,.\,2\,.\,3} + \dots\,.$$

The theorem of § 193, Ex. 15 would lead to the same conclusion as to one to one correspondence, and afford an alternative generator of all seminvariants from power enders.

194 (*bis*). In proving (§ 193) that every G is an ΩF, we noticed that F might have to involve more advanced letters in the series $a_0, a_1, a_2, \dots$ than G does.

Another way of expressing G as an ΩF will make it clear that there is always an F in which these more advanced letters enter, if at all, to the first degree only.

Denote by ψ_w the operator

$$\psi_w \equiv \frac{\partial}{\partial a_w} - \frac{1}{w}\Omega\frac{\partial}{\partial a_{w-1}} + \frac{1}{w(w-1)}\Omega^2\frac{\partial}{\partial a_{w-2}} - \dots + (-1)^w\frac{1}{w!}\Omega^w\frac{\partial}{\partial a_0}\,.$$

Then

$$\begin{aligned}\psi_w\Omega = &\left\{(w+1)\frac{\partial}{\partial a_{w+1}} + \Omega\frac{\partial}{\partial a_w}\right\} - \frac{1}{w}\Omega\left\{w\frac{\partial}{\partial a_w} + \Omega\frac{\partial}{\partial a_{w-1}}\right\} \\ &+ \frac{1}{w(w-1)}\Omega^2\left\{(w-1)\frac{\partial}{\partial a_{w-1}} + \Omega\frac{\partial}{\partial a_{w-2}}\right\} \\ &- \dots + (-1)^w\frac{1}{w!}\Omega^w\left\{\frac{\partial}{\partial a_1} + \Omega\frac{\partial}{\partial a_0}\right\} \\ = &(w+1)\frac{\partial}{\partial a_{w+1}} + (-1)^w\frac{1}{w!}\Omega^{w+1}\frac{\partial}{\partial a_0}\,. \qquad \dots (1)\end{aligned}$$

This, we notice, annihilates any F of weight w or less. If then we take a $G = \Omega F$ of weight w, so that F is of weight $w+1$, we have $\psi_{w+1}G = 0$.

Now

$$\psi_{w+1}G + \frac{1}{w+1}\Omega\psi_w G = \frac{\partial}{\partial a_{w+1}}G, \text{ i. e. } \frac{1}{w+1}\Omega\psi_w G = 0,$$

$$\psi_w G + \frac{1}{w}\Omega\psi_{w-1}G = \frac{\partial}{\partial a_w}G,$$

$$\psi_{w-1}G + \frac{1}{w-1}\Omega\psi_{w-2}G = \frac{\partial}{\partial a_{w-1}}G,$$

. . . .

$$\psi_1 G + \Omega\psi_0 G = \frac{\partial}{\partial a_1}G,$$

$$\psi_0 G = \frac{\partial}{\partial a_0}G.$$

Hence, multiplying by $a_{w+1}, a_w, a_{w-1}, \dots a_1, a_0$ respectively and adding,

$$\Omega\left\{\frac{1}{w+1}a_{w+1}\psi_w+\frac{1}{w}a_w\psi_{w-1}+\dots+a_1\psi_0\right\}G=iG; \qquad \dots (2)$$

and this is a relation $G=\Omega F$ such as desired. Letters more advanced than those occurring in G present themselves to the first degree only, if at all, in F, because $\psi_w G$, $\psi_{w-1} G, \dots$ do not involve the more advanced letters.

We can use the equality here proved to obtain another generator of seminvariants from gradients. Take any F of type w, i, so that ΩF, if not zero, is of type $w-1$, i, and contains no more advanced letter than F does. Taking ΩF for G in (2), with $w-1$ for w, we at once obtain that

$$\left\{1-\frac{1}{i}\left(\frac{1}{w}a_w\psi_{w-1}+\frac{1}{w-1}a_{w-1}\psi_{w-2}+\dots+a_1\psi_0\right)\Omega\right\}F$$

is annihilated by Ω, so that it is a seminvariant or zero.

A much simpler form may be given to this by substitution for $\psi_{w-1}\Omega$, $\psi_{w-2}\Omega, \dots$ from equalities (1), and use of Euler's Theorem as to homogeneous functions. This is

$$\frac{1}{i}\left\{a_0-a_1\Omega+\frac{1}{1\,.\,2}a_2\Omega^2-\dots+(-1)^w\frac{1}{w\,!}a_w\Omega^w\right\}\frac{\partial}{\partial a_0}F.$$

The verification that this is annihilated by Ω, because $\dfrac{\partial}{\partial a_0}F$ is only of weight w, is immediate.

The generator thus provided, continued to infinity, i. e.

$$\frac{1}{i}\left\{a_0-a_1\Omega+\frac{1}{1\,.\,2}a_2\Omega^2-\frac{1}{1\,.\,2\,.\,3}a_3\Omega^3+\dots\right\}\frac{\partial}{\partial a_0}$$

produces all seminvariants from gradients. For the first form in which it was obtained shows that it produces any F satisfying $\Omega F=0$ from itself. The second, and better, form gives the same information, as when $\Omega F=0$ it simply yields

$$i^{-1}\left\{a_0(\partial/\partial a_0)+a_1(\partial/\partial a_1)+a_2(\partial/\partial a_2)+\dots\right\}F,$$

for it is easy to prove that $\Omega^r\partial F/\partial a_0=(-1)^r r\,!\,\partial F/\partial a_r$ when $\Omega F=0$. It does not, however, produce a complete system of seminvariants from a complete system of power enders; for it annihilates those power enders which do not involve a_0.

The seminvariant thus produced from any gradient F cannot be of degree above the first in letters beyond those present in F.

Notice that if F is general of degree i, $(\partial/\partial a_0)F$ is general of degree $i-1$. Thus we have that, if G is the general gradient of weight w and degree $i-1$, then

$$\left\{a_0 - a_1\Omega + \frac{1}{1.2}a_2\Omega^2 - \frac{1}{1.2.3}a_3\Omega^3 + \ldots\right\} G$$

is a sum of arbitrary multiples of all seminvariants of weight w and degree i.

Remembering § 93, we can hence derive the theorem that any seminvariant of weight w is the wth transvectant (lineo-linear invariant) of the w-ic $(a_0, a_1, \ldots a_w)(x, y)^w$ and a w-ic which is a rational integral function of some or all of the former w-ic and its successive x-derivatives. (See also § 262 *bis*.)

ADDITIONAL EXAMPLES (MISCELLANEOUS).

Ex. 16. A non-unitary symmetric function of the roots of an equation of order p, i.e. one whose expression in terms of $s_1, s_2, \ldots s_p$ does not involve s_1, or, if p be not less than the weight $l+m+n+\ldots$, one $\Sigma(a_1{}^l a_2{}^m a_3{}^n \ldots)$ in which none of $l, m, n, \ldots$ is unity, has its full expression in terms of the coefficients determinate when the non-unitary part of that expression, i.e. the part of it free from the unitary coefficient b, is known, just as the full expression of a seminvariant is determinate from its non-unitary portion. (*MacMahon.*)

Ex. 17. Prove that

$$\tfrac{1}{2}a^2\partial_b + ab\partial_c + (ac + \tfrac{1}{2}b^2)\partial_d + (ad + bc)\partial_e + (ae + bd + \tfrac{1}{2}c^2)\partial_f + \ldots$$

and

$$2 . \tfrac{1}{2}a^2\partial_c + 3ab\partial_d + 4(ac + \tfrac{1}{2}b^2)\partial_e + 5(ad + bc)\partial_f + 6(ae + bd + \tfrac{1}{2}c^2)\partial_g + \ldots$$

generate seminvariants from seminvariants. (*MacMahon.*)

Ans. Form the alternants with the infinitely continued Ω.

Ex. 18. Every invariant I of a binary p-ic u is a numerical multiple of the pth transvectant or lineo-linear invariant of u and a p-ic covariant

$$y^p e^{\frac{x}{y}\Omega} \partial I/\partial a_0, \text{ i.e. } \left(\frac{\partial I}{\partial a_0}, \frac{\partial I}{\partial a_1}, \ldots \frac{\partial I}{\partial a_p}\right)(y, -x)^p.$$

Ex. 19. Every seminvariant S of extent p is a numerical multiple of the pth transvectant of the p-ic u and a p-ic $y^p e^{\frac{x}{y}\Omega}\partial S/\partial a_0$ which is annihilated by $\Omega - y\partial/\partial x$.

Ans. Use § 194 (*bis*) and $\Omega^r \partial S/\partial a_0 = (-1)^r r!\,\partial S/\partial a_r$.

Ex. 20. The coefficients of powers of x in the expansion of

$$\left(a - b\frac{ix}{1} + c\frac{i^2x^2}{1.2} - d\frac{i^3x^3}{1.2.3} + \ldots\right)$$
$$\left(a + b\frac{x}{1} + c\frac{x^2}{1.2} + d\frac{x^3}{1.2.3} + \ldots\right)^i,$$

where i is any positive integer, are all seminvariants, except such as are zero.

Ex. 21. If ϑ is the infinitely continued operator defined in § 192, and if S_1, S_2 are two seminvariants of degrees i_1, i_2 respectively, then $i_2 S_2 \vartheta S_1 - i_1 S_1 \vartheta S_2$ is a seminvariant, unless it vanishes. (*D'Ocagne.*)

Ex. 22. Prove that Ω annihilates the product

$$\{a+b(x-y)+\frac{c}{1.2}(x-y)^2+\dots\}\{a+b(y-z)+\dots\}$$
$$\dots\{a+b(u-v)+\dots\}\{a+b(v-x)+\dots\},$$

where $x, y, z, \dots u, v$ are arbitrary, and the series in brackets extend to infinity; and hence that all non-vanishing coefficients in the product expanded by powers and products of $x, y, z, \dots u, v$ are seminvariants. (*S. Roberts.*)

Ex. 23. If S is a seminvariant of $(a, b, c, d, \dots)(x, y)^\infty$, prove that $(2w\vartheta - i\phi)S$, where the notation is that of § 192, is another seminvariant of the same degree, and weight one higher, unless it vanishes. (*Cayley.*)

Ans. Cf. § 165 (*bis*), Exx. 16, 17.

Ex. 24. If in any seminvariant of $(a, b.1, c.1.2, d.1.2.3, \dots)(x, y)^\infty$, $a, b, c, d, \dots$ are replaced by $b, c, d, e, \dots$ the result gives the terms free from a in a seminvariant of the same degree and higher weight. (*MacMahon.*)

Ex. 25. A seminvariant of $(a, b, c, d, e, \dots)(x, y)^\infty$ is a seminvariant of the system

$$\begin{array}{l} (a,\ b.1,\ c.1.2,\ d.1.2.3, \dots)(x, y)^\infty \\ (b,\ c.1,\ d.1.2,\ e.1.2.3, \dots)(x, y)^\infty \\ (c,\ d.1,\ e.1.2, \dots \qquad\qquad)(x, y)^\infty \end{array}$$

&c., &c. (*MacMahon.*)

Ex. 26. If $\{a_0, a_1, \dots a_p\}(x, y)^p$ denotes

$$a_0x^p + pa_1x^{p-1}y + p(p-1)a_2x^{p-2}y^2 + \dots + p!\,a_py^p,$$

then the part free from a_0 in any seminvariant of $\{a_0, a_1, \dots a_p\}(x, y)^p$ is a seminvariant of $\{a_1, a_2, \dots a_p\}(x, y)^{p-1}$, and is reducible if the first seminvariant is.

Ex. 27. The seminvariant leader of a covariant of degree i and order ϖ greater than $i+p-2$ of $\{a_1, a_2, \dots a_p\}(x, y)^{p-1}$ is the part free from a_0 in a seminvariant of $\{a_0, a_1, \dots a_p\}(x, y)^p$; and if the first is irreducible so is the second.

Ex. 28. If G is any gradient of weight w degree i and extent p, and if σ is the sum of its numerical coefficients, then, whatever x be,

$$x^{-w}\left(\frac{\partial}{\partial a_0}+x\frac{\partial}{\partial a_1}+x^2\frac{\partial}{\partial a_2}+\dots+x^p\frac{\partial}{\partial a_p}\right)^i G = i!\,\sigma.$$

Ex. 29. Hence any seminvariant of weight w and degree i is annihilated by the operator which is the coefficient of x^w in the expansion of

$$(\partial_a + x\partial_b + x^2\partial_c + x^3\partial_d + \ldots)^i.$$

Ex. 30. Referring to § 174, Ex. 22 for the notation, show that, if δ_r denotes $r\,!\,(p-r)\,!\,\dfrac{\partial}{\partial a_r}$, and δ_r' denotes $r\,!\,(p-r)\,!\,\dfrac{\partial}{\partial \mathrm{a}_r}$, $\delta_p, \delta_{p-1}, \ldots \delta_0$ are the same functions of $\delta_p', \delta'_{p-1}, \ldots \delta_0'$ and m as $\mathrm{a}_0, \mathrm{a}_1, \ldots \mathrm{a}_p$ are of $a_0, a_1, \ldots a_p$ and m.

Ex. 31. In the same notation $\delta_p', \delta_{p-1}', \ldots \delta_0'$ are the same functions of $\delta_p, \delta_{p-1}, \ldots \delta_0$ and $-m$ as $\mathrm{a}_0, \mathrm{a}_1, \ldots \mathrm{a}_p$ are of $a_0, a_1, \ldots a_p$ and m.

Ex. 32. If, upon the substitution of $X+mY$, Y for x, y,

$$(a_0, a_1, a_2, \ldots a_p)\,(x, y)^p$$

becomes $$(\mathrm{a}_0, \mathrm{a}_1, \mathrm{a}_2, \ldots \mathrm{a}_p)\,(X, Y)^p,$$

then $$(\delta_p, -\delta_{p-1}, \delta_{p-2}, \ldots (-1)^p\delta_0)\,(x, y)^p$$

becomes $$(\delta_p', -\delta'_{p-1}, \delta'_{p-2}, \ldots (-1)^p\delta_0')\,(X, Y)^p. \quad (\textit{Sylvester.})$$

Ex. 33. Any seminvariant of $(a_0, a_1, a_2, \ldots a_p)\,(x, y)^p$ becomes, when in it $\delta_p, -\delta_{p-1}, \delta_{p-2}, \ldots (-1)^p\delta_0$ are put for $a_0, a_1, a_2, \ldots a_p$, an operator which has the same effect on any function of $a_0, a_1, a_2, \ldots a_p$ as the result of replacing in it $\delta_p, \delta_{p-1}, \ldots$ by $\delta_p', \delta'_{p-1}, \ldots$ has on the equivalent function of $\mathrm{a}_0, \mathrm{a}_1, \mathrm{a}_2, \ldots \mathrm{a}_p$, and may be called a seminvariant operator. (*Sylvester.*)

Ex. 34. More generally, any operator obtained by writing down a seminvariant of the two quantics

$$(a_0, a_1, a_2, \ldots a_p)\,(x, y)^p, \; (\delta_p, -\delta_{p-1}, \delta_{p-2}, \ldots (-1)^p\delta_0)\,(x, y)^p,$$

the symbols δ being written last in every term, is a seminvariant operator. (*Sylvester.*)

Ex. 35. Hence obtain the results (cf. § 186) that

$$i, \;\Omega, \; w-\frac{a_1}{a_0}\Omega, \; O-\frac{a_1}{a_0}(pi-2w)-\frac{a_1^{\,2}}{a_0^{\,2}}\Omega$$

are four seminvariant operators.

Ex. 36. If $\alpha_1, \alpha_2, \ldots \alpha_i$ are i symbols, and

$$(\alpha_1-\alpha_2)^{n_{12}}\,(\alpha_1-\alpha_3)^{n_{13}}\,(\alpha_2-\alpha_3)^{n_{23}}\ldots$$

any product of w differences between pairs of them which is such that not more than p factors involve any one of the symbols, and if the product is expanded and multiplied by $a_0^{\,i}$, and in the result a_1/a_0 is put for every one of the first powers $\alpha_1, \alpha_2, \ldots \alpha_i$, a_2/a_0 for every one of $\alpha_1^2, \alpha_2^2, \ldots \alpha_i^2$, and generally a_r/a_0 for every one of $\alpha_1^r, \alpha_2^r, \ldots \alpha_p^r$, the result is a seminvariant of $(a_0, a_1, a_2, \ldots a_p)\,(x, y)^p$ of degree i

and weight w; and all seminvariants are linear functions of seminvariants which can be thus expressed. (*Stroh.*)

Ans. Such a function is annihilated by $\frac{\partial}{\partial a_1}+\frac{\partial}{\partial a_2}+\dots+\frac{\partial}{\partial a_i}$, and a seminvariant is annihilated by Ω. Now both these operators are expressed by

$$\frac{\partial}{\partial a_1}+\frac{\partial}{\partial a_2}+\dots+\frac{\partial}{\partial a_i}+2\left\{a_1\frac{\partial}{\partial (a_1^2)}+\dots+a_i\frac{\partial}{\partial (a_i^2)}\right\}$$
$$+3\left\{a_1^2\frac{\partial}{\partial (a_1^3)}+\dots\right\}+\dots+p\left\{a_1^{p-1}\frac{\partial}{\partial (a_1^p)}+\dots\right\}.$$

Or again, the functions lead hyperdeterminants (§ 60 *bis*).

Ex. 37. If $\lambda_1, \lambda_2, \dots \lambda_i$ are i quantities whose sum is zero, then, after expansion and substitution as in the last example,

$$a_0^i(\lambda_1 a_1+\lambda_2 a_2+\dots+\lambda_i a_i)^w$$

is a seminvariant of degree i and weight w, provided that w do not exceed p. (*Stroh.*)

Ex. 38. If p is infinite, or not less than w, and if $e_1\,(=0), e_2, e_3, \dots e_i$ are the elementary symmetric functions

$$\Sigma(\lambda)\,(=0),\quad \Sigma(\lambda_1\lambda_2),\quad \Sigma(\lambda_1\lambda_2\lambda_3),\ \dots,\quad \lambda_1\lambda_2\dots\lambda_i,$$

then, when the function of the last example is expanded and expressed in terms of powers and products of $e_2, e_3, \dots e_p$, and substitution for the a's and their powers made as before, the coefficients of the various products of e's are a complete system of $(w\,;\,\infty, i)-(w-1\,;\,\infty, i)$ linearly independent seminvariants of weight w and degree i. (*Stroh.*)

Ex. 39. If the numbers of powers and products of $e_2, e_3, \dots e_i$ in the sum of Ex. 38 are diminished as much as possible by means of the relations in $e_2, e_3, \dots e_i$ any one of which expresses that in some way $\lambda_1+\lambda_2+\dots+\lambda_i$ is a sum of two sums

$$\lambda_1+\dots+\lambda_\phi,\quad \lambda_{\phi+1}+\dots+\lambda_i$$

each of which vanishes, the coefficients of powers and products of the e's which remain are non-perpetuant seminvariants, and the number of perpetuants of degree i and weight w is the number of powers and products which have disappeared. (*Stroh.*)

Ans. Seminvariants which do not disappear are reducible in terms of seminvariants of lower degree, and others which are not syzygetic with these are not so reducible.

Ex. 40. Perpetuants of degree i and weight w are just as numerous as products of $e_2, e_3, \dots e_i$ and powers of them which when multiplied by $\quad \Pi\lambda\,.\,\Pi(\lambda_1+\lambda_2)\,.\,\Pi(\lambda_1+\lambda_2+\lambda_3)\dots\Pi(\lambda_1+\lambda_2+\dots+\lambda_\nu)$

are raised to weight w in e-suffixes, i. e. to dimensions w in the λ's. Here

$$\Pi\lambda = e_i,\ \Pi(\lambda_1+\lambda_2) = (\lambda_1+\lambda_2)(\lambda_1+\lambda_3)\ldots(\lambda_2+\lambda_3)\ldots(\lambda_{i-1}+\lambda_i),$$

&c., and ν is $\frac{1}{2}i$ or $\frac{1}{2}(i-1)$ according as i is even or odd. (If i is even, two conjugate sums $\lambda_1+\lambda_2+\ldots+\lambda_\nu$, $\lambda_{\nu+1}+\lambda_{\nu+2}+\ldots+\lambda_i$ are not both written in the last product.) (*Stroh.*)

Ex. 41. The product $\Pi\lambda \,.\, \Pi(\lambda_1+\lambda_2)\ldots\Pi(\lambda_1+\lambda_2+\ldots+\lambda_\nu)$ is of weight $2^{i-1}-1$, whether i be even or odd. Consequently the weight of the lowest perpetuant of degree i is $2^{i-1}-1$. (*Stroh.*)

Ans. For instance, i even gives the weight

$$i + \frac{i(i-1)}{1\,.\,2} + \ldots + \tfrac{1}{2}\frac{i(i-1)\ldots(\frac{1}{2}i+1)}{1\,.\,2\ldots\frac{1}{2}i} = \tfrac{1}{2}2^i - 1.$$

Ex. 42. The number of perpetuants of a higher weight w than this, and of degree i, is the number of solutions in positive integral and zero values of $\mu_2, \mu_3, \mu_4, \ldots$ of

$$2^{i-1}-1+2\mu_2+3\mu_3+4\mu_4+\ldots+i\mu_i = w.$$

Ex. 43. Deduce the generating function for perpetuants (§ 189), viz.

$$\frac{x^{2^{i-1}-1}}{(1-x^2)(1-x^3)\ldots(1-x^i)}.$$

Ex. 44. If, in the θ-notation of § 60 *bis*, $F(\theta_1, \theta_2, \ldots \theta_i)\,a_0a_0a_0\ldots$, i factors, is a seminvariant of degree i, so that

$$(\partial/\partial\theta_1+\partial/\partial\theta_2+\ldots+\partial/\partial\theta_i)\,F(\theta_1, \theta_2, \ldots \theta_i) = 0,$$

prove that it must be a product, or sum of numerical multiples of products, of seminvariants of lower degrees if $F(\theta_1, \theta_2, \ldots \theta_i)$ is also annihilated by a sum of some but not all of $\partial/\partial\theta_1, \partial/\partial\theta_2, \ldots \partial/\partial\theta_i$.

Ex. 45. The symbol F of every seminvariant of degree i which is not a perpetuant is annihilated by the product of the

$$1 + \binom{i-1}{1} + \binom{i-2}{2} + \ldots + \binom{i-1}{i-2} = 2^{i-1}-1$$

parts of $\partial/\partial\theta_1+\partial/\partial\theta_2+\ldots+\partial/\partial\theta_i$ which do not contain $\partial/\partial\theta_1$.

Ex. 46. Conversely, if F is annihilated by this product, it is a sum of parts each annihilated by a sum-operator not containing $\partial/\partial\theta_1$, and is not a perpetuant.

Ans. Cf. *Quarterly Journal*, XXXVI, p. 132.

Ex. 47. Hence also the lowest possible weight of a perpetuant of degree i is $2^{i-1}-1$.

Ex. 48. Show that

$$(\theta_1-\theta_2)^{2^{i-2}}(\theta_2-\theta_3)^{2^{i-3}}\ldots(\theta_{i-2}-\theta_{i-1})^2(\theta_{i-1}-\theta_i)\,a_0a_0a_0\ldots$$

is a perpetuant of this weight. (*Grace.*)

Ex. 49. Prove that $\{\theta_2+\theta_3+\ldots+\theta_i-(i-1)\,\theta_1\}^{2^{i-1}-1}a_0a_0a_0\ldots$ is a linear function of the perpetuant of Ex. 48 and reducible seminvariants.

Ans. The operating product of Ex. 45 reduces both to constants, and so annihilates a linear function of the two.

Ex. 50. Show that

$$F(\theta_1,\theta_2,\ldots\theta_i)\,\{\theta_2+\theta_3+\ldots+\theta_i-(i-1)\,\theta_1\}^{2^{i-1}-1}a_0a_0a_0\ldots,$$

i factors, expresses a complete system of perpetuants of degree i.

Ex. 51. If ϕ_r denotes $\theta_1+\theta_2+\ldots+\theta_i-i\theta_r$, and $p_2, p_3, \ldots p_i$ denote the sums of products 2, 3, ... i together of $\phi_1, \phi_2, \ldots \phi_i$, a complete system of perpetuants of degree i is given by the expansion of

$$\Sigma\phi^{2^{i-1}-1}/(1-p_2)\,(1-p_3)\ldots(1-p_i).$$

(*Proc. Lond. Math. Soc.*, Ser. 2, IV, p. 233.)

Ex. 52. The lowest weight of a seminvariant of the quantic $a_0(x-a_1y)\,(x-a_2y)\ldots(x-a_py)$ which is not expressible as a sum of numerical multiples of products of seminvariants of quantics which are complementary factors of this quantic, is $2^{p-1}-1$; and

$$\Sigma\,(a_1-a_2)^{2^{p-2}}(a_2-a_3)^{2^{p-3}}\ldots(a_{p-2}-a_{p-1})^2\,(a_{p-1}-a_p)$$

is, but for a power of a_0 as factor, such a seminvariant for this weight. (Theory dual to perpetuants.)

CHAPTER XII

CANONICAL FORMS, ETC.

195. WHEN a binary quantic $(a_0, a_1, a_2, \dots a_p)(x, y)^p$ is transformed by the linear substitution

$$x = lX + mY, \quad y = l'X + m'Y,$$

four constants l, m, l', m' are introduced whose values may be assigned at will. These may be so chosen that the form of the transformed quantic is simplified by the absence of certain of its coefficients, or by relations among certain coefficients. The quantic is thus reduced to a simpler form without any loss of generality.

For instance, we know perfectly well that by giving l, m, l', m' the values $1, -a_1/a_0, 0, 1$ the quantic is transformed into one wanting its second term. The quantic without a second term is then not a special one, but is in effect just as general as one with its second term present. Any binary quantic can be so expressed by means of a linear transformation.

Moreover, it is to be noticed that the deprivation of a quantic of its second term is not something which can be done by linear transformation in one way only, but that there is a wide class of linear substitutions any one of which will effect the purpose. In fact, if by the general linear substitution $(a_0, a_1, a_2, \dots a_p)(x, y)^p$ is transformed into $(A_0, A_1, A_2, \dots A_p)(X, Y)^p$, we see at once that

$$A_1 = a_0 l^{p-1} m + a_1 \{l^{p-1} m' + (p-1) l^{p-2} m l'\} + \dots + a_p l'^{p-1} m',$$

in which we may give to l, m, l' any non-vanishing values we please, and obtain, by solution of an equation of the first degree, a value of m' which, going with those values of l, m, l', will make A_1 vanish. The usual way of depriving a quantic of its second term is then only the simplest of many ways.

We see, in fact, that by proper choice of the four quantities l, m, l', m' we may in general impose four conditions on the coefficients in a binary quantic, and still have a form to which the quantic can be reduced by a linear substitution without losing its generality. These may not be any four conditions we choose, for the equations in l, m, l', m' which express four conditions may not prove to be consistent with one another.

In particular, for instance, we can never make four separate coefficients in the quantic vanish. For to express this we should have to make l, m, l', m' satisfy four homogeneous equations, i.e. to choose the ratios l/m, l'/m, m'/m, three quantities, so as to satisfy four independent equations, which cannot be done.

196. **Definition of canonical forms.** Now the binary p-ic contains $p+1$ coefficients. Taking 4 from this number, we see that no binary p-ic with less than $p-3$ perfectly arbitrary coefficients can be equivalent to a perfectly general binary p-ic subjected to linear transformation, but that there is a certain presumption in favour of one which has $p-3$ perfectly arbitrary coefficients, or whose coefficients involve $p-3$ perfectly arbitrary quantities, being equivalent to the general binary p-ic, which presumption must, however, in every case be tested before it can be stated as a certainty.

A form of binary p-ic whose coefficients involve $p-3$ perfectly arbitrary quantities, and which is proved to be a form to which the general binary p-ic can be reduced by a linear substitution, is called a *Canonical Form* of the binary p-ic. There may be different forms for the same value of p which have equal claims to the name canonical, but in practice, for the cubic, quartic, &c., respectively, one canonical form is chosen because of symmetry of shape and convenience of treatment, and often spoken of as *the* canonical form.

The case $p=2$ of the quadratic stands by itself in that $p-3$ is negative. Of course the three coefficients of a binary quadratic cannot be subjected to more than three conditions. To each of the simple forms X^2+Y^2, XY a quadratic can be reduced in an infinite number of ways, since one of l, m, l', m' is arbitrary. Indeed, the general binary quadratic

$$ax^2+2bxy+cy^2$$

can be given the form of any quadratic $a'X^2+2b'XY+c'Y^2$ whatever whose discriminant $a'c'-b'^2$ does not vanish. The like fact is true as to quadratics in any number of variables.

197. Canonical forms have here been defined for binary quantics only. For quantics in more variables than two the definition is similar. A form of q-ary p-ic which is a simplest form to which linear transformation can reduce the general q-ary p-ic is a canonical form of the q-ary p-ic, one form being regarded as more simple than another when of its coefficients a smaller number are arbitrary, or, as is the same thing, when its coefficients are known functions of a smaller number of arbitrary quantities.

The number of coefficients in the q-ary p-ic being easily seen to be

$$\frac{(p+1)(p+2)\dots(p+q-1)}{(q-1)!},$$

and the number of constants in the general scheme of linear substitution being q^2, the number of perfectly arbitrary coefficients left in a canonical form will be

$$\frac{(p+1)(p+2)\dots(p+q-1)}{(q-1)!}-q^2,$$

when the degree p is sufficiently great for this to be positive.

198. The knowledge of invariants and covariants both aids and is aided by the determination of canonical forms of quantics. On the one hand, as we shall illustrate by examples, invariants and covariants supply information as to forms which are canonical and the reduction of general quantics to those forms, and on the other, since invariants and covariants of a quantic have relations to one another, expressed by homogeneous isobaric syzygies, which hold however the quantic be linearly transformed, it suffices, in order to discover those relations, to consider the quantic and the invariants and covariants in simpler forms which they can assume without loss of generality.

Geometrical interpretation of invariants and covariants is also greatly assisted by the simplification afforded by canonical forms.

199. **Canonical form of binary cubic.** The binary cubic

$$ax^3+3bx^2y+3cxy^2+dy^3$$

can be expressed in the canonical form

$$X^3+Y^3.$$

In other words, constants λ, μ, λ', μ' can be found such that

$$ax^3+3bx^2y+3cxy^2+dy^3 \equiv (\lambda x+\mu y)^3+(\lambda' x+\mu' y)^3$$

is an identity.

A presumption in favour of this is afforded by the fact that the identification of coefficients of x^3, x^2y, xy^2, y^3, on the left and right gives four equations for the determination of λ, μ, λ', μ'; but we have to be sure that the four equations are consistent and independent and can actually be solved. This will first be proved without any reference to the invariant theory.

With a change of notation, we have to see that p, q, α, β can be found so as to make

$$ax^3+3bx^2y+3cxy^2+dy^3 \equiv p(x+\alpha y)^3+q(x+\beta y)^3,$$

i.e. so as to make simultaneously

$$\begin{aligned} p \ \ + q \ \ &= a, \\ p\alpha \ + q\beta \ &= b, \\ p\alpha^2 + q\beta^2 &= c, \\ p\alpha^3 + q\beta^3 &= d. \end{aligned}$$

The first three of these are consistent for the determination of p, q if

$$\begin{vmatrix} 1, & 1, & a \\ \alpha, & \beta, & b \\ \alpha^2, & \beta^2, & c \end{vmatrix} = 0,$$

and the values of $p\alpha$, $q\beta$ which satisfy the second and third also satisfy the fourth if

$$\begin{vmatrix} 1, & 1, & b \\ \alpha, & \beta, & c \\ \alpha^2, & \beta^2, & d \end{vmatrix} = 0.$$

We have thus two equations for the determination of α, β. We may write them

$$Pa + Qb + Rc = 0,$$

and

$$Pb + Qc + Rd = 0,$$

where also $P + Q\alpha + R\alpha^2 = 0$, and $P + Q\beta + R\beta^2 = 0$. These are made consistent by taking for α and β the two roots of the quadratic

$$\begin{vmatrix} a, & b, & c \\ b, & c, & d \\ 1, & \alpha, & \alpha^2 \end{vmatrix} = 0.$$

Having thus found α and β, any two of the first set of four equations suffice to determine p and q. Thus the possibility of reducing the cubic to the canonical form $X^3 + Y^3$ is proved, and the means of doing it, by solution of quadratic and linear equations, afforded.

The student should notice that there is failure to effect what is desired when a, b, c, d have such specially connected values that the quadratic for α and β has equal roots, i.e. when

$$(ad - bc)^2 - 4\,(ac - b^2)\,(bd - c^2) = 0,$$

that is to say, when the discriminant of the cubic vanishes, so that the cubic has a square factor. The canonical form for cubics with a square factor is not $X^3 + Y^3$ but X^2Y.

This leads to the general remark that a canonical form of the general quantic of any type is one to which a quantic of that type can be reduced when general, but not necessarily one to which every special quantic of that type can be reduced.

Ex. 1. Verify that

$$(pq)^2 (\alpha-\beta)^6 = (ad-bc)^2 - 4(ac-b^2)(bd-c^2).$$

Ex. 2. One binary cubic with general coefficients can be linearly transformed into any other.

Ans. Through X^3+Y^3 as an intermediary.

200. The reduction of the cubic to the form

$$p(x+\alpha y)^3 + q(x+\beta y)^3$$

and thence to its canonical form X^3+Y^3 is most easily effected by means of its one quadratic covariant, the Hessian

$$(ac-b^2)x^2 + (ad-bc)xy + (bd-c^2)y^2.$$

Regard the cubic

$$ax^3 + 3bx^2y + 3cxy^2 + dy^3$$

as the transformed form obtained by the substitution

$$x' = x+\alpha y,\ y' = x+\beta y,$$

whose modulus is $\beta-\alpha$, from the form $px'^3+qy'^3$.

The Hessian of the transformed is the Hessian of the untransformed multiplied by the square of the modulus. Thus

$$(ac-b^2)x^2 + (ad-bc)xy + (bd-c^2)y^2 = (\beta-\alpha)^2 pqx'y'$$
$$= pq(\alpha-\beta)^2 (x+\alpha y)(x+\beta y).$$

Consequently if the Hessian

$$(ac-b^2)x^2 + (ad-bc)xy + (bd-c^2)y^2$$

has for its factors

$$(ac-b^2)(x+\alpha y)(x+\beta y),$$

the cubic must have the form

$$p(x+\alpha y)^3 + q(x+\beta y)^3,$$

in which p and q may be found from the equations

$$p+q = a,\quad p\alpha+q\beta = b.$$

Thus $p^{\frac{1}{3}}(x+\alpha y)$ and $q^{\frac{1}{3}}(x+\beta y)$, the X and Y of the canonical form, are found.

The determination of the canonical form of the binary cubic effects the solution of a cubic equation. (Cf. § 11, Exx. 14, 15.) For it reduces the cubic equation to the form

$$X^3+Y^3 = 0,$$

i. e. to the three linear equations

$$X+Y=0,\quad X+\omega Y = 0,\quad X+\omega^2 Y = 0.$$

The student is advised to illustrate this by an example, e. g. to solve $x^3 - 3x^2 \tan\alpha - 3x + \tan\alpha = 0$.

201. **Concomitants of cubic in canonical form.** We have seen in § 169 and elsewhere that the cubic

$$u \equiv ax^3 + 3bx^2y + 3cxy^2 + dy^3$$

has, besides its Hessian

$$H \equiv (ac-b^2)x^2 + (ad-bc)xy + (bd-c^2)y^2,$$

a cubicovariant

$$G \equiv (a^2d - 3abc + 2b^3)x^3 + 3(abd - 2ac^2 + b^2c)x^2y$$
$$+ 3(2b^2d - acd - bc^2)xy^2 + (3bcd - ad^2 - 2c^3)y^3,$$

and one invariant, its discriminant

$$\Delta \equiv (ad-bc)^2 - 4(ac-b^2)(bd-c^2).$$

The same functions of the coefficients and variables in the canonical form are

$$X^3 + Y^3,$$
$$XY,$$
$$X^3 - Y^3,$$
$$1.$$

Now let M' be the modulus of the substitution which expresses X and Y in terms of x and y, so that, in the two notations of § 199,

$$M' = \lambda\mu' - \lambda'\mu = (pq)^{\frac{1}{3}}(\beta - \alpha).$$

We remember from Chapters II, III, that the index of the power of the modulus, which has to multiply an invariant or covariant of a binary quantic to produce the equivalent of the same invariant or covariant of the transformed quantic, is equal to the weight of the invariant or of the leading coefficient in the covariant. Thus the information given by invariant algebra as to a binary cubic and its canonical form is presented in the four identities

$$u = X^3 + Y^3,$$
$$H = M'^2 . XY,$$
$$G = M'^3(X^3 - Y^3),$$
$$\Delta = M'^6.$$

Of these the last tells us at once that the modulus of the substitution which expresses X and Y in terms of x and y, i.e. the reciprocal (§ 23) of the modulus of that which expresses x and y in terms of X and Y, is equal to the sixth root of the discriminant.

We have also in a clear form before us the fact that u, H, G, Δ, though irreducible in that none of them can be expressed rationally and integrally in terms of the rest, are not independent, but are connected by the syzygy (cf. § 169)

$$u^2\Delta = G^2 + 4H^3,$$

which is obtained by eliminating X, Y and M'. Moreover, no other syzygy connects them, for there is no other way of eliminating those three quantities.

It is of interest to notice that we have also readily given by these identities the values of the p, q, a, β of § 199. We have

$$u = X^3 + Y^3 = p(x+ay)^3 + q(x+\beta y)^3,$$
$$\Delta^{-\frac{1}{2}} G = X^3 - Y^3 = p(x+ay)^3 - q(x+\beta y)^3.$$

Thus, taking the full expressions for u and G, and attending only to the equalities of the coefficients of x^3 and x^2y,

$$p+q = a,$$
$$pa + q\beta = b,$$
$$p-q = \Delta^{-\frac{1}{2}}(a^2d - 3abc + 2b^3),$$
$$pa - q\beta = \Delta^{-\frac{1}{2}}(abd - 2ac^2 + b^2c);$$

whence

$$2p = a + \Delta^{-\frac{1}{2}}(a^2d - 3abc + 2b^3),$$
$$2q = a - \Delta^{-\frac{1}{2}}(a^2d - 3abc + 2b^3),$$
$$2pa = b + \Delta^{-\frac{1}{2}}(abd - 2ac^2 + b^2c),$$
$$2q\beta = b - \Delta^{-\frac{1}{2}}(abd - 2ac^2 + b^2c).$$

We have also X^3 and Y^3 themselves; viz.

$$\tfrac{1}{2}(u + \Delta^{-\frac{1}{2}}G) \text{ and } \tfrac{1}{2}(u - \Delta^{-\frac{1}{2}}G).$$

The solutions of the cubic equation

$$(a, b, c, d)(x, y)^3 = 0$$

in $x:y$ are then given by the three linear equations

$$(u + \Delta^{-\frac{1}{2}}G)^{\frac{1}{3}} + (u - \Delta^{-\frac{1}{2}}G)^{\frac{1}{3}} = 0,$$
$$(u + \Delta^{-\frac{1}{2}}G)^{\frac{1}{3}} + \omega(u - \Delta^{-\frac{1}{2}}G)^{\frac{1}{3}} = 0,$$
$$(u + \Delta^{-\frac{1}{2}}G)^{\frac{1}{3}} + \omega^2(u - \Delta^{-\frac{1}{2}}G)^{\frac{1}{3}} = 0.$$

202. **Geometry of concomitants of cubic.** Geometrically, taking $(a, b, c, d)(x, y)^3 = 0$ to represent three straight lines through a point, the reduction of the cubic to its canonical form is the reference to the lines which form the Hessian. As examples of geometrical information yielded by the canonical form the following are left to the student.

Ex. 3. The cubicovariant of a pencil of three lines L, M, N represents the pencil L', M', N' which consists of the harmonic conjugate of L with regard to M and N, that of M with regard to N and L, and that of N with regard to L and M.

Ans. It suffices to prove that $X-Y$ and $X+Y$ are harmonic with regard to $X+\omega Y$ and $X+\omega^2 Y$.

Ex. 4. L, L'; M, M'; N, N' are pairs of an involution, of which H the Hessian represents the double lines.

By means of the expressions for u, H, G, Δ in terms of X, Y, M' in § 201 we may readily prove the following theorem due to Cayley.

Ex. 5. The Hessian, cubicovariant, and discriminant of $ku+k'G$ are respectively

$$(k^2-k'^2\Delta)H, \quad (k^2-k'^2\Delta)(kG+k'\Delta u), \quad (k^2-k'^2\Delta)^2\Delta.$$

Ex. 6. If L', M', N' are the harmonic conjugates of L with regard to M and N, of M with regard to N and L, and of N with regard to L and M, then L, M, N are respectively the harmonic conjugates of L' with regard to M' and N', of M' with regard to N' and L', and of N' with regard to L' and M'.

203. **Canonical reduction of binary** $(2n-1)$-ic. The proposition of § 199 is a case of a general one due, like the rest of the elementary theory of canonical forms, to Sylvester. This is that a general binary quantic of odd order $2n-1$ is a sum of $(2n-1)$th powers of n linear forms.

As indicating the likelihood of this, we notice that the sum

$$(\lambda_1 x+\mu_1 y)^{2n-1}+(\lambda_2 x+\mu_2 y)^{2n-1}+\ldots+(\lambda_n x+\mu_n y)^{2n-1},$$

or its equivalent

$$p_1(x+a_1 y)^{2n-1}+p_2(x+a_2 y)^{2n-1}+\ldots+p_n(x+a_n y)^{2n-1},$$

is a binary $(2n-1)$-ic with no obvious connexion among its coefficients, which coefficients are functions of $2n$ constants that may be chosen at will, this number $2n$ being exactly that of coefficients in the general binary $(2n-1)$-ic

$$(a_0, a_1, a_2, \ldots a_{2n-1})(x, y)^{2n-1}.$$

We have to see, however, that values of the $2n$ a's and p's, to adopt the second notation, actually exist, which make the sum and the quantic identical. We shall prove that the a's are the roots of an equation of degree n, and so do exist, though general expressions cannot algebraically be found for them when n exceeds 4, and that, when the a's are known, the p's are determinate by solution of equations of the first degree.

For the identity

$$(a_0, a_1, a_2, \ldots a_{2n-1})(x, y)^{2n-1} \equiv p_1(x+a_1 y)^{2n-1} + p_2(x+a_2 y)^{2n-1}+\ldots+p_n(x+a_n y)^{2n-1}$$

to hold, we must have simultaneously

$$\begin{array}{lllll} p_1 & +p_2 & +\ldots+p_n & = a_0, \\ p_1 a_1 & +p_2 a_2 & +\ldots+p_n a_n & = a_1, \\ p_1 a_1^2 & +p_2 a_2^2 & +\ldots+p_n a_n^2 & = a_2, \\ \cdot\ \cdot\ \cdot & \cdot\ \cdot\ \cdot & \cdot\ \cdot\ \cdot & \cdot\ \cdot \\ p_1 a_1^{2n-1} & +p_2 a_2^{2n-1} & +\ldots+p_n a_n^{2n-1} & = a_{2n-1}; \end{array}$$

and to find solutions of these equations it suffices to take for $a_1, a_2, \dots a_n$ the n roots of an equation

$$a^n + q_1 a^{n-1} + q_2 a^{n-2} + \dots + q_n = 0,$$

where $q_1, q_2, \dots q_n$ are determined by the n equations

$$\begin{array}{l} a_n + q_1 a_{n-1} + q_2 a_{n-2} + \dots + q_n a_0 = 0, \\ a_{n+1} + q_1 a_n + q_2 a_{n-1} + \dots + q_n a_1 = 0, \\ a_{n+2} + q_1 a_{n+1} + q_2 a_n + \dots + q_n a_2 = 0, \\ \cdot \quad \cdot \quad \cdot \quad \cdot \quad \cdot \quad \cdot \quad \cdot \quad \cdot \quad \cdot \quad \cdot \\ a_{2n-1} + q_1 a_{2n-2} + q_2 a_{2n-3} + \dots + q_n a_{n-1} = 0; \end{array}$$

and then to solve for $p_1, p_2, \dots p_n$ the first n of the $2n$ equations of the first degree in these which have been made consistent.

The equation whose roots are $a_1, a_2, \dots a_n$ has the form

$$\begin{vmatrix} a_n, & a_{n-1}, & a_{n-2}, & \dots a_0 \\ a_{n+1}, & a_n, & a_{n-1}, & \dots a_1 \\ a_{n+2}, & a_{n+1}, & a_n, & \dots a_2 \\ \cdot & \cdot & \cdot & \cdot \\ a_{2n-1}, & a_{2n-2}, & a_{2n-3}, & \dots a_{n-1} \\ a^n, & a^{n-1}, & a^{n-2}, & \dots 1 \end{vmatrix} = 0,$$

as is at once seen by elimination of $q_1, q_2, \dots q_n$.

For the quintic $(a, b, c, d, e, f)\ (x, y)^5$, and the septimic $(a, b, c, d, e, f, g, h)\ (x, y)^7$, n has the values 3 and 4 respectively. Thus the reduction of the quintic to a sum of three fifth powers, and that of the septimic to a sum of four seventh powers, can actually be effected algebraically. For quantics of higher odd orders the reduction would depend on the solution of equations in a of degrees above the fourth. For such higher cases the quantic is proved to have an equivalent expression as a sum of powers, but the algebraic reduction to the form is not effected.

204. **Case of canonizing equation having equal roots.** There is failure to effect the required reduction when the coefficients in the $(2n-1)$-ic are special in such a way that the equation of the nth degree in a has equal roots.

The condition for such equality of roots is the vanishing of the discriminant of the n-ic in a. This is of degree $2(n-1)$ in the coefficients of the n-ic, which themselves are of degree n in $a_0, a_1, a_2, \dots a_{2n-1}$. The condition is then the vanishing of a function of degree $2n(n-1)$ in the coefficients of the

$(2n-1)$-ic. This function is an invariant, being the discriminant of what will presently be exhibited as a covariant. For the case of the quintic $n = 3$, and the invariant is of degree 12.

Let us discuss the failure for the case of the quintic. If the cubic $\alpha^3 + q_1\alpha^2 + q_2\alpha + q_3 = 0$ has one root α and two roots equal to β, so that $3\beta^2 + 2q_1\beta + q_2 = 0$ as well as

$$\beta^3 + q_1\beta^2 + q_2\beta + q_3 = 0,$$

the six linear equations made consistent as above are not those of § 203 (with $n = 3$) for p_1, p_2, p_3, but

$$\begin{aligned} p + q &= a, \\ p\alpha + (q+r)\beta &= b, \\ p\alpha^2 + (q+2r)\beta^2 &= c, \\ p\alpha^3 + (q+3r)\beta^3 &= d, \\ p\alpha^4 + (q+4r)\beta^4 &= e, \\ p\alpha^5 + (q+5r)\beta^5 &= f, \end{aligned}$$

of which any three determine p, q, r.

Now these give the quintic the form

$$p(x+\alpha y)^5 + q(x+\beta y)^5 + 5r\beta y(x+\beta y)^4,$$

i. e.

$$p(x+\alpha y)^5 + q(x+\beta y)^5 + \frac{5r\beta}{\alpha-\beta}\{(x+\alpha y) - (x+\beta y)\}(x+\beta y)^4,$$

whose form is

$$p(x+\alpha y)^5 + 5r'(x+\alpha y)(x+\beta y)^4 + q'(x+\beta y)^5.$$

Thus the canonical form of a quintic which is special in that its invariant of the twelfth degree above vanishes is most simply written

$$X^5 + 5\lambda XY^4 + Y^5,$$

in which three consecutive coefficients are wanting.

When α, β, γ are all equal, it is easy to see that the degenerate form is

$$(x+\alpha y)^3\{p(x+\alpha y)^2 + 5q(x+\alpha y)y + 10ry^2\},$$

so that the quintic has a perfect cube for a factor.

205. **Canonical forms of quintic, septimic, &c.** In the identity

$$(a, b, c, d, e, f)(x, y)^5 \equiv p(x+\alpha y)^5 + q(x+\beta y)^5 + r(x+\gamma y)^5,$$

we may write X for $p^{\frac{1}{5}}(x+\alpha y)$ and Y for $q^{\frac{1}{5}}(x+\beta y)$, and consequently $\lambda X+\mu Y$ for $r^{\frac{1}{5}}(x+\gamma y)$, where λ and μ are constants. We thus have as a canonical form of the general binary quintic

$$X^5+Y^5+(\lambda X+\mu Y)^5,$$

which involves two free constants only. More symmetrically we may write it

$$X^5+Y^5+Z^5,$$

where X, Y, Z are connected by a linear relation without constant term; or again, we may write it

$$\lambda' x'^5+\mu' y'^5+z'^5,$$

where

$$x'+y'+z'=0.$$

In like manner a canonical form of the general binary septimic is

$$X^7+Y^7+(\lambda X+\mu Y)^7+(\lambda' X+\mu' Y)^7;$$

and similarly for binary quantics of higher odd orders.

206. **Canonizants.** In § 200 it was seen that the $x+\alpha y$, $x+\beta y$ of the cubic have for their product multiplied by a function of the coefficients a certain covariant, the Hessian, which may be written in either of the forms

$$\begin{vmatrix} ax+by, & bx+cy \\ bx+cy, & cx+dy \end{vmatrix},$$

$$\begin{vmatrix} a, & b, & c \\ b, & c, & d \\ y^2, & -xy, & x^2 \end{vmatrix}.$$

There are corresponding facts for the quintic, septimic, ... $(2n-1)$-ic.

The covariant whose factors are

$$x+\alpha_1 y,\ x+\alpha_2 y, \dots x+\alpha_n y$$

is not, after the cubic, the Hessian, but its form is analogous to either of the forms of the Hessian of the cubic here written down.

Regard the equation whose roots are $\alpha_1, \alpha_2, \dots \alpha_n$ which has been exhibited in § 203; and remember that, if $\alpha_1, \alpha_2, \dots \alpha_n$ are the roots of

$$\alpha^n+q_1\alpha^{n-1}+q_2\alpha^{n-2}+\dots+q_n=0,$$

then $x+\alpha_1 y, x+\alpha_2 y, \dots x+\alpha_n y$ are the factors of

$$x^n-q_1x^{n-1}y+q_2x^{n-2}y^2-\dots+(-1)^n q_n y^n.$$

We at once gather, altering the arrangement of rows in the canonizing determinant, that

$$\begin{vmatrix} x^n, & -x^{n-1}y, & x^{n-2}y^2, & -x^{n-3}y^3, & \ldots & (-1)^n y^n \\ a_n, & a_{n-1}, & a_{n-2}, & a_{n-3}, & \ldots & a_0 \\ a_{n+1}, & a_n, & a_{n-1}, & a_{n-2}, & \ldots & a_1 \\ a_{n+2}, & a_{n+1}, & a_n, & a_{n-1}, & \ldots & a_2 \\ \cdot & \cdot & \cdot & \cdot & \cdot & \cdot \\ a_{2n-1}, & a_{2n-2}, & a_{2n-3}, & a_{2n-4}, & \ldots & a_{n-1} \end{vmatrix}$$

$$\equiv (x+\alpha_1 y)(x+\alpha_2 y)\ldots(x+\alpha_n y) \begin{vmatrix} a_{n-1}, & a_{n-2}, & a_{n-3}, & \ldots & a_0 \\ a_n, & a_{n-1}, & a_{n-2}, & \ldots & a_1 \\ a_{n+1}, & a_n, & a_{n-1}, & \ldots & a_2 \\ \cdot & \cdot & \cdot & \cdot & \cdot \\ a_{2n-2}, & a_{2n-3}, & a_{2n-4}, & \ldots & a_{n-1} \end{vmatrix}$$

Accordingly the determination of the

$$x+\alpha_1 y,\ x+\alpha_2 y, \ldots x+\alpha_n y$$

of the canonical expression of the $(2n-1)$-ic is effected by the breaking up of the n-ic which is the determinant on the left into its n factors.

To reduce the determinant to its other form, we best proceed by multiplying it, according to the ordinary rule, by another determinant of the same number of rows and columns, viz.

$$\begin{vmatrix} y, & x, & 0, & 0, & \ldots & 0, & 0 \\ 0, & y, & x, & 0, & \ldots & 0, & 0 \\ 0, & 0, & y, & x, & \ldots & 0, & 0 \\ \cdot & \cdot & \cdot & \cdot & \cdot & \cdot & \cdot \\ 0, & 0, & 0, & 0, & \ldots & y, & x \\ 0, & 0, & 0, & 0, & \ldots & 0, & 1 \end{vmatrix},$$

whose value is y^n. Combining rows with rows the product is

$$\begin{vmatrix} 0, & 0, & 0, & \ldots & 0, & (-1)^n y^n \\ a_n y + a_{n-1}x, & a_{n-1}y + a_{n-2}x, & a_{n-2}y + a_{n-3}x, & \ldots & a_1 y + a_0 x, & a_0 \\ a_{n+1}y + a_n x, & a_n y + a_{n-1}x, & a_{n-1}y + a_{n-2}x, & \ldots & a_2 y + a_1 x, & a_1 \\ \cdot & \cdot & \cdot & \cdot & \cdot & \cdot \\ a_{2n-1}y + a_{2n-2}x, & a_{2n-2}y + a_{2n-3}x, & a_{2n-3}y + a_{2n-4}x, & \ldots & a_n y + a_{n-1}x, & a_{n-1} \end{vmatrix}$$

i. e., rearranging columns, is

$$(-1)^{\frac{1}{2}n(n-1)}y^n \begin{vmatrix} a_0x+a_1y, & a_1x+a_2y & ,\ldots, & a_{n-1}x+a_ny \\ a_1x+a_2y, & a_2x+a_3y & ,\ldots, & a_nx+a_{n+1}y \\ \cdot & \cdot & \cdot & \cdot \\ a_{n-1}x+a_ny, & a_nx+a_{n+1}y, & \ldots, & a_{2n-2}x+a_{2n-1}y \end{vmatrix}.$$

The omission of the factor y^n from each side now establishes the identity, but for sign at most, of this last determinant with the first.

The determinant is a covariant, viz. the catalecticant of the $(2n-2)$th emanant (§ 56, cf. also § 17, Ex. 20). In the last written form of determinant the convention of § 71 as to sign and numerical multiple will be seen to have been adopted. The covariant, from the property here developed in connexion with canonical forms, is called the *canonizant* of the $(2n-1)$-ic.

To realize the conclusion by particularization let us restate it for the quintic only. To reduce the quintic

$$(a, b, c, d, e, f)(x, y)^5$$

to its canonical form $X^5+Y^5+Z^5$, form the canonizant

$$\begin{vmatrix} ax+by, & bx+cy, & cx+dy \\ bx+cy, & cx+dy, & dx+ey \\ cx+dy, & dx+ey, & ex+fy \end{vmatrix},$$

and break it up into three linear factors $\lambda_1x+\mu_1y$, $\lambda_2x+\mu_2y$, $\lambda_3x+\mu_3y$. X, Y, Z respectively are multiples of these. To determine the multiples assume them arbitrarily. Then, by equating the coefficients of x^5, $5x^4y$, $10x^3y^2$ in $X^5+Y^5+Z^5$ to a, b, c respectively, we obtain three equations of the first degree for their determination.

And in like manner for the septimic, nonic, &c.

The failing case when the coefficients are special in such a way that the canonizant has a square factor has been considered in § 204.

Ex. 7. If the canonizant of a quintic is a perfect cube the quintic can be reduced to the form $(A_0, A_1, A_2, 0, 0, 0)(X, Y)^5$; and all invariants vanish.

Ans. Cf. § 204, and § 28, Ex. 5.

Ex. 8. If the canonizant of a septimic is a fourth power the septimic can be reduced to the form

$$(A_0, A_1, A_2, A_3, 0, 0, 0, 0,)(X, Y)^7,$$

so that all invariants vanish. (*Booth.*)

207. **Apolarity.** It will be observed that the second transvectant of a cubic and its Hessian, i.e. the result obtained when we operate on the cubic with the result of putting $\frac{\partial}{\partial y}, -\frac{\partial}{\partial x}$ for x, y in the Hessian, vanishes identically; and generally that the covariant which results from operating on a $(2n-1)$-ic with its canonizant vanishes. The latter fact is clear because, taking the canonizant in the first of the two forms of § 206, the coefficients of $x^{n-1}, x^{n-2}y, \ldots$ in the result of operating are all one multiple of results of replacing in the determinant the first row by other rows.

We express this fact by saying that a $(2n-1)$-ic and its canonizant are *apolar* to one another. Two binary quantics of orders p and p', $p \ngtr p'$, are *apolar* when the pth transvectant of the two, i.e. the result of operating with the former on the latter, vanishes for all values of x, y.

In particular two p-ics are apolar when the lineo-linear invariant of the two vanishes. A p-ic is apolar to itself if its invariant of degree 2 vanishes when p is even. When p is odd the p-ic is certainly apolar to itself.

The fact that a $(2n-1)$-ic is a sum of constant multiples of the $(2n-1)$th powers of the n linear factors of its canonizant, provided the latter has no repeated factor, is a consequence of the following theorem.

If a binary p-ic and p′-ic, $p \ngtr p'$, are apolar, and if the p-ic has only unrepeated factors, then the p′-ic is equal to a sum of constant multiples of the p′th powers of those factors.

Let $a_1, a_2, \ldots a_p$ be the roots of the p-ic, and let v be the p'-ic. The expression of the apolarity is

$$\left(\frac{\partial}{\partial y}+a_1\frac{\partial}{\partial x}\right)\left(\frac{\partial}{\partial y}+a_2\frac{\partial}{\partial x}\right)\left(\frac{\partial}{\partial y}+a_3\frac{\partial}{\partial x}\right)\ldots\left(\frac{\partial}{\partial y}+a_p\frac{\partial}{\partial x}\right)v=0.$$

Now this equation tells us that

$$\left(\frac{\partial}{\partial y}+a_2\frac{\partial}{\partial x}\right)\left(\frac{\partial}{\partial y}+a_3\frac{\partial}{\partial x}\right)\ldots\left(\frac{\partial}{\partial y}+a_p\frac{\partial}{\partial x}\right)v=\phi\,(x-a_1y).$$

But the left-hand side here is homogeneous in x, y and of order $p'-p+1$. Hence $\phi\,(x-a_1y)=A\,(x-a_1y)^{p'-p+1}$, for a constant value of A.

A second integration gives

$$\left(\frac{\partial}{\partial y}+a_3\frac{\partial}{\partial x}\right)\ldots\left(\frac{\partial}{\partial y}+a_p\frac{\partial}{\partial x}\right)v$$
$$=\frac{1}{p'-p+2}\cdot\frac{A}{a_2-a_1}(x-a_1y)^{p'-p+2}+\psi\,(x-a_2y);$$

and here the homogeneity and dimensions of the rest of the equality tell us that $\psi\,(x-a_2y)=B\,(x-a_2y)^{p'-p+2}$. A third integration, and the fact of homogeneity, give us in like manner

$$\left(\frac{\partial}{\partial y}+a_4\frac{\partial}{\partial x}\right)\dots\left(\frac{\partial}{\partial y}+a_p\frac{\partial}{\partial x}\right)v=\frac{A'}{(a_2-a_1)(a_3-a_1)}(x-a_1y)^{p'-p+3}$$
$$+\frac{B'}{a_3-a_2}(x-a_2y)^{p'-p+3}+C(x-a_3y)^{p'-p+3};$$

and so on. Finally, after p integrations and repetitions of the argument we arrive at an identity of the form

$$v=C_1(x-a_1y)^{p'}+C_2(x-a_2y)^{p'}+\dots+C_p(x-a_py)^{p'}.$$

As an example we have, from the fact that a $(2n-1)$-ic is apolar to itself, the conclusion that, whatever number n be, there are constants $A_1, A_2, \dots A_{2n-1}$ dependent on $a_1, a_2, \dots a_{2n-1}$, which make

$$(x-a_1y)(x-a_2y)\dots(x-a_{2n-1}y)=A_1(x-a_1y)^{2n-1}$$
$$+A_2(x-a_2y)^{2n-1}+\dots+A_{2n-1}(x-a_{2n-1}y)^{2n-1}$$

for all values of x and y. There is no corresponding identity in the case of an even number $2n$ of factors unless $a_1, a_2, \dots a_{2n}$ are connected by a relation expressing that the product is a $2n$-ic apolar to itself.

For more on the subject of apolarity, and in particular for a consideration of apolar quantics with repeated factors, reference is made to Grace and Young's *Algebra of Invariants*.

208. **Quantics of even order. Catalecticants interpreted.** The general binary quantic of even order $2n$ cannot be expressed as a sum of n $2n$th powers. For the $2n$-ic has $2n+1$ coefficients, and the sum of n terms like $(\lambda x+\mu y)^{2n}$ contains only $2n$ free constants like λ, μ, which cannot be so chosen as to satisfy $2n+1$ conditions. On the other hand, a sum of $n+1$ $2n$th powers contains $2n+2$ free constants, one more than the number of coefficients in the $2n$-ic. We should expect then that the $2n$-ic can be expressed as a sum of $n+1$ $2n$th powers in an infinite number of ways, and not definitely in one or a few ways. That it can, and that in general one of the $n+1$ powers may be the power of a multiple of any linear function of x and y we like to choose, is clear because when u is homogeneous in X, Y, and $\partial u/\partial X$ is a sum of n $(2n-1)$th powers, u is by integration expressed as a sum of n $2n$th powers and a multiple of Y^{2n}. Proper canonical forms of binary quantics of even order must not therefore be expected to be mere sums of $2n$th powers. A sum of n $2n$th powers together with one additional term is, however, a form to be reasonably anticipated.

Before seeking such a canonical form for the quartic it will be interesting to investigate the special relation which must hold among the coefficients of the $2n$-ic

$$(a_0, a_1, a_2, \dots a_{2n})(x, y)^{2n}$$

that it may be identical with a sum of n $2n$th powers.

If we pay attention to the method of § 203 it will be clear that the necessary and sufficient condition is that n quantities $q_1, q_2, \dots q_n$ exist which satisfy simultaneously the $n+1$ equations

$$\begin{array}{llllll} a_n & +q_1 a_{n-1} & +q_2 a_{n-2} & +\dots+q_n a_0 & = 0, \\ a_{n+1} & +q_1 a_n & +q_2 a_{n-1} & +\dots+q_n a_1 & = 0, \\ \cdot & \cdot & \cdot & \cdot & \cdot \\ a_{2n-1} & +q_1 a_{2n-2} & +q_2 a_{2n-3} & +\dots+q_n a_{n-1} & = 0, \\ a_{2n} & +q_1 a_{2n-1} & +q_2 a_{2n-2} & +\dots+q_n a_n & = 0. \end{array}$$

Now the necessary and sufficient condition for this is that, reversing the order of the columns,

$$\begin{vmatrix} a_0, & a_1 & , a_2 & , \dots a_n \\ a_1, & a_2 & , a_3 & , \dots a_{n+1} \\ a_2, & a_3 & , a_4 & , \dots a_{n+2} \\ \cdot & \cdot & \cdot & \cdot \\ a_n, & a_{n+1}, & a_{n+2}, & \dots a_{2n} \end{vmatrix} = 0,$$

i.e. that the invariant defined as the *catalecticant* (§ 17 Examples) vanish.

Ex. 9. The binary quartic $(a, b, c, d, e)(x, y)^4$ will be a sum of two fourth powers if

$$J \equiv ace + 2bcd - ad^2 - b^2e - c^3 = 0.$$

Ex. 10. The binary sextic $(a, b, c, d, e, f, g)(x, y)^6$ will be a sum of three sixth powers if

$$\begin{vmatrix} a, & b, & c, & d \\ b, & c, & d, & e \\ c, & d, & e, & f \\ d, & e, & f, & g \end{vmatrix} = 0.$$

209. **Catalecticants are invariants.** It is instructive to notice that what we have before us affords a reason why the catalecticant of a binary quantic of even order is an invariant. Its vanishing expresses the necessary and sufficient condition that the quantic may have a special property, that of being a sum of n $2n$th powers, which is entirely independent of any linear transformation. If, in fact, the most general linear substitution possible in $(a_0, a_1, a_2, \dots a_{2n})(x, y)^{2n}$ transforms

that $2n$-ic into $(A_0, A_1, A_2, \ldots A_{2n})(X, Y)^{2n}$, the vanishing of the same function of $A_0, A_1, A_2, \ldots A_{2n}$ expresses the necessary and sufficient condition for the same special property. Moreover, the A's being of the first degree in the a's, the degree in the a's of the catalecticants of the original and transformed $2n$-ics are the same. The one, then, can only differ from the other by a factor involving merely the constants of the substitution. The catalecticant is therefore an invariant by the definition (§ 3). That the factor is a power of the modulus has been established in general in § 23.

The student is advised to establish that the canonizant of § 206 is a covariant of a binary $(2n-1)$-ic by similar reasoning.

210. In § 208 it was proved that if the catalecticant vanishes the $2n$-ic is a sum of n $2n$th powers, and that conversely if a $2n$-ic is a sum of n $2n$th powers its catalecticant vanishes. The latter fact is well exhibited as follows. For brevity of writing the case of the quartic alone is taken.

The catalecticant of $p(x+ay)^4 + q(x+\beta y)^4$ is

$$\begin{vmatrix} p+q, & pa+q\beta, & pa^2+q\beta^2 \\ pa+q\beta, & pa^2+q\beta^2, & pa^3+q\beta^3 \\ pa^2+q\beta^2, & pa^3+q\beta^3, & pa^4+q\beta^4 \end{vmatrix}.$$

Now this is a sum of $8\,(=2^3)$ determinants, of which the first is

$$\begin{vmatrix} p, & pa, & pa^2 \\ pa, & pa^2, & pa^3 \\ pa^2, & pa^3, & pa^4 \end{vmatrix},$$

the other seven being obtained from this one by replacing p and a by q and β in one or more of its columns.

But in every one of these eight determinants there are either two (p, a) columns at least or two (q, β) columns at least. Moreover, taking one which contains two (p, a) columns, we notice that the constituents in one of these two columns are either a or a^2 times those in the other of the two, so that the determinant is either a or a^2 times one with two columns identical, and therefore vanishes. Similarly every one of the eight which has two (q, β) columns vanishes. All the eight then vanish, and consequently their sum the catalecticant vanishes.

211. **Canonical form of quartic.** We now proceed to show that the general binary quartic may be reduced to the canonical form

$$X^4 + Y^4 + 6mX^2Y^2,$$

in favour of which there is a presumption as the form contains one ($=4-3$, cf. § 196) free coefficient m.

We have to see that p, q, a, β and μ can be found so as to make

$$(a, b, c, d, e)(x, y)^4$$
$$\equiv p(x+ay)^4+q(x+\beta y)^4+6\mu(x+ay)^2(x+\beta y)^2$$

an identity. It is not enough to notice that the number of free constants on the right is equal to the number of coefficients on the left.

Knowledge that a quartic equation has four roots is assumed. Thus $(a, b, c, d, e)(x, y)^4$ can be broken up into linear factors, and consequently into two quadratic factors in three ways, corresponding to the arrangements (12, 34), (13, 24), (14, 23) of the linear factors. Let one of the quadratic factorizations be

$$(a'x^2+2b'xy+c'y^2)(a''x^2+2b''xy+c''y^2).$$

What we have to prove will be established if we can find p', q', p'', q'', a, β so that simultaneously

$$a'x^2+2b'xy+c'y^2 \equiv p'(x+ay)^2+q'(x+\beta y)^2,$$
$$a''x^2+2b''xy+c''y^2 \equiv p''(x+ay)^2+q''(x+\beta y)^2.$$

The six equations for finding the constants on the right, that this may be the case, are

$$p'+q' = a', \quad p''+q'' = a'',$$
$$p'a+q'\beta = b', \quad p''a+q''\beta = b'',$$
$$p'a^2+q'\beta^2 = c', \quad p''a^2+q''\beta^2 = c''.$$

Now of these the first three are consistent for the determination of p', q' if

$$c'-b'(a+\beta)+a'a\beta = 0,$$

as we see by eliminating p' and q', and the last three are consistent for the determination of p'', q'' if

$$c''-b''(a+\beta)+a''a\beta = 0;$$

and these two conditions are satisfied by taking

$$\frac{1}{a'b''-a''b'} = \frac{a+\beta}{a'c''-a''c'} = \frac{a\beta}{b'c''-b''c'},$$

i.e. by taking for a, β the roots of the quadratic

$$(a'b''-a''b')a^2-(a'c''-a''c')a+b'c''-b''c' = 0,$$

which are finite and unequal if a', b', c', a'', b'', c'' are unconnected, i.e. if the quartic is general. For cases of speciality see § 215 below.

We see then that the required reduction is in general possible, and possible in three distinct ways, one corresponding to each way of breaking up the quartic into two quadratic factors.

The quartic in the form

$$p(x+\alpha y)^4+q(x+\beta y)^4+6\mu(x+\alpha y)^2(x+\beta y)^2,$$

into which it is now shown capable of being thrown, is given the canonical form

$$X^4+Y^4+6mX^2Y^2$$

by taking for X either $\pm p^{\frac{1}{4}}(x+\alpha y)$ or $\pm\iota p^{\frac{1}{4}}(x+\alpha y)$, where ι denotes $\sqrt{-1}$, and for Y either $\pm q^{\frac{1}{4}}(x+\beta y)$ or $\pm\iota q^{\frac{1}{4}}(x+\beta y)$. It is thus seen that m may have either of the two values $\pm(pq)^{-\frac{1}{2}}\mu$. Each of the three reductions above produces then two varieties of the canonical form differing only in the sign of m. The equation to be found for the determination of m should consequently prove to be a cubic in m^2.

We thus encounter a striking difference between the quartic, and other quantics of even order, and the cubic, and quantics of odd order, in the matter of canonical forms. The reduction of the cubic to its canonical form X^3+Y^3 is unique. On the other hand, the reduction of the quartic to its canonical form $X^4+Y^4+6mX^2Y^2$ is sixfold.

212. We now proceed to exhibit the information given by invariant algebra with reference to the general binary quartic

$$u\equiv(a,\ b,\ c,\ d,\ e)\,(x,\ y)^4$$

and its canonical form

$$X^4+Y^4+6mX^2Y^2\equiv(1,\ 0,\ m,\ 0,\ 1)\,(X,\ Y)^4.$$

Suppose that X and Y, expressed in terms of x and y, are $\lambda x+\mu y$ and $\lambda' x+\mu' y$ respectively. Let M' denote $\lambda\mu'-\lambda'\mu$, so that M' is the modulus of the substitution which reduces the canonical form to the general, and consequently M'^{-1} the modulus of that which reduces the general to the canonical.

By § 170 the irreducible concomitants of the quartic are, including itself, five in number. They are

(1) the quartic itself

$$u\equiv(a,\ b,\ c,\ d,\ e)\,(x,\ y)^4,$$

(2, 3) its two invariants

$$I\equiv ae-4bd+3c^2,$$

$$J\equiv ace+2bcd-ad^2-b^2e-c^3,$$

of which the latter is its catalecticant,

(4) its quartic covariant, or Hessian,

$$H\equiv\begin{vmatrix} ax^2+2bxy+cy^2, & bx^2+2cxy+dy^2 \\ bx^2+2cxy+dy^2, & cx^2+2dxy+ey^2 \end{vmatrix},$$

of which the seminvariant leader is $ac-b^2$, and

(5) a sextic covariant of which the seminvariant leader is $a^2d-3abc+2b^3$, which, written at length by the method of § 110, is

$$\begin{aligned}G \equiv &(a^2d-3abc+2b^3)x^6+(a^2e+2abd-9ac^2+6b^2c)x^5y\\ &+(5abe-15acd+10b^2d)x^4y^2+(10b^2e-10ad^2)x^3y^3\\ &+(15bce-5ade-10bd^2)x^2y^4+(9c^2e-ae^2-2bde-6cd^2)xy^5\\ &+(3cde-be^2-2d^3)y^6.\end{aligned}$$

The power of the modulus in the equality expressive of invariancy or covariancy of any one of these has for its index, it will be remembered, the weight of the invariant or of the seminvariant leader of the covariant. Thus we have the five equalities

$$u = X^4+Y^4+6mX^2Y^2, \qquad \ldots(1)$$

$$I = M'^4(1+3m^2), \qquad \ldots(2)$$

$$J = M'^6(m-m^3), \qquad \ldots(3)$$

$$H = M'^2\{m(X^4+Y^4)+(1-3m^2)X^2Y^2\}, \qquad \ldots(4)$$

$$G = M'^3(1-9m^2)XY(X^4-Y^4). \qquad \ldots(5)$$

The first observation made on an inspection of these equalities is that the two invariants I and J alone supply us with the equation for the determination of the m's of the six canonical forms, and with the values of the modulus M', going with the several values of m, of the substitutions which express X and Y in terms of x and y.

Elimination of M' between (2) and (3) gives at once

$$I^3m^2(1-m^2)^2 = J^2(1+3m^2)^3, \qquad \ldots(6)$$

the cubic whose roots are the three values of m^2. To each value of m there corresponds a value of M'^2 given by

$$M'^2 = \frac{J}{I}\cdot\frac{1+3m^2}{m-m^3}, \qquad \ldots(7)$$

so that with each value of m go two of M', equal but of opposite signs. This is reasonable, for a canonical form is unaltered when we interchange X and Y, but the modulus is changed in sign. The equation for all the values of M' should then be a cubic in M'^4, the two values $\pm m$ of m giving two values $\pm M'^2$ of M'^2. This cubic comes at once from elimination of m between (2) and (3), and is

$$J^2 = M'^{12}\frac{I-M'^4}{3M'^4}\left\{1-\left(\frac{I-M'^4}{3M'^4}\right)\right\}^2,$$

i. e. $$(M'^4-I)(4M'^4-I)^2+27J^2=0. \qquad \ldots(8)$$

The cubic for $M'^2 m$ is simpler than either that for m^2 or that for M'^4, and is given by taking

$$\frac{J}{M'^2 m} - I = -4M'^4 m^2,$$

and so is

$$4(M'^2 m)^3 - I(M'^2 m) + J = 0, \qquad \ldots(9)$$

which will be recognized as the ordinary reducing cubic of a quartic equation.

We shall consider this cubic further presently. Meanwhile let us pay a little close attention to the cubic (6) for m^2, the solution of which is the one which at once affords the canonical forms themselves. Written at length the cubic is

$$(I^3 - 27J^2)m^6 - (2I^3 + 27J^2)m^4 + (I^3 - 9J^2)m^2 - J^2 = 0. \ldots(10)$$

The one parameter involved in it is the absolute invariant I^3/J^2.

We proceed to draw in the following article certain conclusions as to the reduction of special classes of quartics, which obey invariant conditions suggested by the coefficients in this cubic.

213. **Quartics for which** $I = 0$. If a quartic belong to the special class for which

$$I \equiv ae - 4bd + 3c^2 = 0,$$

the cubic for m^2 becomes

$$(1 + 3m^2)^3 = 0,$$

so that the three pairs of reductions to a canonical form coalesce in form into a single pair, the alternative canonical forms being

$$X^4 + Y^4 \pm 2\iota\sqrt{3}\, X^2 Y^2,$$

and being thus of imaginary shape. From (3) we find, as corresponding to the values $\pm\iota\sqrt{\tfrac{1}{3}}$ of m respectively,

$$M'^6 = \mp\tfrac{3}{4}\iota\sqrt{3}J,$$

so that the values of the modulus as well as of m are all imaginary.

Since the relation $1 + 3m^2 = 0$ may be written

$$\frac{1 - 3m^2}{6m} = -\frac{m}{1},$$

we see from (1) and (4) that the Hessian of

$$X^4 + Y^4 \pm 2\iota\sqrt{3}\, X^2 Y^2$$

is, but for the factor $M'^2 m$,

$$X^4 + Y^4 \mp 2\iota\sqrt{3}\, X^2 Y^2.$$

Thus a quartic for which $I = 0$ and its Hessian have reciprocal properties, each being, but for a constant factor, the Hessian of the other. Moreover they have, but for a constant factor, the same sextic covariant G.

Ex. 11. Prove that

$$X^4 + Y^4 \pm 2\iota\sqrt{3}X^2Y^2 \equiv \frac{1}{2 \mp 2\iota\sqrt{3}}\{(X+Y)^4 + (X-Y)^4 \mp 2\iota\sqrt{3}(X+Y)^2(X-Y)^2\}$$
$$\equiv \frac{1}{2 \pm 2\iota\sqrt{3}}\{(X+\iota Y)^4 + (X-\iota Y)^4 \pm 2\iota\sqrt{3}(X+\iota Y)^2(X-\iota Y)^2\},$$

thus exhibiting the connexion between the three like pairs of canonical forms when $I = 0$.

Ex. 12. Three of the six anharmonic ratios of the range or pencil denoted by a binary quartic for which $I = 0$ are equal to $-\omega$, and the other three to $-\omega^2$, where ω and ω^2 are the imaginary cube roots of unity.

Ex. 13. When $I = 0$, $M'^6 m^3 = -\frac{1}{4}J$.

Ex. 14. When $I = 0$,

$$u + \frac{4^{\frac{1}{3}}}{J^{\frac{1}{3}}}H,\quad u + \omega\frac{4^{\frac{1}{3}}}{J^{\frac{1}{3}}}H,\quad u + \omega^2\frac{4^{\frac{1}{3}}}{J^{\frac{1}{3}}}H$$

are perfect squares; viz. numerical multiples of the squares of the products XY for canonical forms.

Ex. 15. When $I = 0$, $Ju^3 + 4H^3 = -G^2$. Hence also prove Ex. 14.

214. **Quartics for which $J = 0$.** When the catalecticant

$$J \equiv ace + 2bcd - ad^2 - b^2e - c^3 = 0,$$

so that (§ 208) one canonical form is a sum of two fourth powers, the cubic (6) or (10) of § 212 for m^2 is

$$m^2(m^2-1)^2 = 0.$$

The second and third pairs of canonical forms coalesce then in the shape

$$X^4 + Y^4 \pm 6X^2Y^2.$$

The connexion of the different canonical forms for this case is exhibited in the identities

$$\begin{aligned} X^4 + Y^4 &\equiv X^4 + (\iota Y)^4, \\ &\equiv \tfrac{1}{8}\{(X+Y)^4 + (X-Y)^4 + 6(X+Y)^2(X-Y)^2\}, \\ &\equiv \tfrac{1}{8}\{(X+Y)^4 + (\iota X-\iota Y)^4 - 6(X+Y)^2(\iota X-\iota Y)^2\}, \\ &\equiv \tfrac{1}{8}\{(X+\iota Y)^4 + (X-\iota Y)^4 + 6(X+\iota Y)^2(X-\iota Y)^2\}, \\ &\equiv \tfrac{1}{8}\{(X+\iota Y)^4 + (\iota X+Y)^4 - 6(X+\iota Y)^2(\iota X+Y)^2\}. \end{aligned}$$

By § 212 (2), $M'^4 = I$ goes with $m = 0$, and $M'^4 = \frac{1}{4}I$ with $m = \pm 1$.

Ex. 16. When $J = 0$, the Hessian is, but for a constant factor, the square of the product of the X and Y of the canonical form $X^4 + Y^4$.

Ex. 17. In the same case, the two expressions $u \pm 2 I^{-\frac{1}{2}} H$ are eight times the squares of the products XY for the other two essentially distinct canonical forms, the third and fourth, and the fifth and sixth, of the above forms not being reckoned as essentially distinct.

Ex. 18. In the same case, $(Iu^2 - 4H^2)H = G^2$.

Ex. 19. The range or pencil denoted by a binary quartic for which $J = 0$ is harmonic.

Ex. 20. So is the range or pencil composed of any two out of three pairs of elements which constitute what is denoted by the sextic covariant G.

215. **Quartics for which $I^3 = 27J^2$.** When the coefficients in the quartic are such that $I^3 - 27J^2 = 0$, i.e. when the discriminant vanishes, so that the quartic has a square factor, one value of m^2 given by § 212 (10) is infinite, and the quadratic for the other two values of m^2 is

$$(9m^2 - 1)^2 = 0.$$

But we are here confronted with a case in which the reduction to the canonical form $X^4 + Y^4 + 6mX^2Y^2$ is impossible unless a further condition is satisfied. The value $m = \infty$ would make this canonical form an infinite multiple of X^2Y^2, i.e. of a perfect square, and the values $m = \pm\frac{1}{3}$ would make it $X^4 + Y^4 \pm 2X^2Y^2$, again perfect squares. Now obviously a quartic with a square factor must have its conjugate quadratic factor also a perfect square for such a reduction to be possible.

For the explanation of this we must refer back to § 211. If the two conjugate quadratic factors there assumed have a common linear factor their eliminant

$$(a'c'' - a''c')^2 - 4(a'b'' - a''b')(b'c'' - b''c')$$

vanishes, and the quadratic in α has equal roots, so that $\alpha = \beta$, and the method followed fails to find a distinct X and Y, and indeed fails to lead to any result which is not more obvious otherwise. And again, if one of the quadratic factors, $a'x^2 + 2b'xy + c'y^2$ suppose, is a perfect square, so that $a'c' = b'^2$, it follows that $p'q'(\alpha - \beta)^2 = 0$, so that either $\alpha = \beta$, and there is failure as before, or else either $p' = 0$ or $q' = 0$, which leads not to the form $X^4 + Y^4 + 6mX^2Y^2$ but to the form $X^4 + 6mX^2Y^2$.

It is this form, or rather its further simplification

$$X^4 + 6X^2Y^2,$$

which is canonical for a quartic for which $I^3 - 27J^2 = 0$.

The more special quantic still which has not only one square factor but two square factors, i.e. which is a constant multiple of the square of a quadratic, can, however, it is clear, be given the form $(X^2+Y^2)^2$ or the form $(X^2-Y^2)^2$ as above. An even simpler form for such a quantic is $6X^2Y^2$.

When the quartic has a cubed factor its canonical form is of course $4X^3Y$. All its invariants vanish.

Ex. 21. The Hessian of a binary quartic with a square factor has that same square factor. (This fact is easily proved for a binary quantic of any order with a square factor.)

Ex. 22. The sextic covariant G of a quartic with a square factor $(lx+my)^2$ has the factor $(lx+my)^5$.

Ex. 23. If a binary quartic be the square of a quadratic it must be the same but for a constant factor as its Hessian, so that

$$\frac{ac-b^2}{a} = \frac{ad-bc}{2b} = \frac{ae+2bd-3c^2}{6c} = \frac{be-cd}{2d} = \frac{ce-d^2}{e}.$$

Ans. $2IH = 3Ju$. (*Cayley.*)

Ex. 24. In the same case the sextic covariant G vanishes identically. Hence also determine the same conditions as in Ex. 23.

216. **The general binary quartic.** We now proceed to apply the equalities of § 212 to the case of the general quartic.

A pair of canonical forms $X^4+Y^4 \pm 6mX^2Y^2$ are not essentially distinct, the X and Y of one being merely the X and ιY of the other.

The sextic covariant G helps us to decide what are the X and Y of each of the two other essentially distinct canonical forms of the same shape as one $X^4+Y^4+6mX^2Y^2$. This covariant G has, § 212 (5), the X and Y of $X^4+Y^4+6mX^2Y^2$ for factors. For the same reason it must have for factors the X and Y of each of the other canonical forms. It is therefore, but for a factor free from the variables, the product of the three X's and the three Y's of the essentially distinct canonical forms. We are thus led to expect that X^2-Y^2 and X^2+Y^2 are, but for constant factors, the products XY corresponding to the two other forms.

And it is in fact quite easy so to assign k', k'', m', m'' as to satisfy the identities

$$\begin{aligned} X^4+Y^4+6mX^2Y^2 &\equiv \{k'(X+Y)\}^4 + \{k'(X-Y)\}^4 \\ &\qquad + 6m'\{k'(X+Y)\}^2\{k'(X-Y)\}^2 \\ &\equiv \{k''(X+\iota Y)\}^4 + \{k''(X-\iota Y)\}^4 \\ &\qquad + 6m''\{k''(X+\iota Y)\}^2\{k''(X-\iota Y)\}^2. \end{aligned}$$

Thus for k', m' we have only to secure that

$$k'^4(2+6m') = 1, \quad k'^4(12-12m') = 6m,$$

i.e. to take

$$m' = \frac{1-m}{3m+1}, \quad k'^4 = \tfrac{1}{8}(3m+1),$$

and similarly for k'', m''.

217. **Reduction of general quartic to canonical form.** Let us now take the simplest of the cubics of § 212, viz. (9)

$$4(M'^2m)^3 - I(M'^2m) + J = 0.$$

The solution of this affords a ready way of determining the X and Y of either of the canonical forms. The equations (1) and (4) of § 212 give us at once

$$u - \frac{H}{M'^2m} = \left(9m - \frac{1}{m}\right)X^2Y^2.$$

Solve then the cubic above for M'^2m, and, taking either of its roots, form the corresponding $M'^2mu - H$. This, but for a multiplier free from the variables, is a perfect square, namely the square of XY. Break up the square root of $M'^2mu - H$, or any convenient multiple of it, into two factors $gx+hy$, $g'x+h'y$. The identity must hold

$$u \equiv (a, b, c, d, e)(x, y)^4 \equiv a'(gx+hy)^4 + 6c'(gx+hy)^2(g'x+h'y)^2 + e'(g'x+h'y)^4,$$

for some values of a', c', e'. These values can be found by identifying three of the coefficients on the left with those which correspond on the right. Having found them,

$a'^{\frac{1}{4}}(gx+hy)$, $e'^{\frac{1}{4}}(g'x+h'y)$ are X, Y, and $c'a'^{-\frac{1}{2}}e'^{-\frac{1}{2}}$ is m.

218. **Syzygy among** u, I, J, H, G. That XY is, but for a factor free from x, y, the square root of $M'^2mu - H$, and consequently that the product of the three values of XY for the three essentially distinct canonical forms is, but for such a factor, the square root of the product of the three values of $M'^2mu - H$ corresponding to the three roots of the cubic for M'^2m, tells us, when taken in connexion with § 216, that this product

$$(M_1'^2m_1u - H)(M_2'^2m_2u - H)(M_3'^2m_3u - H)$$

can only differ by a factor free from the variables from G^2.

Now by the theory of equations

$$4z^3 - Iz + J = 4(z - M_1'^2m_1)(z - M_2'^2m_2)(z - M_3'^2m_3).$$

Consequently an identity must hold of the form

$$kG^2 = -4H^3 + Iu^2H - Ju^3.$$

That k here is merely a numerical constant, and not a function of the coefficients, is indicated by the fact that G^2 and the right-hand side are both of degree 6 in the coefficients. To find its value we may either substitute for u, I, J, H, G their values in terms of X, Y, M', m from § 212 and examine the identity of the coefficients of one term, say of $X^{10}Y^2$, on the two sides, or may notice that § 213, Ex. 15 gives us the particular form which the relation takes when $I = 0$. We thus find $k = 1$.

Accordingly the irreducible but not independent concomitants u, I, J, H, G of the binary quartic u are connected by the syzygy

$$Iu^2H - 4H^3 - Ju^3 = G^2,$$

the invariants and seminvariant leaders of the covariants being themselves connected by the syzygy

$$Ia^2(ac-b^2) - 4(ac-b^2)^3 - Ja^3 = (a^2d - 3abc + 2b^3)^2.$$

These syzygies have been otherwise obtained in previous chapters.

219. **Canonical reduction with unit modulus.** There is often convenience in using, not the strictly canonical form of a quantic, i.e. the simplest form to which the quantic may be reduced by any linear substitution, but the simplest form to which it may be reduced by a substitution of unit modulus.

If the substitution which reduces the quartic $(a, b, c, d, e)(x, y)^4$ to its canonical form $X^4 + Y^4 + 6mX^2Y^2$ be

$$x = lX + mY, \quad y = l'X + m'Y,$$

so that $lm' - l'm = M'^{-1}$ in what precedes, the substitution

$$(lm' - l'm)^{\frac{1}{2}}x = lx' + my', \quad (lm' - l'm)^{\frac{1}{2}}y = l'x' + m'y',$$

whose modulus is unity, reduces the quartic to

$$M'^2(x'^4 + y'^4 + 6mx'^2y'^2).$$

Thus $a'(x'^4 + y'^4) + 6c'x'^2y'^2 \equiv (a', 0, c', 0, a')(x', y')^4$ is a form to which the general binary quartic can be reduced by a substitution whose modulus is unity. We also see that c' is the M'^2m of §§ 212, 217, so that the reducing cubic of the quartic is the one whose roots are the three values of c'. We may find it very easily as follows. Since the modulus is 1,

$$I = a'^2 + 3c'^2, \quad J = a'^2c' - c'^3,$$

whence, eliminating a'^2,

$$Ic' - J = 4c'^3,$$

the same cubic as that already found for M'^2m.

We might equally have found in this way the same cubic for c' if all that we had assumed were that a substitution of unit modulus reduces the quartic to the form

$$a'x'^4 + 6c'x'^2y'^2 + e'y'^4.$$

Adopting, however, the fact known as above that a' and e' may be made equal, the equalities (1) to (5) of § 212 are replaced by

$$\begin{aligned} u &= a'(x'^4 + y'^4) + 6c'x'^2y'^2, \\ I &= a'^2 + 3c'^2, \\ J &= a'^2c' - c'^3, \\ H &= a'c'(x'^4 + y'^4) + (a'^2 - 3c'^2)x'^2y'^2, \\ G &= a'(a'^2 - 9c'^2)x'y'(x'^4 - y'^4), \end{aligned}$$

whose right-hand sides are obviously connected by a syzygy, as they involve only four quantities a', c', x', y'. This is readily seen to be that of the preceding article.

Ex. 25. Prove that, if H' is the Hessian of the Hessian H of u, $H' = \frac{1}{4}Ju - \frac{1}{12}IH$.

Ex. 26. The sextic covariant G' of H is $-\frac{1}{4}JG$.

Ex. 27. Find the Hessian and the sextic covariant of $ku + k'H$.

220. The cubic for c' may be found in a different manner, which exhibits it in a form having its analogue in the case of higher binary quantics of even order.

It has been seen that the identity

$$\begin{aligned} &ax^4 + 4bx^3y + 6cx^2y^2 + 4dxy^3 + ey^4 \\ &\qquad \equiv a'(lx+my)^4 + e'(l'x+m'y)^4 + 6c'(lx+my)^2(l'x+m'y)^2 \end{aligned}$$

is one which can be satisfied simultaneously with

$$lm' - l'm = 1,$$

and in fact that we may take $e' = a'$.

Now operate on both sides of the identity with

$$\left(l\frac{\partial}{\partial y} - m\frac{\partial}{\partial x}\right)\left(l'\frac{\partial}{\partial y} - m'\frac{\partial}{\partial x}\right),$$

noticing that this annihilates both $lx+my$ and $l'x+m'y$, and that

$$\begin{aligned} &\left(l\frac{\partial}{\partial y} - m\frac{\partial}{\partial x}\right)\left(l'\frac{\partial}{\partial y} - m'\frac{\partial}{\partial x}\right)\{(lx+my)^2(l'x+m'y)^2\} \\ &\qquad\qquad = -4(lm'-l'm)^2(lx+my)(l'x+m'y) \\ &\qquad\qquad = -4(lx+my)(l'x+m'y). \end{aligned}$$

Equating coefficients of x^2, xy, y^2 in the results of operating on the left and right-hand sides of the identity, we obtain

$$amm'-b(lm'+l'm)+cll' = -2c'll',$$
$$bmm'-c(lm'+l'm)+dll' = -c'(lm'+l'm),$$
$$cmm'-d(lm'+l'm)+ell' = -2c'mm',$$

equations linear in ll', $lm'+l'm$, mm'. By elimination of these we at once obtain the cubic for c'

$$\begin{vmatrix} a, & b, & c+2c' \\ b, & c-c', & d \\ c+2c', & d, & e \end{vmatrix} = 0,$$

i.e. $ace+2bcd-ad^2-b^2e-c^3-(ae-4bd+3c^2)c'+4c'^3=0$,

i.e. $J-Ic'+4c'^3=0$,

the reducing cubic already obtained otherwise.

Taking either root c' of this cubic we can solve the linear equations in ll', $lm'+l'm$, mm', and so obtain their ratios, i.e. obtain the product $ll'x^2+(lm'+l'm)xy+mm'y^2$ of $lx+my$, $l'x+m'y$ but for a constant factor.

221. **Solution of a quartic equation.** When a quartic is reduced to its canonical form, or to the form $a'x^4+6c'x^2y^2+e'y^4$, it is at once broken up into quadratic factors and solved. Two methods suggested by the articles which precede are here exemplified. They are not so simple in their use as some of those given in works on the theory of equations.

Ex. 28. By use of § 220 solve the quartic equation

$$3x^4-4x^3+24x^2-16x+48=0.$$

Here a, b, c, d, e have the values 3, -1, 4, -4, 48. Thus $I=176$, $J=448$, and the cubic for c' is $c'^3-44c'+112=0$, of which 4 is a root. The corresponding ratios $ll' : lm'+l'm : mm'$ of § 220 are $1:0:-4$. The quartic has then the form

$$a''(x+2)^4+e''(x-2)^4+6c''(x^2-4)^2=0,$$

and is in fact seen to be

$$(x+2)^4+2(x-2)^4+3(x^2-4)^2=0,$$

i.e. $\{(x+2)^2+(x-2)^2\}\{(x+2)^2+2(x-2)^2\}=0$,

i.e. $(x^2+4)(3x^2-4x+12)=0$,

so that the roots are $\pm 2\iota$ and $\frac{1}{3}(2\pm 4\iota\sqrt{2})$.

Ex. 29. To the same quartic apply the method of § 217.

Here

$$H \equiv (3x^2-2x+4)(4x^2-8x+48)-(-x^2+8x-4)^2$$
$$\equiv 11x^4-16x^3+104x^2-64x+176.$$

Also a value of M'^2m, or c', is, as above, 4. Thus

$$c'u-H \equiv x^4-8x^2+16 \equiv \{(x+2)(x-2)\}^2.$$

Hence the given equation has the form

$$a''(x+2)^4+e''(x-2)^4+6c''(x^2-4)^2=0,$$

and the solution is completed as above.

222. There is a symmetrical expression given by Cayley for a linear factor of the general binary quartic u.

If c_1, c_2, c_3 are the roots of $4c'^3-Ic'+J=0$, it has been seen in § 217 that c_1u-H, c_2u-H, c_3u-H are multiples of squares of quadratics in the variables.

Thus

$$\lambda\sqrt{(c_1u-H)}+\mu\sqrt{(c_2u-H)}+\nu\sqrt{(c_3u-H)}$$

is a rational quadratic function of x and y. We seek λ, μ, ν that it may be the square of a factor of u.

A value of x/y which makes u vanish, i. e. a root of u, will make the quadratic function vanish if

$$(\lambda+\mu+\nu)\,\iota\sqrt{H}=0,$$

i. e. if

$$\lambda+\mu+\nu=0.$$

The same value will make its differential coefficient with respect to x, i. e.

$$\frac{\lambda}{\sqrt{(c_1u-H)}}\left\{c_1\frac{\partial u}{\partial x}-\frac{\partial H}{\partial x}\right\}+\frac{\mu}{\sqrt{(c_2u-H)}}\left\{c_2\frac{\partial u}{\partial x}-\frac{\partial H}{\partial x}\right\}$$
$$+\frac{\nu}{\sqrt{(c_3u-H)}}\left\{c_3\frac{\partial u}{\partial x}-\frac{\partial H}{\partial x}\right\},$$

vanish, if it make

$$\frac{1}{\iota\sqrt{H}}\left\{(\lambda c_1+\mu c_2+\nu c_3)\frac{\partial u}{\partial x}-(\lambda+\mu+\nu)\frac{\partial H}{\partial x}\right\}=0,$$

as it will do if the further condition

$$\lambda c_1+\mu c_2+\nu c_3=0$$

is satisfied.

Now these two conditions are satisfied by taking

$$\frac{\lambda}{c_2-c_3}=\frac{\mu}{c_3-c_1}=\frac{\nu}{c_1-c_2}.$$

Also nothing has been said as to which of the two quadratics having either c_1u-H or c_2u-H or c_3u-H for square has been chosen in taking the square root; but the same signs have been adhered to throughout. Hence the four squares of linear factors of u are constant multiples of

$$(c_2-c_3)\sqrt{(c_1u-H)}\pm(c_3-c_1)\sqrt{(c_2u-H)}\pm(c_1-c_2)\sqrt{(c_3u-H)}.$$

Ex. 30. Prove that

$$(c_2-c_3)\sqrt{[c_1(c_1u-H)]}\pm(c_3-c_1)\sqrt{[c_2(c_2u-H)]}\pm(c_1-c_2)\sqrt{[c_3(c_3u-H)]}$$

are the squares of linear factors of the Hessian; and that

$$(c_2-c_3)\sqrt{[(k+k'c_1)(u-c_1H)]}\pm(c_3-c_1)\sqrt{[(k+k'c_2)(c_2u-H)]}\pm(c_1-c_2)\sqrt{[(k+k'c_3)(c_3u-H)]}$$

are those of linear factors of $ku+k'H$.

223. **Geometry of concomitants of quartic.** The invariant and covariant geometry of a binary quartic is a geometry of anharmonic properties. The student of geometry will know that, if ρ is an anharmonic ratio of a pencil or range of four elements, the other five anharmonic ratios are

$$\frac{1}{\rho},\ 1-\rho,\ \frac{1}{1-\rho},\ 1-\frac{1}{\rho},\ \frac{\rho}{\rho-1}.$$

Some parts of the geometry have already been obtained. Thus (§ 213, Ex. 12) $I=0$ is the condition that one anharmonic ratio of the pencil or range denoted by the quartic be $-\omega$, and consequently that two others be also $-\omega$, and the remaining three $-\omega^2$. In fact, if we take for ρ the anharmonic ratio $\frac{\gamma-\beta}{\gamma-\delta}:\frac{\alpha-\beta}{\alpha-\delta}$, where α, β, γ, δ are the roots, and notice that this is $-u/w$ in the notation of § 80, we obtain

$$\begin{aligned}I &= \tfrac{1}{24}a^2(u^2+v^2+w^2)\\ &= \tfrac{1}{24}a^2\{u^2+w^2+(u+w)^2\}\\ &= \tfrac{1}{12}a^2(u^2+uw+w^2)\\ &= \tfrac{1}{12}a^2w^2(\rho^2-\rho+1),\end{aligned}$$

so that $I=0$ means, unless two roots are equal which would imply a further invariant condition,

$$\rho=-\omega \text{ or } -\omega^2.$$

Again, $J=0$ is the condition (§ 214, Ex. 19) that the pencil or range be harmonic, i. e. that one anharmonic ratio be -1, and consequently the rest -1, 2, $\frac{1}{2}$, $\frac{1}{2}$, 2. In fact, referring again to § 80,

$$\begin{aligned}J &= -\tfrac{1}{432}a^3(v-w)(w-u)(u-v)\\ &= -\tfrac{1}{432}a^3(-u-2w)(w-u)(2u+w)\\ &= \quad\tfrac{1}{432}a^3w^3(\rho-2)(\rho+1)(2\rho-1),\end{aligned}$$

so that $J=0$ necessitates that ρ be either -1 or 2 or $\frac{1}{2}$.

We have at once, by elimination of aw, the equation whose roots are the six values of ρ, i. e. the six anharmonic ratios of the general quartic; namely,

$$\frac{I^3}{J^2} = 108 \frac{(\rho^2-\rho+1)^3}{(\rho+1)^2(\rho-2)^2(2\rho-1)^2},$$

which may be given the simpler shape

$$\frac{(\rho^2-\rho+1)^3}{\rho^2(\rho-1)^2} = \frac{27I^3}{4(I^3-27J^2)},$$

a cubic, in $\rho(1-\rho)$. The left-hand side of this may also be written

$$\frac{(\rho+\rho^{-1}-1)^3}{\rho+\rho^{-1}-2},$$

so that it is also a cubic in $\rho+\rho^{-1}$.

To interpret the sextic covariant G we remember that it is, but for a constant factor, the product of the XY's of the three essentially distinct canonical forms. Now, if the canonical form $X^4+6mX^2Y^2+Y^4$ is broken up into

$$(X^2+\mu Y^2)(X^2+\mu^{-1}Y^2),$$

we recognize that XY represents the common pair of harmonic conjugates of the pairs $X^2+\mu Y^2$, $X^2+\mu^{-1}Y^2$. We thus conclude that G represents the three pairs of common harmonic conjugates of pairs into which the four factors of the quartic u can be separated, i. e. the double elements of the three involutions which are determined by taking the four linear factors of u in pairs.

It is clear, from the similarity of the canonical reduction (§ 212 (4)) of H the Hessian of u to that of u itself, that G has the same property with regard to H as it has with regard to u. It has also the same property with regard to $ku+k'H$, where k and k' have any values which do not make this a perfect square.

We notice the further property of G, gathering it from the canonical reduction, that its six linear factors occur in pairs XY, X^2-Y^2, X^2+Y^2 such that either pair constitutes the double elements of the involution determined by the other pairs of elements.

The Hessian H determines with u an infinite system of quartics $ku+k'H$, the factors of any one of which can in three ways be taken in pairs so as to have a pair chosen out of six elements constituting G for the double elements of the involution which they determine. For a specification of H itself in the system see Ex. 33 below.

If we describe a conic through the origin, the four points in which it is cut again by the lines u, the four in which it is cut by the lines H, and the four in which it is cut by any $ku+k'H$, are vertices of quadrangles with a common harmonic triangle; and the sides of this triangle cut the conic in the six points where the latter is cut by the six lines G.

For a given u, H is unique; but for a given H, u is not, since to be given $(1-3m^2)/m$ in § 212 (3) is to be given a quadratic for m. The two u's which go with a given H in a system $ku+k'H$ are apolar to one another.

Ex. 31. Find a covariant which represents the four harmonic conjugates of the factors of u, each with regard to the Hessian of the other three factors.

Ans. $(I^3-3J^2)u+8IJH$. To find it take the quartic in the form $4(x^3+y^3)(x+ay)$, so that $I=12a$, $J=-4(a^3+1)$, and determine θ, so that $\theta u-H$, where H is the Hessian of the quartic, may have $x-ay$ for a factor.

Ex. 32. In terms of the roots of u, the quadratic factors of G which give the products XY for canonical forms are

$$\big(\delta+a-\beta-\gamma,\ \beta\gamma-a\delta,\ \delta a(\beta+\gamma)-\beta\gamma(\delta+a)\big)(x,\ y)^2,$$

and two similar.

Ex. 33. A quartic u is represented by four lines through the origin O, and a conic through O cuts the lines in A, B, C, D. If LMN is the harmonic triangle of the complete quadrangle $ABCD$, there are three of the conics having LMN for a common self-conjugate triangle each of which touches two pairs of sides of the complete quadrangle, and there is another conic with regard to which every one of these three conics is its own reciprocal. Prove that if this last conic cuts the conic $(OABCD)$ in A', B', C', D', then the lines OA', OB', OC', OD' represent the Hessian of u.

Ex. 34. Prove that $\quad 4xy(x^2+y^2)=\mu(x^2-y^2)^2$
is a general canonical form of $u=0$, suitable for exhibiting the geometry when two roots of $u=0$ are real and two imaginary.

If $\mu\mu'=3$, to replace μ by μ' in this form gives the $u'=0$ apolar to $u=0$ in the system $ku+k'H=0$, and to replace it by $-\frac{1}{2}(\mu+\mu')$ gives $H=0$.

224. **Higher binary quantics of even order.** We now pass to consider briefly the reduction to canonical forms of $2n$-ics, where n exceeds 2.

It has been seen (§ 208) that a binary $2n$-ic whose catalecticant vanishes can be expressed as a sum of n $2n$th powers.

Now let u be the general binary $2n$-ic, whose catalecticant therefore does not vanish, and let v be any particular binary $2n$-ic with coefficients definitely chosen, either as constants or as functions of the coefficients in u. Let λ be a constant free to have any value.

Write down the catalecticant of $u-\lambda v$ and equate it to zero. The result is, as a rule, an equation in λ; it certainly will be if the catalecticant of v does not vanish. This equation has a root or roots, i.e. there is a value, or values, of λ for which $u-\lambda v$ is a sum of n $2n$th powers.

A right form to assume for the general binary $2n$-ic u is then a sum of n $2n$th powers together with a free multiple of any particular $2n$-ic v whose catalecticant does not vanish. The latter restriction is in excess of the requirements.

The most natural form to assume for the sextic would appear to be
$$X^6+Y^6+Z^6+\lambda X^2Y^2Z^2,$$
but the reduction to this form has not, as a matter of fact, been effected.

The octavic, however, as we shall presently see, has been brought by Sylvester to the corresponding form.
$$X^8+Y^8+Z^8+W^8+\lambda X^2Y^2Z^2W^2.$$

225. **The binary sextic.** The usual canonical form for the sextic is
$$p(X+Y)^6+q(X+\omega Y)^6+r(X+\omega^2Y)^6+\mu(X^6-Y^6),$$
or, putting x', y', z' for $X+Y$, $\omega(X+\omega Y)$, $\omega^2(X+\omega^2Y)$ respectively,
$$px'^6+qy'^6+rz'^6+\lambda x'y'z'(y'-z')(z'-x')(x'-y').$$
It contains one superfluous constant. Thus we may hope to express the sextic in the form by a transformation of modulus unity.

We seek X and Y that
$$(a, b, c, d, e, f, g)(x, y)^6$$
$$=p(X+Y)^6+q(X+\omega Y)^6+r(X+\omega^2Y)^6+\mu(X^6-Y^6)$$
may be an identity. Suppose that
$$a'x^3+3b'x^2y+3c'xy^2+d'y^3\equiv X^3+Y^3.$$
Then, by § 46, the modulus being unity, we have also the equivalence of operations
$$a'\frac{\partial^3}{\partial y^3}-3b'\frac{\partial^3}{\partial x\,\partial y^2}+3c'\frac{\partial^3}{\partial x^2\partial y}-d'\frac{\partial^3}{\partial x^3}=\frac{\partial^3}{\partial Y^3}-\frac{\partial^3}{\partial X^3}.$$
Operate with the left-hand side here upon
$$(a, b, c, d, e, f, g)(x, y)^6,$$
and with the right on its supposed equivalent in terms of X and Y. Remembering that
$$\left(\frac{\partial}{\partial Y}-\frac{\partial}{\partial X}\right)(X+Y)=0,\quad \left(\frac{\partial}{\partial Y}-\omega\frac{\partial}{\partial X}\right)(X+\omega Y)=0,$$
$$\left(\frac{\partial}{\partial Y}-\omega^2\frac{\partial}{\partial X}\right)(X+\omega^2Y)=0,$$
we see that the result on the right-hand side is
$$-120\mu(X^3+Y^3),$$
which is the same as
$$-120\mu(a'x^3+3b'x^2y+3c'xy^2+d'y^3).$$

This is exhibited as the equivalent of another cubic in x and y. Equating the coefficients in the two, we have at once

$$\begin{aligned} a'd-3b'c+3c'b-d'a &= -a'\mu, \\ a'e-3b'd+3c'c-d'b &= -b'\mu, \\ a'f-3b'e+3c'd-d'c &= -c'\mu, \\ a'g-3b'f+3c'e-d'd &= -d'\mu, \end{aligned}$$

which are made consistent for finding the mutual ratios of a', b', c', d' by choosing μ so as to satisfy

$$\begin{vmatrix} d+\mu, & c & , b & , a \\ e & , d-\frac{1}{3}\mu, & c & , b \\ f & , e & , d+\frac{1}{3}\mu, & c \\ g & , f & , e & , d-\mu \end{vmatrix} = 0,$$

i. e. by solving a quartic equation; so that there are four such values of μ.

Substitute one of these values of μ. The ratios $a' : b' : c' : d'$ are at once determined by any three of the linear equations made consistent. It is now a matter of the solution of a cubic equation to split up

$$a'x^3+3b'x^2y+3c'xy^2+d'y^3$$

into its three factors, which must, but for constant multipliers, be the $X+Y$, $X+\omega Y$, $X+\omega^2 Y$.

Now we have secured above that X^3+Y^3 is apolar to

$$(a, b, c, d, e, f, g)(x, y)^6-\mu(X^6-Y^6).$$

This latter then is of the form

$$p(X+Y)^6+q(X+\omega Y)^6+r(X+\omega^2 Y)^6;$$

and p, q, r can be found by identifying three coefficients when both forms are expressed in terms of x, y. We have thus proved the canonical form valid, and shown how to find it.

The coefficients of the canonizing quartic equation in μ must be invariants, as their property is quite independent of any linear transformation. The equation is in fact

$$\begin{vmatrix} d, & c, & b, & a \\ e, & d, & c, & b \\ f, & e, & d, & c \\ g, & f, & e, & d \end{vmatrix} + \tfrac{1}{9}(ag-6bf+15ce-10d^2)\mu^2+\tfrac{1}{9}\mu^4 = 0,$$

whose coefficients are the catalecticant and the quadric invariant.

It will be seen that the four values of μ go in pairs $\pm\mu_1$, $\pm\mu_2$.

226. Another useful canonical form of the general binary sextic is
$$(1, 0, C, D, E, 0, 1)(X, Y)^6.$$

It suffices to show that linear transformations exist which deprive the sextic of its second and penultimate coefficients. After the application of one of them we can make the first and last coefficients unity by a further substitution of some λX, μY for X and Y.

Apply the transformation
$$x = lX + mY, \quad y = X + Y$$
to the general sextic
$$u \equiv (a, b, c, d, e, f, g)(x, y)^6.$$

The coefficients of X^5Y and XY^5 in the transformed sextic will both vanish if
$$m(al^5 + 5bl^4 + 10cl^3 + 10dl^2 + 5el + f) + bl^5 + 5cl^4 + 10dl^3 + 10el^2 + 5fl + g = 0,$$
and
$$l(am^5 + 5bm^4 + 10cm^3 + 10dm^2 + 5em + f) + bm^5 + 5cm^4 + 10dm^3 + 10em^2 + 5fm + g = 0.$$

These two equations will in particular be satisfied if
$$l = m \text{ and } (a, b, c, d, e, f, g)(l, 1)^6 = 0;$$
but the transformation thus led to is unlawful, because the modulus $l - m$ may not vanish. In the equation for l found by eliminating m the factor $(a, b, c, d, e, f, g)(l, 1)^6$ will occur, and must be discarded.

Now the elimination of m gives
$$(al + b, bl + c, cl + d, dl + e, el + f, fl + g)(bl^6 + 5cl^4 + \ldots + g, -al^5 - 5bl^4 - \ldots - f)^5 = 0,$$
an equation of the 26th degree; and on removing the superfluous sextic factor one of degree 20 remains. Changing sign, this begins with
$$(a^4f - 5a^3be + 10a^2b^2d - 10ab^3c + 4b^5)\,l^{20}.$$
The leading coefficient is then a seminvariant, the A_5 of § 163.

In fact, the whole left-hand side of the equation of degree 26 is the result of replacing x, y by l, 1 in a numerical multiple of
$$\left(\frac{\partial^5 u}{\partial x^5}, \frac{\partial^5 u}{\partial x^4\,\partial y}, \frac{\partial^5 u}{\partial x^3\,\partial y^2}, \frac{\partial^5 u}{\partial x^2\,\partial y^3}, \frac{\partial^5 u}{\partial x\,\partial y^4}, \frac{\partial^5 u}{\partial y^5}\right)\left(\frac{\partial u}{\partial y}, -\frac{\partial u}{\partial x}\right)^5,$$
which is a covariant of the sextic u, being written down as an invariant of its first and fifth emanants. Its leading coefficient is a numerical multiple of aA_5, so that (§ 111) u itself is a factor of the covariant, and the remaining factor is a covariant of order 20 led by A_5.

By the fundamental theorem of Algebra the equation in l of degree 20 has roots. Any one of these may be taken for l; and then the first of the two equations in l, m gives uniquely a second of the 20 as an m which goes with the first l in satisfying our requirement.

Since $x-ly=(m-l)Y$, and $x-my=(l-m)X$, a sextic is reduced to the desired form by taking for the new variables any linear factor of the 20-ic covariant and a uniquely corresponding second factor. The factorization is not algebraically practicable; but the lawfulness of the canonical form is not thus prejudiced.

Stephanos and Brill, following other methods, have made the reduction of a sextic to the desired form depend on the solution of quintic and lower equations.

Ex. 35. The general binary p-ic can be deprived of second and penultimate coefficients by taking for new variables any first and a corresponding second factor of a $(p-1)(p-2)$-ic covariant led by the seminvariant A_{p-1} of § 163. Treat the problems of §§ 199, 211 as particular cases.

227. **The binary octavic.** The canonical form of the octavic $(a_0, a_1, \ldots a_8)(x, y)^8$ is

$$X^8+Y^8+Z^8+W^8+\lambda X^2Y^2Z^2W^2,$$

where X, Y, Z, W are linear in x and y. The form is certainly lawful by § 224. We have to see that λ and the product

$$\begin{aligned} XYZW &\equiv (l_1x+m_1y)(l_2x+m_2y)(l_3x+m_3y)(l_4x+m_4y) \\ &\equiv (a', b', c', d', e')(x, y)^4, \text{ say,} \end{aligned}$$

can be found.

The operator $(a', b', c', d', e')(\partial/\partial y, -\partial/\partial x)^4$ annihilates X^8, Y^8, Z^8, W^8, as is clear, since $\left(l\frac{\partial}{\partial y}-m\frac{\partial}{\partial x}\right)(lx+my)=0$. We can further see that the same operator produces from $X^2Y^2Z^2W^2$ a constant multiple of $XYZW$. To do so affords a good example of the use of the concomitants of a quartic.

We have to see, in fact, that

$$(a', b', c', d', e')\left(\frac{\partial}{\partial y}, -\frac{\partial}{\partial x}\right)^4\{(a', b', c', d', e')(x, y)^4\}^2$$

is a constant multiple of $(a', b', c', d', e')(x, y)^4$.

The expression is a covariant of the quartic by § 47. Its degree in the coefficients of the quartic is 3, and its order in the variables is 4. Now, referring to the complete list, § 212, of the irreducible concomitants of the quartic, we see that these, u, I, J, H, G, are of degree-orders (1, 4), (2, 0), (3, 0), (2, 4), (3, 6), and that the only covariant of degree-order

(3, 4) which can be formed by combining them is the product Iu of the first two, i.e. is a constant multiple of u or

$$(a', b', c', d', e')\,(x, y)^4.$$

The result of operating with $(a', b', c', d', e')\left(\frac{\partial}{\partial y}, -\frac{\partial}{\partial x}\right)^4$ on the identity of the octavic and its canonical form is then the production of an identity

$$(a', b', c', d', e')\left(\frac{\partial}{\partial y}, -\frac{\partial}{\partial x}\right)^4 . (a_0, a_1, \ldots a_8)(x, y)^8$$
$$\equiv \mu'(a', b', c', d', e')(x, y)^4$$

of two quartics, μ' being a constant quâ x, y, namely a numerical multiple of the product of λ and the invariant I of the quartic on the right. Let us write $8 . 7 . 6 . 5 . \mu$ for μ'. We obtain, by equating coefficients of x^4, x^3y, x^2y^2, xy^3, y^4 on the two sides, the equations

$$\begin{aligned}
a'a_4 - 4b'a_3 + 6c'a_2 - 4d'a_1 + e'a_0 &= a'\mu,\\
a'a_5 - 4b'a_4 + 6c'a_3 - 4d'a_2 + e'a_1 &= b'\mu,\\
a'a_6 - 4b'a_5 + 6c'a_4 - 4d'a_3 + e'a_2 &= c'\mu,\\
a'a_7 - 4b'a_6 + 6c'a_5 - 4d'a_4 + e'a_3 &= d'\mu,\\
a'a_8 - 4b'a_7 + 6c'a_6 - 4d'a_5 + e'a_4 &= e'\mu,
\end{aligned}$$

which are made consistent for determining $a' : b' : c' : d' : e'$ by taking for μ one of the roots of the canonizing quintic equation

$$\begin{vmatrix}
a_4 - \mu, & a_3 & , a_2 & , a_1 & , a_0 \\
a_5 & , a_4 + \frac{1}{4}\mu, & a_3 & , a_2 & , a_1 \\
a_6 & , a_5 & , a_4 - \frac{1}{6}\mu, & a_3 & , a_2 \\
a_7 & , a_6 & , a_5 & , a_4 + \frac{1}{4}\mu, & a_3 \\
a_8 & , a_7 & , a_6 & , a_5 & , a_4 - \mu
\end{vmatrix} = 0,$$

a quintic all whose non-vanishing coefficients are invariants of the octavic.

228. **General binary** $2n$-ic. The success of the method adopted with variations in §§ 220, 225, 227 for the canonizing of a $2n$-ic depends on the knowledge, for the cases $n = 2, 3, 4$, of an auxiliary n-ic covariant V of an n-ic

$$(a_0', a_1', \ldots a_n')(x, y)^n \equiv X_1 X_2 \ldots X_n,$$

which is such that the derived n-ic covariant

$$(a_0', a_1', \ldots a_n')\left(\frac{\partial}{\partial y}, -\frac{\partial}{\partial x}\right)^n \{(a_0', a_1', \ldots a_n')(x, y)^n . V\}$$

is of the form

$$k(a_0', a_1', \ldots a_n')(x, y)^n,$$

where k is a function of $a_0', a_1', \ldots a_n'$ only.

If in the case of any higher value of n such a covariant V of the n-ic can be found, then the method of the preceding article will establish that the general binary $2n$-ic has the canonical form

$$X_1^{2n}+X_2^{2n}+\ldots+X_n^{2n}+\lambda X_1X_2\ldots X_n \,.\, V,$$

where V is this covariant of $X_1X_2\ldots X_n$, and μ, a determinate constant multiple of λ, is any one of the roots of the canonizing $(n+1)$-ic equation, all whose coefficients are invariants, and which for odd values of n is a $\frac{1}{2}(n+1)$-ic in μ^2 only,

$$\begin{vmatrix} a_n-\mu, & a_{n-1}, & a_{n-2}, & \ldots, & a_0 \\ a_{n+1}, & a_n+\frac{1}{n}\mu, & a_{n-1}, & \ldots, & a_1 \\ a_{n+2}, & a_{n+1}, & a_n-\frac{1.2}{n(n-1)}\mu, & \ldots, & a_2 \\ \cdot & \cdot & \cdot & \cdot & \cdot \\ a_{2n}, & a_{2n-1}, & a_{2n-2}, & \ldots, & a_n-(-1)^n\mu \end{vmatrix}=0.$$

That the terms other than $\lambda X_1X_2\ldots X_n \,.\, V$ in the canonical form are $2n$th powers of factors of $X_1X_2\ldots X_n$ will follow from the fact that we have made $(a_0', a_1', \ldots a_n')(x, y)^n$ apolar to the difference of the $2n$-ic and a constant multiple of $(a_0', a_1', \ldots a_n')(x, y)^n \,.\, V$.

229. The ternary cubic. For the reduction to canonical forms of ternary and quaternary quantics works (e.g. Salmon's) on geometry of two and three dimensions should be consulted. The case of the ternary cubic is alone considered here.

The canonical form, due to Hesse, of the general ternary cubic is

$$X^3+Y^3+Z^3+6mXYZ. \qquad \ldots(1)$$

To this form can be reduced by linear transformation any cubic whose discriminant (§ 15) does not vanish. The number of free constants ($=3\times 3+1$) in the form is the same as that of coefficients in the general cubic, a fact which indicates the likelihood of the correctness of the form.

But in proving the correctness we shall have to assume that the discriminant is different from zero, i.e. shall have to exclude from the conclusion the special classes of cubics which are called *singular*. We shall see that there are two classes of singular cubics, a class of *nodal* cubics for which the canonical form is

$$X^3+Y^3+6XYZ, \qquad \ldots(2)$$

and a class of *cuspidal* cubics for which it is

$$X^3+3Y^2Z. \qquad \ldots(3)$$

Let us first consider a singular cubic u, i.e. one of vanishing discriminant. Because the discriminant vanishes, $\partial u/\partial x$, $\partial u/\partial y$, $\partial u/\partial z$ can be made to vanish simultaneously by giving to x, y, z suitable values not all zero. Suppose that they vanish for values of x, y, z which make

$$x' \equiv \lambda x + \mu y + \nu z = 0, \text{ and } y' \equiv \lambda' x + \mu' y + \nu' z = 0,$$

then, if by linear transformation we express u in terms of x', y', z, we must give it the form

$$(ax' + by' + cz)x'^2 + 2(a'x' + b'y' + c'z)x'y' + (a''x' + b''y' + c''z)y'^2,$$

i.e. $Ax'^3 + 3Bx'^2y' + 3Cx'y'^2 + Dy'^3 + z(cx'^2 + 2c'x'y' + c''y'^2)$.

Two cases now arise. The quadratic $cx'^2 + 2c'x'y' + c''y'^2$ may either be a product of two different factors, or a square.

In the former case let XY be the factors. The form arrived at may be written

$$A'X^3 + 3B'X^2Y + 3C'XY^2 + D'Y^3 + zXY,$$

i.e. $$A'X^3 + D'Y^3 + (z + 3B'X + 3C'Y)XY,$$

i.e. with a change of notation,

$$X^3 + Y^3 + 6XYZ. \qquad \text{... (2)}$$

In the latter case let Y^2 be the square. The form arrived at may be written

$$A'x'^3 + 3B'x'^2Y + 3C'x'Y^2 + D'Y^3 + zY^2,$$

or, putting X for $x' + \dfrac{B'}{A'}Y$,

$$A'X^3 + 3C''XY^2 + D''Y^3 + zY^2,$$

i.e. $$A'X^3 + Y^2(z + 3C''X + D''Y),$$

or, with a change of notation,

$$X^3 + 3Y^2Z. \qquad \text{... (3)}$$

Having thus obtained canonical forms for the two classes of singular cubics, we proceed to show that any cubic which is not singular can be given the canonical form (1). This will be shown by proving that, starting from any one cubic of non-vanishing discriminant which can be given the form, we may pass by infinitesimal gradations through a succession of cubics which can be given the form to any cubic of non-vanishing discriminant whatever.

Take $u \equiv X^3 + Y^3 + Z^3 + 6mXYZ$ one such cubic, X, Y, Z being given linear functions of x, y, z the variables in u. Since the discriminant does not vanish, $\dfrac{\partial u}{\partial x}, \dfrac{\partial u}{\partial y}, \dfrac{\partial u}{\partial z}$ cannot be made to vanish by any values of x, y, z not all zero. Consequently X, Y, Z cannot be made all to vanish by any such values of x, y, z. In other words, X, Y, Z are linearly independent. Moreover, $1+8m^3$ cannot vanish, as otherwise u would break up into three linear factors, and its discriminant would vanish.

Now give to X, Y, Z, and to m, increments

$$\xi \equiv \epsilon_1 X + \epsilon_2 Y + \epsilon_3 Z, \quad \eta \equiv \zeta_1 X + \zeta_2 Y + \zeta_3 Z, \quad \zeta \equiv \eta_1 X + \eta_2 Y + \eta_3 Z,$$

and μ, where $\epsilon_1, \epsilon_2, \epsilon_3, \zeta_1, \zeta_2, \zeta_3, \eta_1, \eta_2, \eta_3, \mu$ are infinitesimal constants. The increment of u is, by differentiation,

$$3(X^2+2mYZ)\xi + 3(Y^2+2mZX)\eta + 3(Z^2+2mXY)\zeta + 6\mu XYZ.$$

This may be identified with the most general cubic in X, Y, Z, with infinitesimal coefficients, by choosing $\epsilon_1, \ldots \zeta_1, \ldots, \eta_1, \ldots, \mu$ to satisfy ten linear equations which are at once written down. It will be found that the values determined by the equations all have $1+8m^3$ for denominator; and this, as seen above, does not vanish, so that there is no failure. Moreover, as X, Y, Z are linearly independent linear functions of x, y, z, the most general cubic with infinitesimal coefficients in X, Y, Z is also the most general cubic with infinitesimal coefficients in x, y, z. Thus any cubic with coefficients infinitesimally differing from the chosen one, which has the form

$$X^3+Y^3+Z^3+6mXYZ,$$

can itself be given the form

$$(X+\xi)^3+(Y+\eta)^3+(Z+\zeta)^3+6(m+\mu)(X+\xi)(Y+\eta)(Z+\zeta).$$

We may pass by an infinite succession of stages like the above to any cubic of which the discriminant does not vanish. We have only to secure that in the course of the passage we do not pass through a cubic whose discriminant vanishes. And, as we can so control at each stage the relative rates of change of the various coefficients that a particular relation in the coefficients (discriminant $=0$) shall not become satisfied, we are sure that any cubic of non-vanishing discriminant can be thus in the end attained to. If confined to the real in our passage we could not of course pass from discriminant positive to discriminant negative without passing through discriminant zero. But we are not so confined.[1]

Thus any non-singular cubic can be given the canonical form

$$X^3+Y^3+Z^3+6mXYZ, \qquad \ldots (1)$$

as stated at the outset.

[1] For instance we can pass from $F(x, y) = c$ to $F(x, y) = -c$ without having to pass through $F(x, y) = 0$ by first passing from c to $c+\iota d$, keeping c constant, then from $c+\iota d$ to $-c+\iota d$, keeping d constant, and then from $-c+\iota d$ to $-c$, keeping $-c$ constant.

It will be noticed that

$$AX^3 + BY^3 + CZ^3 + 6DXYZ \qquad \dots (4)$$

is a semi-canonized form which includes the canonical forms both of non-singular cubics and of nodal cubics. For the latter one of A, B, C is zero. Cuspidal cubics are, however, exceptional even to this form, or only included if we allow two of X, Y, Z to be the same.

229 (*bis*). Besides general, or non-singular, and singular ternary cubics, there are also degenerate cubics, which break up into factors. Cubics which break up into three linear factors can be given the form

$$XYZ,$$

which is included in (4), if the factors are linearly independent, or again the form

$$X^3 + Y^3 + Z^3 - 3XYZ,$$

which is included not only in (4) but in (1). If the factors are not linearly independent we have the form

$$X^3 + Y^3,$$

which comes under (4). In particular, if the factors are all the same, we have X^3. Cubics which break up into a linear and a quadratic factor may be given the form

$$X(X^2 + YZ),$$

which comes under (4); for a ternary quadratic can be given the form $X^2 + YZ$ with any X we choose, as we know from the reference of a conic to any chord X and the tangents at its ends.

Thus of ternary cubics, general, singular, and degenerate, only cuspidal cubics, and degenerate cubics X^2Y with two but not three factors the same, are exceptional to the form (4) with X, Y, Z independent.

Ex. 36. Apply this method to show (§ 199) that $X^3 + Y^3$ is a canonical form of the binary cubic, and (§ 211) $X^4 + Y^4 + 6mX^2Y^2$ one of the binary quartic.

230. **Catalecticant of ternary quartic.** We conclude this chapter with a theorem due to Sylvester as to the impossibility in general of a reduction which a mere counting of the constants might lead us hastily to assume possible. This will illustrate the necessity of a care which in much that has preceded may have seemed superfluous.

The general ternary *quartic*

$$(a, b, c, \ldots)(x, y, z)^4$$

contains fifteen $(= 1+2+3+4+5)$ coefficients; and the sum of five fourth powers

$$\sum_{r=1}^{r=5} (l_r x + m_r y + n_r z)^4$$

contains exactly the same number of constants, which may be chosen at will.

It would then be expected that a canonical form of the general ternary quartic would be a sum of five fourth powers. But this is not the case. The fifteen coefficients in the sum of powers are, as we shall see, connected by a relation, which must consequently also connect the coefficients in the ternary quartic for the reduction to be possible.

The fact is akin to that of §§ 208, 210, in which, however, there is nothing in the same way paradoxical, as in the sum of two binary fourth powers the number of constants is obviously one less than in the general binary quartic.

The function of the coefficients in a ternary quartic which must vanish that the quartic may be a sum of five fourth powers is an invariant, called in analogy with the catalecticant of a binary quartic its catalecticant, i.e. is the eliminant of its six second partial differential coefficients, which are linear functions of x^2, y^2, z^2, yz, zx, xy. Let us use a triple suffix notation according to which a_{rst}, where $r+s+t = 4$, is the coefficient in the ternary quartic of the term $k_{rst} x^r y^s z^t$ which occurs in the expansion of $(x+y+z)^4$ by the multinomial theorem. The catalecticant is

$$\begin{vmatrix} a_{400} & a_{310} & a_{301} & a_{220} & a_{211} & a_{202} \\ a_{310} & a_{220} & a_{211} & a_{130} & a_{121} & a_{112} \\ a_{301} & a_{211} & a_{202} & a_{121} & a_{112} & a_{103} \\ a_{220} & a_{130} & a_{121} & a_{040} & a_{031} & a_{022} \\ a_{211} & a_{121} & a_{112} & a_{031} & a_{022} & a_{013} \\ a_{202} & a_{112} & a_{103} & a_{022} & a_{013} & a_{004} \end{vmatrix}.$$

The same function of the coefficients in $(lx+my+nz)^4$ is

$$\begin{vmatrix} l^4 & l^3m & l^3n & l^2m^2 & l^2mn & l^2n^2 \\ l^3m & l^2m^2 & l^2mn & lm^3 & lm^2n & lmn^2 \\ l^3n & l^2mn & l^2n^2 & lm^2n & lmn^2 & ln^3 \\ l^2m^2 & lm^3 & lm^2n & m^4 & m^3n & m^2n^2 \\ l^2mn & lm^2n & lmn^2 & m^3n & m^2n^2 & mn^3 \\ l^2n^2 & lmn^2 & ln^3 & m^2n^2 & mn^3 & n^4 \end{vmatrix},$$

in which it will be noticed that the columns are respectively l^2, lm, ln, m^2, mn, n^2 times the one column l^2, lm, ln, m^2, mn, n^2. The columns are then identical, but for different multipliers applied to them severally.

For the sum of five fourth powers the catalecticant is a determinant, obtained from that last written by writing for each constituent in it a sum of five like ones obtained by giving to l, m, n, or such of them as occur in it, the suffixes 1, 2, 3, 4, 5 in succession.

Now the determinant thus obtained is a sum of 5^6 determinants like the last written, except that the constituents have suffixes, which in any one of the determinants are the same in any column, but not, except in the case of five of the determinants, the same in all columns. All possibilities of applying the suffixes 1, 2, 3, 4, 5 to columns, one suffix to each, in fact occur in different determinants of the whole set of 5^6.

But there are six columns and only five suffixes. In every one of the 5^6 determinants there must therefore be at least two columns with the same suffix. By the above, then, every one of the determinants contains two columns which, upon removal of factors such as two of l^2, lm, ln, m^2, mn, n^2 for some suffix or other, are identical. Every one therefore vanishes. Consequently their sum, the catalecticant of the sum of five fourth powers, vanishes.

231. The student will easily convince himself in like manner of the following facts.

The quaternary quartic $(a, b, \ldots)(x, y, t, u)^4$ contains thirty-five coefficients, and the sum of nine fourth powers of linear forms contains thirty-six constants, apparently one more than is necessary. Yet a quaternary quartic cannot be expressed as a sum of nine fourth powers unless its catalecticant, i.e. the eliminant of its second partial derivatives, vanishes. For ten, the number of these derivatives, exceeds nine, the number of squares.

The quinary quartic $(a, b, \ldots)(x, y, z, u, v)^4$ contains seventy coefficients, and the sum of fourteen fourth powers of linear functions of x, y, z, u, v contains seventy free constants. Yet a quinary quartic cannot be written as a sum of fourteen fourth powers unless its catalecticant vanishes, since $15 > 14$.

CHAPTER XIII

INVARIANTS AND COVARIANTS OF THE BINARY QUINTIC AND SEXTIC.

232. THE study of the binary quintic and its concomitants has been carried to a high degree of completeness by investigators, among whom Hermite, Cayley, Sylvester, Salmon, Clebsch, Gordan, and Faà de Bruno should be named. The present chapter contents itself with calling attention to the main facts, and some of the simpler applications thereof. It is beyond the scope of an introductory treatise to give a full synopsis of the mass of results at which the theory has arrived, or to endeavour to reproduce in outline more than the most elementary of the investigations which have produced those results.

The three absolutely independent invariants of lowest degrees have been encountered in previous chapters, and are of degrees 4, 8, 12 respectively. Any other invariant is a function of these by § 30: but there is a fourth of degree 18 (§ 114, Ex. 22), discovered by Hermite, which is irreducible in that it is not a rational integral function of them, but is connected with them by a syzygy which will be exhibited later. A method by which the existence of the syzygy is proved has been noticed in § 143.

The whole number of irreducible covariants and invariants of the quintic, the quintic itself being counted as one, is twenty-three, a number which the arithmetical method by analysis of a generating function, whose beginnings have been sketched in Chapter VIII, has been successful in indicating. The honour, not only of pointing out the number, but of exhibiting symbolically the concomitants themselves, is Gordan's. Their explicit forms have been investigated in Cayley's second, third, fifth, eighth and ninth memoirs on quantics.

233. **Canonical and semi-canonical forms.** For the detailed study of the quintic much use has been made of the form to which it may be reduced

$$aX^5 + bY^5 + c'(X+Y)^5,$$

or, say, $$aX^5+bY^5+cZ^5,$$
where $$X+Y+Z\equiv 0.$$

One of the three coefficients a, b, c may, in accordance with § 205, be taken as unity; or, if we allow a, b, c to be all arbitrary, we may suppose that the modulus of the substitution which reduces the general quintic to the form is unity. Chapter XVIII of Salmon's *Higher Algebra* gives the forms, symmetrical of course in a, b, c and in X, Y, Z, of the concomitants for this symmetrical shape of canonical form.

A very convenient canonical form is Hammond's
$$x'^5+5b'x'^4y'+5e'x'y'^4+y'^5,$$
i. e. $$(1, b', 0, 0, e', 1)(x', y')^5,$$
in which the two end coefficients are units and the two middle ones zero. He uses more the form
$$(a, b, 0, 0, e, f)(x, y)^5,$$
which contains too many free coefficients to be properly called canonical, but to which a substitution of unit modulus reduces any quintic, and which has the advantage of not excluding some special classes of quintics, whose coefficients obey invariant conditions, to which the more restricted canonical form does not apply.

We must see that the reduction to this form is possible.

Take the quintic in the form
$$aX^5+bY^5+c(X+Y)^5,$$
from which the most general linear substitution produces
$$a(lx+my)^5+b(l'x+m'y)^5+c\{(l+l')x+(m+m')y\}^5.$$
In this the coefficients of $10x^3y^2$ and $10x^2y^3$ are
$$al^3m^2+bl'^3m'^2+c(l+l')^3(m+m')^2$$
and $$al^2m^3+bl'^2m'^3+c(l+l')^2(m+m')^3.$$
Adding and subtracting, we find that these will both vanish if l, m, l', m' satisfy the two equations
$$\{al^2m^2+c(l+l')^2(m+m')^2\}(l\pm m)$$
$$+\{bl'^2m'^2+c(l+l')^2(m+m')^2\}(l'\pm m')=0.$$
Now, since
$$(l-m)(l'+m')-(l+m)(l'-m')=2(lm'-l'm)\neq 0,$$
these are the same as
$$al^2m^2=bl'^2m'^2=-c(l+l')^2(m+m')^2,$$
i. e. $$\pm a^{\frac{1}{2}}lm=\pm b^{\frac{1}{2}}l'm'=\iota c^{\frac{1}{2}}(l+l')(m+m'),$$
which suffice to determine l/l' and m/m'; whence $lm'-l'm=1$

derives lm and $l'm'$, leaving still one of l, m, l', m' which may be assigned arbitrarily.

In case (cf. § 204) the assumed reduction to the form

$$aX^5+bY^5+c(X+Y)^5$$

is impossible, there is as a rule no exception to the reducibility to Hammond's form. In fact it has been seen in § 204 that in the ordinary special case, when $\beta=\gamma$ only, the special form

$$ax^5+5exy^4+fy^5$$

is assumed, which is the case of Hammond's when b as well as c and d is zero. This is the case when I_{12}, the irreducible invariant of degree 12, vanishes.

In the more special case, when $\alpha=\beta=\gamma$, we saw in the article referred to that the form

$$x^3(a'x^2+5b'xy+10c'y^2)$$

is taken, and this, if we take for a new y one of the factors of $a'x^2+5b'xy+10c'y^2$, becomes

$$x^3(5bxy+10cy^2).$$

This is the one case of exception to the general applicability of Hammond's form.

It might be thought from mere counting of the constants that it would be possible in general to make the coefficient of x^4y as well as those of x^3y^2 and x^2y^3 vanish. It will be seen later, however, that this can only be done when an invariant condition $I_{12}=0$ is satisfied. That it can be done when $I_{12}=0$ has been seen earlier, as stated above.

Ex. 1. There are four essentially distinct reductions of a general quintic to the form $(a', b', 0, 0, e', f')(x, y)^5$; and the four products $x'y'$ are quadratic factors of an octavic covariant

$$\{(ad-bc)^2-4(ac-b^2)(bd-c^2)\}x^8+\dots. \qquad (\textit{Newson.})$$

Ex. 2. Another canonical form to which the general quintic can be reduced by a substitution of unit modulus is $(a, b, c, a, b, c)(x, y)^5$. (*Hammond.*)

Ans. Take $\lambda(\omega x+\omega^2 y)$, $\lambda(\omega^2 x+\omega y)$, with a proper λ, for X, Y in $lX^5+mY^5-n(X+Y)^5$. The x, y are the variables in the canonical form of the canonizant $C_{3,3}$. They are also the factors of $C_{6,2}$.

234. List of concomitants of binary quintic. The twenty-three concomitants of a quintic, arranged in the order of Cayley's ninth memoir on quantics, are as follows. Many of them have been already met with. It will be seen that all are invariants or covariants from their methods of formation. That they are irreducible, and form the complete irreducible system, it is beyond our scope to establish here. The usual proof reposes on the method of transvectants (cf. § 61). We use the notation $C_{i,\varpi}$ to denote a covariant of degree i in the coefficients and order ϖ in the variables, and I_i to denote an invariant of degree i. The arrangement is according to degree, and for the same degree according to order.

(1) u or $C_{1,5}$ is the quintic $(a, b, c, d, e, f)(x, y)^5$ itself.

(2) $C_{2,2}$ is the quadratic covariant whose leading coefficient is the seminvariant $ae-4bd+3c^2$. It is the fourth transvectant of u and itself, or the quadratic invariant $a'e'-4b'd'+3c'^2$ of the fourth emanant of u.

(3) $C_{2,6}$ is the Hessian of u. Its leading coefficient is $ac-b^2$.

(4) $C_{3,3}$ has for its leading coefficient

$$ace+2bcd-ad^2-b^2e-c^3.$$

It is obtained as this invariant of the fourth emanant of u, or as the result of putting $\partial/\partial y$, $-\partial/\partial x$ for x and y in (2) and operating on u, or, let us say, of operating with (2) on u. It is the canonizant (§ 206) of the quintic.

(5) $C_{3,5}$ is the Jacobian of u and (2). Its leading coefficient is $a^2f-5abe+2acd+8b^2d-6bc^2$.

(6) $C_{3,9}$ is the covariant whose leading coefficient is

$$a^2d-3abc+2b^3.$$

It is the Jacobian of u and its Hessian (3).

(7) I_4 is the invariant of lowest degree. It is the discriminant of (2), viz.

$$(af-3be+2cd)^2-4(ae-4bd+3c^2)(bf-4ce+3d^2).$$

(8) $C_{4,4}$ is formed by adding nine times the square of (2) to the result of operating with (2) on (3), in the manner described in connexion with (4), and dividing by fifteen. Its leading coefficient is

$$a^2(e^2-df)+a(3bcf-3bde-4c^2e+4cd^2)$$
$$+5b^2ce+2b^2d^2-2b^3f-8bc^2d+3c^4.$$

It will be noticed that we have given it a different sign from that of our general convention in § 71.

(9) $C_{4,6}$, a second sextic covariant, is the Jacobian of u and (4). Its leading coefficient is

$$a^2(cf-de)-a(b^2f+2bce-4bd^2+c^2d)+3b^3e-6b^2cd+3bc^3.$$

(10) $C_{5,1}$, the linear covariant of lowest degree in the coefficients, is the result of operating with (2) on (4), with sign changed.

(11) $C_{5,3}$, a second cubic covariant, is the Jacobian of (4) and (2).

(12) $C_{5,7}$ is the Jacobian of (3) and (4).

(13) $C_{6,2}$, a second quadratic covariant, is given by operation with (2) on (8).

(14) $C_{6,4}$, a second quartic covariant, is given by operation with (10) on u.

(15) $C_{7,1}$, a second linear covariant, is the Jacobian of (10) and (2).

(16) $C_{7,5}$, a third quintic covariant, reckoning u itself as one, is the Jacobian of (13) and u.—(N.B. The quintic covariant (16) of Salmon's *Higher Algebra*, § 232, or Faà de Bruno's *Formes Binaires*, No. 12, Table v, is the result of subtracting from this $C_{7,5}$ the product $C_{2,2}\,C_{5,3}$ of (2) and (11).)

(17) I_8, the second invariant, is found as the invariant $ac'+a'c-2bb'$ of (2) and (13).

(18) $C_{8,2}$, a third quadratic covariant, is found as the Jacobian of (4) and (10).

(19) $C_{9,3}$, a third cubic covariant, is the Jacobian of (13) and (4).—(N.B. The covariant of degree 9 and order 3 in Faà de Bruno's *Formes Binaires*, No. 15, Table v, is $96\,C_{9,3}-16\,C_{2,2}\,C_{7,1}+7\,I_4\,C_{5,3}$.)

(20) $C_{11,1}$, a third linear covariant, is given by operation with (2) on (19).

(21) I_{12}, the third invariant, is the discriminant, but for a numerical factor, of (13) or of (4).

(22) $C_{13,1}$, the fourth linear covariant, is the result of operating with (19) on (8). (Faà de Bruno's, No. 17, Table v, is $-6\,C_{13,1}-2\,I_8\,C_{5,1}$.)

(23) I_{18}, the fourth irreducible invariant, is the eliminant of the two linear covariants (10) and (22). It is also the catalecticant of (14).

Thus, to sum up, the irreducible concomitants of a binary quintic are

4	invariants	I_4, I_8, I_{12}, I_{18},
4	linear covariants	$C_{5,1}$, $C_{7,1}$, $C_{11,1}$, $C_{13,1}$,
3	quadratic ,,	$C_{2,2}$, $C_{6,2}$, $C_{8,2}$,
3	cubic ,,	$C_{3,3}$, $C_{5,3}$, $C_{9,3}$,
2	quartic ,,	$C_{4,4}$, $C_{6,4}$,
3	quintic ,,	u, $C_{3,5}$, $C_{7,5}$,
2	sextic ,,	$C_{2,6}$, $C_{4,6}$,
1	septimic ,,	$C_{5,7}$,
1	nonic ,,	$C_{3,9}$.

235. **Forms of the concomitants when $c=0$, $d=0$.** The

kindness of Mr. Hammond has supplied me with the forms taken by the twenty-three concomitants when the quintic is given his form $(a, b, 0, 0, e, f)(x, y)^5$, in which the two middle terms are wanting. None of the expressions are of great complexity. They are

(1) $C_{1,5} \equiv u = ax^5 + 5bx^4y + 5exy^4 + fy^5,$

(2) $C_{2,2} = aex^2 + (af - 3be)xy + bfy^2,$

(3) $C_{2,6} = -(b^2x^6 + e^2y^6) + 3(aex^2 + bfy^2)x^2y^2 + (af + 7be)x^3y^3,$

(4) $C_{3,3} = -\{b^2ex^3 + b^2fx^2y + ae^2xy^2 + be^2y^3\},$

(5) $C_{3,5} = (af - 5be)(ax^5 - fy^5) + (5af - 9be)(bx^3 - ey^3)xy + 8(b^2fx - ae^2y)x^2y^2,$

(6) $C_{3,9} = 2(b^3x^9 - e^3y^9) + 2(a^2ex^7 - bf^2y^7)xy + (af + 11be)(ax^5 - fy^5)x^2y^2 + (7af + 29be)(bx^3 - ey^3)x^3y^3 + 16(b^2fx - ae^2y)x^4y^4,$

(7) $I_4 = a^2f^2 - 10abef + 9b^2e^2,$

(8) $C_{4,4} = (a^2e^2 - 2b^3f)x^4 + (b^2f^2 - 2ae^3)y^4 + 4be(aex^2 + bfy^2)xy + 18b^2e^2x^2y^2,$

(9) $C_{4,6} = (3be - af)(b^2x^6 - e^2y^6) - 2(a^2e^2 + b^3f)x^5y + 2(b^2f^2 + ae^3)xy^5 - 10be(aex^2 - bfy^2)x^2y^2,$

(10) $C_{5,1} = (a^2e^3 - ab^2f^2 + 6b^3ef)x + (b^3f^2 - a^2e^2f + 6abe^3)y,$

(11) $C_{5,3} = be(9be - af)(bx^3 - ey^3) + (4a^2e^3 - ab^2f^2 - 3b^3ef)x^2y - (4b^3f^2 - a^2e^2f - 3abe^3)xy^2,$

(12) $C_{5,7} = 2(b^4fx^7 - ae^4y^7) + 10b^2e^2(ax^5 - fy^5)xy + 3be(af + 9be)(bx^3 - ey^3)x^2y^2 + (ab^2f^2 - 6a^2e^3 + 19b^3ef)x^4y^3 - (a^2e^2f - 6b^3f^2 + 19abe^3)x^3y^4,$

(13) $C_{6,2} = (3ae^3 - b^2f^2)b^2x^2 - (af - 9be)b^2e^2xy + (3b^3f - a^2e^2)e^2y^2,$

(14) $C_{6,4} = (a^3e^2f - 5a^2be^3 - 2ab^3f^2 + 6b^4ef)x^4 - (ab^2f^3 - 5b^3ef^2 - 2a^2e^3f + 6abe^4)y^4 + 4(a^2e^2f - 6abe^3 - b^3f^2)bx^3y - 4(ab^2f^2 - 6b^3ef - a^2e^3)exy^3,$

(15) $C_{7,1} = (3a^3e^3f - a^2b^2f^3 - 15a^2be^4 + 7ab^3ef^2 - 18b^4e^2f)x - (3ab^3f^3 - a^3e^2f^2 - 15b^4ef^2 + 7a^2be^3f - 18ab^2e^4)y,$

(16) $C_{7,5} = (a^2e^2f - 3abe^3 - 2b^3f^2)b^2x^5 + (2a^3e^2 - 3ab^3f - 27b^4e)e^2x^4y + 8(a^2e^2 - 3b^3f)be^2x^3y^2 - 8(b^2f^2 - 3ae^3)b^2ex^2y^3 - (2b^2f^3 - 3ae^3f - 27be^4)b^2xy^4 - (ab^2f^2 - 3b^3ef - 2a^2e^3)e^2y^5,$

(17) $I_8 = a^2b^2e^2f^2 - 2a^3e^5 - 2b^5f^3 + 27b^4e^4,$

(18) $C_{8,2}=(4a^2e^3f-ab^2f^3-18abe^4+3b^3ef^2)b^2x^2$
$+2(a^3e^5-b^5f^3)xy$
$-(4ab^3f^2-a^3e^2f-18b^4ef+3a^2be^3)e^2y^2$,

(19) $C_{9,3}=(2b^2f^3-9ae^3f+27be^4)b^4x^3$
$+3(ab^2f^2+9b^3ef-6a^2e^3)b^2e^2x^2y$
$-3(a^2e^2f+9abe^3-6b^3f^2)b^2e^2xy^2$
$-(2a^3e^2-9ab^3f+27b^4e)e^4y^3$,

(20) $C_{11,1}=(5a^3e^5f-a^2b^2e^2f^3-27a^2be^6-9ab^3e^3f^2+2b^5f^4$
$+54b^4e^4f)b^2x-(5ab^5f^3-a^3b^2e^2f^2-27b^6ef^2$
$-9a^2b^3e^3f+2a^4e^5+54ab^4e^4)e^2y$,

(21) $I_{12}=b^2e^2(a^2b^2e^2f^2-4a^3e^5-4b^5f^3+18ab^3e^3f-27b^4e^4)$,

(22) $C_{13,1}=(a^5e^7+b^8f^4-8a^3b^3e^5f+9ab^6e^3f^2+27a^2b^4e^6$
$-54b^7e^4f)ex+(b^7f^5+a^4e^8-8ab^5e^3f^3$
$+9a^2b^3e^6f+27b^6e^4f^2-54ab^4e^7)by$,

(23) $I_{18}=(a^3e^5-b^5f^3)\{(af-5be)(a^3e^5+b^5f^3)$
$-10a^2b^3e^3f^2+90ab^4e^4f-216b^5e^5\}$.

236. **Discriminant of quintic.** It will be noticed that the discriminant of the quintic does not occur among the irreducible invariants I_4, I_8, I_{12}, I_{18}. Its degree is $2(5-1)=8$. It might have been taken instead of I_8, being, as will be seen, the difference of a multiple of I_8 and $I_4{}^2$; but, as I_8 itself is the simpler of the two, we prefer to speak of that and not of the discriminant as the irreducible invariant.

For the quintic in its form $(a, b, 0, 0, e, f)(x, y)^5$ the discriminant is easily formed by elimination between the two first derivatives

$$ax^4+4bx^3y+ey^4, \quad bx^4+4exy^3+fy^4,$$

and is found to be

$$a^4f^4-20a^3bef^3+256(a^3e^5+b^5f^3)-10a^2b^2e^2f^2$$
$$-180ab^3e^3f-3375b^4e^4,$$

which may be written

$$(a^2f^2-10abef+9b^2e^2)^2$$
$$-128(a^2b^2e^2f^2-2a^3e^5-2b^5f^3+27b^4e^4),$$

so that, by § 235 (7) and (17), the expression for the discriminant in terms of I_4 and I_8 is

$$\Delta=I_4{}^2-128I_8.$$

237. **Syzygy among the invariants.** The four invariants I_4, I_8, I_{12}, I_{18}, though irreducible, must, as we have often seen, be connected by a syzygy. This may be expected to give the square of I_{18} in terms of the others. It is here sought.

As the quintic can be brought to the form

$$(a, b, 0, 0, e, f)(x, y)^5$$

by a substitution of modulus unity, it can in general be further brought to the canonical form

$$(a', 1, 0, 0, 1, f')(x', y')^5$$

by a further linear substitution which replaces bx^4y and exy^4 by x'^4y' and $x'y'^4$. Let the modulus of the resultant substitution which brings the quintic from its general to this last form be M. Then, from the expressions in § 235,

$$\begin{aligned} M^{10} I_4 &= a'^2 f'^2 - 10 a' f' + 9 \\ &= (a'f' - 1)(a'f' - 9), \\ M^{20} I_8 &= a'^2 f'^2 - 2a'^3 - 2f'^3 + 27, \\ M^{30} I_{12} &= a'^2 f'^2 - 4a'^3 - 4f'^3 + 18 a' f' - 27, \\ M^{45} I_{18} &= (a'^3 - f'^3)\{(a'f' - 5)(a'^3 + f'^3) \\ &\qquad - 10 a'^2 f'^2 + 90 a' f' - 216\}. \end{aligned}$$

It is possible to eliminate a', f' and M between these four equations and obtain the syzygy required.

As a guidance see what happens when $a' = f'$ so that $I_{18} = 0$. Writing J_4, J_8, J_{12} for the values taken by I_4, I_8, I_{12}, we have

$$\begin{aligned} M^{10} J_4 &= (a'^2 - 1)(a'^2 - 9) \\ M^{20} J_8 &= a'^4 - 4a'^3 + 27 = (a' - 3)^2 (a'^2 + 2a' + 3) \\ M^{30} J_{12} &= a'^4 - 8a'^3 + 18 a'^2 - 27 = (a' - 3)^3 (a' + 1), \end{aligned}$$

or, writing μ for $M^{10}/(a' - 3)$,

$$\begin{aligned} \mu J_4 &= (a'^2 - 1)(a' + 3) \\ \mu^2 J_8 &= a'^2 + 2a' + 3, \\ \mu^3 J_{12} &= a' + 1. \end{aligned}$$

These give, by substitution for a' from the last in the others,

$$\begin{aligned} \mu J_4 &= \mu^3 J_{12} (\mu^6 J_{12}^2 - 4), \\ \mu^2 J_8 &= \mu^6 J_{12}^2 + 2, \end{aligned}$$

by combination of which

$$J_4 = \mu^2 J_{12} (\mu^2 J_8 - 6).$$

We thus have a simple quadratic and cubic from which to eliminate μ^2. The result is

$$J_4 J_8^4 + 8 J_8^3 J_{12} - 2 J_4^2 J_8^2 J_{12} - 72 J_4 J_8 J_{12}^2 - 432 J_{12}^3 + J_4^3 J_{12}^2 = 0.$$

It is suggested then to try whether the same function of I_4, I_8, I_{12} as this on the left is of J_4, J_8, J_{12}, a function whose degree is 36, is of the form λI_{18}^2, where λ is a constant. This proves to be the case with $\lambda = 16$. Thus

$$16 I_{18}^2 = I_4 I_8^4 + 8 I_8^3 I_{12} - 2 I_4^2 I_8^2 I_{12} - 72 I_4 I_8 I_{12}^2 - 432 I_{12}^3 + I_4^3 I_{12}^2$$

is the syzygy required.

A usual and elegant way of obtaining this syzygy is to show that, formed by the methods of § 234, the values of the invariants for the canonical form of unit modulus

$$lX^5 + mY^5 - n(X+Y)^5$$

are
$$I_4 = (mn + nl + lm)^2 - 4lmn(l+m+n),$$
$$I_8 = l^2m^2n^2(mn+nl+lm),$$
$$I_{12} = l^4m^4n^4,$$
$$I_{18} = l^5m^5n^5(m-n)(n-l)(l-m),$$

so that l, m, n are the roots of the cubic

$$l^3 + \frac{I_4 I_{12} - I_8^2}{4 I_{12}^{\frac{5}{4}}} l^2 + \frac{I_8}{I_{12}^{\frac{1}{2}}} l - I_{12}^{\frac{1}{4}} = 0,$$

and $I_{18}^2 I_{12}^{-\frac{5}{2}}$ is the product of the squares of differences between roots of this cubic.

238. The quintic in a form with invariant coefficients. Hermite's Formes-types. It is an interesting proposition that if a quintic is so transformed that its variables are any two of its linear covariants, the coefficients are all invariants; and the same is true for any binary quantic whatever which has two linear covariants.

Let $$X = Px + Qy, \quad Y = P'x + Q'y$$

be any two of the linear covariants $C_{5,1}$, $C_{7,1}$, $C_{11,1}$, $C_{13,1}$ of the quintic $(a, b, c, d, e, f)(x, y)^5$. We have

$$x = \frac{Q'X - QY}{PQ' - P'Q}, \quad y = \frac{-P'X + PY}{PQ' - P'Q},$$

in which the denominator is the modulus of the (X, Y) to (x, y) substitution, and is also an invariant, being the eliminant of two covariants.

We have now to show that in

$$(a, b, c, d, e, f)(Q'X - QY, \; -P'X + PY)^5$$

all the coefficients are invariants. This will be proved if we can show that they are annihilated by Ω and by O, of which the first is
$$a\partial_b + 2b\partial_c + 3c\partial_d + 4d\partial_e + 5e\partial_f.$$

Now, if u, v stand for $Q'X - QY$, $-P'X + PY$,

$$\Omega(a, b, c, d, e, f)(u, v)^5 = 5v(a, b, c, d, e)(u, v)^4$$
$$+ 5(a, b, c, d, e)(u, v)^4 \Omega u + 5(b, c, d, e, f)(u, v)^4 \Omega v.$$

We here mean that the operation is not on X and Y, but only on coefficients of powers and products of powers of X and Y when the quintic is expressed in terms of a, b, c, d, e, f;

P, Q, P', Q'; X, Y. Now since (§ 109) $\Omega P = 0$, $\Omega Q = P$, $\Omega P' = 0$, $\Omega Q' = P'$, the operation being in this sense,

$$\Omega u = \Omega(Q'X - QY) = P'X - PY = -v,$$

and $$\Omega v = \Omega(-P'X + PY) = 0.$$

Consequently

$$\Omega(a, b, c, d, e, f)(u, v)^5 = 0,$$

i.e. $$\Omega(a, b, c, d, e, f)(Q'X - QY, \ -P'X + PY)^5 = 0,$$

the operation not being on X, Y, but only on coefficients of $X^5, X^4Y, \ldots, Y^5$.

All these coefficients are then annihilated by Ω. Similarly all are annihilated by O. Accordingly all are invariants.

239. **Quintics for which $I_{12} = 0$.** In § 233 it was stated that a quintic can only be linearly transformed to the form $(a, 0, 0, 0, e, f)(x, y)^5$, wanting its second as well as its third and fourth terms, when an invariant condition is satisfied. And it was seen that the said reduction can be effected when I_{12}, which is the discriminant of the canonizant, vanishes. To prove the necessity of this condition take Hammond's forms of the invariants (§ 235) of $(a, b, 0, 0, e, f)(x, y)^5$, and put $b = 0$ in them. We get

$$\begin{aligned} I_4 &= a^2 f^2, \\ I_8 &= -2a^3e^5, \\ I_{12} &= 0, \\ I_{18} &= a^7e^{10}f, \end{aligned}$$

of which the third proves the necessity stated.

From the values here of I_4, I_8, I_{12} it follows that for a quintic which can be reduced to the form now contemplated

$$16 I_{18}^2 = I_4 I_8^4,$$

and this is correctly what the syzygy of § 237 becomes when $I_{12} = 0$.

It is not hard to prove from the expressions for the invariants I_4, I_8, I_{12} of $(a, b, 0, 0, e, f)(x, y)^5$, which involve af, be and $a^3e^5 + b^5f^3$ only, that be, which call β, is given by the equation

$$\left(I_4 - \frac{2I_8}{\beta^2} + \frac{I_{12}}{\beta^4}\right)^2 = 64\left(2I_8 - \frac{I_{12}}{\beta^2}\right),$$

so that the product of all the values which be can have for reductions of the form $(a, b, 0, 0, e, f)(x, y)^5$ is

$$I_{12}^2(I_4^2 - 128 I_8)^{-1},$$

unless the discriminant $I_4^2 - 128 I_8$ vanishes, when the product is still a multiple of I_{12}. We thus have it clearly exhibited that when I_{12} vanishes some one at least of these values of *be* is zero, so that a reduction to the form $(a, 0, 0, 0, e, f)(x, y)^5$ or the in fact equivalent form $(a, b, 0, 0, 0, f)(x, y)^5$ is possible. The conclusion converse to that proved above, which was in effect arrived at before as stated already, is thus confirmed.

A quintic for which $I_{12} = 0$ cannot be expressed as a sum of three fifth powers, as was seen in § 204. In fact, the canonizant of $ax^5 + 5exy^4 + y^5$, to which form it can be reduced, is

$$C_{8,3} \equiv -ae^2xy^2.$$

Thus, if the reduction were possible, one of the X, Y, Z would be a multiple of x and the other two of y. Now

$$ax^5 + 5exy^4 + fy^5 \equiv lx^5 + my^5 + ny^5$$

is an impossibility unless $e = 0$, i.e. unless $I_8 = 0$ and $I_{18} = 0$ as well as $I_{12} = 0$.

We are thus guarded against an erroneous conclusion which might hastily be drawn from the last forms of the invariants in § 237. It might appear from those expressions that, whenever $I_{12} = 0$, either $l = 0$ or $m = 0$ or $n = 0$, and therefore $I_8 = 0$ and $I_{18} = 0$. But this is not the case, the forms not being applicable to the case when $I_{12} = 0$.

240. **Formes-types when $I_{12} = 0$** Another interesting fact as to quintics for which $I_{12} = 0$ may be derived from observing what the four linear covariants of the quintic become when $b = 0$, $c = 0$, $d = 0$.

Putting $b = 0$ in (10) (15) (20) and (22) of § 235 we obtain

$$\begin{aligned} L_5 \equiv C_{5,1} &= a^2e^2(ex - fy), \\ L_7 \equiv C_{7,1} &= a^3e^2f(3ex + fy), \\ L_{11} \equiv C_{11,1} &= -2a^4e^7y, \\ L_{13} \equiv C_{13,1} &= a^5e^8x. \end{aligned}$$

Thus the y and x of the form $(a, 0, 0, 0, e, f)(x, y)^5$, to which a quintic for which $I_{12} = 0$ may be reduced by a linear substitution of modulus unity, are multiples of the linear covariants of the 11th and 13th degrees, and are easily expressed also as sums of multiples of any two of the four linear covariants. We have, in fact, using the values of I_4, I_8, I_{18} in § 239,

$$\begin{aligned} ax^5 &= a^{-24}e^{-40}L_{13}^5 = 256 I_8^{-8} L_{13}^5, \\ exy^4 &= \tfrac{1}{16} a^{-21}e^{-35}L_{13}L_{11}^4 = -8 I_8^{-7} L_{13} L_{11}^4, \\ fy^5 &= -\tfrac{1}{32} a^{-20}e^{-35} f L_{11}^5 = 16 I_8^{-9} I_{18} L_{11}^5. \end{aligned}$$

Thus the quintic reduced to the form $(a, 0, 0, 0, e, f)(x, y)^5$ with modulus unity, is

$$8 I_8^{-9}\{32 I_8 L_{13}^5 - 5 I_8^2 L_{13} L_{11}^4 + 2 I_{18} L_{11}^5\}.$$

Consequently when $I_{12} = 0$ one of Hermite's six ways (§ 238) of expressing the quintic with invariant coefficients expresses it in the reduced form.

Ex. 3. When $I_{12} = 0$ prove that the other five expressions of the quintic with invariant coefficients are

(2) $I_8^{-18}(-8, 0, 0, 0, 4I_8^9, 16I_8^9I_{18})(4I_{18}L_{11}+I_8^3L_5, L_{11})^5$,

(3) $3^{-5}I_4^{-2}I_8^{-6}I_{18}^{-1}(2, 0, 0, 0, -81I_4^2I_8, 243I_4^3I_8)$
$(I_8L_7+I_4L_{11}, L_{11})^5$,

(4) $2^{-6}I_{18}^{-4}(64I_4^2, 0, 0, 0, -2I_8, -I_8)(L_{13}, 2L_{13}+I_8L_5)^5$,

(5) $2^7I_4^{-7}I_8^{-12}(2I_4^7I_8^4, 0, 0, 0, -I_4I_8, 1)$
$(L_{13}, 3I_4I_8L_{13}-2I_{18}L_7)^5$,

(6) $2^{-10}I_4^{-4}I_8^{-11}I_{18}^{-1}(2I_4^2, 0, 0, 0, -I_8, -I_8)$
$(I_8^2L_7-4I_{18}L_5, I_8^2L_7+12I_{18}L_5)^5$. (*Hammond.*)

241. The classes of quintics for which respectively $I_4 = 0$ and $I_8 = 0$ will not long occupy us. We content ourselves with noticing first that when $I_4 = 0$ for the quintic

$$(a, b, 0, 0, e, f)(x, y)^5$$

the condition satisfied is, by § 235 (7),

$$(af-be)(af-9be) = 0.$$

Thus when $I_4 = 0$ a quintic may be reduced by a substitution of unit modulus with one degree of arbitrariness in its coefficients to one or other of the forms

$$ax^5+5bx^4y+5exy^4+\frac{be}{a}y^5,$$

$$ax^5+5bx^4y+5exy^4+\frac{9be}{a}y^5.$$

By a linear substitution of non-unit modulus it can then be given one of the forms

$$ax^5+\frac{1}{a}y^5+5xy(x^3+y^3),$$

$$ax^5+\frac{9}{a}y^5+5xy(x^3+y^3),$$

or, equally, one or other of the forms

$$x^5+y^5+5xy\left(bx^3+\frac{1}{b}y^3\right),$$

$$x^5+y^5+5xy\left(bx^3+\frac{1}{9b}y^3\right).$$

Secondly when $I_8 = 0$, provided I_{12} does not also vanish, by the last expressions in § 237, the quintic can by substitution of unit modulus be given the form

$$lX^5 + mY^5 - n(X+Y)^5,$$

where $l^{-1} + m^{-1} + n^{-1} = 0$, i. e. the form

$$lX^5 + mY^5 + \frac{lm}{l+m}(X+Y)^5.$$

By a substitution of non-unit modulus it can be given the form

$$\frac{X^5}{\lambda} + \frac{Y^5}{1-\lambda} + (X+Y)^5.$$

When both $I_8 = 0$ and $I_{12} = 0$, or both $I_4 = 0$ and $I_{12} = 0$, we gather from § 239 that also $I_{18} = 0$, and the cases are such as will occur below.

242. **Quintics for which $I_{18} = 0$.** Quintics for which the skew invariant I_{18} vanishes have a special simplicity in that they are soluble. I_{18} is skew, for its weight is $\frac{1}{2} . 18 . 5 = 45$, i. e. is odd.

Consider the canonical form of unit modulus

$$lX^5 + mY^5 + nZ^5, \quad \text{where } X + Y + Z = 0.$$

Referring to § 237, we see that if $I_{18} = 0$, and if I_{12} does not vanish, so that the reduction to this form is possible, and $lmn \neq 0$, then $(m-n)(n-l)(l-m) = 0$, which requires that two of l, m, n be equal. Thus a quintic for which $I_{18} = 0$ and $I_{12} \neq 0$ can be given by linear transformation of modulus unity the form

$$l(X^5 + Y^5) - m(X+Y)^5,$$

i. e. the form

$$(X+Y)\{(l-m)(X^4+Y^4) \\ -(l+4m)XY(X^2+Y^2) + (l-6m)X^2Y^2\},$$

i. e. $(X+Y)\{(l-m)(X^2+Y^2)^2$

$$-(l+4m)XY(X^2+Y^2) - (l+4m)X^2Y^2\},$$

which can be broken up into $X+Y$ and two quadratic, and then into five linear, factors.

Thus, so far, a quintic for which $I_{18} = 0$ and $I_{12} \neq 0$ can be solved.

Moreover the factors are of the forms

$$X+Y,$$
$$X^2 + Y^2 + pXY,$$
$$X^2 + Y^2 + qXY,$$

and of these the single one which comes first is, speaking geometrically, one of the common harmonic conjugates $X^2 - Y^2$ of the other two pairs.

Thus, if for a binary quintic $I_{18} = 0$, and $I_{12} \neq 0$, some one of its five linear factors is a double element of one of the three involutions determined by the other four factors taken in pairs.

Putting x for $X+Y$ and y for $X-Y$ the quintic above may be written in the form

$$kx(x^2 - \lambda y^2)(x^2 - \mu y^2),$$

i.e.
$$ax^5 + 10cx^3y^2 + 5exy^4,$$

a form in which all the coefficients of odd weight are wanting.

Conversely, if one of the five factors of a quintic is one of the common harmonic conjugates of two pairs which together constitute the other four factors, then $I_{18} = 0$.

For such a quintic can be given the form

$$ax(x^2 - \lambda y^2)(x^2 - \mu y^2),$$

i.e.
$$ax^5 + 10cx^3y^2 + 5exy^4,$$

in which no non-vanishing coefficient, and therefore no non-vanishing rational integral function of the coefficients, and consequently, in particular, no non-vanishing invariant, can be of odd weight.

Now all skew invariants (§ 95), and I_{18} in particular, are of odd weight. For such a quintic as contemplated therefore, I_{18} and all other skew invariants vanish.

Granting then, as we shall see in the next article, that the temporarily reserved case when $I_{12} = 0$ as well as $I_{18} = 0$ is only special and not exceptional, we have arrived at the fact that the condition $I_{18} = 0$ is the necessary and sufficient one that the quintic may have the special property which has been expressed geometrically above.

We can also conclude that I_{18} is the only irreducible skew invariant which a quintic possesses. If $I_{18} = 0$ the quintic has the above property. If it have that property all skew invariants must vanish. Thus every skew invariant vanishes if I_{18} vanishes. I_{18} is then a factor of every skew invariant, and the invariant obtained by removing that factor is no longer skew. If its expression in terms of irreducible invariants involves another skew invariant, this may be analysed in like manner; and so on.

Ex. 4. Solve the quintic equation

$$ax^5 + 5bx^4 + 5ex + \sqrt[3]{(a^3e^5/b^5)} = 0.$$

Ex. 5. By actual substitution, as in § 233, prove that

$$a(X^5 + Y^5) - c(X+Y)^5$$

can be transformed with modulus unity into

$$a'x^5 + 5b'x^4y + 5e'xy^4 + f'y^5,$$

where $a'^8 e'^5 = b'^5 f'^3$.

Ans. As in § 233 a way to make $c' = 0$, $d' = 0$ is given by taking $a^{\frac{1}{2}}lm = a^{\frac{1}{2}}l'm' = c^{\frac{1}{2}}(l+l')(m+m')$; whence, if

$$t = \frac{l}{m'} = \frac{l'}{m} = \frac{l+l'}{m+m'}, \text{ we get } \frac{a'}{f'} = t^5 \text{ and } \frac{b'}{e'} = t^8.$$

Ex. 6. Hence the form of Ex. 4 is a general one for quintics for which $I_{18} = 0$, but $I_{12} \neq 0$.

Ex. 7. Prove that

$$\begin{vmatrix} 1, & 2a, & a^2 \\ 1, & \beta+\gamma, & \beta\gamma \\ 1, & \delta+\epsilon, & \delta\epsilon \end{vmatrix} = 0$$

is the condition that $x - ay$ be a common harmonic conjugate of the pairs

$$(x-\beta y)(x-\gamma y),\ (x-\delta y)(x-\epsilon y);$$

and that the determinant is a function of differences between pairs of $a, \beta, \gamma, \delta, \epsilon$.

Ans. It is annihilated by

$$\frac{\partial}{\partial a} + \frac{\partial}{\partial \beta} + \frac{\partial}{\partial \gamma} + \frac{\partial}{\partial \delta} + \frac{\partial}{\partial \epsilon}.$$

It is $\qquad (a-\delta)(a-\beta)(\epsilon-\gamma) + (a-\gamma)(a-\epsilon)(\delta-\beta).$

Ex. 8. Prove that the product of

$$(a-\delta)(a-\beta)(\epsilon-\gamma) + (a-\epsilon)(a-\gamma)(\delta-\beta),$$
$$(a-\beta)(a-\gamma)(\epsilon-\delta) + (a-\epsilon)(a-\delta)(\beta-\gamma),$$
$$(a-\gamma)(a-\delta)(\epsilon-\beta) + (a-\epsilon)(a-\beta)(\gamma-\delta)$$

is symmetric in $\beta, \gamma, \delta, \epsilon$, and hence that a^{18} times the product of 5×3 determinants like that of Ex. 7 is an invariant of degree 18 and weight 45, so that it is a numerical multiple of I_{18}.

(*Hermite* and *Cayley*.)

243. We temporarily reserved in § 242 the case of quintics for which $I_{12} = 0$ as well as $I_{18} = 0$.

When $I_{12} = 0$ the quintic can (§ 239) be given by substitution of unit modulus the form

$$ax^5 + 5exy^4 + fy^5,$$

and the condition $I_{18} = 0$ is then

$$a^7 e^{10} f = 0,$$

so that either $f = 0$ or $e = 0$ or $a = 0$.

We also see from the syzygy $16 I_{18}^2 = I_4 I_8^4$, which holds when $I_{12} = 0$, that the conditions $I_{12} = 0$, $I_{18} = 0$ necessitate also that either $I_4 = 0$ or $I_8 = 0$.

When $f = 0$ the form taken is

$$ax^5 + 5exy^4,$$

i.e.
$$X(X^4 + Y^4).$$

This is the case when $I_4 = 0$ as well as $I_{12} = 0$, $I_{18} = 0$. There is no exception here to the geometrical property in § 242.

When $e = 0$ the form taken is

$$ax^5 + fy^5,$$

i.e.
$$X^5 + Y^5,$$

and again there is no exception. The case is that of quintics for which $I_8 = 0$ as well as $I_{12} = 0$ and $I_{18} = 0$.

When $a = 0$ the form taken is

$$5exy^4 + fy^5,$$

i.e.
$$Y^4(X + Y),$$

for which the property holds in a limiting form, for $X + Y$ or any other linear form in X and Y is one of a pair of harmonic conjugates, the other being Y, of the coincident factors of Y^2.

This last class of cases is included in the class for which all the invariants vanish, but is not coextensive with that class. As we have seen in § 28, Ex. 3, all invariants vanish for a quintic
$$X^3(X + Y)(pX + qY)$$
with a perfect cube for factor, for such a quintic can be given the form
$$a_0x^5 + 5a_1x^4y + 10a_2x^3y^2,$$
and no product of i factors chosen from among a_0, a_1, a_2 can have a weight so great as to satisfy $5i = 2w$.

It will be remembered from § 233 that this case of a quintic with a cubed factor is the one of irreducibility to Hammond's form. It is not one of exception to the geometrically expressed theorem as to quintics for which $I_{18} = 0$, for X is one of the common harmonic conjugates of the pairs

$$X^2, \quad (X + Y)(pX + qY).$$

244. **The binary sextic.** We will only give a list of what prove to be the complete system of irreducible concomitants of the sextic.

As indicated in § 143 the sextic has five irreducible invariants. Of these four I_2, I_4, I_6, I_{10} are independent. The fifth, I_{15}, is skew, and its square is given in terms of the rest by a syzygy of degree 30.

Clebsch and Gordan have found that the whole number of irreducible covariants and invariants, including the sextic itself, is 26, and the method of Cayley and Sylvester by means of generating functions, which has been referred to in Chapter VIII, confirms the result. The complete system has been exhibited as follows, the arrangement being, as in the case of the quintic, according to degrees in the coefficients, and for the same degree according to orders in the variables.

(1) u, or $C_{1,6}$, is the sextic $(a, b, c, d, e, f, g)(x, y)^6$ itself.

(2) I_2, the invariant of degree 2, is $ag-6bf+15ce-10d^2$. Cf. § 48.

(3) $C_{2,4}$, the first quartic covariant, is the covariant whose leading coefficient is the seminvariant

$$ae-4bd+3c^2.$$

It is the fourth transvectant of u and itself.

(4) $C_{2,8}$, an octavic covariant, is the Hessian, whose leading coefficient is $ac-b^2$.

(5) $C_{3,2}$ is a quadratic covariant obtained by operation with u, having replaced in it x and y by $\partial/\partial y$ and $-\partial/\partial x$, on the Hessian $C_{2,8}$. The seminvariant which leads it is

$$(ac-b^2)g-3(ad-bc)f+2ae^2-bde-3c^2e+2cd^2.$$

It can also be obtained by operation with $C_{2,4}$ on u.

(6) $C_{3,6}$ is a sextic covariant whose leader is

$$ace+2bcd-ad^2-b^2e-c^3$$

(§ 114, Ex. 13), the catalecticant of the fourth emanant.

(7) $C_{3,12}$ is a duodecimic with the seminvariant

$$a^2d-3abc+2b^3$$

(§ 114, Ex. 15) for leader.

(8) $C_{3,8}$, a second octavic covariant, has for its leader

$$a^2f-5abe+2acd-6bc^2+8b^2d$$

(§ 165).

(9) I_4, the irreducible invariant of degree 4, is the result of operating with u on $C_{3,6}$. It is the catalecticant (§ 208)

$$\begin{vmatrix} a, & b, & c, & d \\ b, & c, & d, & e \\ c, & d, & e, & f \\ d, & e, & f, & g \end{vmatrix}.$$

(10) $C_{4,4}$ is a second quartic covariant, the Hessian, but for a numerical factor, of the first quartic covariant $C_{2,4}$. Its seminvariant leader is

$$2(ae-4bd+3c^2)(ag-9ce+8d^2)-3(af-3be+2cd)^2,$$

where the coefficient 2 is, contrary to the usual convention of

§ 71, given to the alphabetically leading term a^2eg in order to avoid fractional coefficients.

(11) $C_{4, 6}$, a third sextic covariant, is the Jacobian of u and $C_{3, 2}$.

(12) $C_{4, 10}$, a decimic, is the Jacobian of $C_{2, 8}$ and $C_{2, 4}$.

(13) $C_{5, 2}$, a second quadratic, is the result of operating on $C_{2, 4}$ with $C_{3, 2}$.

(14) $C_{5, 4}$, a third quartic, is the Jacobian of $C_{2, 4}$ and $C_{3, 2}$.

(15) $C_{5, 8}$, a third octavic, is the Jacobian of $C_{2, 8}$ and $C_{3, 2}$.

(16) I_6, the irreducible invariant of degree 6, is the discriminant of $C_{3, 2}$.

(17) $C_{6, 6}$, a fourth sextic covariant, is the Jacobian of u and $C_{5, 2}$.

(18) $K_{6, 6}$, another covariant of the same degree and order 6, 6 as the last, is the Jacobian of $C_{3, 6}$ and $C_{3, 2}$.

(19) $C_{7, 2}$, a third quadratic, is the result of operating on $C_{2, 4}$ with $C_{5, 2}$.

(20) $C_{7, 4}$, a fourth quartic, is the Jacobian of $C_{4, 4}$ and $C_{3, 2}$.

(21) $C_{8, 2}$, a fourth quadratic, is the Jacobian $C_{3, 2}$ and $C_{5, 2}$.

(22) $C_{9, 4}$, a fifth quartic, is the Jacobian of $C_{4, 4}$ and $C_{5, 2}$.

(23) I_{10}, the invariant of degree 10, is the discriminant of $C_{5, 2}$.

(24) $C_{10, 2}$, a fifth quadratic, is the Jacobian of $C_{3, 2}$ and $C_{7, 2}$.

(25) $C_{12, 2}$, a sixth quadratic, is the Jacobian of $C_{5, 2}$ and $C_{7, 2}$.

(26) I_{15}, the skew invariant of degree 15 and weight $\frac{1}{2} 6 . 15 = 45$, is the determinant (§ 17, Ex. 25) of the quadratics $C_{3, 2}$, $C_{5, 2}$, $C_{7, 2}$. It is the criterion for those three quadratic covariants forming an involution.

245. There are then altogether for the sextic the following irreducible concomitants:—

5 invariants I_2, I_4, I_6, I_{10}, I_{15}, of which the last is skew,		
6 quadratic covariants		$C_{3, 2}$, $C_{5, 2}$, $C_{7, 2}$, $C_{8, 2}$, $C_{10, 2}$, $C_{12, 2}$,
5 quartic	”	$C_{2, 4}$, $C_{4, 4}$, $C_{5, 4}$, $C_{7, 4}$, $C_{9, 4}$,
5 sextic	”	u, $C_{3, 6}$, $C_{4, 6}$, $C_{6, 6}$, $K_{6, 6}$,
3 octavic	”	$C_{2, 8}$, $C_{3, 8}$, $C_{5, 8}$,
1 decimic	”	$C_{4, 10}$,
1 duodecimic	”	$C_{3, 12}$.

None of the covariants are of odd order. Indeed, we have seen (§ 39) that no binary quantic of even order can have a covariant of odd order. In particular a sextic, or other binary quantic of even order, has no linear covariant.

We notice the occurrence of two irreducible covariants $C_{6,6}$, $K_{6,6}$ of the sixth order and the sixth degree, i.e. of two covariants of that order and degree which are linearly independent of one another, and of the covariants of the same order and degree which can be formed as products of lower covariants and invariants. This is the first instance of a state of things which often occurs in connexion with quantics above the sixth order, but only in this one instance up to the sextic inclusively.

In forming covariants and invariants by operations which involve only differentiations with respect to variables, as for instance in the ordinary methods of finding them as hyperdeterminants or transvectants, or, in particular, as Hessians, Jacobians, or results of operating with one covariant or quantic on another, we may, it is clear, with safety use canonical forms. Only operations of this class occur in the determinations of the more complicated of the above concomitants from the simpler ones. We may apply them to the canonical form of unit modulus

$$a(x^6+y^6)+15cx^4y^2+20dx^3y^3+15ex^2y^4,$$

which (§ 226) is a valid one, although the actual reduction of a sextic to the form has not been effected by solving equations of degree less than 5.

It should be mentioned, however, as of general applicability, that methods which use differentiations with regard to coefficients, such as that of evectants (§§ 67, 68), cannot as a rule be used in connexion with canonical forms. Such methods are not contemplated above.

246. Complete systems of concomitants of the binary septimic and octavic have been symbolically exhibited by von Gall, and a good deal has been done with regard to quantics of a few orders higher. For no higher quantic, however, have explicit results been arrived at with completeness, except for that of infinite order, whose theory has been touched upon in Chapter XI.

ADDITIONAL EXAMPLES.

Ex. 9. Prove that a quintic, deprived of its second term by writing $x = X - bY$, $y = aY$, may be written

$$a(1, 0, C, D, a^2E-3C^2, a^2F-2CD)(X, Y)^5,$$

where

$$C = ac-b^2,\ D = a^2d-3abc+2b^3,\ E = ae-4bd+3c^2,$$
$$F = a^2f-5abe+8b^2d+2acd-6bc^2;$$

and that, if

$$J = ace+2bcd-ad^2-b^2e-c^3,$$

the relation $D^2 = -a^3J + a^2CE - 4C^3$ can be used to reduce any expression to the first degree in D. (*Cayley.*)

Ex. 10. If $\alpha, \beta, \gamma, \delta, \epsilon$ are the roots of a quintic, prove that

$$a^2\Sigma(\alpha-\beta)^2(x-\gamma y)^2(x-\delta y)^2(x-\epsilon y)^2 = -100\,C_{2,6}.$$

Ex. 11. If $\alpha, \beta, \gamma, \delta, \epsilon, \zeta$ are the roots of a sextic, prove that

$$a^2\Sigma(\alpha-\beta)^2(x-\gamma y)^2(x-\delta y)^2(x-\epsilon y)^2(x-\zeta y)^2 = -180\,C_{2,8}.$$

Ex. 12. For the quintic $a^4\Sigma(\alpha-\beta)^2(\beta-\gamma)^2(\gamma-\alpha)^2(\delta-\epsilon)^4$ is an invariant, and must be a numerical multiple of I_4.

Ex. 13. For the quintic $a^2\Sigma(\alpha-\beta)^2(\gamma-\delta)^2(x-\epsilon y)^2$ is a covariant, and a numerical multiple of $C_{2,2}$.

Ex. 14. For the sextic $a^4\Sigma(\alpha-\beta)^2(\gamma-\delta)^2(x-\epsilon y)^2(x-\zeta y)^2$ is a numerical multiple of $C_{2,4}$.

Ex. 15. Prove that

$$a^4\Sigma(\alpha-\beta)^2(\beta-\gamma)^2(\gamma-\alpha)^2(\delta-\epsilon)^2(x-\delta y)^2(x-\epsilon y)^2$$

is a covariant of a quintic which vanishes identically when the quintic has three equal roots. It must be a linear function of $C_{4,4}$ and $C^2_{2,2}$. Show by considering the quintic $x^5+10cx^3y^2$, which has three equal roots, that it is a multiple of $C^2_{2,2}-3C_{4,4}$. (*Cayley.*)

Ex. 16. Prove that

$$a^5\Sigma(\alpha-\delta)(\alpha-\epsilon)(\beta-\delta)(\beta-\epsilon)(\gamma-\delta)(\gamma-\epsilon)(\delta-\epsilon)^2$$
$$(x-\alpha y)^3(x-\beta y)^3(x-\gamma y)^3$$

is a covariant of degree 5 and order 9 of a quintic, which vanishes for a quintic having two pairs of equal roots. It must be a linear function of $uC^2_{2,2}$, $uC_{4,4}$ and $C_{2,6}C_{3,3}$. Prove that it is a numerical multiple of $50\,C_{2,6}C_{3,3} - u(C_{4,4}+3C^2_{2,2})$. (*Cayley.*)

Ex. 17. Prove that

$$a^4\Sigma(\alpha-\beta)(\alpha-\gamma)(\alpha-\delta)(\alpha-\epsilon)(x-\beta y)^3(x-\gamma y)^3(x-\delta y)^3(x-\epsilon y)^3$$

is a covariant of degree 4 and order 12, which vanishes for a quintic having three roots equal and the other two roots equal, and express it as $k(3u^2C_{2,2}-25C^2_{2,6})$. (*Cayley.*)

Ex. 18. For the sextic

$$I_2 = -\tfrac{1}{240}a^2\Sigma(\alpha-\beta)^2(\gamma-\delta)^2(\epsilon-\zeta)^2. \quad (\textit{Sylvester.})$$

Ex. 19. For the sextic

$$120(71\,I_2^{\,2}+900\,I_4) = a^4\Sigma(\alpha-\beta)^4(\gamma-\delta)^4(\epsilon-\zeta)^4. \quad (\textit{Sylvester.})$$

Ex. 20. Show that

$$\begin{vmatrix} \alpha\beta, & \alpha+\beta, & 1 \\ \gamma\delta, & \gamma+\delta, & 1 \\ \epsilon\zeta, & \epsilon+\zeta, & 1 \end{vmatrix},$$

i.e. $\alpha\beta(\gamma+\delta-\epsilon-\zeta)+\gamma\delta(\epsilon+\zeta-\alpha-\beta)+\epsilon\zeta(\alpha+\beta-\gamma-\delta)$,

whose vanishing expresses that the quadratics

$$(x-\alpha y)(x-\beta y),\quad (x-\gamma y)(x-\delta y),\quad (x-\epsilon y)(x-\zeta y)$$

form an involution, is a function of the differences between pairs of $\alpha, \beta, \gamma, \delta, \epsilon, \zeta$.

Ex. 21. The six letters $\alpha, \beta, \gamma, \delta, \epsilon, \zeta$ can be divided into pairs $\alpha, \beta ; \gamma, \delta ; \epsilon, \zeta$, in fifteen ways. Take each triad of pairs in a definite order, and write down the fifteen values of the function of differences in Ex. 20. Show that the product is symmetric in the roots, and must be a numerical multiple of $a^{-15} I_{15}$, where I_{15} is the skew invariant of the sextic of which $\alpha, \beta, \gamma, \delta, \epsilon, \zeta$ are the roots.

(*Joubert.*)

Ex. 22. The vanishing of the skew invariant I_{15} of a sextic is the necessary and sufficient condition that the sextic be the product of three quadratics which form an involution, and consequently that, except in a very special case, it can be written as a cubic in X^2, Y^2, where X and Y are linear in the original variables.

Ex. 23. All skew invariants vanish for a sextic which can be thrown into the form $aX^6+15cX^4Y^2+15eX^2Y^4+gY^6$.

Ex. 24. From the last two examples a sextic has no irreducible skew invariant but I_{15}.

Ex. 25. Prove that

$$a^5 \Sigma (\alpha-\beta)(\alpha-\gamma)(\alpha-\delta)(\alpha-\epsilon)(\beta-\gamma)^4(\delta-\epsilon)^4(x-\alpha y)$$

and

$$a^7 \Sigma (\alpha-\beta)^3(\alpha-\gamma)^2(\alpha-\delta)(\beta-\gamma)^2(\beta-\delta)^2(\gamma-\epsilon)^3(\delta-\epsilon)^4(x-\alpha y)$$

are the unique linear covariants of degrees 5 and 7, respectively, of a quintic with $\alpha, \beta, \gamma, \delta, \epsilon$ for roots.

Ex. 26. Prove that

$$a^{11} \Sigma (\alpha-\beta)^5(\alpha-\gamma)^3(\alpha-\delta)^2(\beta-\gamma)^3(\beta-\delta)^3(\gamma-\epsilon)^5(\delta-\epsilon)^6(x-\alpha y)$$

and

$$a^{13} \Sigma (\alpha-\beta)^3(\alpha-\gamma)^3(\alpha-\delta)^3(\alpha-\epsilon)^3(\beta-\gamma)^{10}(\delta-\epsilon)^{10}(x-\alpha y)$$

are linear covariants of degrees 11 and 13 of the quintic, and are not reducible as invariant multiples of L_7 and L_5 respectively.

Ex. 27. The 20-ic covariant of a sextic u, which (§ 226) is a constant multiple of the product of the ten products XY for canonical forms $(1, 0, C, D, E, 0, 1)(X, Y)^6$, is reducible as $u^2 C_{3,8} - 2C_{2,8} C_{3,12}$.

Ex. 28. The 12-ic covariant of a quintic u, which is a constant multiple of the six products XY in canonical forms

$$(1, 0, C, D, 0, 1)(X, Y)^5,$$

is reducible as $u^2 C_{2,2} - 3C^2_{2,6}$.

Ex. 29. Prove that

$$(\epsilon-\alpha)(\gamma-\beta)(x-\delta y)-(\epsilon-\beta)(\gamma-\delta)(x-\alpha y) \\ -(\epsilon-\delta)(\gamma-\alpha)(x-\beta y),$$

of which the leading coefficient is

$$\alpha\beta+\beta\gamma+\gamma\delta+\delta\epsilon+\epsilon\alpha-\alpha\gamma-\gamma\epsilon-\epsilon\beta-\beta\delta-\delta\alpha,$$

is a covariant of the five linear forms $x-ay$, $x-\beta y$, $x-\gamma y$, $x-\delta y$, $x-\epsilon y$, which is the same, but for sign in the last ten cases, for the same forms in the 20 orders in which the cyclical arrangement is one of

$$(a\beta\gamma\delta\epsilon),\ (\epsilon\delta\gamma\beta a),\ (a\gamma\epsilon\beta\delta),\ (\delta\beta\epsilon\gamma a);$$

and that the product of six such covariants is the sextic covariant $uC_{5,1}-25C^2_{3,3}$ of $(x-ay)(x-\beta y)(x-\gamma y)(x-\delta y)(x-\epsilon y)$.

Ex. 30. Corresponding to each vertex A_r of a pentagon $A_1A_2A_3A_4A_5$ inscribed in a conic, construct a vertex B_r of another inscribed pentagon $B_1B_2B_3B_4B_5$ as the second intersection with the conic of the line joining A_r to the intersection of the connectors of the two vertices adjacent to A_r and the two remote from A_r in the cycle $(A_1A_2A_3A_4A_5)$. Let the connector A_rA_s of two vertices of the one pentagon, and the connector B_rB_s of the two corresponding vertices of the other, meet in Q_{rs}. Then the lines $Q_{34}Q_{52}$, $Q_{45}Q_{13}$, $Q_{51}Q_{24}$, $Q_{12}Q_{35}$, $Q_{23}Q_{41}$ pass respectively through A_1, A_2, A_3, A_4, A_5, and meet the conic again in the same point X. (*Quarterly Journal*, Vol. XXVIII, p. 265.)

Ex. 31. If a conic through the origin O cuts the five lines $u=0$ in P_1, P_2, P_3, P_4, P_5; if Q_1 is the point conjugate to P_1 for all conics through P_2, P_3, P_4, P_5, and Q_2, Q_3, Q_4, Q_5 have like meanings; if the polar of Q_1 with regard to the harmonic triangle of the quadrangle $P_2P_3P_4P_5$ meets the tangent at P_1 in R_1, and R_2, R_3, R_4, R_5 are similarly constructed; these five points lie on a straight line whose intersections A, B with the conic $OP_1P_2P_3P_4P_5$ specify OA, OB the factors of the covariant $C_{2,2}$ of u. (*Morley.*)

Ex. 32. If C is the pole of the above AB with regard to the conic $OP_1P_2P_3P_4P_5$; D, E the points where CA, CB meet again the conic $CP_2P_3P_4P_5$; and F the pole of DE for that conic; if CP_1 meets the conic $OP_1P_2P_3P_4P_5$ again in Q_1, and FQ_1 meets it again in Q; and if CQ meets the same conic again in P; then OQ and OP specify the linear covariants $C_{5,1}$ and $C_{7,1}$ of the quintic u.

(*Proc. Lond. Math. Soc.*, Ser. 2, Vol. VI, p. 227.)

Ex. 33. If P_1R, P_1R' are the harmonic conjugates of the tangent at P_1 with regard to P_1P_2, P_1P_3 and P_1P_4, P_1P_5 respectively; and P_1R_1, the harmonic conjugate of the same tangent with regard to P_1R, P_1R', meets the conic $OP_1P_2P_3P_4P_5$ again in R_1; then OR_1 specifies one of the five factors of a covariant of degree 7 and order 5 of the quintic u.

Ex. 34. By means of this quintic covariant of u, and the AB of Ex. 31, two linear covariants of degrees 11, 13 can be constructed as in Ex. 32.

CHAPTER XIV

SEVERAL BINARY QUANTICS.

247. IT will be remembered (§§ 103, 115) that an invariant of several binary quantics

$$a_0x^p + pa_1x^{p-1}y + \frac{p(p-1)}{1.2}a_2x^{p-2}y^2 + \dots + a_py^p,$$

$$a_0'x^{p'} + p'a_1'x^{p'-1}y + \frac{p'(p'-1)}{1.2}a_2'x^{p'-2}y^2 + \dots + a'_{p'}y^{p'},$$

&c., &c.,

has the two annihilators

$$\Sigma\Omega \equiv \left(a_0\frac{\partial}{\partial a_1} + 2a_1\frac{\partial}{\partial a_2} + \dots + pa_{p-1}\frac{\partial}{\partial a_p}\right)$$
$$+ \left(a_0'\frac{\partial}{\partial a_1'} + 2a_1'\frac{\partial}{\partial a_2'} + \dots + p'a'_{p'-1}\frac{\partial}{\partial a'_{p'}}\right) + \dots,$$

$$\Sigma O \equiv \left(pa_1\frac{\partial}{\partial a_0} + p-1\,.\,a_2\frac{\partial}{\partial a_1} + \dots + a_p\frac{\partial}{\partial a_{p-1}}\right)$$
$$+ \left(p'a_1'\frac{\partial}{\partial a_0'} + p'-1\,.\,a_2'\frac{\partial}{\partial a_1'} + \dots + a'_{p'}\frac{\partial}{\partial a'_{p'-1}}\right) + \dots;$$

that any covariant has the two annihilators

$$\Sigma\Omega - y\frac{\partial}{\partial x}, \qquad \Sigma O - x\frac{\partial}{\partial y};$$

and that any seminvariant, the leading coefficient in a covariant, has the one annihilator $\Sigma\Omega$.

It will also be remembered (§§ 103, 115) that for any invariant

$$ip + i'p' + \dots = 2w,$$

and that for any seminvariant which is not an invariant $ip + i'p' + \dots$ exceeds $2w$, the excess

$$ip + i'p' + \dots - 2w$$

being the order in the variables of the covariant which the seminvariant leads. We here and throughout this chapter mean by seminvariant *rational integral* seminvariant.

We proceed to illustrate the theory of concomitants of several binary quantics by consideration of a few early cases.

248. Linear form and p-ic. Let the linear form and the p-ic be

$$u \equiv \xi x + \eta y,$$
$$v \equiv (a_0, a_1, a_2, \dots a_p)(x, y)^p.$$

The linear form alone has no invariant, and no covariant distinct from itself.

The p-ic alone has a system of invariants and covariants which, in the preceding pages, have been investigated for values of p up to 4, and given for the values 5 and 6 of p.

The other *invariants* of the system are (§ 69) given by substituting ξ for y and $-\eta$ for x in the covariants of the p-ic, including the p-ic itself. They are the eliminants of u and the covariants of v. They are also spoken of (§ 68) as the contravariants of v alone, if we regard u as the universal concomitant (§ 66) of two contragredient systems x, y ; ξ, η. We shall dwell comparatively little on this aspect of them, but the ξ, η notation is chosen so as to accord with it.

We seek information as to the other *covariants* of the system, or as to the *mixed concomitants* (§ 66) of v. The quest for these covariants is that for the *seminvariants* of the system which lead them.

These seminvariants are rational integral functions of ξ and η and $a_0, a_1, \dots a_p$, which are homogeneous, of different degrees i, i' it may be, both in ξ and η and in $a_0, a_1, \dots a_p$, and are isobaric in the two sets of coefficients taken together, ξ and η being of weights 0, 1 respectively. They have the one annihilator

$$\xi \frac{\partial}{\partial \eta} + \Omega.$$

Suppose that

$$\xi^i P_w + i\xi^{i-1}\eta P_{w-1} + \frac{i(i-1)}{1 \cdot 2}\xi^{i-2}\eta^2 P_{w-2} + \dots + \eta^i P_{w-i}$$

is such a seminvariant, where $P_w, P_{w-1}, \dots P_{w-i}$ are gradients, all of degree i', in $a_0, a_1, \dots a_p$, the weight of each being indicated by its suffix.

Expressing the fact of annihilation by $\xi \frac{\partial}{\partial \eta} + \Omega$, by equating to zero the terms in the result of operation with it which multiply $\xi^i, \xi^{i-1}\eta, \dots \eta^i$ separately, we obtain

$$\begin{aligned}
\Omega P_w \quad &+ \quad iP_{w-1} &= 0,\\
\Omega P_{w-1} &+ (i-1)P_{w-2} &= 0,\\
\cdots & \cdots & \\
\Omega P_{w-i+2} &+ \quad 2P_{w-i+1} &= 0,\\
\Omega P_{w-i+1} &+ \quad P_{w-i} &= 0,\\
\Omega P_{w-i} & &= 0,
\end{aligned}$$

of which the last shows that P_{w-i} is a seminvariant of the p-ic alone, and from which, as in § 109, we also draw the conclusions that

$$P_{w-r} = (-1)^r \frac{1}{i(i-1)\dots(i-r+1)} \Omega^r P_w,$$

for every value of r from 1 to i inclusive, and that the full expression for the seminvariant is consequently

$$\xi^i P_w - \frac{1}{1}\xi^{i-1}\eta\Omega P_w + \frac{1}{1\,.\,2}\xi^{i-2}\eta^2\Omega^2 P_w - \dots + (-1)^i \frac{1}{i!}\eta^i \Omega^i P_w,$$

which may be written

$$\xi^i e^{-\frac{\eta}{\xi}\Omega} P_w,$$

since the addition of terms multiplying $\Omega^{i+1}P_w$, $\Omega^{i+2}P_w, \dots$ is a mere addition of zeros.

It will also be recognized, from § 93 or § 160, that this expression for the joint seminvariant is the result of substituting in P_w for $a_0, a_1, a_2, \dots a_p$ respectively, the expressions

$$\begin{aligned}
a_0 &\equiv a_0 \\
a_1 &\equiv a_1\xi - a_0\eta \\
a_2 &\equiv a_2\xi^2 - 2a_1\xi\eta + a_0\eta^2 \\
a_3 &\equiv a_3\xi^3 - 3a_2\xi^2\eta + 3a_1\xi\eta^2 - a_0\eta^3 \\
&\dots\dots\dots\dots\dots\dots \\
a_p &\equiv a_p\xi^p - pa_{p-1}\xi^{p-1}\eta + \frac{p(p-1)}{1\,.\,2}a_{p-2}\xi^{p-2}\eta^2 - \dots + (-1)^p a_0\eta^p,
\end{aligned}$$

i.e. by the results of replacing x and y by $-\eta$ and ξ in

$$\frac{1}{p!}\frac{\partial^p v}{\partial x^p}, \quad \frac{1!}{p!}\frac{\partial^{p-1} v}{\partial x^{p-1}}, \quad \frac{2!}{p!}\frac{\partial^{p-2} v}{\partial x^{p-2}}, \dots \frac{1}{p}\frac{\partial v}{\partial x}, \quad v,$$

and after substitution dividing through by ξ^{w-i}.

Any seminvariant which is not a mere power of ξ, or, in particular, any invariant, is then a gradient in $a_0, a_1, \dots a_p$, or such a gradient multiplied or divided by a power of ξ. Moreover, any gradient in $a_0, a_1, \dots a_p$ is a seminvariant or, in particular, invariant. For $a_0, a_1, \dots a_p$ are seminvariants themselves—the last of them, in fact, an invariant—being all annihilated by

$$\xi\frac{\partial}{\partial\eta} + \Omega.$$

248 (*bis*). From the last paragraph we draw the interesting conclusion that *every* gradient P_w in $a_0, a_1, \dots a_p$, and in particular every single coefficient and product of coefficients, is the coefficient of the highest power of ξ in some covariant of the p-ic and linear form. This highest power of ξ is not

uniquely determinate for a given P_w, but may not be lower than the ith, where Ω^{i+1} is the first power of Ω which annihilates P_w. Having obtained the seminvariant of the p-ic and linear form which has the term $\xi^i P_w$, we know that there is another with first term $\xi^{i+n} P_w$ for every positive n. The covariant which it leads is the product of $(\xi x + \eta y)^n$ and the covariant led by the seminvariant with the term $\xi^i P_w$.

If ϖ is the order of the covariant led by the seminvariant with the term $\xi^i P_w$, i.e. by the seminvariant

$$\xi^i e^{-\frac{\eta}{\xi}\Omega} P_w,$$

and if i' is the degree of P_w, we have

$$i + i'p - 2w = \varpi,$$

and (§ 115) the covariant is

$$x^{\varpi} e^{\frac{y}{x}\left(O + \eta\frac{\partial}{\partial \xi}\right)} \left\{ \xi^i e^{-\frac{\eta}{\xi}\Omega} P_w \right\},$$

which may be written in other forms; for instance

$$x^{\varpi} e^{\frac{y}{x}\eta\frac{\partial}{\partial \xi}} \left\{ \xi^i e^{\frac{y}{x} O} e^{-\frac{\eta}{\xi}\Omega} P_w \right\},$$

i.e., since by Taylor's theorem $e^{h\frac{d}{dx}} F(x)$ means $F(x+h)$,

$$x^{\varpi - i} (\xi x + \eta y)^i e^{\frac{y}{x} O} e^{-\frac{\eta x}{\xi x + \eta y}\Omega} P_w.$$

Contrary to appearances this is integral in x even when $\varpi < i$.

We have noticed that these covariants are the concomitants (in general mixed) of the p-ic only. Changing the notation by writing ϖ' and i in place of i and i', we are led to the following theorem.

Every gradient G whatever of degree i and weight w in $a_0, a_1, \ldots a_p$ is either an invariant or the coefficient of $x^{\varpi}\xi^{\varpi'}$ in some rational integral covariant (with $\varpi' = 0$), contravariant (with $\varpi = 0$), or mixed concomitant, of $(a_0, a_1, \ldots a_p)(x, y)^p$.

The value of ϖ' is the smallest number for which $\Omega^{\varpi'+1} G = 0$, that of ϖ is $ip - 2w + \varpi'$, and an expression for the concomitant is

$$x^{ip-2w} (\xi x + \eta y)^{\varpi'} e^{\frac{y}{x} O} e^{-\frac{\eta x}{\xi x + \eta y}\Omega} G.$$

The same expression also gives a mixed concomitant if ϖ' is any greater number than the smallest for which $\Omega^{\varpi'+1} G = 0$, but in such a case a power of $\xi x + \eta y$ is a factor of the concomitant.

Let us call ϖ the *order* of a covariant or mixed concomitant, and ϖ' the *class* of a mixed concomitant or contravariant.

Taking for G the general gradient of type w, i, p, containing $(w; i, p)$ arbitrary numerical coefficients, we thus derive from it a concomitant including as many arbitraries

$$x^{ip-2w}(\xi x+\eta y)^w e^{\frac{y}{x}O} e^{-\frac{\eta x}{\xi x+\eta y}\Omega} G,$$

of order $ip-w$ and class w.

This may be separated into parts which give us the concomitants of lowest orders and classes with leading coefficients included in G. In § 128 (*bis*) we have seen how to write the general G as a sum of parts

$$G_1+G_2+G_3+\ldots+G_{w+1}$$

which are annihilated, respectively, by Ω, by Ω^2 but not by Ω, by Ω^3 but not $\Omega^2, \ldots$, by Ω^{w+1} but not Ω^w. If $ip-2w$ is negative the parts $G_1, G_2, \ldots G_{2w-ip}$ do not occur in the sum (§ 128 (*bis*), Ex. 14). The concomitant of order $ip-w$ and class w derived from G as above is now a sum of parts

$$(\xi x+\eta y)^w C_1+(\xi x+\eta y)^{w-1}C_2+(\xi x+\eta y)^{w-2}C_3+\ldots+C_{w+1},$$

where

$$C_r = x^{ip-2w}(\xi x+\eta y)^{r-1} e^{\frac{y}{x}O} e^{-\frac{\eta x}{\xi x+\eta y}\Omega} G_r,$$

for every r from 1 to $w+1$ if $ip-2w$ is not, and for every r from $2w-ip+1$ to $w+1$ if $ip-2w$ is, negative. In the latter case $C_1, C_2, \ldots C_{2w-ip}$ are zero. Here $C_1, C_2, \ldots C_{w+1}$ are the concomitants of lowest orders and classes desired.

Ex. 1. Prove that the operator $\xi(\partial/\partial y)-\eta(\partial/\partial x)$ produces concomitants from concomitants, and hence that a cubic

$$A \equiv ax^3+3bx^2y+3cxy^2+dy^3$$

has concomitants with b, c, d respectively for leading coefficients, namely

$$B \equiv (bx^2+2cxy+dy^2)\xi-(ax^2+2bxy+cy^2)\eta,$$
$$C \equiv (cx+dy)\xi^2-2(bx+cy)\xi\eta+(ax+by)\eta^2,$$
$$D \equiv d\xi^3-3c\xi^2\eta+3b\xi\eta^2-a\eta^3.$$

Ex. 2. Hence also any gradient $G(a, b, c, d)$ is the leading coefficient in a concomitant $G(A, B, C, D)$ of the cubic. Prove in like manner the general fact as to concomitants of a p-ic.

249. **Irreducible systems.** Let us return to the notation of § 248. All seminvariants and invariants, including those of u and v singly, being rational integral functions of some or all of ξ and $a_0, a_1, a_2, \ldots a_p$, or such rational integral functions divided by powers of ξ, the search for the complete system of *irreducible* concomitants of the linear u and the p-ic v is the search for homogeneous isobaric functions of ξ

and $a_0, a_1, a_2, \dots a_p$, from which, when they are expressed in terms of ξ, η and $a_0, a_1, a_2, \dots a_p$, powers of ξ may be removed by division, leaving the result integral. Such new forms have again to be combined with ξ, $a_0, a_1, a_2, \dots a_p$ and with one another, or with such of them as in the process are not excluded as themselves composite, and new forms derived by removal of ξ factors, till the process can be continued no longer. The method for thus arriving at all the irreducible concomitants is that illustrated in §§ 169, 170. Two early cases follow.

250. **Case of two linear forms.** Let the two forms be

$$\xi x + \eta y, \quad ax + by.$$

The seminvariants ξ, a_0, a_1 are

$$\xi, \quad a, \quad b\xi - a\eta;$$

and ξ is not a factor of any combination of them. These then are the only seminvariants and invariant; so that the complete system for two linear forms consists of the two forms themselves and one invariant, their eliminant.

251. **Case of linear form and quadratic.** For the system

$$u \equiv \xi x + \eta y,$$
$$v \equiv ax^2 + 2bxy + cy^2,$$

the independent seminvariants ξ, a_0, a_1, a_2 are

$$\xi, \quad a, \quad b\xi - a\eta, \quad c\xi^2 - 2b\xi\eta + a\eta^2.$$

Here, if ξ were zero, we should have $a_0 a_2 = a_1{}^2$. Thus $a_0 a_2 - a_1{}^2$ is divisible by ξ. In fact,

$$a_0 a_2 - a_1{}^2 = (ac - b^2)\,\xi^2.$$

Thus $ac - b^2$ is a seminvariant (invariant) newly given. It is irreducible, for it is no function of the other one a which does not involve ξ.

Further examining the results of putting $\xi = 0$ in the seminvariants now before us, i.e.

$$0, \quad a, \quad -\eta a, \quad \eta^2 a, \quad ac - b^2,$$

we see that no new relation connects them. We have before us therefore the complete system of irreducible covariants and invariants, viz.

(1) the linear form itself, led by ξ;

(2) the quadratic itself, led by a;

(3) a covariant led by $b\xi - a\eta$. It is a linear covariant, the Jacobian

$$(b\xi - a\eta)\,x + (c\xi - b\eta)\,y.$$

Geometrically it is the harmonic conjugate of the linear form with regard to the quadratic;

(4) an invariant $c\xi^2 - 2b\xi\eta + a\eta^2$, the eliminant;
(5) an invariant $ac - b^2$, the discriminant of the quadratic.

252. Another method, which might be pursued in examining the system of a linear form and p-ic, consists in using instead of

$$\xi, \quad a_0, a_1, a_2, \ldots a_p$$

the system of $p+2$ protomorphs of § 168,

$$\xi,\ b\xi - a\eta,\ a_0,\ a_0a_2 - a_1^2,\ a_0^2a_3 - 3a_0a_1a_2 + 2a_1^3,$$
$$a_0a_4 - 4a_1a_3 + 3a_2^2, \ldots .$$

A third method, which will be adopted, depends on the fact that if S is a seminvariant, or invariant, of $\xi x + \eta y$ and v, which involves ξ and η, i.e. which is not either a power of ξ or a seminvariant of v alone, then $\partial S/\partial\eta$ is another.

The fact is an immediate consequence of the identity of operators

$$\left(\xi\frac{\partial}{\partial\eta} + \Omega\right)\frac{\partial}{\partial\eta} = \frac{\partial}{\partial\eta}\left(\xi\frac{\partial}{\partial\eta} + \Omega\right),$$

which tells us that when $\xi\dfrac{\partial}{\partial\eta} + \Omega$ annihilates S, so that

$$\frac{\partial}{\partial\eta}\left(\xi\frac{\partial}{\partial\eta} + \Omega\right)S = 0,$$

then $\xi\dfrac{\partial}{\partial\eta} + \Omega$ also annihilates $\dfrac{\partial}{\partial\eta}S$.

Thus from an *invariant*

$$(Q_{w-i}, Q_{w-i+1}, \ldots Q_w)(\eta, -\xi)^i$$

of $\xi x + \eta y$ and v, formed as in § 248 from v or a covariant of v, are derived the series of seminvariants

$$(Q_{w-i}, Q_{w-i+1}, \ldots Q_{w-1})(\eta, -\xi)^{i-1},$$
$$(Q_{w-i}, Q_{w-i+1}, \ldots Q_{w-2})(\eta, -\xi)^{i-2},$$
$$\cdots\cdots\cdots\cdots$$
$$Q_{w-i}\eta - Q_{w-i+1}\xi,$$
$$Q_{w-i},$$

of which the last is the corresponding seminvariant of v only.

The way in which, in the following two cases, this is utilized for the determination of complete systems of $\xi x + \eta y$ and v, when the complete system of v is known, is general. We shall see that ξ, the irreducible invariants of v, the invariants of $\xi x + \eta y$ and v obtained by putting $\eta, -\xi$ for x, y in the irreducible covariants of v, and the successive derivatives of these with regard to η, constitute together the complete system of seminvariants and invariants.

253. Case of linear form and cubic. Take the linear form

$$\xi x + \eta y$$

and the cubic

$$ax^3 + 3bx^2y + 3cxy^2 + dy^3.$$

The complete system for the linear form alone is itself.

The complete system for the cubic alone consists (§ 169) of three covariants

$$(a, b, c, d)(x, y)^3, \text{ i.e. the cubic itself,}$$

$$(ac - b^2)x^2 + (ad - bc)xy + (bd - c^2)y^2,$$

$$(a^2d - 3abc + 2b^3,\ abd - 2ac^2 + b^2c,\ -acd + 2b^2d - bc^2,\\ -ad^2 + 3bcd - 2c^3)(x, y)^3,$$

and one invariant

$$(ad - bc)^2 - 4(ac - b^2)(bd - c^2).$$

Thus the system has

(1) the seminvariant ξ;

(2) the invariant $(a, b, c, d)(\eta, -\xi)^3$,

by § 248, from which flow, by § 252, the seminvariants

(3) $(a, b, c)(\eta, -\xi)^2$,

(4) $a\eta - b\xi$,

(5) a;

(6) the invariant $(ac - b^2)\eta^2 - (ad - bc)\eta\xi + (bd - c^2)\xi^2$,

from which flow the seminvariants

(7) $2(ac - b^2)\eta - (ad - bc)\xi$,

(8) $ac - b^2$;

(9) the invariant $(a^2d - 3abc + 2b^3,\ -abd + 2ac^2 - b^2c,\ -acd + 2b^2d - bc^2,\ ad^2 - 3bcd + 2c^3)(\eta, \xi)^3$,

from which flow the seminvariants

(10) $(a^2d - 3abc + 2b^3,\ -abd + 2ac^2 - b^2c,\ -acd + 2b^2d - bc^2)(\eta, \xi)^2$,

(11) $(a^2d - 3abc + 2b^3)\eta - (abd - 2ac^2 + b^2c)\xi$,

(12) $a^2d - 3abc + 2b^3$;

and lastly the invariant

(13) $(ad - bc)^2 - 4(ac - b^2)(bd - c^2)$.

None of these thirteen is a rational integral function of any of the others. That (5), (8), (12) and (13) are irreducible is the theory of the single cubic (§ 169). That (1) is irreducible is obvious. We have still to see that none of the rest of the thirteen, i.e. none of those which involve ξ and η, is a rational integral function of others of the thirteen. Now if

$$P\eta^m + Q\eta^{m-1}\xi + \ldots + Z\xi^m,$$

where $P, Q, \dots Z$ do not involve ξ and η, is the expansion of a rational integral function of some of the thirteen, its P must be a rational integral function of some or all of

$$a,\ ac-b^2,\ a^2d-3abc+2b^3,\ (ad-bc)^2-4(ac-b^2)(bd-c^2);$$

and, as none of these is a rational integral function of the rest, P can only be one of them when actually presented as one. Thus none of (2) to (13) could be reducible except as a product of another of them and a seminvariant involving η but none of a, b, c, d. But the only seminvariants free from a, b, c, d are powers of ξ, and do not involve η.

We have still to show that this system of thirteen irreducible seminvariants and invariants is complete.

254. **The system is complete.** We have to see that any seminvariant or invariant whatever of the linear form and cubic can be rationally and integrally expressed in terms of the system (1) to (13) of the preceding article.

Firstly, any seminvariant or invariant in which only a, b, c, d occur is a rational integral function of (5), (8), (12), (13), by the theory of the single cubic.

Secondly, any seminvariant in which a, b, c, d do not occur is a mere power of ξ.

It remains to consider seminvariants and invariants in which both sets a, b, c, d and ξ, η are represented. Let

$$S \equiv P\eta^i + Q\eta^{i-1}\xi + R\eta^{i-2}\xi^2 + \dots + Z\xi^i$$

be one, from which factors which are powers of ξ have been removed. $P, Q, \dots Z$ are rational integral functions of degree i' in a, b, c, d or some of them.

By § 248, P is a seminvariant in a, b, c, d. It can therefore be rationally and integrally expressed in terms of

$$a,\ ac-b^2,\ a^2d-3abc+2b^3,\ (ad-bc)^2-4(ac-b^2)(bd-c^2),$$

which call a, C, D, Δ.

If w is the whole weight of S, we have (§ 247)

$$i+3i' \not< 2w.$$

Now P consists of a sum of positive and negative numerical multiples of such products as $a^pC^qD^r\Delta^s$, where

$$p+2q+3r+4s=i'.$$

The term $P\eta^i$ in S is then a sum of numerical multiples of such terms as

$$a^pC^qD^r\Delta^s.\eta^i,$$

for which, expressing that $i+3i' \not< 2w$, we have

$$i+3(p+2q+3r+4s) \not< 2(i+2q+3r+6s),$$

i. e. $$3p+2q+3r \nless i$$
$$= i+t, \text{ say},$$

where t is a positive integer or zero. It is important to see that this implies, among other things, that p, q, r cannot all vanish, since i does not.

Now in the product
$$(2)^p (6)^q (9)^r (13)^s$$
the highest term in η is
$$a^p C^q D^r \Delta^s . \eta^{3p+2q+3r},$$
and the product
$$(5)^p (8)^q (12)^r (13)^s$$
is
$$a^p C^q D^r \Delta^s;$$
and, if in this last we replace one of the p factors (5) by (4), or one of the q factors (8) by half of (7), or one of the r factors (12) by (11), we produce a first term
$$a^p C^q D^r \Delta^s . \eta,$$
and again, by a like process of retrogression, we produce
$$a^p C^q D^r \Delta^s . \eta^2,$$
and so on. Continuing the process of unit retrogression we must arrive, before or upon finally reaching the first term
$$a^p C^q D^r \Delta^s . \eta^{3p+2q+3r},$$
at the desired first term
$$a^p C^q D^r \Delta^s . \eta^{3p+2q+3r-t},$$
i. e.
$$a^p C^q D^r \Delta^s . \eta^i,$$
as a rule in a number of different ways.

Similarly for any other term of which $P\eta^i$ consists.

Thus we can, and as a rule in a number of ways, obtain by composition of (2) to (13) a seminvariant
$$P\eta^i + Q'\eta^{i-1}\xi + R'\eta^{i-2}\xi^2 + \ldots + Z'\xi^i,$$
whose η^i term is the same as that of S.

Subtracting it from S, and removing the seminvariant factor ξ, we obtain a seminvariant
$$(Q-Q')\eta^{i-1} + (R-R')\eta^{i-2}\xi + \ldots + (Z-Z')\xi^{i-1}.$$

Let the same process be repeated. We can form a combination of (2) to (13) whose highest term in η is $(Q-Q')\eta^{i-1}$. Subtracting this, and dividing by ξ, we have a seminvariant
$$(R-R'-R'')\eta^{i-2} + \ldots + (Z-Z'-Z'')\xi^{i-2}.$$

Repeat the process again; and continually as long as necessary. We get, lastly, unless at some stage or other the result of subtraction has vanished, in which case the desired expression of S has been obtained, a residual

$$Z - Z' - Z'' - \dots - Z_i,$$

which is a seminvariant free from ξ, η, and so a rational integral function of (5), (8), (12), (13).

Thus, finally, we have S expressed as

$$S_1 + \xi S_2 + \xi^2 S_3 + \dots + \xi^i S_i,$$

where $S_1, S_2, S_3, \dots S_i$ are rational integral functions of (2) to (13) or some of them.

We see then that every seminvariant or invariant of the linear form and cubic is a rational integral function of (1) to (13) or some of them. These were seen to be irreducible. The proof is now complete that they form the complete system of irreducible seminvariants and invariants.

The complete system of irreducible covariants and invariants follows at once from the complete system of irreducible seminvariants and invariants. The covariant corresponding to any one of the seminvariants S is, by § 115,

$$x^{\varpi} e^{\frac{y}{x}\left(\eta \frac{\partial}{\partial \xi} + O\right)} S,$$

where $$\varpi = i + 3i' - 2w.$$

255. Case of linear form and quartic. The irreducible covariants and invariants of the quartic

$$(a, b, c, d, e)(x, y)^4,$$

are, § 170, the quartic itself, the covariants

$$(ac - b^2)x^4 + 2(ad - bc)x^3 y + (ae + 2bd - 3c^2)x^2 y^2 + 2(be - cd)xy^3 + (ce - d^2)y^4,$$

and $$x^6 e^{\frac{y}{x}O}(a^2 d - 3abc + 2b^3),$$

and the invariants

$$I \equiv ae - 4bd + 3c^2,$$
$$J \equiv ace + 2bcd - ad^2 - b^2 e - c^3.$$

The invariants of the system consisting of $\xi x + \eta y$ and the quartic are then

(1) I,

(2) J,

(3) $(a, b, c, d)(\eta, -\xi)^4$,

(4) $(ac - b^2)\eta^4 - 2(ad - bc)\eta^3\xi + (ae + 2bd - 3c^2)\eta^2\xi^2 - 2(be - cd)\eta\xi^3 + (ce - d^2)\xi^4$,

(5) $\eta^6 e^{-\frac{\xi}{\eta}O}(a^2 d - 3abc + 2b^3)$,

and the other seminvariants are, as in the last two articles, ξ, the four successive differential coefficients of (3), the four successive differential coefficients of (4), and the six successive differential coefficients of (5), all with respect to η.

Altogether we have twenty seminvariants and invariants.

The twenty are all irreducible. This is established exactly as in § 253.

Moreover, as in § 254, any seminvariant or invariant whatever can be rationally and integrally expressed in terms of the twenty or some of them. They form, then, the complete irreducible system of seminvariants and invariants.

From every seminvariant of the system the corresponding irreducible covariant is formed by the operation and multiplication

$$x^{i+4i'-2w} e^{\frac{y}{x}\left(\eta \frac{\partial}{\partial \xi} + O\right)}.$$

256. **Case of n linear forms.** For the case of n linear forms

$$a_1x+b_1y,\ a_2x+b_2y, \dots ,\ a_nx+b_ny,$$

an *algebraically* complete system of concomitants, i.e. a system of which all other covariants and invariants are functions, though not necessarily rational integral functions, consists of the n linear forms themselves and the $n-1$ invariants

$$a_1b_2-a_2b_1,\ a_1b_3-a_3b_1, \dots ,\ a_1b_n-a_nb_1,$$

which are the eliminants of a chosen one of the forms and the other $n-1$.

For

$$a_1,\ a_2, \dots a_n,\ a_1b_2-a_2b_1,\ a_1b_3-a_3b_1, \dots ,\ a_1b_n-a_nb_1$$

are all independent, each involving a letter which does not occur in any previous one, and their whole number $2n-1$ is less by 4, the number of l, m, l', m', than $2n+2+1$, i.e. than the number of equations which express the equalities of coefficients of X and Y in the given forms and their linear transformations together with the equations of substitution

$$x=lX+mY, \quad y=l'X+m'Y$$

and the one equation

$$M=lm'-l'm. \quad \text{(Cf. § 42.)}$$

The complete *irreducible* system consists of the above and the other eliminants

$$a_2b_3-a_3b_2,\ a_2b_4-a_4b_2, \dots ,\ a_3b_4-a_4b_3, \dots , \dots ,\ a_{n-1}b_n-a_nb_{n-1}$$

of pairs of the n forms. The whole number of the system is the sum of n, the number of linear forms, and $\frac{1}{2}n(n-1)$, the number of eliminants, i.e. is

$$\tfrac{1}{2}n(n+1).$$

We must see that they are all irreducible, and that there is no other covariant or invariant which is not a rational integral function of them.

They are all irreducible. For the leaders

$$a_1, a_2, \dots a_n$$

of the forms themselves, being different and of the first degree, are irreducible, and the eliminants $a_1b_2 - a_2b_1, \dots$ are all of degree 2, so that any one of them if not irreducible would have to be a linear function of the rest and of the squares and products of $a_1, a_2, \dots a_n$. These last cannot enter with the others in any linear relation, for they are all of weight zero, and the rest are of weight 1: and no linear relation can connect the eliminants alone, for they are of different partial degrees in the coefficients of the n forms separately.

To prove that every other seminvariant is reducible in terms of $a_1, a_2, \dots a_n$ and the eliminants, we may proceed by mathematical induction. Assume it true for the above n forms, and take an $(n+1)$th $\xi x + \eta y$. Exactly as in § 254, any seminvariant of the system of $n+1$ forms is a rational integral function of

$$a_1b_2 - a_2b_1,\ a_1b_3 - a_3b_1, \dots,\ a_2b_3 - a_3b_2, \dots, \dots,\ a_{n-1}b_n - a_nb_{n-1},$$
$$a_1\eta - b_1\xi,\ a_2\eta - b_2\xi, \dots,\ a_n\eta - b_n\xi,$$

and the η-derivatives of these

$$a_1, a_2, \dots a_n,$$

together with ξ.

This proves the theorem for $n+1$ forms when we know it for n. But (§ 250) we know it for $n = 2$. Consequently it is true for $n = 3, 4, 5, \dots$, i.e. universally.

In proofs by the method of § 254 the critical fact is that, in the inequalities like the

$$3p + 2q + 3r \nless i$$

of that article, the non-vanishing coefficients on the left are all positive. This is a universal fact, for every coefficient is the $\Sigma(ip) - 2w$ of a seminvariant, and this is never negative (§ 247).

257. System of two quadratics. This is the only system of two quantics neither of which is linear which we shall discuss at length.

Let the two quadratics be

$$u \equiv ax^2 + 2bxy + cy^2,$$
$$v \equiv a'x^2 + 2b'xy + c'y^2.$$

Six seminvariants and invariants we have at once the means of writing down, viz.

(1) a, the leading coefficient of u,

(2) a', the leading coefficient of v,

(3) $ac-b^2$, the one invariant of u alone, its discriminant,

(4) $a'c'-b'^2$, the one invariant of v alone, its discriminant,

(5) $ac'+a'c-2bb'$, the invariant of u and v intermediate to (3) and (4), found in § 18.

(6) $ab'-a'b$, the leading coefficient of the Jacobian of u and v.

These six form the complete irreducible system. This may be seen as follows.

Firstly none of them is a rational integral function of the rest. This is clearly the case with regard to the two a, a' of the first degree. As to the rest all are of the second degree. If any one of them is a rational integral function of the rest it must be a linear function of a^2, aa', a'^2 and of the other three of (3) to (6). Now it is clear that every one of (3) to (6) consists of terms which do not occur in the rest or in a^2, aa', a'^2.

The six, however, are not all independent, but are connected by one syzygy. For, combining (1) to (5) so as to get an expression free from c and c', we find

$$aa'(ac'+a'c-2bb')-a^2(a'c'-b'^2)-a'^2(ac-b^2)$$
$$=(ab'-a'b)^2. \quad \ldots (7)$$

We have still to see that any seminvariant or invariant can be expressed rationally and integrally in terms of (1) to (6). Writing C, C', Γ for (3), (4) and (5), we have

$$c=(C+b^2)/a, \quad c'=(C'+b'^2)/a',$$

so that any rational integral function of a, b, c, a', b', c' may be written as a sum of such terms as

$$\lambda a^m a'^n b^p b'^q (C+b^2)^r (C'+b'^2)^s,$$

where the indices are integers, zero allowed, and, with the exception of m and n, certainly positive. This again is a sum of such terms as

$$\lambda' a^m a'^n b^{p'} b'^{q'} C^{r'} C'^{s'}.$$

If the sum is a seminvariant or invariant it is annihilated by

$$\left(a\frac{\partial}{\partial b}+2b\frac{\partial}{\partial c}\right)+\left(a'\frac{\partial}{\partial b'}+2b'\frac{\partial}{\partial c'}\right),$$

which also annihilates a, a', C, C' separately, and so in its effect on the sum is the same as

$$a\frac{\partial}{\partial b}+a'\frac{\partial}{\partial b'}$$

on it as a function of b and b' as they occur explicitly. Now the annihilation by this implies, as the theory of partial differential equations tells us, that b and b' only occur in the connexion

$$ab' - a'b.$$

Any seminvariant or invariant is then a sum of such terms as

$$\mu a^{m'} a'^{n'} (ab' - a'b)^t C^{r'} C'^{s'},$$

and consequently, by use of the syzygy (7), can be written as a sum of terms each belonging to one of the types

$$\mu' a^\alpha a'^\beta C^\rho C'^\sigma \Gamma^\tau,$$
$$\mu' a^\alpha a'^\beta (ab' - a'b)\, C^\rho C'^\sigma \Gamma^\tau.$$

Terms of both types cannot occur, for the whole weights of the two types are one even and the other odd.

Thus a seminvariant or invariant is, either a sum of terms like

$$\mu' a^\alpha a'^\beta C^\rho C'^\sigma \Gamma^\tau,$$

or such a sum multiplied by $ab' - a'b$. Here ρ, σ, τ are positive integers, zero not excluded, and α, β are integral or zero, but not yet proved positive. The factors a, a', C, C', Γ of any term are absolutely independent, and the last three are invariants.

We have to see that for no term as above can α or β be negative. Suppose if possible that there are terms in which α, for instance, is negative, and let α' be the greatest positive value of $-\alpha$ which occurs in any term. We remember that the seminvariant must lead a covariant, and that the last coefficient in the covariant is, but for a numerical factor, obtained by operating on the seminvariant with $(O + O')^\varpi$, where

$$O + O' \equiv \left(2b\frac{\partial}{\partial a} + c\frac{\partial}{\partial b}\right) + \left(2b'\frac{\partial}{\partial a'} + c'\frac{\partial}{\partial b'}\right),$$

and ϖ is the order of the covariant, i.e. $\Sigma(ip) - 2w$ (in this case $2(\alpha + \beta)$, which is accordingly non-negative and constant throughout). This last coefficient is annihilated by $O + O'$, so that the seminvariant is annihilated by $(O + O')^{\varpi+1}$. Now the result of operating with this upon it, if as supposed it contains a sum of terms

$$a^{-\alpha'} \Sigma (a'^\beta C^\rho C'^\sigma \Gamma^\tau)$$

and none with the factor $a^{-\alpha'-1}$, contains the terms

$$(-1)^{\varpi+1} \alpha'(\alpha' + 1) \ldots (\alpha' + \varpi)\, a^{-\alpha' - \varpi - 1} \Sigma (a'^\beta C^\rho C'^\sigma \Gamma^\tau)\, 2^{\varpi+1} b^{\varpi+1},$$

and no other terms involving $a^{-\alpha'-\varpi-1}$ against which they can cancel. The result then cannot vanish; and the supposition was unsound.

It is then completely established that any seminvariant or

invariant is either a rational integral function of (1), (2), (3), (4), (5), or such a function multiplied by (6).

The system (1) to (6) is then the complete system of irreducible seminvariants and invariants.

Consequently also the complete system of irreducible covariants and invariants consists of the two quadratics themselves, the three invariants (3), (4), (5), and a third covariant, the Jacobian

$$(ab'-a'b)\,x^2+(ac'-a'c)\,xy+(bc'-b'c)\,y^2.$$

258. **Canonical forms of two quadratics.** It is easily seen that by a linear substitution of modulus unity the two quadratics can be given the simultaneous forms

$$aX^2+cY^2, \quad a'X^2+c'Y^2,$$

with new values of a, c, a', c'.

For to make simultaneously

$$\begin{aligned} all'+b\,(lm'+l'm)+cmm' &= 0,\\ a'll'+b'\,(lm'+l'm)+c'mm' &= 0, \end{aligned}$$

we have only so to choose $l:m$ as to make

$$\frac{al+bm}{a'l+b'm}=\frac{bl+cm}{b'l+c'm},$$

i.e. to solve a quadratic, and then to take for $l':m'$

$$-\frac{bl+cm}{al+bm}.$$

The absolute values of l, m and l', m', whose ratios in pairs are thus determined, may then be taken, and still with one degree of freedom, so as to make $lm'-l'm=1$.

For these canonical forms of unit modulus the six concomitants are

$$\begin{array}{l} aX^2+cY^2 \quad ,\\ a'X^2+c'Y^2 \quad ,\\ \quad ac \quad ,\\ \quad a'c' \quad ,\\ ac'+a'c \quad ,\\ (ac'-a'c)\,XY. \end{array}$$

The X and Y of the canonical forms are then factors of the Jacobian.

The failing case of two quadratics which are special in that their Jacobian has equal roots is left as an exercise to the student.

Ex. 3. Interpret geometrically the vanishing of the invariant $ac'+a'c-2bb'$.

Ex. 4. The Jacobian of two quadratics represents the double elements of the involution which they determine.

Ex. 5. Express the seminvariant $ab'^2-2ba'b'+ca'^2$ in terms of (1) to (6).

Ans. $a'(ac'+a'c-2bb')-a(a'c'-b'^2)$.

Ex. 6. By means of the canonical forms prove that the covariant led by the seminvariant of Ex. 5, represents the harmonic conjugates of the factors of $ax^2+2bxy+cy^2$ with regard to $a'x^2+2b'xy+c'y^2$.

Ex. 7. Prove the same by means of § 251 (3).

Ex. 8. Find the covariant which consists of the harmonic conjugates of the factors of v with regard to u.

Ex. 9. Prove that the covariants of Ex. 6 and Ex. 8 are quadratics which belong to the involution of Ex. 4.

Ex. 10. Express the eliminant $(ac'-a'c)^2-4(ab'-a'b)(bc'-b'c)$ of u and v in terms of the invariants (3), (4), (5) of § 257.

Ans. $(ac'+a'c-2bb')^2-4(ac-b^2)(a'c'-b'^2)$. Use the canonical forms.

259. **Linear form and two quadratics.** Let the quadratics be as before

$$u \equiv ax^2+2bxy+cy^2,$$
$$v \equiv a'x^2+2b'xy+c'y^2,$$

and the linear form $\xi x+\eta y$.

Of the linear form alone the one seminvariant is

$$\xi,$$

and of the quadratics the irreducible concomitants are

$$ax^2+2bxy+cy^2,$$
$$a'x^2+2b'xy+c'y^2,$$
$$(ab'-a'b)x^2+(ac'-a'c)xy+(bc'-b'c)y^2,$$
$$ac-b^2,$$
$$a'c'-b'^2,$$
$$ac'+a'c-2bb'.$$

As in § 248 the invariants of the system are these last three, and the eliminants of $\xi x+\eta y$, and the preceding three, i.e.

$$a\eta^2-2b\eta\xi+c\xi^2,$$
$$a'\eta^2-2b'\eta\xi+c'\xi^2,$$
$$(ab'-a'b)\eta^2-(ac'-a'c)\eta\xi+(bc'-b'c)\xi^2;$$

and as in §§ 253, 254 the remaining irreducible seminvariants of the system are the successive η-derivatives of these three last, i. e.

$$\begin{aligned}&a\eta - b\xi,\\&a,\\&a'\eta - b'\xi,\\&a',\\&2(ab'-a'b)\eta - (ac'-a'c)\xi,\\&ab'-a'b.\end{aligned}$$

The covariants which these lead are readily written down. The last, last but two, and last but four, occur above.

Ex. 11. The vanishing of the invariant

$$(ab'-a'b)\eta^2 - (ac'-a'c)\eta\xi + (bc'-b'c)\xi^2$$

expresses that the linear form is a double element of the involution determined by the quadratics.

Ex. 12. The covariant $(a\eta - b\xi)x + (b\eta - c\xi)y$ represents the harmonic conjugate of $\xi x + \eta y$ with regard to u.

Ex. 13. Interpret the linear covariants led by

$$a'\eta - b'\xi, \quad 2(ab'-a'b)\eta - (ac'-a'c)\xi.$$

260. **System of quadratic and cubic.** Take the forms

$$\begin{aligned}u &\equiv ax^2 + 2bxy + cy^2,\\ v &\equiv a'x^3 + 3b'x^2y + 3c'xy^2 + d'y^3.\end{aligned}$$

For the quadratic only the irreducible concomitants are

(1) $$u,$$

and the invariant

(2) $$ac - b^2.$$

For the cubic only they are

(3) $$v,$$

the covariants

(4) $$(a'c'-b'^2)x^2 + (a'd'-b'c')xy + (b'd'-c'^2)y^2,$$

(5) $$(a'^2d' - 3a'b'c' + 2b'^3)x^3 + \ldots,$$

and the invariant,

(6) $$(a'd'-b'c')^2 - 4(a'c'-b'^2)(b'd'-c'^2).$$

The remaining irreducible concomitants of the system prove to be nine in number. They may be taken to be the following:

(7) the Jacobian of u and v

$$(ab'-a'b)x^3 + \ldots,$$

(8) the Jacobian of u and (4)

$$\{a(a'd'-b'c') - 2b(a'c'-b'^2)\}x^2 + \ldots,$$

(9) the result of operating with u on v, after substituting $\partial/\partial y$, $-\partial/\partial x$ for x, y in u,

$$(ac'+a'c-2bb')\,x+(ad'+cb'-2bc')\,y,$$

(10) the result of operating with (9) on u

$$-\{a^2d'-3abc'+(ac+2b^2)\,b'-bca'\}\,x$$
$$+\{c^2a'-3bcb'+(ac+2b^2)\,c'-abd'\}\,y,$$

(11) the result of operating with u on (5)

$$\{a(-a'c'd'+2b'^2d'-b'c'^2)+2b(-a'b'd'+2a'c'^2-b'^2c')$$
$$+c(a'^2d'-3a'b'c'+2b'^3)\}\,x-\{c(-a'b'd'+2a'c'^2-b'^2c')$$
$$+2b(-a'c'd'+2b'^2d'-b'c'^2)+a(a'd'^2-3b'c'd'+2c'^3)\}\,y,$$

(12) the result of operating with (11) on u, a linear covariant (the fourth) of degree 2 in the coefficients of u and 3 in those of v,

(13) the intermediate invariant $AC'+A'C-2BB'$ of u and (4), i.e.

$$a(b'd'-c'^2)-b(a'd'-b'c')+c(a'c'-b'^2),$$

(14) an invariant of partial degrees 3, 2, the eliminant of u and v,

(15) an invariant of partial degrees 3, 4, the eliminant of the two linear covariants (9) and (12), or (10) and (11).

Of the system five are invariants, (2), (6), (13), (14), (15), four are linear covariants (9), (10), (11), (12), three are quadratics, u, (4), (8), and three cubics v, (5) and (7).

The above is Salmon's list (*Higher Algebra*, § 198). They are, though all irreducible, connected by many syzygies, which have been fully exhibited by Hammond (*Am. J.*, Vol. VIII). There is of course a considerable freedom allowed in choosing the complete list of fifteen, it being allowable to take, in place of any one of the more complicated ones above, any linear function of that one and compounds of the right order and partial degrees of those that are simpler. In fact Hammond finds it convenient to modify the last linear covariant (12) and the last invariant but one (14) by addition of products of others of the set in a way suggested in the next article.

261. We may, in accordance with the chapter on canonical forms, reduce the cubic by linear transformation of modulus unity to the form

$$a'x^3+d'y^3,$$

with different a', d', x, y. The same substitution does not affect the form of

$$ax^2+2bxy+cy^2,$$

but only makes the a, b, c different.

For purposes, then, of the study of the combinations of the concomitants, it suffices to consider u, v in the forms

$$u \equiv ax^2 + 2bxy + cy^2,$$
$$v \equiv a'x^3 + d'y^3.$$

With this simplification it is easy to form all of (1) to (15) by the methods described. In the following notation I, L, Q, C denote respectively invariants and linear, quadratic, and cubic covariants. The first suffix denotes degree in the coefficients of u, and the second degree in those of v. The list is, in the same order as before,

(1) $Q_{10} \equiv u \equiv ax^2 + 2bxy + cy^2,$

(2) $I_{20} \equiv ac - b^2,$

(3) $C_{01} \equiv v \equiv a'x^3 + d'y^3,$

(4) $Q_{02} \equiv a'd'xy,$

(5) $C_{03} \equiv a'd'(a'x^3 - d'y^3),$

(6) $I_{04} \equiv a'^2d'^2,$

(7) $C_{11} \equiv -b(a'x^3 - d'y^3) - (ca'x - ad'y)xy,$

(8) $Q_{12} \equiv a'd'(ax^2 - cy^2),$

(9) $L_{11} \equiv ca'x + ad'y,$

(10) $L_{21} \equiv (bca' - a^2d')x - (abd' - c^2a')y$
$\equiv b(ca'x - ad'y) - (a^2d'x - c^2a'y),$

(11) $L_{13} \equiv a'd'(ca'x - ad'y),$

(12) $L_{23} \equiv a'd'\{(a^2d' + bca')x + (abd' + c^2a')y\}$
$\equiv a'd'(a^2d'x + c^2a'y) + ba'd'(ca'x + ad'y)$
$\equiv a'd'(a^2d'x + c^2a'y) - I_{12}L_{11},$

(13) $I_{12} \equiv -ba'd',$

(14) $I_{32} \equiv a^3d'^2 + (6abc - 8b^3)a'd' + c^3a'^2$
$\equiv a^3d'^2 - 2abca'd' + c^3a'^2 - 8I_{12}I_{20},$

(15) $I_{34} \equiv a'd'(c^3a'^2 - a^3d'^2).$

Mr. Hammond's modification is to take instead of L_{23} and I_{32} the concomitants of like type, but simpler canonical shape,

$$L'_{23} \equiv L_{23} + I_{12}L_{11} \equiv a'd'(a^2d'x + c^2a'y),$$
$$I'_{32} \equiv I_{32} + 8I_{12}I_{20} \equiv a^3d'^2 - 2abca'd' + c^3a'^2.$$

This last is the eliminant of (9) and (10). Its full value in the notation of § 260 is

$$a^3d'^2 + c^3a'^2 - 6a^2bc'd' - 6bc^2a'b' + 2(ac + 2b^2)(ab'd' + ca'c')$$
$$+ (ac + 8b^2)(ac'^2 + cb'^2) - 2abca'd' - 2b(5ac + 4b^2)b'c'.$$

Many good exercises in geometrical interpretation are afforded by the above canonical expressions.

262. Linear form quadratic and cubic. From the system

for the quadratic and cubic, the system for them and a linear form $\xi x+\eta y$, is derived exactly as in § 259.

The invariants of the system are the invariants I_{20}, I_{04}, I_{12}, I_{32}, I_{34} of the quadratic and cubic, and the results of replacing x by η and y by $-\xi$ in the quadratic and cubic and their covariants. The other seminvariants are ξ and the successive derivatives of the invariants which contain ξ, η with regard to η.

Ex. 14. Any *seminvariant* of $ax^3+3bx^2y+3cxy^2+dy^3$ is a rational integral function of a and *invariants* of the system

$$ax+by,\ ax^2+2bxy+cy^2,\ ax^3+3bx^2y+3cxy^2+dy^3. \quad (\textit{Kempe.})$$

Ans. It is a rational integral function of

$$a,\ ac-b^2,\ a^2d-3abc+2b^3,\ \text{and}\ (ad-bc)^2-4(ac-b^2)(bd-c^2),$$

of which the second and fourth are invariants of the quadratic and cubic respectively, and the third is the invariant of the linear form quadratic and cubic given by § 260 (9).

Ex. 15. Any seminvariant of $(a,\ b,\ c,\ d,\ e)(x,\ y)^4$ is a rational integral function of a and invariants of the system consisting of the quartic and its successive derivatives with regard to x. (*Kempe.*)

Ans. Since it is a rational integral function of

$$a,\ ac-b^2,\ a^2d-3abc+2b^3,\ ae-4bd+3c^2,\ ace+2bcd-ad^2-b^2e-c^3.$$

Ex. 16. Express the seminvariant $a^2f-5abe+2acd+8b^2d-6bc^2$ of extent 5 as an invariant of the quintic and its successive derivatives with regard to x.

Ans. Form a covariant of the system by operating on the quintic with its first x-derivative, and substitute $-b$ for x and a for y.

Ex. 17. All *invariants* of a linear form a quadratic and a cubic are functions, not necessarily rational integral functions, of the discriminant of the quadratic and the eliminants of the linear form with the quadratic, the cubic, the Hessian and cubicovariant of the latter, and the Jacobian of the quadratic and cubic. (*Forsyth.*)

262 (*bis*). The Examples 14 to 16 are cases of a fact called attention to by Kempe, that all seminvariants of a binary quantic in x, y are *invariants* of the system consisting of that quantic and its partial derivatives with regard to x. This is readily proved by use of the θ-notation of § 60 (*ter*). The seminvariant of degree i of

$$(x+y\theta_1)^p a_0 \equiv (x+y\theta_2)^p a_0 \equiv \ldots \equiv (x+y\theta_i)^p a_0$$

which leads the covariant

$$(\theta_1-\theta_2)^{n_{12}}(\theta_1-\theta_3)^{n_{13}}(\theta_2-\theta_3)^{n_{23}}\ldots(\theta_{i-1}-\theta_i)^{n_{i-1\,i}}$$
$$(x+y\theta_1)^{\varpi_1}a_0\,(x+y\theta_2)^{\varpi_2}a_0\ldots(x+y\theta_i)^{\varpi_i}a_0$$

is

$$(\theta_1-\theta_2)^{n_{12}}(\theta_1-\theta_3)^{n_{13}}(\theta_2-\theta_3)^{n_{23}}\dots(\theta_{i-1}-\theta_i)^{n_{i-1\,i}}a_0a_0a_0\dots \quad (i \text{ factors}),$$

where

$$n_{12}+n_{13}+\dots+n_{1i}=p-\varpi_1,$$
$$n_{12}+n_{23}+\dots+n_{2i}=p-\varpi_2,$$
&c., &c.

Now this is an invariant of the derivatives

$$(x+y\theta_1)^{p-\varpi_1}a_0,\ (x+y\theta_2)^{p-\varpi_2}a_0,\dots(x+y\theta_i)^{p-\varpi_i}a_0.$$

263. **Case of $p+1$ binary quantics of orders p, $p-1$, $p-2,\dots 1, 0$.** An *algebraically* complete system of seminvariants, i.e. a system in terms of which all other seminvariants can be expressed (*not* of course a complete *irreducible* system in terms of which all can be expressed rationally and integrally) of a system of binary quantics

$$(a_0, b_0, c_0, d_0, \dots k_0, l_0, m_0)(x, y)^p,$$
$$(a_1, b_1, c_1, d_1, \dots k_1, l_1)(x, y)^{p-1},$$
$$\cdot\quad\cdot\quad\cdot\quad\cdot\quad\cdot\quad\cdot\quad\cdot\quad\cdot\quad\cdot\quad\cdot\quad\cdot\quad\cdot$$
$$(a_{p-2}, b_{p-2}, c_{p-2})(x, y)^2,$$
$$(a_{p-1}, b_{p-1})(x, y),$$
$$a_p,$$

in which notice the presence of the last of zero order, a mere constant which is its own only irreducible concomitant, consists of the results of replacing x and y by b_{p-1} and $-a_{p-1}$ in the quantics and their successive derivatives with regard to x.

Thus, for the case $p=4$, an algebraically complete system for the five quantics

$$(a_0, b_0, c_0, d_0, e_0)(x, y)^4,\quad (a_1, b_1, c_1, d_1)(x, y)^3,$$
$$(a_2, b_2, c_2)(x, y)^2,\quad (a_3, b_3)(x, y),\quad a_4$$

consists of

$$(a_0, b_0, c_0, d_0, e_0)(b_3, -a_3)^4,\ (a_0, b_0, c_0, d_0)(b_3, -a_3)^3,$$
$$(a_0, b_0, c_0)(b_3, -a_3)^2,\ (a_0, b_0)(b_3, -a_3),\ a_0,$$
$$(a_1, b_1, c_1, d_1)(b_3, -a_3)^3,\ (a_1, b_1, c_1)(b_3, -a_3)^2,$$
$$(a_1, b_1)(b_3, -a_3),\ a_1,$$
$$(a_2, b_2, c_2)(b_3, -a_3)^2,\ (a_2, b_2)(b_3, -a_3),\ a_2,$$
$$[(a_3, b_3)(b_3, -a_3)=0],\ a_3,$$
$$a_4.$$

Their formation accords with § 252. They are all independent, for taken from last to first each one involves a coefficient which has not previously occurred. Also their number, excluding the always vanishing last but two, is

$$\tfrac{1}{2}(p+1)(p+2)-1=\tfrac{1}{2}p(p+3),$$

which is easily seen as in §§ 42, 256 to be the maximum possible number of perfectly independent concomitants.

The system appears to have been first given by Forsyth.

An alternative algebraically complete system consists, §§ 168, 252, of sets of $p, p-1, p-2, \dots 2, 1, 1$ protomorphs of the $p+1$ quantics, and the Jacobians of the linear one and the $p-1$ of higher orders.

264. **Systems of quantics of one order. Combinants.** We will conclude this chapter by alluding to an important class of invariants of several binary p-ics, to which their first discoverer, Sylvester, has given the name *Combinants.* There are also combinants of systems of q-ary p-ics, for any the same q as well as the same p.

A combinant of a number of p-ics $u, v, w, \dots$, in the same variables, is an invariant which differs only by a function of $\lambda, \mu, \nu, \dots, \lambda', \mu', \nu', \dots, \dots$ as factor, by a power of

$$\begin{vmatrix} \lambda, & \mu, & \nu, & \dots \\ \lambda', & \mu', & \nu', & \dots \\ \lambda'', & \mu'', & \nu'', & \dots \\ \cdot & \cdot & \cdot & \cdot \end{vmatrix}$$

in fact, from the same invariant of

$$\lambda u+\mu v+\nu w+\dots,\ \lambda' u+\mu' v+\nu' w+\dots,$$
$$\lambda'' u+\mu'' v+\nu'' w+\dots, \dots.$$

It is, in fact, an invariant quâ linear transformation of the p-ics as well as quâ linear transformations of the variables.

If $a, b, c, \dots; a', b', c', \dots; a'', b'', c'', \dots; \dots$ are corresponding coefficients in $u, v, w, \dots$ it is readily seen that the conditions for an invariant to be a combinant are that it have the pairs of annihilators

$$a'\frac{\partial}{\partial a}+b'\frac{\partial}{\partial b}+c'\frac{\partial}{\partial c}+\dots,$$

$$a\frac{\partial}{\partial a'}+b\frac{\partial}{\partial b'}+c\frac{\partial}{\partial c'}+\dots,$$

corresponding to pairs of the p-ics $u, v, w, \dots$.

There are also combinant covariants.

265. A few of the more obvious facts with regard to combinants are the following.

The eliminant or resultant of two binary p-ics u, v is

a combinant. For if u, v have a common factor so have $\lambda u+\mu v$, $\lambda' u+\mu' v$, so that the eliminant of u, v is a factor of that of $\lambda u+\mu v$, $\lambda' u+\mu' v$. The remaining factor involves λ, μ, λ', μ' only, as we are told by consideration of dimensions in the coefficients of u, v.

The eliminant or resultant of three ternary p-ics is also a combinant; and so on.

A combinant of $u, v, w, \ldots$ is of equal partial degrees in the coefficients of $u, v, w, \ldots$ separately. For, if we denote

$$a'\frac{\partial}{\partial a}+b'\frac{\partial}{\partial b}+c'\frac{\partial}{\partial c}+\ldots,$$

$$a\frac{\partial}{\partial a'}+b\frac{\partial}{\partial b'}+c\frac{\partial}{\partial c'}+\ldots$$

by ϕ', ϕ respectively,

$$\phi'\phi-\phi\phi'=\left(a'\frac{\partial}{\partial a'}+b'\frac{\partial}{\partial b'}+c'\frac{\partial}{\partial c'}+\ldots\right)$$
$$-\left(a\frac{\partial}{\partial a}+b\frac{\partial}{\partial b}+c\frac{\partial}{\partial c}+\ldots\right),$$

whose effect is, by Euler's theorem, the same as that of the multiplier $i'-i$. Thus, if $\phi C=0$ and $\phi' C=0$, the first and second partial degrees i, i' of C are equal. In like manner the first and third, the first and fourth, &c., partial degrees are equal.

An intermediate invariant (§§ 18, 19) is *not* a combinant. Consider two p-ics u, v only. The operation ϕ repeated a number of times on an intermediate invariant produces the invariant of u only, between which and the same invariant of v the supposed invariant is intermediate. This intermediate invariant is not then annihilated by ϕ. In like manner as to intermediate invariants of more p-ics than two.

Let I be any invariant of u, and form the same invariant of $\lambda u+\mu v$, as in §§ 18, 19. This is

$$\lambda^i I+\frac{1}{1}\lambda^{i-1}\mu\phi' I+\frac{1}{1\,.\,2}\lambda^{i-2}\mu^2\phi'^2 I+\ldots+\frac{1}{i\,!}\mu^i\phi'^i I,$$

or, as it may be also written,

$$\frac{1}{i\,!}\lambda^i\phi^i I'+\frac{1}{(i-1)\,!}\lambda^{i-1}\mu\phi^{i-1}I'+\ldots+\frac{1}{1}\lambda\mu^{i-1}\phi I'+\mu^i I'.$$

Call it

$$A\lambda^i+iB\lambda^{i-1}\mu+\frac{i(i-1)}{1\,.\,2}C\lambda^{i-2}\mu^2+\ldots+iJ\lambda\mu^{i-1}+K\mu^i,$$

so that

$$\phi' A = iB, \quad \phi' B = (i-1)\, C,$$
$$\phi' C = (i-2)\, D, \ldots, \quad \phi' J = K, \quad \phi' K = 0.$$

We thus have

$$\phi' F(A, B, C, \ldots J, K) = \frac{\partial F}{\partial A} \phi' A + \frac{\partial F}{\partial B} \phi' B + \ldots + \frac{\partial F}{\partial K} \phi' K$$

$$= \left(iB \frac{\partial}{\partial A} + (i-1)\, C \frac{\partial}{\partial B} + \ldots + K \frac{\partial}{\partial J} \right) F(A, B, C, \ldots J, K),$$

where the operator on the right is of the form of O. In like manner

$$\phi F(A, B, C, \ldots J, K)$$
$$= \left(A \frac{\partial}{\partial B} + 2B \frac{\partial}{\partial C} + \ldots + iJ \frac{\partial}{\partial K} \right) F(A, B, C, \ldots J, K),$$

where the operator on the right is of the form of Ω.

We thus see that any invariant of an invariant of $\lambda u + \mu v$ regarded as a quantic in λ, μ is a combinant of u and v. For it is an invariant of u and v, being a rational integral homogeneous isobaric function of invariants $A, B, \ldots K$, and it is annihilated by ϕ and ϕ'.

In like manner any invariant of an invariant of $\lambda u + \mu v + \nu w$ regarded as a quantic in λ, μ, ν is a combinant of u, v, w, by the principles of the next chapter but one; and so in general.

Ex. 18. If u, v are binary quadratics, the combinant obtained as the discriminant of the quadratic in λ, μ which is the discriminant of $\lambda u + \mu v$ is the eliminant of u, v. (*Boole.*)

Ex. 19. The lineo-linear invariant of two binary p-ics is a combinant if p is odd, but not if p is even. (*Cayley.*)

Ex. 20. The criterion of an involution

$$\begin{vmatrix} a_1, & b_1, & c_1, \\ a_2, & b_2, & c_2, \\ a_3, & b_3, & c_3, \end{vmatrix}$$

of three binary quadratics is a combinant.

Ex. 21. A combinant of the fewer than $p+1$ p-ics

$$(a_1, b_1, c_1, \ldots)(x, y, \ldots)^p, \ (a_2, b_2, c_2, \ldots)(x, y, \ldots)^p, \ (a_3, b_3, c_3, \ldots)(x, y, \ldots)^p, \ldots$$

is a function of determinants obtained by erasing columns from

$$\left\| \begin{matrix} a_1, & b_1, & c_1, & d_1, & e_1, \ldots \\ a_2, & b_2, & c_2, & d_2, & e_2, \ldots \\ a_3, & b_3, & c_3, & d_3, & e_3, \ldots \\ . & . & . & . & . \end{matrix} \right\|$$

(*Sylvester.*)

CHAPTER XV

RESTRICTED SUBSTITUTIONS. BINARY QUANTICS IN CARTESIAN GEOMETRY.

266. BESIDES actual or full invariants and covariants, which have the invariantic or covariantic connexion with a quantic or quantics whatever be the linear substitution for the variables, there exist functions which possess the property of invariancy or covariancy for particular classes or sub-groups of substitutions.

Thus, for instance, seminvariants of binary quantics are not invariants for all linear substitutions, but are invariantic for the sub-group of substitutions $x = lX + mY$, $y = m'Y$.

A very important class of invariants and covariants for restricted substitutions is that of functions which are invariants and covariants so far as all substitutions are concerned which in Cartesian geometry express change of reference from one set of axes to another, the old and new variables being both sets of coordinates in the ordinary sense.

Confining attention to plane geometry, the most general equations of substitution, those which express change from old axes at an angle ω to new axes at an angle $\omega' = \beta - a$, through a point (h, k), and inclined at angles a, β respectively to the old axis of x, are

$$x = X\frac{\sin(\omega - a)}{\sin\omega} + Y\frac{\sin(\omega-\beta)}{\sin\omega} + [Z]h,$$

$$y = X\frac{\sin a}{\sin\omega} + Y\frac{\sin\beta}{\sin\omega} + [Z]k,$$

$$[z] = \qquad [Z] = 1.$$

Of these, whether h, k be present or absent, i.e. whether the substitution be taken as ternary or binary, the modulus is

$$\frac{\sin(\omega - a)\sin\beta - \sin(\omega-\beta)\sin a}{\sin^2\omega} = \frac{\sin\omega\sin(\beta - a)}{\sin^2\omega}$$

$$= \frac{\sin(\beta - a)}{\sin\omega} = \frac{\sin\omega'}{\sin\omega}.$$

267. **Boolian and orthogonal invariants, &c.** The study of certain invariants and covariants for Cartesian transformations preceded and led to the investigation of invariants and covariants generally. The chief early contribution to the study is in a paper by Boole (*Cambridge Math. Journal*, Vol. III), to which reference has already been made in § 18. It is proposed here to give the name *Boolian* invariants and covariants to functions which have the restricted invariantic and covariantic properties contemplated, the name being given without in the least implying that Boole confined his attention to such restricted invariants and covariants. His work not only led to the study of the more general invariant algebra, but began that study.

The original theorem was that a binary quadratic

$$ax^2 + 2bxy + cy^2$$

has the two Boolian invariants

$$ac - b^2, \quad a + c - 2b\cos\omega;$$

in fact that, if $a'X^2 + 2b'XY + c'Y^2$ is the quadratic transformed so as to be referred to new axes at an angle ω',

$$a'c' - b'^2 = \left(\frac{\sin\omega'}{\sin\omega}\right)^2 (ac - b^2),$$

$$a' + c' - 2b'\cos\omega' = \left(\frac{\sin\omega'}{\sin\omega}\right)^2 (a + c - 2b\cos\omega).$$

The first of these Boolian invariants is known to be an invariant for all linear substitutions. The second is not.

Boole's well-known method depends on the fact that, the transformation being a binary one, i.e. one with no change of origin,

$$x^2 + 2xy\cos\omega + y^2 = X^2 + 2XY\cos\omega' + Y^2.$$

He in fact determines, by his method § 18, the invariants in the ordinary sense of the system

$$ax^2 + 2bxy + cy^2,$$
$$x^2 + 2xy\cos\omega + y^2.$$

In like manner Boolian invariants and covariants of a binary quantic, among which are included the full invariants and covariants of that quantic, are obtained as the full invariants and covariants of the system consisting of that quantic and the quadratic

$$x^2 + 2xy\cos\omega + y^2.$$

If we take $\cos\omega' = \cos\omega = 0$, i.e. if we consider only transformations from one pair to another of *rectangular* axes, Boolian invariants and covariants take particular forms which may be called *orthogonal* invariants and covariants.

268. As a first instance of a Boolian covariant we may take the Jacobian of the quadratic

$$ax^2 + 2bxy + cy^2,$$

and $$x^2 + 2xy \cos \omega + y^2,$$

which proves to be

$$(a \cos \omega - b) x^2 + (a - c) xy + (b - c \cos \omega) y^2.$$

This must be a pair of lines having an invariable geometrical relation to the pair of lines denoted by the given quadratic and the pair of lines $x^2 + 2xy \cos \omega + y^2$ to the circular points at infinity.

To see what the relation is take $2xy$ for the given quadratic. The Boolian covariant is at once

$$y^2 - x^2,$$

and so represents the bisectors of the angles between the lines forming the quadratic $2xy$. These bisectors are presented as the common harmonic conjugates of the lines xy and

$$x^2 + 2xy \cos \omega + y^2.$$

Quite generally, a Boolian covariant represents a pencil of lines having an invariable geometrical relation to the pencil represented by a binary quantic and the pencil

$$x^2 + 2xy \cos \omega + y^2$$

from the vertex to the circular points at infinity, i.e. represents a pencil having an invariable relation to the pencil represented by the quantic, into the expression of which relation magnitudes of angles enter or may enter as well as descriptive and projective connexions.

The vanishing of a Boolian *invariant* expresses a geometrical relation between the lines of a pencil denoted by the binary quantic to which the invariant belongs, into the expression of which relation magnitudes of angles may enter as well as descriptive and projective connexions.

For instance, $a + c - 2b \cos \omega = 0$ expresses that a quadratic denotes lines harmonically conjugate with regard to the lines to the circular points, i.e. denotes lines at right angles.

269. The method of emanants (§§ 52, &c.) applies to Boolian invariants and covariants. It was proved that any invariant of an emanant of u is a covariant, or, in particular, invariant, of u. Now, just as this was seen, it follows also that any function which is for a sub-group of linear substitutions an invariant of the emanant is for the same sub-group a covariant, or invariant, of u. In particular, this is the case for the substitutions of Cartesian geometry.

For instance, the second emanant of u

$$x'^2 \frac{\partial^2 u}{\partial x^2} + 2x'y' \frac{\partial^2 u}{\partial x\, \partial y} + y'^2 \frac{\partial^2 u}{\partial y^2}$$

has the Boolian invariant

$$\frac{\partial^2 u}{\partial x^2} + \frac{\partial^2 u}{\partial y^2} - 2 \frac{\partial^2 u}{\partial x\, \partial y} \cos \omega.$$

This, then, is a Boolian covariant of the binary quantic u, if the order of u exceeds 2. For the order 2 of u it is the Boolian invariant used in its production.

The expression of the fact of covariancy of the function before us is

$$\frac{\partial^2 u}{\partial X^2} + \frac{\partial^2 u}{\partial Y^2} - 2 \frac{\partial^2 u}{\partial X\, \partial Y} \cos \omega'$$
$$= \left(\frac{\sin \omega'}{\sin \omega}\right)^2 \left\{\frac{\partial^2 u}{\partial x^2} + \frac{\partial^2 u}{\partial y^2} - 2 \frac{\partial^2 u}{\partial x\, \partial y} \cos \omega\right\}.$$

In particular, $\dfrac{\partial^2 u}{\partial x^2} + \dfrac{\partial^2 u}{\partial y^2}$ is an *orthogonal* covariant, i.e., since $(\sin \omega'/\sin \omega)^2 = 1$ for all orthogonal substitutions, is unaltered by any change of rectangular axes without change of origin.

270. **Cogrediency identical with contragrediency for orthogonal substitutions.** This last fact as to an orthogonal covariant is a case of an interesting theorem due to Boole.

It should be noticed that there are two discrete classes of orthogonal substitutions, which may be called *direct* and *skew* respectively. In the direct class the sense of rotation from the axis of X to that of Y is the same as that from the axis of x to that of y, while in the skew class the senses of rotation are opposite. The modulus for the direct class is $+1$, whereas that for the skew class is -1.

The formulae for orthogonal substitution are

$$x = X \cos \theta \mp Y \sin \theta,$$
$$y = X \sin \theta \pm Y \cos \theta,$$

where the upper signs refer to direct and the lower to skew substitutions. From these there follow

$$\frac{\partial}{\partial X} = \cos \theta \frac{\partial}{\partial x} + \sin \theta \frac{\partial}{\partial y},$$

$$\frac{\partial}{\partial Y} = \mp \sin \theta \frac{\partial}{\partial x} \pm \cos \theta \frac{\partial}{\partial y},$$

so that

$$\frac{\partial}{\partial x} = \cos\theta \frac{\partial}{\partial X} \mp \sin\theta \frac{\partial}{\partial Y},$$

$$\frac{\partial}{\partial y} = \sin\theta \frac{\partial}{\partial X} \pm \cos\theta \frac{\partial}{\partial Y}.$$

Thus for all orthogonal substitutions $\partial/\partial x$ and $\partial/\partial y$ are cogredient with x and y (§ 51). For orthogonal substitutions then contragrediency is identical with cogrediency (cf. §§ 46, 68). This is readily seen to be the case if we take ξ, η, any quantities or symbols contragredient with x and y, instead of $\partial/\partial x$ and $\partial/\partial y$ in particular.

The application of the cogrediency now before us is as follows. If the result of transforming a binary quantic orthogonally is

$$u \equiv (a_0, a_1, a_2, \dots a_p)(x, y)^p = (A_0, A_1, A_2, \dots A_p)(X, Y)^p, \quad \dots (1)$$

while of course $$x^2 + y^2 = X^2 + Y^2, \quad \dots (2)$$

and the modulus of the substitution is in magnitude $\cos^2\theta + \sin^2\theta$, i.e. unity, we have also

$$(a_0, a_1, a_2, \dots a_p)\left(\frac{\partial}{\partial x}, \frac{\partial}{\partial y}\right)^p$$
$$= (A_0, A_1, A_2, \dots A_p)\left(\frac{\partial}{\partial X}, \frac{\partial}{\partial Y}\right)^p \quad \dots (3)$$

and $$\left(\frac{\partial}{\partial x}\right)^2 + \left(\frac{\partial}{\partial y}\right)^2 = \left(\frac{\partial}{\partial X}\right)^2 + \left(\frac{\partial}{\partial Y}\right)^2. \quad \dots (4)$$

Moreover, if $K(a_0, a_1, a_2, \dots a_p)(x, y)^\varpi$ is any covariant or orthogonal covariant,

$$K(a_0, a_1, a_2, \dots a_p)\left(\frac{\partial}{\partial x}, \frac{\partial}{\partial y}\right)^\varpi$$
$$= \pm K(A_0, A_1, A_2, \dots A_p)\left(\frac{\partial}{\partial X}, \frac{\partial}{\partial Y}\right)^\varpi, \quad \dots (5)$$

the upper sign being correct except when both the covariant and the substitution are skew.

Thus by operation with any combination of the left-hand sides of (3) and (4), or with any covariant operator such as the left of (5), on any combination of the left-hand sides of (1) and (2), or on any covariant or orthogonal covariant, we obtain an orthogonal covariant or invariant.

Consider in particular the quadratic

$$ax^2 + 2bxy + cy^2.$$

We have by (3) on (1) an orthogonal invariant

$$a^2 + 2b^2 + c^2,$$

and by (4) on (1) another

$$a+c.$$

The known invariant $ac-b^2$ is, of course,

$$\tfrac{1}{2}\{(a+c)^2-(a^2+2b^2+c^2)\}.$$

Again, from the cubic

$$ax^3+3bx^2y+3cxy^2+dy^3$$

we have by (3) on (1) an orthogonal invariant

$$a^2+3b^2+3c^2+d^2,$$

by (4) on (1) an orthogonal covariant

$$(a+c)x+(b+d)y,$$

and again, by operating on this with $(a+c)\frac{\partial}{\partial x}+(b+d)\frac{\partial}{\partial y}$, another orthogonal invariant

$$(a+c)^2+(b+d)^2.$$

For another example take the quintic $(a, b, c, d, e, f)(x, y)^5$. We obtain at once ($\alpha$) the orthogonal invariant

$$a^2+5b^2+10c^2+10d^2+5e^2+f^2,$$

(β) a cubic orthogonal covariant which leads to the orthogonal invariant

$$(a+c)^2+3(b+d)^2+3(c+e)^2+(d+f)^2,$$

and from it again (γ) a linear orthogonal covariant and the orthogonal invariant

$$(a+2c+e)^2+(b+2d+f)^2,$$

besides two other orthogonal invariants obtained by operations with orthogonal covariants found above on others.

Observe that orthogonal invariants and covariants arising as invariants and covariants of a p-ic and x^2+y^2 are all of real form, and are all absolute for direct orthogonal transformations. For skew substitutions some have -1 and not $+1$ for factor in the expression of invariancy. We will call them all absolute, but when need for discrimination arises will characterize those that are absolute only for direct transformations as semi-skew. Later we shall encounter orthogonal invariants and covariants which are neither of real form nor absolute.

The number of independent absolute orthogonal invariants of a p-ic is p. This will be proved later.

The difficulty of discovering complete irreducible systems would have to be attacked separately in the case of every order p. After the quadratic more than p are irreducible.

Ex. 1. In orthogonal transformations in three dimensions prove that $\partial/\partial x$, $\partial/\partial y$, $\partial/\partial z$ are cogredient with x, y, z. (*Boole.*)

Ex. 2. For orthogonal transformations covariants and contravariants coincide. (*Sylvester.*)

Ex. 3. The ternary cubic

$$ax^3+by^3+cz^3+3dx^2y+3exy^2+3fx^2z+3gxz^2+3hy^2z+3iyz^2+6kxyz$$

has the orthogonal invariants

$$a^2+b^2+c^2+3(d^2+e^2+f^2+g^2+h^2+i^2)+6k^2,$$
$$(a+e+g)^2+(b+d+i)^2+(c+f+h)^2. \quad (\textit{Boole.})$$

271. **Annihilator of absolute orthogonal covariants and invariants.** Sylvester has expressed by a linear differential equation the condition that a function be an absolute orthogonal covariant or invariant of a binary quantic.

A turning of the axes through a finite angle can be effected gradually. If we express absolute invariancy for the infinitesimal transformation which means an infinitesimal turning, we express it for any amount of turning whatever, i.e. for any direct orthogonal transformation.

Now the formulae of substitution for turning through an infinitesimal angle θ are

$$x = X-\theta Y, \qquad y = \theta X+Y,$$

omitting infinitesimals of the second order. The modulus of this, to the first order of infinitesimals, is 1. Indeed 1 is its absolute value, as in all cases of direct orthogonal substitution, when infinitesimals of higher orders are expressed in the formulae of substitution. Now these are, to the same order of infinitesimals,

$$X = x+\theta y, \qquad Y = y-\theta x.$$

Thus the substitution amounts to giving x and y the increments θy and $-\theta x$.

Again, if the quantic under consideration is

$$(a_0, a_1, a_2, \ldots a_p)(x, y)^p,$$

the substitution may be effected, correctly to the first order in θ, by first writing it

$$(a_0, a_1, a_2, \ldots a_p)(X-\theta y, y)^p,$$

which makes it $\quad (a_0', a_1', a_2', \ldots a_p')(X, y)^p,$

where (§ 91)

$$a_0' = a_0,\ a_1' = a_1-a_0\theta,\ a_2' = a_2-2a_1\theta, \ldots,\ a_p' = a_p-pa_{p-1}\theta,$$

and then writing it

$$(a_0', a_1', a_2', \ldots a_p')(X, \theta X+Y)^p,$$

i.e. $$(A_0, A_1, A_2, \dots A_p)(X, Y)^p,$$
where (§ 94)

$$\begin{aligned}
A_0 &= a_0' + pa_1'\theta &&= a_0 + pa_1\theta, && \text{to the first order in } \theta,\\
A_1 &= a_1' + (p-1)a_2'\theta &&= a_1 + (p-1)a_2\theta - a_0\theta, && \quad ,, \quad ,, \quad ,\\
A_2 &= a_2' + (p-2)a_3'\theta &&= a_2 + (p-2)a_3\theta - 2a_1\theta, && \quad ,, \quad ,, \quad ,\\
&\dots\\
A_{p-1} &= a'_{p-1} + a_p'\theta &&= a_{p-1} + a_p\theta - (p-1)a_{p-2}\theta, && \quad ,, \quad ,, \quad ,\\
A_p &= a_p' &&= a_p \qquad - pa_{p-1}\theta, && \quad ,, \quad ,, \quad .
\end{aligned}$$

Thus $X, Y, A_0, A_1, A_2, \dots A_{p-1}, A_p$ differ from

$$x, y, a_0, a_1, a_2, \dots a_{p-1}, a_p$$

by the increments

$$\delta x = \theta y,\ \delta y = -\theta x,\ \delta a_0 = pa_1\theta,\ \delta a_1 = \{(p-1)a_2 - a_0\}\theta,$$
$$\delta a_2 = \{(p-2)a_3 - 2a_1\}\theta, \dots, \delta a_p = -pa_{p-1}\theta,$$

whence it follows that the increment of

$$F(x, y, a_0, a_1, a_2, \dots a_p)$$

is
$$\theta\left\{y\frac{\partial}{\partial x} - x\frac{\partial}{\partial y} + \left(pa_1\frac{\partial}{\partial a_0} + (p-1)a_2\frac{\partial}{\partial a_1} + \dots + a_p\frac{\partial}{\partial a_{p-1}}\right) - \left(a_0\frac{\partial}{\partial a_1} + 2a_1\frac{\partial}{\partial a_2} + \dots + pa_{p-1}\frac{\partial}{\partial a_p}\right)\right\}F.$$

The necessary and sufficient condition that F may be a covariant for *direct* orthogonal substitutions is, then, if as usual we adopt the notation of Chapter VI, that F have the annihilator

$$y\frac{\partial}{\partial x} - x\frac{\partial}{\partial y} + O - \Omega.$$

For it to be a covariant also for *skew* orthogonal substitutions a further condition is necessary and sufficient. It must be either unaltered or only changed in sign when y and the alternate coefficients $a_1, a_3, a_5, \dots$ have their signs altered. For the most general skew orthogonal transformation may be performed by replacing x, y by $x, -y$, i.e. reversing the direction of the axis of y, and then performing the most general direct orthogonal transformation. Should, however, a function $K_1 + K_2$, which has the above annihilator, become $K_1 - K_2$ upon making these changes of sign, it is readily seen that $K_1 - K_2$ also has the annihilator, since this annihilator is only altered in sign by the changes of sign of y and $a_1, a_3, a_5, \dots$. In this case K_1 and K_2 are orthogonal covariants for skew as well as direct substitutions, while $K_1 + K_2$ and $K_1 - K_2$ are not. K_1 and K_2 have in fact for their factors powers of the modulus ± 1 of which one is even and the other odd.

In particular, absolute orthogonal *invariants* for direct transformations are functions of the coefficients only which have the annihilator $O-\Omega$. One which is not invariant also for skew transformations is a sum of two which are—one of them being semi-skew.

272. **Annihilator of Boolian covariants and invariants.** We may also find an annihilator of any *Boolian* covariant or invariant from the consideration that any one is unchanged when the oblique axes are turned through an infinitesimal angle θ.

For such a turning the formulae are, by § 266, since $\alpha=\theta$, $\beta=\omega+\theta$,

$$x = X - X\cot\omega\,.\,\theta - Y\operatorname{cosec}\omega\,.\,\theta,$$
$$y = Y + X\operatorname{cosec}\omega\,.\,\theta + Y\cot\omega\,.\,\theta.$$

Thus x and y have the increments

$$\delta x = x\cot\omega\,.\,\theta + y\operatorname{cosec}\omega\,.\,\theta,\quad \delta y = -x\operatorname{cosec}\omega\,.\,\theta - y\cot\omega\,.\,\theta.$$

Also it is readily seen that the increments of $a_0, a_1, a_2, \dots a_p$ may be exhibited as follows:

$$\begin{array}{rllllll}
& \delta a_0, & \delta a_1, & \delta a_2, \dots, & \delta a_{p-1}, & \delta a_p & \\
=(& -pa_0, & -(p-1)a_1, & -(p-2)a_2, \dots, & -a_{p-1}, & 0 &)\cot\omega\,.\,\theta \\
+(& 0, & -a_0, & -2a_1, \dots, & -(p-1)a_{p-2}, & -pa_{p-1} &)\operatorname{cosec}\omega\,.\,\theta \\
+(& pa_1, & (p-1)a_2, & (p-2)a_3, \dots, & a_p, & 0 &)\operatorname{cosec}\omega\,.\,\theta \\
+(& 0, & a_1, & 2a_2, \dots, & (p-1)a_{p-1}, & pa_p &)\cot\omega\,.\,\theta.
\end{array}$$

Hence the expression of the fact that the increment of a Boolian covariant vanishes is that it is annihilated by

$$\cot\omega\left\{x\frac{\partial}{\partial x} - y\frac{\partial}{\partial y} - pa_0\frac{\partial}{\partial a_0} - (p-2)a_1\frac{\partial}{\partial a_1} - (p-4)a_2\frac{\partial}{\partial a_2} - \dots + (p-2)a_{p-1}\frac{\partial}{\partial a_{p-1}} + pa_p\frac{\partial}{\partial a_p}\right\}$$
$$+\operatorname{cosec}\omega\left\{y\frac{\partial}{\partial x} - x\frac{\partial}{\partial y} + O - \Omega\right\},$$

which correctly becomes the annihilator of the preceding article when $\omega=\frac{1}{2}\pi$, i.e. when the covariant is orthogonal.

In particular, Boolian *invariants* have the annihilator

$$O-\Omega-\cos\omega\left\{pa_0\frac{\partial}{\partial a_0} + (p-2)a_1\frac{\partial}{\partial a_1} + \dots - (p-2)a_{p-1}\frac{\partial}{\partial a_{p-1}} - pa_p\frac{\partial}{\partial a_p}\right\}.$$

The second part of this annihilator has the effect of multiplying every isobaric part of weight w of a Boolian invariant of degree i by $-\cos\omega$ times $ip-2w$. But this multiplier is not constant throughout, as Boolian invariants other than full invariants are not isobaric in the coefficients of the quantic to which they belong—the fact of annihilation tells us that when a Boolian invariant B is isobaric we have separately $OB=0$, $\Omega B=0$, $ip=2w$.

Boolian covariants and invariants have also to obey a further law, which is perhaps best expressed by saying that they must be unaltered or changed at most in sign when x and y, a_0 and a_p, a_1 and a_{p-1}, a_2 and a_{p-2}, &c., are interchanged. The supplementary necessity of the last article as to orthogonal covariants and invariants might have been expressed in the same way.

Ex. 4. By turning the axis of y through an angle $d\omega$, keeping that of x unchanged, prove that, μ being the index of the power to which the modulus $\sin\omega'/\sin\omega$ enters in the equality expressing that F is a Boolian covariant,

$$\mu F=\left\{\left(a_1\frac{\partial}{\partial a_1}+2a_2\frac{\partial}{\partial a_2}+\dots+pa_p\frac{\partial}{\partial a_p}-y\frac{\partial}{\partial y}\right)\right.$$
$$\left.+\sec\omega\left(y\frac{\partial}{\partial x}-\Omega\right)+\tan\omega\frac{\partial}{\partial\omega}\right\}F.$$

Ans. Express that the increment of $(\sin\omega)^{-\mu}F$ vanishes.

273. **Boolian complete systems.** In Chapter XIV there have been given systems of irreducible covariants and invariants for a linear form and a quadratic (§ 251), for two quadratics (§ 257), for a linear form and two quadratics (§ 259), and for a quadratic and cubic (§ 260). If for the quadratic, or one of the quadratics when there are two, we take $x^2+2xy\cos\omega+y^2$, i.e. if for a, b, c the coefficients in this quadratic we write 1, $\cos\omega$, 1, we deduce in the several cases systems of Boolian covariants and invariants of a linear form, a quadratic, a linear form and a quadratic, and a cubic, in terms of which all other Boolian covariants and invariants, in each case, can be rationally and integrally expressed. The student is recommended to write down these systems, and to interpret geometrically the vanishing of the various Boolian invariants, and the relationship between the pencils represented by equating to zero the Boolian covariants and the pencil or pencils represented by equating to zero the quantic or quantics of which they are Boolian covariants, remembering that rectangularity may be expected to be a feature of the relationship, since harmonic conjugates with regard to $x^2+2xy\cos\omega+y^2=0$ are at right angles. He will be aided by giving to a quadratic other than $x^2+2xy\cos\omega+y^2$ or a cubic, as the case may be, a canonical form to which

it may be reduced without loss of generality by a change of axes, e.g. the form ax^2+cy^2 or $2bxy$ for a quadratic, and $3xy(bx+cy)$ for a cubic with real factors or ax^3+dy^3 for one with two factors imaginary.

In forming other Boolian covariants and invariants as rational integral functions of those written down as above, it will be well to retain a double suffix notation, such as used in § 261, for the various members of the system used. For dimensions in 1, $\cos\omega$, 1, which have replaced the a, b, c of a quadratic, have no clear meaning in coefficients before us, and yet must not be disregarded.

273 (*bis*). If in the complete system of irreducibles for a quantic or quantics and a quadratic we take x^2+y^2 for the quadratic, instead of $x^2+2xy\cos\omega+y^2$, we obtain a system of *orthogonal* covariants and invariants of the quantic or quantics, in terms of which all others, so far as at present contemplated, can be rationally and integrally expressed. All are absolute, but some semi-skew (§ 270), as the multiplying factor in the expression of the invariancy of every one of them is 1 for direct and one of ± 1 for skew orthogonal transformations. This fact justifies much greater freedom in deriving from them other orthogonal concomitants than was admissible when we had to attend to factors which must be powers of $\sin\omega'/\sin\omega$. We may in fact compound them and x^2+y^2 rationally and integrally *in any way*, and produce other absolute covariants and invariants for all *direct* orthogonal transformations. For *skew* transformations only those compounds have the invariant property which are throughout of either even or odd dimensions in those of the ground-forms which are semi-skew. A compound in general will be a sum of two absolute orthogonal covariants or invariants, of which one is semi-skew.

Thus, much greater freedom of rational integral combination being allowed in the case of the orthogonal covariants and invariants than in the case of the full covariants and invariants from which they were derived, we have no authority for asserting that the irreducible system of full invariants and covariants of a quadratic and another form or other forms yields, upon taking x^2+y^2 for the quadratic, such a system of orthogonal invariants and covariants of the other form or forms that every member of it is irreducible quâ orthogonal concomitant. The system yielded is likely to be sufficiently, but may be excessively, numerous. A case of excess actually arises for the cubic. This has a full covariant

$$(a^2d-3abc+2b^3)x^3+\ldots$$

which is irreducible as a member of the system of covariants of the cubic and a general quadratic; but quâ orthogonal covariant of the cubic it proves to be reducible.

We shall presently (§ 278 *bis*) be in position to specify irreducible systems.

274. **Every product of coefficients leads an absolute orthogonal covariant.** In the rest of this chapter we consider *orthogonal* concomitants only.

In § 270 we have seen that for orthogonal transformations x and y are contragredient to themselves. In the conclusions of § 248 (*bis*) as to contravariants and mixed concomitants of a quantic or quantics we can then write x and y for ξ and η, and derive conclusions as to orthogonal covariants of the quantic or quantics.

Or we may proceed independently. From the equalities in § 270 it at once follows that for orthogonal transformations

$$x\frac{\partial}{\partial y} - y\frac{\partial}{\partial x} = \pm\left(X\frac{\partial}{\partial Y} - Y\frac{\partial}{\partial X}\right),$$

with upper or lower sign on the right according as the transformation is direct or skew. Thus the left-hand member is an operator deriving orthogonal covariants from others. From an absolute one it derives another which is or is not, according as the first is not or is, semi-skew.

Operate once, twice, ... p times with $x\frac{\partial}{\partial y} - y\frac{\partial}{\partial x}$ on a p-ic

$$(a_0, a_1, \ldots a_p)(x, y)^p.$$

There are thus derived from it, in succession, orthogonal covariants with

$$a_1x^p,\ a_2x^p, \ldots a_px^p$$

respectively for their terms free from y. All of them are absolute, those with odd-weighted coefficients of x^p being semi-skew.

Accordingly the product of any number i of the $p+1$ forms now before us is an absolute orthogonal invariant, semi-skew or not according as the coefficient of x^{ip} in it is of odd or even weight. This coefficient is a product, and may be any product, of i of $a_0, a_1, \ldots a_p$, repetitions allowed.

It follows that every rational integral function of degree i throughout in $a_0, a_1, \ldots a_p$—it need not be isobaric—is the coefficient of x^{ip} in an absolute orthogonal covariant for direct transformations. If it contains terms of both even and odd weights, it is the sum of two for skew transformations, the one led by the terms of odd weights being semi-skew.

It may be, and in fact is, possible so to choose rational integral functions of degree i in $a_0, a_1, \ldots a_p$ that the covariants led are divisible by x^2+y^2, by $(x^2+y^2)^2, \ldots$ or by $(x^2+y^2)^r$, where r is any number not exceeding $\frac{1}{2}ip$. On rejecting these absolute covariant factors, absolute orthogonal covariants will be obtained, with coefficients of degree i, of all those orders not exceeding ip which are even or odd according as ip is. In particular, absolute orthogonal invariants will be given in the case $r = \frac{1}{2}ip$ when ip is even.

275. **An annihilator of all rational integral functions of degree i in $a_0, a_1, \ldots a_p$.** We can obtain the condition satisfied by a rational integral function C_0 of degree i throughout in $a_0, a_1, \ldots a_p$ which leads an absolute orthogonal covariant, of order $\varpi = ip - 2r$,

$$C_0 x^{\varpi} + C_1 x^{\varpi-1} y + \ldots + C_{\varpi} y^{\varpi}.$$

By § 271 this is annihilated by

$$O - \Omega - x\frac{\partial}{\partial y} + y\frac{\partial}{\partial x}.$$

We have then the chain of equations

$$\begin{aligned}
&(O-\Omega)\,C_0 \quad - C_1 && = 0,\\
&(O-\Omega)\,C_1 \quad - 2C_2 + \varpi C_0 && = 0,\\
&(O-\Omega)\,C_2 \quad - 3C_3 + (\varpi-1)\,C_1 && = 0,\\
&\cdots\cdots\cdots\cdots\cdots\cdots\cdots\cdots\\
&(O-\Omega)\,C_{\varpi-1} - \varpi C_{\varpi} + 2C_{\varpi-2} && = 0,\\
&(O-\Omega)\,C_{\varpi} \qquad\qquad + C_{\varpi-1} && = 0.
\end{aligned}$$

The first, second, ..., last but one, of these determine $C_1, C_2, \ldots C_{\varpi}$ in succession in terms of $C_0, (O-\Omega)\,C_0, \ldots (O-\Omega)^{\varpi} C_0$; and the result of substituting for $C_{\varpi-1}, C_{\varpi}$ in the last gives a differential equation which must be satisfied by C_0. Moreover it is all that need be satisfied to make consistent values of $C_1, C_2, \ldots C_{\varpi}$ determinate from C_0. With some difficulty—see also § 278 below—the equation is found to be

$$\{(O-\Omega)^2+\varpi^2\}\,\{(O-\Omega)^2+(\varpi-2)^2\} \ldots \{(O-\Omega)^2+2^2\}\,(O-\Omega)\,C_0 = 0,$$

or

$$\{(O-\Omega)^2+\varpi^2\}\,\{(O-\Omega)^2+(\varpi-2)^2\} \ldots \{(O-\Omega)^2+1^2\}\,C_0 = 0,$$

according as ϖ is even or odd. The theorem is due to Mr. Berry.

Now we have seen that *every* rational integral function of degree i throughout in $a_0, a_1, \ldots a_p$ is the coefficient of x^{ip} in an absolute orthogonal covariant of order ip, or a sum of two such, one semi-skew. Hence, according as ip is even or odd,

$$\{(O-\Omega)^2+(ip)^2\}\{(O-\Omega)^2+(ip-2)^2\}\ldots\{(O-\Omega)^2+2^2\}(O-\Omega),$$

or $$\{(O-\Omega)^2+(ip)^2\}\{(O-\Omega)^2+(ip-2)^2\}\ldots\{(O-\Omega)^2+1^2\},$$

annihilates every rational integral homogeneous function of degree i in $a_0, a_1, \ldots a_p$.

Ex. 5. If ip is odd every rational integral function of degree i throughout in $a_0, a_1, \ldots a_p$ is the result of operating with $(O-\Omega)^2$ on some other. If ip is even this is in general not the case.

Ex. 6. A binary quantic of odd order has no absolute orthogonal invariants of odd degree.

Ans. With ip odd and $(O-\Omega)G=0$ we must have

$$\{ip(ip-2)\ldots 1\}^2 G=0,$$

i.e. $G=0$.

Ex. 7. If H is the most general rational integral function of degree i throughout in the coefficients of a p-ic, apply the method of § 128 (*bis*) to express it as a sum of rational integral solutions of the separate equations

$$\{(O-\Omega)^2+(ip)^2\}\,h=0,\ \{(O-\Omega)^2+(ip-2)^2\}\,h=0,\ldots$$
$$\{(O-\Omega)^2+m_0^{\,2}\}\,h=0,$$

where m_0 is 1 or 0 according as ip is odd or even; and in particular, when ip is even, obtain the most general absolute orthogonal invariant of degree i.

Ans.

$$\{(O-\Omega)^2+(ip)^2\}\ \{(O-\Omega)^2+(ip-2)^2\}\ \ldots\ \{(O-\Omega)^2+2^2\}\ H.$$

276. **Non-absolute orthogonal concomitants.** The orthogonal covariants and invariants so far exhibited are all absolute, for direct transformations at any rate. They are also all of real form. We now introduce others which are neither of real form nor absolute.

The facts are of striking simplicity. For direct orthogonal transformations there are two universal linear covariants $x\pm\iota y$, where ι denotes $\sqrt{-1}$, and $p+1$ independent linear invariants of the p-ic $(a_0, a_1, \ldots a_p)(x, y)^p$. In terms of these invariants and universal covariants all orthogonal invariants and covariants, including absolute ones, can be rationally and integrally expressed. Sylvester was the first to call attention to the system.

The proof in § 23, that in an expression of invariancy the factor depending on the constants of transformation must be a power of the modulus M, rested on the facts that we were considering the *general* group of linear transformations, and that the general modulus M has no factors. When we consider invariancy for a sub-group of linear transformations, the M of special form may break up into factors, so that the proof does not apply. Now for the sub-group of (direct) orthogonal transformations we have

$$M = \cos^2\theta + \sin^2\theta = (\cos\theta + \iota\sin\theta)(\cos\theta - \iota\sin\theta) = e^{\iota\theta}.e^{-\iota\theta}.$$

We must not be surprised then at discovering that there are orthogonal invariants and covariants of factors which are powers of $e^{\iota\theta}$.

Now from the formulae of transformation in § 270, taking upper signs, i.e. direct transformations, we have

$$X + \iota Y = (\cos\theta - \iota\sin\theta)(x + \iota y) = e^{-\iota\theta}(x + \iota y),$$

and $$X - \iota Y = (\cos\theta + \iota\sin\theta)(x - \iota y) = e^{\iota\theta}(x - \iota y).$$

Thus $x \pm \iota y$ are universal covariants for direct orthogonal transformations, having for factors $e^{\mp\iota\theta}$ respectively.

For skew transformations we have

$$X \pm \iota Y = e^{\pm\iota\theta}(x \mp \iota y),$$

and there is no covariancy of either of $x \pm \iota y$. These are interchanged, as well as multiplied by factors. Their product $x^2 + y^2$ is of course covariant, and absolutely, for skew as well as direct transformations.

Let us put ξ, η for $x \pm \iota y$ respectively, i.e. put

$$x = \tfrac{1}{2}(\xi + \eta), \qquad y = \frac{1}{2\iota}(\xi - \eta),$$

and express a p-ic in x, y in terms of ξ, η by these formulae, getting, say,

$$(a_0, a_1, \ldots a_p)(x, y)^p \equiv (a_0', a_1', \ldots a_p')(\xi, \eta)^p.$$

Here $a_0', a_1', \ldots a_p'$ are linearly independent linear functions of $a_0, a_1, \ldots a_p$. For, by a reversal of the transformation, the independent $a_0, a_1, \ldots a_p$ are definite linear functions of them.

Let $(A_0, A_1, \ldots A_p)(X, Y)^p$ be what the p-ic in x, y becomes after a direct orthogonal transformation, and let $A_0', A_1', \ldots A_p'$ be the same functions of $A_0, A_1, \ldots A_p$ as $a_0', a_1', \ldots a_p'$ are of $a_0, a_1, \ldots a_p$. We obtain

$$\begin{aligned}(a_0', a_1', \ldots a_p')(\xi, \eta)^p &\equiv (a_0, a_1, \ldots a_p)(x, y)^p \\ &\equiv (A_0, A_1, \ldots A_p)(X, Y)^p \\ &\equiv (A_0', A_1', \ldots A_p')(e^{-\iota\theta}\xi, e^{\iota\theta}\eta)^p.\end{aligned}$$

In this identity of quantics in ξ, η, the coefficients of the various products $\xi^r\eta^{p-r}$ on the two sides must be equal. Therefore

$$A_0' = e^{\iota p\theta}a_0', \; A_1' = e^{\iota(p-2)\theta}a_1', \; A_2' = e^{\iota(p-4)\theta}a_2',$$
$$\ldots A_{p-1}' = e^{-\iota(p-2)\theta}a_{p-1}', \; A_p' = e^{-\iota p\theta}a_p'.$$

Thus $a_0', a_1', \dots a_p'$ are $p+1$ linearly independent orthogonal invariants (for direct transformations) of factors $e^{\iota p\theta}$, $e^{\iota(p-2)\theta}$, $\dots e^{-\iota p\theta}$, respectively.

276 (*bis*). Having $p+1$ independent invariants, of factors which are all powers of $e^{\iota\theta}$, we can in many ways, by elimination of $e^{\iota\theta}$, obtain p that are absolute as well as independent. A statement in § 270 is thus justified.

Write
$$I_p, I_{p-2}, \dots I_{-p+2}, I_{-p}$$
for the invariants
$$2^p a_0', 2^p a_1', \dots 2^p a_{p-1}', 2^p a_p'$$
respectively. Every suffix of an I is here the index of the power of $e^{\iota\theta}$ which is the factor in the expression of the invariancy of that I. We have
$$(I_p, I_{p-2}, \dots I_{-p+2}, I_{-p})(\xi, \eta)^p \equiv (a_0, a_1, \dots a_p)(\xi+\eta, \iota(\eta-\xi))^p,$$
and hence readily find that

$$I_p, I_{-p} \text{ are, respectively, } a_0 \mp \iota p a_1 - \frac{p(p-1)}{1.2} a_2 \pm \dots + (\mp\iota)^p a_p,$$

$$I_{p-2}, I_{-p+2} \quad \text{,,} \quad a_0 + a_2 \mp \iota(p-2)(a_1+a_3) - \dots + (\mp\iota)^{p-2}(a_{p-2}+a_p),$$

$$I_{p-4}, I_{-p+4} \quad \text{,,} \quad a_0 + 2a_2 + a_4 \mp \iota(p-4)(a_1+2a_3+a_5) - \dots + (\mp\iota)^{p-4}(a_{p-4}+2a_{p-2}+a_p),$$

and, generally, that for every $2r$ not greater than p, I_{p-2r}, I_{-p+2r} are
$$\big((a_0, a_2, \dots a_{2r})(1, 1)^r, (a_1, a_3, \dots a_{2r+1})(1, 1)^r, \dots (a_{p-2r}, a_{p-2r+2}, \dots a_p)(1, 1)^r\big)(1, \mp\iota)^{p-2r}.$$
If p is odd they go in pairs throughout, but if p is even $(=2p')$ there is in the middle a single
$$I_0 = a_0 + p'a_2 + \frac{p'(p'-1)}{1.2} a_4 + \dots + a_{2p'}.$$
This I_0 is an invariant, and is absolute and of real form.

Any product of suffixed I's is an invariant, of factor $e^{w'\iota\theta}$, where w' is the sum of the suffixes. In particular every product with zero sum of suffixes is absolute. Thus, for instance, there are $\frac{1}{2}p$ or $\frac{1}{2}(p+1)$ absolute invariants of degree 2; namely $I_p I_{-p}, I_{p-2}I_{-p+2}, I_{p-4}I_{-p+4}, \dots$. A quartic $(a, b, c, d, e)(x, y)^4$ has then two absolute orthogonal invariants of degree 2, namely
$$I_4 I_{-4} \equiv (a-6c+e)^2 + 16(b-d)^2,$$
$$I_2 I_{-2} \equiv (a-e)^2 + 4(b+d)^2,$$
as well as a linear one $I_0 \equiv a+2c+e$.

A quintic $(a, b, c, d, e, f)(x, y)^5$ has three, namely,

$$I_5 I_{-5} \equiv (a-10c+5e)^2+(5b-10d+f)^2,$$
$$I_3 I_{-3} \equiv (a-2c-3e)^2+(3b+2d-f)^2,$$
$$I_1 I_{-1} \equiv (a+2c+e)^2+(b+2d+f)^2.$$

See that those given for the quintic in § 270 are linear functions of these.

277. We have here said nothing about skew orthogonal transformations. The absolute linear and quadratic invariants found as above are unaltered when the signs of $a_1, a_3, a_5, \ldots$ are changed; so that these at any rate are invariant for skew as well as direct substitutions.

But we have seen that $\xi \equiv x+\iota y$ and $\eta \equiv x-\iota y$ are covariants, of factors $e^{-\iota\theta}$ and $e^{\iota\theta}$ respectively, only for direct transformations. A skew transformation gives as equal to $e^{-\iota\theta}(x+\iota y)$ not $X+\iota Y$ but $X-\iota Y$, and similarly as to η. Thus a skew transformation, when applied to the p-ic in the preceding article, gives us, not that $e^{\iota m\theta} I_m$ is equal to the function I_m of the coefficients of the transformed p-ic, but that it is equal to the conjugate I_{-m} of the transformed.

Thus, while a product $I_m I_{-m}$ is, as above seen, invariant and absolute, a product such as $I_1{}^3 I_{-3}$, which is not symmetrical in positive and negative suffixes, is not invariant at all for skew transformations, even when the sum of suffixes is zero, and the factor thus made 1. It is equal, in that case, to the conjugate function, $I_{-1}{}^3 I_3$ say, of the coefficients in the transformed quantic.

However, a pair of conjugates with zero for sum of suffixes in each always produce a pair of invariants for skew as well as direct transformations. We have only to take, for instance,

$$\tfrac{1}{2}(I_1{}^3 I_{-3}+I_{-1}{}^3 I_3) \quad \text{and} \quad \frac{1}{2\iota}(I_1{}^3 I_{-3}-I_{-1}{}^3 I_3).$$

The second of such a pair of absolute orthogonal invariants is semi-skew. Notice that ι has disappeared, so that they have real form.

Similarly as to covariants. Take for instance the direct orthogonal covariant

$$I_1{}^2 I_3 (x+\iota y)^5,$$

which is absolute. For skew transformations it is not covariant at all. But it has a conjugate

$$I_{-1}{}^2 I_{-3} (x-\iota y)^5,$$

with which it is only interchanged by a skew transformation. Half the sum and $\dfrac{1}{2\iota}$ times the difference of the two are both covariant for the transformation, the former absolute for it, and the latter semi-skew. Both are in real form.

We may reason in the same way as to conjugate linear functions of products.

278. Annihilators. Separation of rational integral functions into orthogonal invariant parts. In § 271 it was proved that

$$O - \Omega + y\frac{\partial}{\partial x} - x\frac{\partial}{\partial y}$$

annihilates any absolute orthogonal covariant. Applying the same method to a non-absolute orthogonal covariant C of factor $e^{\iota m\theta}$, i.e. to one which has to be multiplied by $e^{\iota m\theta}$ to become equal to the same function of the coefficients and variables in the directly transformed quantic, and so by $1+\iota m\theta$ when the transformation is infinitesimal, we readily find that

$$\left(O - \Omega + y\frac{\partial}{\partial x} - x\frac{\partial}{\partial y}\right)C = \iota m C.$$

In particular, any invariant I of factor $e^{\iota m\theta}$ satisfies

$$(O - \Omega - \iota m)I = 0.$$

Now any quantic of order ϖ in x, y, with coefficients of degree i in the coefficients of $(a_0, a_1, \dots a_p)(x, y)^p$, can be expressed as one of order ϖ in the linearly independent functions $x \pm \iota y$ of x and y, with coefficients of degree i in the $p+1$ linearly independent functions $I_p, I_{p-2}, \dots I_{-p}$ of $a_0, a_1, \dots a_p$. In particular any orthogonal covariant can. The two linear universal covariants, and the $p+1$ linear invariants, form then the complete system of irreducible covariants and invariants for direct orthogonal transformations. Note that the p-ic itself is not one of its own irreducible system, but is reducible as $2^{-p}(I_p, I_{p-2}, \dots I_{-p})(\xi, \eta)^p$ in terms of the system. It belongs of course to its system of irreducible *absolute* orthogonal covariants and invariants, into which system at most one of the more fundamental irreducibles enters.

Now take any *absolute* orthogonal covariant of degree i and order ϖ,

$$C_0 x^{\varpi} + C_1 x^{\varpi-1}y + \dots + C_{\varpi} y^{\varpi}.$$

It can, by the above, be expressed as

$$C_0'(x+\iota y)^{\varpi} + C_1'(x+\iota y)^{\varpi-1}(x-\iota y) + \dots + C_{\varpi}'(x-\iota y)^{\varpi},$$

where $(x+\iota y)^{\varpi}$, $(x+\iota y)^{\varpi-1}(x-\iota y), \dots (x-\iota y)^{\varpi}$ are covariants of factors $e^{-\iota\varpi\theta}$, $e^{-\iota(\varpi-2)\theta}, \dots e^{\iota\varpi\theta}$, respectively. Consequently $C_0', C_1', \dots C_{\varpi}'$, which are invariants, are of factors $e^{\iota\varpi\theta}$, $e^{\iota(\varpi-2)\theta}$, $\dots e^{-\iota\varpi\theta}$, respectively. Thus

$$C_0 = C_0' + C_1' + \dots + C_{\varpi}'$$

is written as a sum of parts annihilated respectively by

$$O-\Omega-\iota\varpi,\ O-\Omega-\iota(\varpi-2),\dots O-\Omega+\iota\varpi,$$

there being (presumably) a middle part, annihilated by $O-\Omega$, if ϖ is even, but not if ϖ is odd. Every part, and therefore the whole C_0, is annihilated by the product of all these operators, i.e. by

$$\{(O-\Omega)^2+\varpi^2\}\{(O-\Omega)^2+(\varpi-2)^2\}\{(O-\Omega)^2+(\varpi-4)^2\}\dots,$$

which ends with $(O-\Omega)^2+1^2$, or with the unrepeated $O-\Omega$, according as ϖ is odd or even. This is the first theorem of § 275.

Further, let H be the most general rational integral function of degree i throughout in $a_0, a_1, \dots a_p$. It is capable of being written as the general rational integral function of degree i throughout in $I_p, I_{p-2}, \dots I_{-p}$. It is therefore a sum of numerical multiples of orthogonal invariants of factors $e^{\iota ip\theta}$, $e^{\iota(ip-2)\theta}, \dots e^{-\iota ip\theta}$. Consequently it is annihilated by a product of $ip+1$ factors as above, with ip for ϖ. This is the second theorem of § 275.

By an application of the method of § 128 (*bis*) (see Ex. 13 after that article), we can express H as a sum of $ip+1$ parts each annihilated by one operating factor $O-\Omega-\iota(ip-2r)$, $r=0, 1, 2, \dots ip$, i.e. as a sum of orthogonal invariants of the various possible factors for degree i. Each part is general of its type. The part composed of the absolute invariants of the type, when ip is even, is a numerical multiple of what is obtained in § 275, Ex. 7; and for every r the corresponding part is a numerical multiple of the result of operating on H with the product of all the operating factors except the corresponding $O-\Omega-\iota(ip-2r)$.

278 (*bis*). **Systems of irreducible absolute orthogonal concomitants.** Writing ρ for $e^{\iota\theta}$, it is clear from what has been said that the products which actually present themselves as multiplying ρ^m in the expansion of

$$\{(1-I_p\rho^p)(1-I_{p-2}\rho^{p-2})\dots(1-I_{-p}\rho^{-p})\}^{-1}$$

constitute a full linearly independent system of direct orthogonal invariants of factor ρ^m; and that the expansion of

$$\{(1-I_p\rho^p)(1-I_{p-2}\rho^{p-2})\dots(1-I_{-p}\rho^{-p})(1-\xi\rho^{-1})(1-\eta\rho)\}^{-1}$$

gives in the same way full linearly independent systems of covariants and invariants together.

If from either of these real generating functions we can extract another which provides the terms free from ρ in its expansion, we thereby obtain a generating function for a full system of linearly independent *absolute* orthogonal invariants (or covariants and invariants), and the form of the generating function will, after the manner of Chapter VIII, give us information as to the complete system of irreducible absolute orthogonal invariants (or covariants and invariants) of a p-ic.

Reference is made to Vol. XXXIII of the *Proceedings of the London Mathematical Society* for a good many such generating functions. It is there proved, for instance, that

$$\{(1-I_0)(1-I_2I_{-2})\}^{-1},$$

$$(1-I_1{}^3I_{-1}{}^3I_3I_{-3})\{(1-I_1I_{-1})(1-I_3I_{-3})(1-I_1{}^3I_{-3})(1-I_{-1}{}^3I_3)\}^{-1},$$

$$(1-I_2{}^2I_{-2}{}^2I_4I_{-4})\{(1-I_0)(1-I_2I_{-2})(1-I_4I_{-4})(1-I_2{}^2I_{-4})(1-I_{-2}{}^2I_4)\}^{-1},$$

are the generating functions for absolute orthogonal invariants of a quadratic, of a cubic, and of a quartic, respectively. It thus follows that a quadratic has two irreducible absolute orthogonal invariants, namely,

$$I_0 = a+c,$$
$$I_2I_{-2} = (a-c)^2+4b^2;$$

that a cubic has four, namely,

$$I_1I_{-1} = (a+c)^2+(b+d)^2,$$
$$I_3I_{-3} = (a-3c)^2+(3b-d)^2,$$
$$\tfrac{1}{2}\{I_1{}^3I_{-3}+I_{-1}{}^3I_3\} = (a+c)(a-3c)\{(a+c)^2-3(b+d)^2\} + (b+d)(3b-d)\{3(a+c)^2-(b+d)^2\},$$
$$\frac{1}{2\iota}\{I_1{}^3I_{-3}-I_{-1}{}^3I_3\} = (a+c)(3b-d)\{(a+c)^2-3(b+d)^2\} -(a-3c)(b+d)\{3(a+c)^2-(b+d)^2\},$$

the last being semi-skew, which are connected by one syzygy expressing the product of the second and the cube of the first in terms of the others; and that a quartic has five, namely,

$$I_0 = a+2c+e,$$
$$I_2I_{-2} = (a-e)^2+4(b+d)^2,$$
$$I_4I_{-4} = (a-6c+e)^2+16(b-d)^2,$$
$$\tfrac{1}{2}\{I_2{}^2I_{-4}+I_{-2}{}^2I_4\} = (a-6c+e)\{(a-e)^2-4(b+d)^2\} + 16(a-e)(b^2-d^2),$$
$$\frac{1}{8\iota}\{I_2{}^2I_{-4}-I_{-2}{}^2I_4\} = (b-d)\{(a-e)^2-4(b+d)^2\} -(a-6c+e)(a-e)(b+d),$$

the last semi-skew, with one syzygy of degree 6 containing a term $(I_4I_{-4})(I_2I_{-2})^2$.

A quintic has 15, and a sextic 14, irreducible absolute orthogonal invariants, connected by many syzygies.

Besides the universal x^2+y^2 and the four invariants, a cubic has in its complete system of irreducibles eight absolute orthogonal covariants, namely,

$$I_1\xi \pm I_{-1}\eta,\ I_3\xi^3 \pm I_{-3}\eta^3,\ I_3 I_{-1}\xi^2 \pm I_{-3} I_1 \eta^2,\ I_3 I_{-1}{}^2\xi \pm I_{-3} I_1{}^2\eta.$$

A quartic has, besides x^2+y^2 and its five invariants, six covariants. These are

$$(a-e)(x^2-y^2)+4(b+d)xy,$$
$$(b+d)(x^2-y^2)-(a-e)xy,$$
$$\{(a-6c+e)(a-e)+8(b^2-d^2)\}(x^2-y^2)$$
$$-4\{(a-6c+e)(b+d)-2(a-e)(b-d)\}xy,$$
$$\{(a-6c+e)(b+d)-2(a-e)(b-d)\}(x^2-y^2)$$
$$+\{(a-6c+e)(a-e)+8(b^2-d^2)\}xy,$$
$$(a-6c+e)(x^4-6x^2y^2+y^4)+16(b-d)xy(x^2-y^2),$$
$$(b-d)(x^4-6x^2y^2+y^4)-(a-6c+e)xy(x^2-y^2).$$

The last but one here may be replaced by the quartic itself, being a linear function of the quartic, the first multiplied by x^2+y^2, and $I_4(x^2+y^2)^2$. The second, fourth, and sixth, given as $\frac{1}{2\iota}$ times differences between conjugate products, are semi-skew, like all covariants and invariants so given.

Ex. 8. Taking $I_2\rho^2$, $I_{-2}\rho^{-2}$ for a, a', use the fact that

$$\frac{1}{(1-a)(1-a')}=\frac{1}{1-aa'}\left\{\frac{1}{1-a}+\frac{1}{1-a'}-1\right\}$$

to obtain the real generating function for absolute orthogonal invariants of a quadratic.

Ex. 9. If $m, n, \ldots$ are positive numbers, prove that the part free from ρ in the expansion of $\{(1-a\rho^{-1})(1-b\rho^m)(1-c\rho^n)\ldots\}^{-1}$ is the expansion of $\{(1-ba^m)(1-ca^n)\ldots\}^{-1}$; and, using this and the formula of Ex. 8, find the real generating functions

(1) for absolute orthogonal covariants of a quadratic,
(2) for absolute orthogonal invariants of a cubic,
(3) for absolute orthogonal invariants of a quartic.

Ex. 10. Prove that two linear forms have four irreducible absolute invariants connected by one syzygy.

Ex. 11. Prove that a linear form and a quadratic have five, connected by one syzygy.

Ex. 12. Two quadratics have six, connected by one syzygy.

CHAPTER XVI

TERNARY QUANTICS. THE QUADRATIC AND CUBIC.

279. A single chapter will be added to what has been said in Chapters I to IV on the concomitants (invariants, covariants, contravariants, and mixed concomitants) of quantics in more variables than two. The importance of ternary and quaternary quantics belongs to geometry of two and three dimensions, and the study of them should be pursued with the aid of Salmon's *Higher Plane Curves*, and *Geometry of Three Dimensions*.

We remember from Chapter IV that, while in the case of binary quantics contravariants are not essentially distinct from covariants, they are essentially distinct in the case of ternary, &c., quantics.

The principles will be briefly exhibited here, by means of which, from invariants and covariants of systems of binary quantics, we may pass on to invariants, covariants, and contravariants of ternary quantics.

280. Let us consider the ternary p-ic in the form

$$\begin{aligned}
&a_p z^p \\
&+ p\,(a_{p-1}x + b_{p-1}y)\,z^{p-1} \\
&+ \frac{p\,(p-1)}{1\,.\,2}\,(a_{p-2}x^2 + 2b_{p-2}xy + c_{p-2}y^2)\,z^{p-2} \\
&+ \quad . \quad . \quad . \quad . \quad . \quad . \quad . \quad . \quad . \quad . \quad . \quad . \\
&+ \left(a_0x^p + pb_0x^{p-1}y + \frac{p\,(p-1)}{1\,.\,2}\,c_0x^{p-2}y^2 + \ldots\right),
\end{aligned}$$

in which the suffixes (weights) of the various coefficients are chosen as in § 27, where we supposed x/z, y/z to be each of unit weight. We might equally have adopted suffix notations appropriate to cases when y/x, z/x in the one case, and z/y, x/y in the other, are of unit weight. Any fact as to weight of concomitants which may be adduced will have two companion facts, arising from it by changes corresponding to cyclical interchange of x, y, z. In one sense, indeed, companion facts are sixfold, one corresponding to every permutation of x, y, z.

In much that follows the notation of the cubic will for simplicity of writing be adopted in our work, and the conclusions only indicated in the notation of the general p-ic. It is important to have before us three ways in which the same cubic may be arranged, namely,

$$\begin{aligned} &a_3 z^3 \\ &+3(a_2 x + b_2 y) z^2 \\ &+3(a_1 x^2 + 2 b_1 xy + c_1 y^2) z \\ &+a_0 x^3 + 3 b_0 x^2 y + 3 c_0 xy^2 + d_0 y^3, \end{aligned} \qquad \ldots \text{(i)}$$

$$\begin{aligned} &a_0 x^3 \\ &+3(b_0 y + a_1 z) x^2 \\ &+3(c_0 y^2 + 2 b_1 yz + a_2 z^2) x \\ &+d_0 y^3 + 3 c_1 y^2 z + 3 b_2 yz^2 + a_3 z^3, \end{aligned} \qquad \ldots \text{(ii)}$$

$$\begin{aligned} &d_0 y^3 \\ &+3(c_1 z + c_0 x) y^2 \\ &+3(b_2 z^2 + 2 b_1 zx + b_0 x^2) y \\ &+a_3 z^3 + 3 a_2 z^2 x + 3 a_1 zx^2 + a_0 x^3. \end{aligned} \qquad \ldots \text{(iii)}$$

The corresponding triple arrangement is general for the ternary p-ic.

281. We first notice that, an invariant or covariant being unaltered, except for a power of the modulus as factor, when we substitute for the coefficients and variables x, y, z the new coefficients and variables given by any linear transformation of x, y, z whatever, the same is true in particular when the linear transformation is one affecting x and y only, leaving z unaltered.

Consider, to begin with, invariants only. We are thus told, using the notation of the cubic, that an invariant is a function of

$$a_3 \qquad \ldots (1)$$

and the coefficients in the quantics

$$a_2 x + b_2 y, \qquad \ldots (2)$$

$$a_1 x^2 + 2 b_1 xy + c_1 y^2, \qquad \ldots (3)$$

$$a_0 x^3 + 3 b_0 x^2 y + 3 c_0 xy^2 + d_0 y^3, \qquad \ldots (4)$$

which is unaffected, except by a power of the modulus as factor, when these quantics are simultaneously linearly transformed. From this we gather that it is a rational integral function of a_3 and invariants of the system (2), (3), (4). Or, regarding a_3 as itself a quantic of zero order, which has itself for its one invariant, we may say that an invariant of the ternary cubic is a rational integral function of invariants of the system (1), (2), (3), (4). It is isobaric on the whole (§ 28), and of course homogeneous on the whole (§ 22), but is not to be expected to be homogeneous in a_3 and the coefficients of (2), (3), (4) separately. It is, in fact, a linear function of invariants of (1), (2), (3), (4) of one whole weight and one whole degree, but different partial weights and degrees.

The invariant has then (§ 247) two annihilators which have been hitherto called $\Sigma\Omega$, ΣO, but will for our present purpose be designated differently, viz.

$$\Omega_{yx} \equiv \left(a_0 \frac{\partial}{\partial b_0} + 2b_0 \frac{\partial}{\partial c_0} + 3c_0 \frac{\partial}{\partial d_0}\right) + \left(a_1 \frac{\partial}{\partial b_1} + 2b_1 \frac{\partial}{\partial c_1}\right) + a_2 \frac{\partial}{\partial b_2},$$

$$\Omega_{xy} \equiv \left(3b_0 \frac{\partial}{\partial a_0} + 2c_0 \frac{\partial}{\partial b_0} + d_0 \frac{\partial}{\partial c_0}\right) + \left(2b_1 \frac{\partial}{\partial a_1} + c_1 \frac{\partial}{\partial b_1}\right) + b_2 \frac{\partial}{\partial a_2}.$$

In the general notation of the p-ic we should have

$$\Omega_{yx} \equiv \sum_{r=0}^{r=p-1} \left\{a_r \frac{\partial}{\partial b_r} + 2b_r \frac{\partial}{\partial c_r} + 3c_r \frac{\partial}{\partial d_r} + \dots\right\},$$

$$\Omega_{xy} \equiv \sum_{r=0}^{r=p-1}$$

$$\left\{(p-r)b_r \frac{\partial}{\partial a_r} + (p-r-1)c_r \frac{\partial}{\partial b_r} + (p-r-2)d_r \frac{\partial}{\partial c_r} + \dots\right\},$$

where only coefficients which actually occur in the p-ic are present.

282. In like manner a covariant of the ternary cubic is a rational integral function, of constant whole order degree and weight throughout, of covariants and invariants of the system (1), (2), (3), (4) of § 281. And analogously for the ternary p-ic. A covariant has then (§ 247) the two annihilators

$$\Omega_{yx} - y\frac{\partial}{\partial x}, \qquad \Omega_{xy} - x\frac{\partial}{\partial y},$$

and these, it is to be noticed, annihilate the ternary p-ic itself, which is of course to be regarded as one of its own covariants.

This fact has led to the frequent use for the operators Ω_{yx}, Ω_{xy} of the symbolical notation $\left[y\frac{\partial}{\partial x}\right]$, $\left[x\frac{\partial}{\partial y}\right]$.

283. Let us now pay attention to the second and third forms (§ 280) in which the cubic or p-ic may be arranged. Attending to the second form we see, just as in §§ 281, 282, that an invariant, or covariant, is a rational integral function of invariants, or of covariants and invariants, of the system of $p+1$ binary quantics which for the case of the cubic are

$$\begin{aligned}&a_0,\\ &b_0 y + a_1 z,\\ &c_0 y^2 + 2b_1 yz + a_2 z^2,\\ &d_0 y^3 + 3c_1 y^2 z + 3b_2 yz^2 + a_3 z^3;\end{aligned}$$

that an invariant has two annihilators, which for the case of the cubic are

$$\Omega_{zy} \equiv \left(d_0 \frac{\partial}{\partial c_1} + 2c_1 \frac{\partial}{\partial b_2} + 3b_2 \frac{\partial}{\partial a_3}\right) + \left(c_0 \frac{\partial}{\partial b_1} + 2b_1 \frac{\partial}{\partial a_2}\right) + b_0 \frac{\partial}{\partial a_1},$$

$$\Omega_{yz} \equiv \left(3c_1 \frac{\partial}{\partial d_0} + 2b_2 \frac{\partial}{\partial c_1} + a_3 \frac{\partial}{\partial b_2}\right) + \left(2b_1 \frac{\partial}{\partial c_0} + a_2 \frac{\partial}{\partial b_1}\right) + a_1 \frac{\partial}{\partial b_0};$$

and that a covariant has the annihilators

$$\Omega_{zy} - z\frac{\partial}{\partial y}, \qquad \Omega_{yz} - y\frac{\partial}{\partial z},$$

which in particular annihilate the cubic itself.

For the p-ic Ω_{zy} and Ω_{yz} are

$$\begin{aligned}\Omega_{zy} \equiv &\left\{\ldots + (p-1)c_{p-2}\frac{\partial}{\partial b_{p-1}} + pb_{p-1}\frac{\partial}{\partial a_p}\right\}\\ &+ \left\{\ldots + (p-2)c_{p-3}\frac{\partial}{\partial b_{p-2}} + (p-1)b_{p-2}\frac{\partial}{\partial a_{p-1}}\right\}\\ &+ \ldots + b_0\frac{\partial}{\partial a_1},\end{aligned}$$

$$\begin{aligned}\Omega_{yz} \equiv &\left\{\ldots + 2b_{p-1}\frac{\partial}{\partial c_{p-2}} + a_p\frac{\partial}{\partial b_{p-1}}\right\}\\ &+ \left\{\ldots + 2b_{p-2}\frac{\partial}{\partial c_{p-3}} + a_{p-1}\frac{\partial}{\partial b_{p-2}}\right\} + \ldots + a_1\frac{\partial}{\partial b_0}.\end{aligned}$$

In like manner, regarding the third form in § 280, we see that an invariant has two additional annihilators Ω_{xz}, Ω_{zx}, and a covariant the two additional annihilators

$$\Omega_{xz} - x\frac{\partial}{\partial z}, \qquad \Omega_{zx} - z\frac{\partial}{\partial x},$$

where, in the case of the cubic,

$$\Omega_{xz} \equiv \left(a_3 \frac{\partial}{\partial a_2} + 2a_2 \frac{\partial}{\partial a_1} + 3a_1 \frac{\partial}{\partial a_0}\right) + \left(b_2 \frac{\partial}{\partial b_1} + 2b_1 \frac{\partial}{\partial b_0}\right) + c_1 \frac{\partial}{\partial c_0},$$

$$\Omega_{zx} \equiv \left(3a_2 \frac{\partial}{\partial a_3} + 2a_1 \frac{\partial}{\partial a_2} + a_0 \frac{\partial}{\partial a_1}\right) + \left(2b_1 \frac{\partial}{\partial b_2} + b_0 \frac{\partial}{\partial b_1}\right) + c_0 \frac{\partial}{\partial c_1},$$

and, in the general case of the p-ic,

$$\Omega_{xz} \equiv \left\{a_p \frac{\partial}{\partial a_{p-1}} + \ldots + (p-1)a_2 \frac{\partial}{\partial a_1} + pa_1 \frac{\partial}{\partial a_0}\right\}$$
$$+ \left\{b_{p-1} \frac{\partial}{\partial b_{p-2}} + \ldots + (p-2)b_2 \frac{\partial}{\partial b_1} + (p-1)b_1 \frac{\partial}{\partial b_0}\right\} + \ldots,$$

$$\Omega_{zx} \equiv \left\{pa_{p-1} \frac{\partial}{\partial a_p} + \ldots + 2a_1 \frac{\partial}{\partial a_2} + a_0 \frac{\partial}{\partial a_1}\right\}$$
$$+ \left\{(p-1)b_{p-2} \frac{\partial}{\partial b_{p-1}} + \ldots + 2b_1 \frac{\partial}{\partial b_2} + b_0 \frac{\partial}{\partial b_1}\right\} + \ldots.$$

284. The facts as to invariants and covariants expressed by the existence of their six annihilators thus found are not all independent. Information as to the nature of their interdependence can be obtained by forming the fifteen alternants of Ω_{yx}, Ω_{xy}, Ω_{zy}, Ω_{yz}, Ω_{xz}, Ω_{zx} in pairs. Taking the forms appropriate to the cubic, we readily obtain first the following triad of alternants:

$$H_3 \equiv \Omega_{yx}\Omega_{xy} - \Omega_{xy}\Omega_{yx} \equiv \left(3a_0 \frac{\partial}{\partial a_0} + b_0 \frac{\partial}{\partial b_0} - c_0 \frac{\partial}{\partial c_0} - 3d_0 \frac{\partial}{\partial d_0}\right)$$
$$+ \left(2a_1 \frac{\partial}{\partial a_1} - 2c_1 \frac{\partial}{\partial c_1}\right) + \left(a_2 \frac{\partial}{\partial a_2} - b_2 \frac{\partial}{\partial b_2}\right), \quad \ldots(3)$$

$$H_1 \equiv \Omega_{zy}\Omega_{yz} - \Omega_{yz}\Omega_{zy} \equiv \left(3d_0 \frac{\partial}{\partial d_0} + c_1 \frac{\partial}{\partial c_1} - b_2 \frac{\partial}{\partial b_2} - 3a_3 \frac{\partial}{\partial a_3}\right)$$
$$+ \left(2c_0 \frac{\partial}{\partial c_0} - 2a_2 \frac{\partial}{\partial a_2}\right) + \left(b_0 \frac{\partial}{\partial b_0} - a_1 \frac{\partial}{\partial a_1}\right), \quad \ldots(1)$$

$$H_2 \equiv \Omega_{xz}\Omega_{zx} - \Omega_{zx}\Omega_{xz} \equiv \left(3a_3 \frac{\partial}{\partial a_3} + a_2 \frac{\partial}{\partial a_2} - a_1 \frac{\partial}{\partial a_1} - 3a_0 \frac{\partial}{\partial a_0}\right)$$
$$+ \left(2b_2 \frac{\partial}{\partial b_2} - 2b_0 \frac{\partial}{\partial b_0}\right) + \left(c_1 \frac{\partial}{\partial c_1} - c_0 \frac{\partial}{\partial c_0}\right). \quad \ldots(2)$$

We here see first that the sum $H_1 + H_2 + H_3$ vanishes identically, whatever be the function operated upon. Thus any function which is annihilated by two of H_1, H_2, H_3, or by two independent sums of multiples of them, is also annihilated by the third, and by any sum of multiples of them.

Before forming the other alternants we proceed to exhibit the information as to invariants of the cubic given by these.

285. Any invariant of the cubic is annihilated by H_1, H_2 and H_3. For every one of these is a difference of two parts each of which annihilates it, since it has the six annihilators Ω. Let us consider the fact that $H_1 - H_2$, the difference of the operators written second and third above, annihilates it. We readily see that

$$H_1 - H_2 \equiv 3\left(a_0\frac{\partial}{\partial a_0} + b_0\frac{\partial}{\partial b_0} + c_0\frac{\partial}{\partial c_0} + d_0\frac{\partial}{\partial d_0}\right.$$
$$\left. + a_1\frac{\partial}{\partial a_1} + b_1\frac{\partial}{\partial b_1} + c_1\frac{\partial}{\partial c_1} + a_2\frac{\partial}{\partial a_2} + b_2\frac{\partial}{\partial b_2} + a_3\frac{\partial}{\partial a_3}\right)$$
$$-3\left(a_1\frac{\partial}{\partial a_1} + b_1\frac{\partial}{\partial b_1} + c_1\frac{\partial}{\partial c_1}\right) - 6\left(a_2\frac{\partial}{\partial a_2} + b_2\frac{\partial}{\partial b_2}\right) - 9a_3\frac{\partial}{\partial a_3}.$$

Hence it follows, by Euler's theorem as to homogeneous functions, and the consequent theorem (§ 117) as to isobaric functions, that $H_1 - H_2$ operating on a function of degree i and weight (sum of suffixes) w has the effect of multiplying it by

$$3i - 3w.$$

Thus since the invariant, which is homogeneous (§ 22), is annihilated by $H_1 - H_2$, it must have a constant weight w throughout given by

$$3i - 3w = 0.$$

If we had taken the forms of H_1, H_2 for the p-ic instead of the cubic, we should have had in like manner

$$pi - 3w = 0.$$

The information given by $H_1 - H_2$ is then that of § 28.

In like manner we have, for the cubic,

$$H_2 - H_3 \equiv 3\left(a_0\frac{\partial}{\partial a_0} + b_0\frac{\partial}{\partial b_0} + c_0\frac{\partial}{\partial c_0} + d_0\frac{\partial}{\partial d_0}\right.$$
$$\left. + a_1\frac{\partial}{\partial a_1} + b_1\frac{\partial}{\partial b_1} + c_1\frac{\partial}{\partial c_1} + a_2\frac{\partial}{\partial a_2} + b_2\frac{\partial}{\partial b_2} + a_3\frac{\partial}{\partial a_3}\right)$$
$$-3\left(c_0\frac{\partial}{\partial c_0} + b_1\frac{\partial}{\partial b_1} + a_2\frac{\partial}{\partial a_2}\right) - 6\left(b_0\frac{\partial}{\partial b_0} + a_1\frac{\partial}{\partial a_1}\right) - 9a_0\frac{\partial}{\partial a_0},$$

the annihilation of the invariant by which tells us, upon observation of the form (ii) of the cubic in § 280, that

$$3i - 3w' = 0,$$

where w' is the weight of the invariant when we consider y/x and z/x as of weight unity. Thus

$$w' = w,$$

which would also follow from the fact that the particular substitution which replaces x, y, z by y, z, x, whose modulus is unity, does not alter the value of the invariant while it replaces c_0, b_1, a_2, b_0, a_1, a_0 by a_1, b_1, c_1, a_2, b_2, a_3.

For the general case of the p-ic we should have had

$$pi - 3w' = 0.$$

In exactly the same way

$$H_3 - H_1 \equiv 3\left(a_0\frac{\partial}{\partial a_0} + b_0\frac{\partial}{\partial b_0} + c_0\frac{\partial}{\partial c_0} + d_0\frac{\partial}{\partial d_0} + a_1\frac{\partial}{\partial a_1} + b_1\frac{\partial}{\partial b_1} + c_1\frac{\partial}{\partial c_1} + a_2\frac{\partial}{\partial a_2} + b_2\frac{\partial}{\partial b_2} + a_3\frac{\partial}{\partial a_3}\right) - 3\left(b_2\frac{\partial}{\partial b_2} + b_1\frac{\partial}{\partial b_1} + b_0\frac{\partial}{\partial b_0}\right) - 6\left(c_1\frac{\partial}{\partial c_1} + c_0\frac{\partial}{\partial c_0}\right) - 9d_0\frac{\partial}{\partial d_0},$$

the annihilation by which requires that an invariant of the cubic have the property

$$3i - 3w'' = 0,$$

where w'' is the weight when each a is of weight 0, each b of weight 1, each c of weight 2, and d_0 of weight 3, i.e. when z/y and x/y are regarded as of unit weight. Thus

$$w'' = w' = w.$$

For the p-ic we should have in like manner

$$pi - 3w'' = 0.$$

Since the sum of $H_2 - H_3$, $H_3 - H_1$ and $H_1 - H_2$ vanishes, any function, not necessarily an invariant, which possesses two of these properties must also possess the third.

Ex. 1. From the fact of annihilation by H_3, which may be written

$$3\left(a_0\frac{\partial}{\partial a_0} + b_0\frac{\partial}{\partial b_0} + c_0\frac{\partial}{\partial c_0} + d_0\frac{\partial}{\partial d_0}\right) + 2\left(a_1\frac{\partial}{\partial a_1} + b_1\frac{\partial}{\partial b_1} + c_1\frac{\partial}{\partial c_1}\right) + \left(a_2\frac{\partial}{\partial a_2} + b_2\frac{\partial}{\partial b_2}\right) - 2\left\{\left(b_0\frac{\partial}{\partial b_0} + 2c_0\frac{\partial}{\partial c_0} + 3d_0\frac{\partial}{\partial d_0}\right) + \left(b_1\frac{\partial}{\partial b_1} + 2c_1\frac{\partial}{\partial c_1}\right) + b_2\frac{\partial}{\partial b_2}\right\},$$

show that if any invariant of a cubic is written as a sum of parts, each separately homogeneous in the sets

$$\begin{array}{l} a_0,\ b_0,\ c_0,\ d_0, \\ a_1,\ b_1,\ c_1, \\ a_2,\ b_2, \\ a_3, \end{array}$$

and if i_3, i_2, i_1 are the degrees of any such part in the first, second, and third of these sets, then throughout the invariant

$$3i_3 + 2i_2 + i_1 = 2w.$$

For an invariant of the p-ic the corresponding fact is

$$pi_p+(p-1)i_{p-1}+\ldots+2i_2+i_1=2w.$$

See §§ 123, 132.

Ex. 2. From the fact of annihilation by H_1 show that throughout an invariant of the cubic

$$3i_3'+2i_2'+i_1'=2w,$$

where i_3', i_2', i_1' are the partial degrees of any term in the sets

$$\begin{array}{l} d_0,\ c_1,\ b_2,\ a_3, \\ c_0,\ b_1,\ a_2, \\ b_0,\ a_1; \end{array}$$

and state the corresponding fact for the p-ic.

Ex. 3. From the fact of annihilation by H_2 show that throughout an invariant of the cubic

$$3i_3''+2i_2''+i_1''=2w,$$

where i_3'', i_2'', i_1'' are the partial degrees of any term in

$$\begin{array}{l} a_3,\ a_2,\ a_1,\ a_0, \\ b_2,\ b_1,\ b_0, \\ c_1,\ c_0; \end{array}$$

and state the corresponding fact for the p-ic.

286. We now form the other alternants of the six Ω's. They occur in cyclical sets of three. Taking the case of the cubic, and referring to §§ 281, 283 for the notation, we find

$$\begin{aligned}\Omega_{yx}\Omega_{zx}-\Omega_{zx}\Omega_{yx} \equiv a_0\frac{\partial}{\partial b_1}+2b_0\frac{\partial}{\partial c_1}+2a_1\frac{\partial}{\partial b_2} \\ -2a_1\frac{\partial}{\partial b_2}-a_0\frac{\partial}{\partial b_1}-2b_0\frac{\partial}{\partial c_1}\end{aligned}$$

$$=0, \qquad \ldots(4)$$

$$\Omega_{zy}\Omega_{xy}-\Omega_{xy}\Omega_{zy}=0, \qquad \ldots(5)$$

$$\Omega_{xz}\Omega_{yz}-\Omega_{yz}\Omega_{xz}=0. \qquad \ldots(6)$$

The same relations hold in the general notation of the p-ic.

In like manner we have another triad

$$\Omega_{xy}\Omega_{xz}-\Omega_{xz}\Omega_{xy}=0, \qquad \ldots(7)$$

$$\Omega_{yz}\Omega_{yx}-\Omega_{yx}\Omega_{yz}=0, \qquad \ldots(8)$$

$$\Omega_{zx}\Omega_{zy}-\Omega_{zy}\Omega_{zx}=0. \qquad \ldots(9)$$

Next we have, for the cubic,

$$\Omega_{xy}\Omega_{zx}-\Omega_{zx}\Omega_{xy} \equiv 3b_0\frac{\partial}{\partial a_1}+2c_0\frac{\partial}{\partial b_1}+d_0\frac{\partial}{\partial c_1}+4b_1\frac{\partial}{\partial a_2}+2c_1\frac{\partial}{\partial b_2}$$

$$+3b_2\frac{\partial}{\partial a_3}-2b_1\frac{\partial}{\partial a_2}-2b_0\frac{\partial}{\partial a_1}-c_0\frac{\partial}{\partial b_1}$$

$$\equiv d_0\frac{\partial}{\partial c_1}+2c_1\frac{\partial}{\partial b_2}+3b_2\frac{\partial}{\partial a_3}$$

$$+c_0\frac{\partial}{\partial b_1}+2b_1\frac{\partial}{\partial a_2}+b_0\frac{\partial}{\partial a_1}$$

$$\equiv \Omega_{zy}, \qquad \ldots (10)$$

and similarly

$$\Omega_{yz}\Omega_{xy}-\Omega_{xy}\Omega_{yz} \equiv \Omega_{xz}, \qquad \ldots (11)$$

$$\Omega_{zx}\Omega_{yz}-\Omega_{yz}\Omega_{zx} \equiv \Omega_{yx}. \qquad \ldots (12)$$

Lastly we have in like manner

$$\Omega_{yx}\Omega_{xz}-\Omega_{xz}\Omega_{yx} \equiv -\Omega_{yz}, \qquad \ldots (13)$$

$$\Omega_{zy}\Omega_{yx}-\Omega_{yx}\Omega_{zy} \equiv -\Omega_{zx}, \qquad \ldots (14)$$

$$\Omega_{xz}\Omega_{zy}-\Omega_{zy}\Omega_{xz} \equiv -\Omega_{xy}. \qquad \ldots (15)$$

All these apply to the general notation of the p-ic, as well as to that of the cubic.

287. The fifteen alternants of pairs of Ω's introduce then no new operators except the H_1, H_2, H_3 of § 284. We complete the theory of the annihilators by forming the alternants of these three with one another and the Ω's. It is quite easy to see that

$$H_2H_3-H_3H_2=0,$$

$$H_3H_1-H_1H_3=0,$$

$$H_1H_2-H_2H_1=0;$$

and that

$$H_3\Omega_{yx}-\Omega_{yx}H_3 \equiv 2\Omega_{yx},$$

$$H_3\Omega_{xy}-\Omega_{xy}H_3 \equiv -2\Omega_{xy},$$

$$H_3\Omega_{zy}-\Omega_{zy}H_3 \equiv -\Omega_{zy},$$

$$H_3\Omega_{yz}-\Omega_{yz}H_3 \equiv \Omega_{yz},$$

$$H_3\Omega_{xz}-\Omega_{xz}H_3 \equiv -\Omega_{xz},$$

$$H_3\Omega_{zx}-\Omega_{zx}H_3 \equiv \Omega_{zx},$$

together with two other sets of six, in the first set of which H_1 occurs and the suffixes x, y, z are interchanged once cyclically, and in the other set H_2 occurs and a second cyclical interchange is made in the suffixes.

Accordingly the nine operators Ω_{yx}, Ω_{zy}, Ω_{xz}, Ω_{xy}, Ω_{yz}, Ω_{zx}, H_1, H_2, H_3 form a group such that, when we form the alternant of any pair of them, some member of the group with a simple numerical multiplier, or else a zero, is produced.

288. **Three cyclical annihilators suffice to define invariants.** We can now see that, if a function of the coefficients is such as to have a cyclical set of three annihilators, such as Ω_{yz}, Ω_{zx}, Ω_{xy} or Ω_{zy}, Ω_{xz}, Ω_{yx}, it has also the other three, and is accordingly, if homogeneous, an invariant.

Suppose, for instance, that Ω_{yz}, Ω_{zx}, Ω_{xy} annihilate a function. By § 286 (10), since Ω_{zx} and Ω_{xy} annihilate it, so does Ω_{zy}. By (11), since Ω_{xy} and Ω_{yz} annihilate it, so does Ω_{xz}. And by (12), since Ω_{yz} and Ω_{zx} annihilate it, so does Ω_{yx}.

And again, to repeat from § 285, since Ω_{yz} and Ω_{zy} annihilate it, so does H_1; and in like manner so do H_2 and H_3. Thus the function has necessarily the degree and weight properties expressed in § 285 and the examples which follow that article.

The property of annihilation by Ω_{yz}, Ω_{zx} and Ω_{xy} includes then all the facts with regard to invariants of ternary quantics except that of homogeneity, just as that of annihilation by Ω and O, i.e. by Ω_{yx} and Ω_{xy}, does with regard to invariants of binary quantics.

We shall see later by another method, which might have been here applied, that the property of having q cyclical annihilators of the Ω form includes all the facts but that of homogeneity as to invariants of q-ary quantics.

289. The six annihilators, as well as going in two triads, go in three pairs Ω_{yx}, Ω_{xy}; Ω_{zy}, Ω_{yz}; Ω_{xz}, Ω_{zx}. It is sometimes most convenient to use the fact that if two pairs of these annihilate a function its annihilation by the third pair is necessitated. For instance, if the first four annihilate it, it follows from § 286 (14) that Ω_{zx} annihilates it, and from (11) that Ω_{xz} does, so that it is an invariant.

The possession of *three* annihilators *not* forming a cyclical set does not suffice.

290. **Invariant of the ternary quadratic.** Let us exemplify some of the above principles by deciding what invariants the ternary quadratic

$$a_2z^2 + 2(a_1x + b_1y)z + a_0x^2 + 2b_0xy + c_0y^2$$

can possess.

Since Ω_{yx} and Ω_{xy} annihilate it, an invariant of the quadratic is an invariant of the system

$$a_2, \quad a_1x + b_1y, \quad a_0x^2 + 2b_0xy + c_0y^2,$$

and so (§ 251) is a rational integral function of

$$a_2,\quad a_0c_0-b_0^2,\quad a_0b_1^2-2b_0a_1b_1+c_0a_1^2. \qquad \ldots(1)$$

Again, since Ω_{zx} and Ω_{xz} annihilate it, it is an invariant of the system

$$c_0,\quad b_1z+b_0x,\quad a_2z^2+2a_1zx+a_0x^2,$$

and so is a rational integral function of

$$c_0,\quad a_0a_2-a_1^2,\quad a_2b_0^2-2a_1b_1b_0+a_0b_1^2. \qquad \ldots(2)$$

Consider the first fact, and let

$$a_2^{\lambda}(a_0c_0-b_0^2)^{\mu}(a_0b_1^2-2b_0a_1b_1+c_0a_1^2)^{\nu}$$

be a part of the invariant. By § 285 its weight measured by sum of suffixes must be equal to its weight considering a's, b's, and c_0 as respectively of weights 0, 1, 2. Thus

$$2\lambda+2\nu=2\mu+2\nu,$$

so that $\lambda=\mu$, and the invariant involves only

$$a_2(a_0c_0-b_0^2),\text{ and } a_0b_1^2-2b_0a_1b_1+c_0a_1^2.$$

Similarly it involves only

$$c_0(a_0a_2-a_1^2),\text{ and } a_2b_0^2-2a_1b_1b_0+a_0b_1^2.$$

Now any function of the first of these pairs which is also a function of the second pair must in particular be so when $c_0=0$. Thus a necessity as to such a function is that the said function of

$$-a_2b_0^2 \text{ and } a_0b_1^2-2b_0a_1b_1$$

is a function of

$$0 \text{ and } a_2b_0^2-2a_1b_1b_0+a_0b_1^2.$$

The difference of the two, and its powers, are obviously the only functions for which this is the case.

Thus

$$a_2(a_0c_0-b_0^2)-(a_0b_1^2-2b_0a_1b_1+c_0a_1^2)$$

and its powers are the only functions which can be invariants, and they can be so only if this is also a function of $c_0(a_0a_2-a_1^2)$ and $a_2b_0^2-2a_1b_1b_0+a_0b_1^2$, as it is, viz. the difference of the two.

The ternary quadratic has then only one irreducible invariant

$$a_0c_0a_2+2b_1a_1b_0-a_0b_1^2-c_0a_1^2-a_2b_0^2,$$

which is, in the more usual notation,

$$abc+2fgh-af^2-bg^2-ch^2,$$

the discriminant.

291. **The ternary cubic.** The general ternary cubic can (§ 229) be linearly transformed into $X^3+Y^3+Z^3+6mXYZ$.

It cannot then have more than two independent invariants. For if it had three it would have two absolute invariants, i.e. there would be two functions of the coefficients equal to functions of m; and by elimination of m we could find a relation in the coefficients only, which there cannot be as the coefficients are all independent.

Two independent invariants S and T, of degrees 4 and 6, will now be found. It will hereafter be seen that not only is there no other independent of these, but that there is no other which cannot be rationally and integrally expressed in terms of them, so that they form the whole system of irreducible invariants.

By § 285, or by § 28, the weight, in either of the three senses, of an invariant of the ternary cubic is equal to its degree. Thus S, which we seek, is of degree 4 and weight 4.

Now suppose that S contains a term or terms of degrees m' in a_3, n in a_2 and b_2, p in a_1, b_1, c_1, and q in a_0, b_0, c_0, d_0. The facts as to degree and weight give us

$$m'+n+p+q=4,$$
$$3m'+2n+p=4,$$

and the only positive integral, including zero, values of m', n, p, q which satisfy these equations are given by the scheme

m',	n,	p,	q
1,	0,	1,	2
0,	2,	0,	2
0,	1,	2,	1
0,	0,	4,	0

Thus S, if it exists, must be of the form

$$a_3(1^1 0^2)+(2^2 0^2)+(2^1 1^2 0^1)+(1^4),$$

where, for instance, the notation $(2^1 1^2 0^1)$ denotes a function of degree 1 in a_2, b_2, degree 2 in a_1, b_1, c_1, and degree 1 in a_0, b_0, c_0, d_0.

Moreover, since $\Omega_{yx}S=0$ and $\Omega_{xy}S=0$, the functions $(1^1 0^2)$, $(2^2 0^2)$, $(2^1 1^2 0^1)$, (1^4) are invariants of the system

$$a_2x+b_2y,$$
$$a_1x^2+2b_1xy+c_1y^2,$$
$$a_0x^3+3b_0x^2y+3c_0xy^2+d_0y^3.$$

Now the invariants of this system are (§ 262) the invariants of the quadratic and cubic given in § 260, and the results of replacing x and y by b_2 and $-a_2$ in the covariants of that article. Those of degree and sum of suffixes not exceeding 4 are given by (2), (4), (6), (9), (10), (13) of the article in question, and are

$A=a_1c_1-b_1^2,$

$B=(a_0c_0-b_0^2)b_2^2-(a_0d_0-b_0c_0)a_2b_2+(b_0d_0-c_0^2)a_2^2,$

$$C = (a_0d_0 - b_0c_0)^2 - 4(a_0c_0 - b_0^2)(b_0d_0 - c_0^2),$$
$$D = (a_1c_0 - 2b_1b_0 + c_1a_0)b_2 - (a_1d_0 - 2b_1c_0 + c_1b_0)a_2,$$
$$E = \{a_1^2d_0 - 3a_1b_1c_0 + (a_1c_1 + 2b_1^2)b_0 - b_1c_1a_0\}b_2$$
$$+ \{c_1^2a_0 - 3b_1c_1b_0 + (a_1c_1 + 2b_1^2)c_0 - a_1b_1d_0\}a_2,$$
$$F = a_1(b_0d_0 - c_0^2) - b_1(a_0d_0 - b_0c_0) + c_1(a_0c_0 - b_0^2).$$

We see then that

$$(1^1\,0^2) = \lambda F,$$
$$(2^2\,0^2) = \mu B,$$
$$(2^1\,1^2\,0^1) = \nu E,$$
$$(1^4) = \varpi A^2,$$

where λ, μ, ν, ϖ are numerical.

Thus we must have

$$S = \lambda a_3\{a_1(b_0d_0 - c_0^2) - b_1(a_0d_0 - b_0c_0) + c_1(a_0c_0 - b_0^2)\}$$
$$+ \mu\{(a_0c_0 - b_0^2)b_2^2 - (a_0d_0 - b_0c_0)a_2b_2 + (b_0d_0 - c_0^2)a_2^2\}$$
$$+ \nu\{a_1^2d_0b_2 - a_1b_1(3c_0b_2 + d_0a_2) + (a_1c_1 + 2b_1^2)(b_0b_2 + c_0a_2)$$
$$- b_1c_1(a_0b_2 + 3b_0a_2) + c_1^2a_0a_2\}$$
$$+ \varpi(a_1c_1 - b_1^2)^2.$$

To determine λ, μ, ν, ϖ we may express that S is annihilated by any of the Ω's, except Ω_{yx} and Ω_{xy} by which we have already secured its annihilation, whatever λ, μ, ν, ϖ be. More easily perhaps we may use the fact that S must be exactly the same function of

$$\begin{array}{l} d_0, \\ c_0,\ c_1, \\ b_0,\ b_1,\ b_2, \\ a_0,\ a_1,\ a_2,\ a_3, \end{array}$$

as of

$$\begin{array}{l} a_3, \\ a_2,\ b_2, \\ a_1,\ b_1,\ c_1, \\ a_0,\ b_0,\ c_0,\ d_0, \end{array}$$

since these sets of coefficients are exactly interchanged by the linear substitution which interchanges y and z leaving x unaltered, whose modulus is -1, which modulus in the expression of invariancy of an invariant of weight 4 is raised to the fourth power, thus producing $+1$ for the factor. For S to be an invariant the above expression must then be the same as

$$\lambda d_0\{b_0(a_1a_3 - a_2^2) - b_1(a_0a_3 - a_1a_2) + b_2(a_0a_2 - a_1^2)\}$$
$$+ \mu\{(a_0a_2 - a_1^2)c_1^2 - (a_0a_3 - a_1a_2)c_0c_1 + (a_1a_3 - a_2^2)c_0^2\}$$

$$+\nu\{b_0^2a_3c_1-b_0b_1(3a_2c_1+a_3c_0)+(b_0b_2+2b_1^2)(a_1c_1+a_2c_0)$$
$$-b_1b_2(a_0c_1+3a_1c_0)+b_2^2a_0c_0\}$$
$$+\varpi(b_0b_2-b_1^2)^2.$$

We at once see that the two forms are identical if

$$\frac{\lambda}{-1}=\frac{\mu}{1}=\frac{\nu}{1}=\frac{\varpi}{-1}.$$

With these values the expression will have Ω_{zx} and Ω_{xz} for annihilators, because of its second form, as well as Ω_{yx} and Ω_{xy} because of its first form. It is then an invariant by § 289. Thus the invariant S looked for is, adopting the second form of writing it,

$$S=(a_0a_2-a_1^2)c_1^2-(a_0a_3-a_1a_2)c_0c_1+(a_1a_3-a_2^2)c_0^2$$
$$+b_0^2a_3c_1-b_0b_1(3a_2c_1+a_3c_0)+(b_0b_2+2b_1^2)(a_1c_1+a_2c_0)$$
$$-b_1b_2(a_0c_1+3a_1c_0)+b_2^2a_0c_0$$
$$-d_0\{b_0(a_1a_3-a_2^2)-b_1(a_0a_3-a_1a_2)+b_2(a_0a_2-a_1^2)\}$$
$$-(b_0b_2-b_1^2)^2.$$

292. The cubic can (§ 229) be linearly transformed to the canonical form

$$X^3+Y^3+Z^3+6mXYZ.$$

By a substitution of modulus unity it can consequently be given the form

$$a'(x^3+y^3+z^3)+6m'xyz.$$

Let us consider it in the less particularized form

$$a_0'x^3+d_0'y^3+a_3'z^3+6b_1'xyz,$$

in which the names of non-vanishing coefficients accord with the notation used in general. The modulus of the transformation which produces this from the general cubic is taken to be unity.

For this form we have, by the above,

$$S=a_0'd_0'a_3'b_1'-b_1'^4=b_1'(a_0'd_0'a_3'-b_1'^3).$$

For the canonical form itself the value is

$$m(1-m^3),$$

which is of course equal not to the S of the untransformed cubic but to that S multiplied by the fourth power of the modulus, which is no longer unity.

Ex. 4. Show that $S=0$ is the condition for the cubic to be capable of expression as a sum of three cubes.

293. The second invariant T of degree 6, and therefore, since $3i=3w$, also of weight 6, can be found as S has been.

For our purposes, however, the labour may be avoided by use of a covariant, the Hessian, which it is already known from § 11 that the cubic possesses.

For the semi-canonized form

$$a_0'x^3+d_0'y^3+a_3'z^3+6b_1'xyz,$$

the Hessian, with the numerical factor 6^3 rejected, is

$$\begin{vmatrix} a_0'x, & b_1'z, & b_1'y \\ b_1'z, & d_0'y, & b_1'x \\ b_1'y, & b_1'x, & a_3'z \end{vmatrix},$$

i.e. $\quad (a_0'd_0'a_3'+2b_1'^3)\,xyz-b_1'^2(a_0'x^3+d_0'y^3+a_3'z^3).$

The Hessian is then a covariant of the third degree and order.

For the canonical form itself the Hessian is

$$(1+2m^3)\,XYZ-m^2(X^3+Y^3+Z^3),$$

i.e. this is equal to the Hessian of the untransformed quantic multiplied by the square of the modulus of the fully canonizing substitution.

Now an invariant of a quantic and a covariant is an invariant of the quantic alone. Also (§ 19) if $ax^3+\ldots$ and $Ax^3+\ldots$ are two quantics of the same order, we may derive an invariant of the two from one of the first only by operation with $A\dfrac{\partial}{\partial a}+\ldots$. Applying this principle to the cubic and its Hessian, both of order 3, we derive from the invariant S another invariant of the sixth degree. This is T, or rather a numerical multiple of T.

We can at once derive the expression for T that goes with the semi-canonized form

$$a_0'x^3+d_0'y^3+a_3'z^3+6b_1'xyz,$$

whose Hessian is as above

$$-b_1'^2a_0'x^3-b_1'^2d_0'y^3-b_1'^2a_3'z^3+(a_0'd_0'a_3'+2b_1'^3)\,xyz,$$

by operating with

$$-b_1'^2a_0'\frac{\partial}{\partial a_0'}-b_1'^2d_0'\frac{\partial}{\partial d_0'}-b_1'^2a_3'\frac{\partial}{\partial a_3'}+\frac{1}{6}(a_0'd_0'a_3'+2b_1'^3)\frac{\partial}{\partial b_1'}$$

on S, which is $\quad b_1'(a_0'd_0'a_3'-b_1'^3).$

The reason for this lawfulness of working with the reduced number of coefficients is that the full expression for S contains, besides the terms $b_1(a_0d_0a_3-b_1^3)$, only terms involving coefficients which vanish for the semi-canonized form—indeed only powers and products of such coefficients, a fact which will be useful later—and that the terms in the generating operator other than those in $\frac{\partial}{\partial a_0}, \frac{\partial}{\partial d_0}, \frac{\partial}{\partial a_3}, \frac{\partial}{\partial b_1}$ contain as factors coefficients in the Hessian which vanish for the semi-canonized form.

The result of performing the operation above, and multiplying by 6, is to obtain

$$T = (a_0' d_0' a_3')^2 - 20 b_1'^3 (a_0' d_0' a_3') - 8 b_1'^6.$$

For the canonical form itself this becomes

$$1 - 20 m^3 - 8 m^6;$$

but this is equal, not to the T of the untransformed cubic, but to the T multiplied by the sixth power of the canonizing modulus.

There is no difficulty in obtaining the lengthy expression for T in the notation of the general cubic, but only tediousness. It will not be here written down. Reference may be made for it to Salmon's *Higher Plane Curves*, §§ 221, 223.

Ex. 5. Prove that b_1' is given by the quartic in $b_1'^2 = \beta$

$$27\beta^4 + 18S\beta^2 + T\beta - S^2 = 0,$$

and that when b_1' is found the corresponding product $a_0' d_0' a_3'$ is uniquely determined.

Ex. 6. The discriminant of this quartic is a perfect square, namely, a numerical multiple of the square of $64S^3 + T^2$, which is a numerical multiple of its catalecticant.

Ex. 7. The discriminant of the ternary cubic is

$$a_0' d_0' a_3' (a_0' d_0' a_3' + 8 b_1'^3)^3, \text{ i.e. } 64S^3 + T^2.$$

Ex. 8. The S of the Hessian of a ternary cubic is a numerical multiple of $48S^3 + T^2$.

294. The result of Ex. 5 above leads us to expect that there are eight distinct ways of reducing the cubic to the form $ax^3 + by^3 + cz^3 + 6mxyz$ by substitutions of such modulus that S and T are absolutely unaltered. (Note that we do not reckon as distinct different ways in which the product xyz is the same.) If M is the modulus of such a substitution, the facts with regard to S and T give us respectively $M^4 = 1$ and $M^6 = 1$. These lead to $M^2 = 1$, i.e. $M = \pm 1$.

It is easy to see that there really are eight ways, and to exhibit their connexion. Take, for instance, the cubic

$$x^3 + y^3 + z^3 + 6mxyz.$$

The substitutions of modulus 1

$$x\sqrt{-3} = X+Y+Z,\ y\sqrt{-3} = X+\omega Y+\omega^2 Z,$$
$$z\sqrt{-3} = X+\omega^2 Y+\omega Z,$$
$$x\sqrt{-3} = X+\omega Y+\omega Z,\ y\sqrt{-3} = X+\omega^2 Y+Z,$$
$$z\sqrt{-3} = X+Y+\omega^2 Z,$$
$$x\sqrt{-3} = X+\omega^2 Y+\omega^2 Z,\ y\sqrt{-3} = X+Y+\omega Z,$$
$$z\sqrt{-3} = X+\omega Y+Z,$$

produce three forms whose m's are respectively

$$m_2 = -(1-m)/\sqrt{-3},\ m_3 = -(\omega^2-m)/\sqrt{-3},$$
$$m_4 = -(\omega-m)/\sqrt{-3},$$

so that

$$mm_2m_3m_4 = m(1-m^3)/3\sqrt{-3} = S/3\sqrt{-3}.$$

Also $x = x'$, $y = y'$, $z = -z'$, whose modulus is -1, gives a form with $-m$ for m, those with $-m_2$, $-m_3$, $-m_4$ for m being obtained in like manner. The product of the eight m's is then

$$(mm_2m_3m_4)^2 = -\tfrac{1}{27}S^2,$$

which accords with § 293, Ex. 5.

295. S **and** T **the only irreducible invariants.** We may prove as follows that any other invariant of the ternary cubic is a rational integral function of S and T.

Write the semi-canonized form of the cubic with the notation of coefficients

$$ax^3+by^3+cz^3+6mxyz, \qquad \ldots (1)$$

so that

$$S = m(abc-m^3),$$
$$T = (abc)^2-20m^3abc-8m^6,$$

and (§ 293, Ex. 5)

$$27m^8+18Sm^4+Tm^2-S^2 = 0. \qquad \ldots (2)$$

We notice here, and from the last article, that the product of the eight values of m for substitutions which leave S and T unaltered, modulus $+1$ or -1, is a numerical multiple of S^2. The product of the four for modulus $+1$ is a numerical multiple of S.

Now if an invariant is such as to vanish when an m vanishes it must when any of the m's vanishes. For its form for (1) has m for a factor, and it is the same thing to say that its form for

$$a_2x^3+b_2y^3+c_2z^3+6m_2xyz$$

has m_2 for a factor. An invariant divisible by m is then divisible by $mm_2m_3m_4$, i.e. by S; and the quotient as well as itself must be an invariant. Equally if divisible by $abc-m^3$

a product of three m's, an invariant is divisible by the fourth, and so by S.

We have then only to consider the reducibility of invariants which are not divisible by m or by $abc - m^3$, which latter call k. In this notation we have

$$S = mk, \quad \dots (3)$$
$$T = k^2 - 18m^3k - 27m^6$$
$$= k^2 - 18Sm^2 - 27m^6. \quad \dots (4)$$

Consider then an invariant I which is not divisible by m or by k. Its degree must be a multiple of 3. For k is of degree 3, so that, if its term free from m is k^n, this is of degree $3n$, and this degree must be preserved throughout. We may suppose then that the invariant is

$$I = k^n + pk^{n-1}m^3 + qk^{n-2}m^6 + \dots + tm^{3n},$$

for it is a function of S and T (§ 291), and consequently of the independent k and m, which are all that S and T involve. It would not be integral were k or m involved fractionally.

Now first use (4) to depress I to the first degree in k, or to the degree zero in k if no odd powers of k occur in I as already exhibited, by substitution for k^2 of $T + 18Sm^2 + 27m^6$. We thus get

$$I = kf(S, T, m) + \phi(S, T, m),$$

where the functions f and ϕ are rational and integral, and where the former may or may not actually occur.

Firstly, if $f(S, T, m)$ do not occur, we have

$$I = \phi(S, T, m).$$

By aid of (2) we may depress this equation below the eighth degree in m by successive substitutions such as that of $\frac{1}{27}(S^2m^r - Tm^{r+2} - 18Sm^{r+4})$ for m^{8+r}, where r is zero or a positive integer. We thus get eventually

$$I = Am^7 + Bm^6 + \dots + K,$$

where $A, B, \dots K$, if they do not vanish, are rational integral functions of S and T.

Now there are (§ 294) eight values of m which must satisfy this equation of degree 7 at most. It must then be an identity. Hence, taking the terms free from m,

$$I = K,$$

i.e. I is a rational integral function of S and T.

Secondly, if $f(S, T, m)$ do occur, let S/m be put for k, by (3), in $kf(S, T, m)$. We have

$$I = F(S, T)\, S/m + \psi(S, T, m),$$

where F and ψ are rational and integral; and this again may be reduced by (2) to

$$Im = A'm^7 + B'm^6 + \dots + H'm + K',$$

where $A', B', \dots H', K'$, if non-vanishing, are rational integral functions of S and T. This equation of degree 7 must be an identity by reasoning as before, and therefore, taking coefficients of m,

$$I = H',$$

so that the conclusion as before is that I is a rational integral function of S and T.

296. Covariants of ternary quantics. By §§ 282, 283 a covariant has three pairs of annihilators, of which the first pair

$$\Omega_{yx} - y\frac{\partial}{\partial x}, \quad \Omega_{xy} - x\frac{\partial}{\partial y}$$

is typical.

Let a covariant of order ϖ be arranged according to powers of z, and written

$$P_\varpi + \varpi P_{\varpi-1}z + \frac{\varpi(\varpi-1)}{1.2}P_{\varpi-2}z^2 + \dots + \varpi P_1 z^{\varpi-1} + P_0 z^\varpi, \quad \dots (1)$$

where P_0 involves coefficients only, and $P_1, P_2, \dots P_\varpi$ are of orders $1, 2, \dots \varpi$ respectively in x and y.

The results of operating on this with $\Omega_{yx} - y\frac{\partial}{\partial x}$ and $\Omega_{xy} - x\frac{\partial}{\partial y}$ must vanish identically. Thus, equating to zero the terms going with different powers of z, we see that

$$P_0, P_1, P_2, \dots P_{\varpi-1}, P_\varpi$$

have all separately the two annihilators $\Omega_{yx} - y\frac{\partial}{\partial x}$, $\Omega_{xy} - x\frac{\partial}{\partial y}$.

In particular P_0, being free from x and y, is annihilated by Ω_{yx} and Ω_{xy}, i.e. is an invariant of the system

$$\begin{array}{l} a_p, \\ a_{p-1}x + b_{p-1}y, \\ a_{p-2}x^2 + 2b_{p-2}xy + c_{p-2}y^2, \\ \cdot \quad \cdot \quad \cdot \quad \cdot \quad \cdot \quad \cdot \quad \cdot \quad \cdot \quad \cdot \quad \cdot \\ a_0x^p + pb_0x^{p-1}y + \frac{p(p-1)}{1.2}c_0x^{p-2}y^2 + \dots . \end{array}$$

As to $P_1, P_2, \dots P_\varpi$ they are, in like manner, covariants of this system. The coefficients of the highest powers of x which occur in them respectively are then seminvariants of the system, i.e. are annihilated by Ω_{yx}.

In particular, the coefficient of x^{ϖ} in P_{ϖ}, i.e. in the covariant (1) itself, is annihilated by Ω_{yx}.

Now suppose again the covariant to be arranged by powers of y instead of by powers of z, and apply like reasoning. The coefficient of x^{ϖ} in the covariant is thus seen to be annihilated by Ω_{zx}.

It has also been seen that the coefficient P_0 of z^{ϖ} in the covariant is annihilated by Ω_{yx} and Ω_{xy}. By the same reasoning the coefficient of x^{ϖ} is annihilated by Ω_{zy} and Ω_{yz}.

Thus the coefficient of x^{ϖ} in the covariant has the four annihilators

$$\Omega_{yx},\ \Omega_{zx},\ \Omega_{zy},\ \Omega_{yz}.$$

In like manner the coefficient of y^{ϖ} has the four annihilators

$$\Omega_{zy},\ \Omega_{xy},\ \Omega_{xz},\ \Omega_{zx};$$

and the coefficient of z^{ϖ} has the four annihilators

$$\Omega_{xz},\ \Omega_{yz},\ \Omega_{yx},\ \Omega_{xy}.$$

297. **A covariant is given by an end coefficient.** When one of these three coefficients is known the whole covariant is known.

Consider the arrangement, (1) of the preceding article, by powers of z. Expressing the fact of annihilation by $\Omega_{xz} - x\dfrac{\partial}{\partial z}$, we have, by taking the coefficients of the successive powers of z,

$$\begin{aligned}
\Omega_{xz}P_{\varpi} - \varpi x P_{\varpi-1} &= 0,\\
\Omega_{xz}P_{\varpi-1} - (\varpi-1)\,x P_{\varpi-2} &= 0,\\
\cdots\cdots\cdots&\\
\Omega_{xz}P_1 - xP_0 &= 0,\\
\Omega_{xz}P_0 &= 0,
\end{aligned}$$

which tell us that (1) may be written

$$\left\{1 + \frac{z}{x}\Omega_{xz} + \frac{1}{1\,.\,2}\frac{z^2}{x^2}\Omega_{xz}^2 + \ldots + \frac{1}{\varpi\,!}\frac{z^{\varpi}}{x^{\varpi}}\Omega_{xz}^{\varpi} + \ldots\right\} P_{\varpi},$$

the terms beyond the last written down vanishing because $\Omega_{xz}P_0 = 0$, i.e. $\Omega_{xz}^{\varpi+1}P_{\varpi} = 0$, and consequently $\Omega_{xz}^{\varpi+r}P_{\varpi} = 0$, for any positive value of the integer r.

Now this expression for the covariant may be written

$$e^{\frac{z}{x}\Omega_{xz}}P_{\varpi}.$$

Again consider P_{ϖ}. It is by the last article annihilated by $\Omega_{yx} - y\dfrac{\partial}{\partial x}$ and $\Omega_{xy} - x\dfrac{\partial}{\partial y}$. Hence as above, or as in § 110, if

S is the coefficient of x^{ϖ} in P_{ϖ}, i.e. in the covariant, we have

$$P_{\varpi} = x^{\varpi} e^{\frac{y}{x}\Omega_{xy}} S.$$

Consequently, upon insertion of this value for P_{ϖ}, the covariant is

$$x^{\varpi} e^{\frac{z}{x}\Omega_{xz}} e^{\frac{y}{x}\Omega_{xy}} S,$$

which, since (§ 286) $\Omega_{xz}\Omega_{xy} = \Omega_{xy}\Omega_{xz}$, so that Ω_{xy} and Ω_{xz} are commutative, and since they do not operate on x, y, z, may without ambiguity be written

$$x^{\varpi} e^{\frac{z}{x}\Omega_{xz}+\frac{y}{x}\Omega_{xy}} S.$$

In like manner, if S' is the coefficient of y^{ϖ} in the covariant, and S'' (the P_0 above) the coefficient of z^{ϖ}, the covariant may also be written in either of the forms

$$y^{\varpi} e^{\frac{x}{y}\Omega_{yx}+\frac{z}{y}\Omega_{yz}} S', \qquad z^{\varpi} e^{\frac{y}{z}\Omega_{zy}+\frac{x}{z}\Omega_{zx}} S''.$$

Ex. 9. Prove that the covariant may also be written

$$z^{\varpi} e^{\frac{x}{y}\Omega_{yx}} e^{\frac{y}{z}\Omega_{zy}} S'',$$

and in two similar forms derived from S and S', but that since Ω_{yx} and Ω_{zy} are not commutative this must *not* be written

$$z^{\varpi} e^{\frac{x}{y}\Omega_{yx}+\frac{y}{z}\Omega_{zy}} S''.$$

298. Another method of obtaining the full expression for a covariant from the coefficient of the highest power of z in it is analogous to that of § 160. Substitute, in the final coefficient S'' or P_0 of a covariant of the ternary p-ic u,

u for a_p,

$\frac{1}{p}\frac{\partial u}{\partial x}, \frac{1}{p}\frac{\partial u}{\partial y}$ for a_{p-1}, b_{p-1},

$\frac{1}{p(p-1)}\frac{\partial^2 u}{\partial x^2}, \frac{1}{p(p-1)}\frac{\partial^2 u}{\partial x\,\partial y}, \frac{1}{p(p-1)}\frac{\partial^2 u}{\partial y^2}$ for $a_{p-2}, b_{p-2}, c_{p-2}$,

. . . .

$\frac{1}{p!}\frac{\partial^p u}{\partial x^p}, \frac{1}{p!}\frac{\partial^p u}{\partial x^{p-1}\partial y}, \ldots$ for $a_0, b_0, \ldots$,

and divide through by the power of z which occurs as a factor in the result.

The proof is easy. We at once see that

$$u = z^p e^{\frac{x}{z}\Omega_{zx}+\frac{y}{z}\Omega_{zy}} a_p,$$

$$\frac{1}{p}\frac{\partial u}{\partial x} = \frac{1}{p} z^{p-1} e^{\frac{x}{z}\Omega_{zx}+\frac{y}{z}\Omega_{zy}} \Omega_{zx} a_p$$

$$= z^{p-1} e^{\frac{x}{z}\Omega_{zx}+\frac{y}{z}\Omega_{zy}} a_{p-1},$$

$$\frac{1}{p}\frac{\partial u}{\partial y} = z^{p-1} e^{\frac{x}{z}\Omega_{zx}+\frac{y}{z}\Omega_{zy}} b_{p-1},$$

$$\frac{1}{p(p-1)}\frac{\partial^2 u}{\partial x^2} = z^{p-2} e^{\frac{x}{z}\Omega_{zx}+\frac{y}{z}\Omega_{zy}} a_{p-2},$$

&c., &c.

Also, if P and Q are two functions of the coefficients,

$$e^{\frac{x}{z}\Omega_{zx}+\frac{y}{z}\Omega_{zy}} PQ = e^{\frac{x}{z}\Omega_{zx}+\frac{y}{z}\Omega_{zy}} P \,.\, e^{\frac{x}{z}\Omega_{zx}+\frac{y}{z}\Omega_{zy}} Q;$$

for

$$\left(\frac{x}{z}\Omega_{zx}+\frac{y}{z}\Omega_{zy}\right)^m PQ = P\,.\left(\frac{x}{z}\Omega_{zx}+\frac{y}{z}\Omega_{zy}\right)^m Q$$

$$+ m\left(\frac{x}{z}\Omega_{zx}+\frac{y}{z}\Omega_{zy}\right) P\,.\left(\frac{x}{z}\Omega_{zx}+\frac{y}{z}\Omega_{zy}\right)^{m-1} Q + \dots$$

$$+ \left(\frac{x}{z}\Omega_{zx}+\frac{y}{z}\Omega_{zy}\right)^m P\,.\,Q,$$

by the method of Leibnitz's theorem. Hence the conclusion is immediate.

Since $z^w = z^\varpi z^{w-\varpi}$, the power of z which divides through is $z^{w-\varpi}$, where w is the weight of the final coefficient on the supposition that z has zero weight, i.e. of the covariant, and ϖ is the order of the latter. The difference $w-\varpi$ is the weight, on the same supposition, of the coefficient of x^ϖ.

299. The search for covariants of ternary quantics is then, as in the case of binary quantics, coextensive with the search for their leading or end coefficients, it being equally reasonable to consider the coefficient of x^ϖ or y^ϖ or z^ϖ a leader.

Take S'', the coefficient of z^ϖ. It has, as has been seen, the four annihilators Ω_{xz}, Ω_{yz}, Ω_{yx}, Ω_{xy}.

By § 286 (13) if Ω_{yx} and Ω_{xz} annihilate a function, then Ω_{yz} must. Thus we may say that S'' has the three annihilators

$$\Omega_{xz},\ \Omega_{yx},\ \Omega_{xy},$$

and, as a consequence, also the fourth Ω_{yz}.

We proceed to see that any rational integral function S''

with these properties is the last coefficient in a covariant, or a sum of last coefficients in more covariants than one. (This latter will be the state of things when S'' is a sum of parts for which ϖ in (5) below has different values.)

Let us adopt the notation of the cubic for simplicity. That Ω_{yx} and Ω_{xy} are annihilators tells us that S'' is a full *invariant* of the system

$$\left.\begin{array}{l} a_3, \\ a_2x + b_2y, \\ a_1x^2 + 2b_1xy + c_1y^2, \\ a_0x^3 + 3b_0x^2y + 3c_0xy^2 + d_0y^3; \end{array}\right\} \quad \ldots (1)$$

and that Ω_{xz} is an annihilator tells us that it is a seminvariant of the system

$$\begin{array}{l} d_0, \\ c_1z + c_0x, \\ b_2z^2 + 2b_1zx + b_0x^2, \\ a_3z^3 + 3a_2z^2x + 3a_1zx^2 + a_0x^3, \end{array}$$

or, let us say, that it is an anti-seminvariant of the system

$$\left.\begin{array}{l} d_0, \\ c_0x + c_1z, \\ b_0x^2 + 2b_1xz + b_2z^2, \\ a_0x^3 + 3a_1x^2z + 3a_2xz^2 + a_3z^3. \end{array}\right\} \quad \ldots (2)$$

The consequence that Ω_{yz} is an annihilator tells us that in virtue of having these properties S'' must be also an anti-seminvariant of the system

$$\left.\begin{array}{l} a_0, \\ b_0y + a_1z, \\ c_0y^2 + 2b_1yz + a_2z^2, \\ d_0y^3 + 3c_1y^2z + 3b_2yz^2 + a_3z^3. \end{array}\right\} \quad \ldots (3)$$

Taking for S'' any solution of $\Omega_{xz}S''=0$, $\Omega_{yx}S''=0$, $\Omega_{xy}S''=0$, let us form from it the function

$$e^{\frac{y}{z}\Omega_{zy}+\frac{x}{z}\Omega_{zx}}S'',$$

remembering that Ω_{zy} and Ω_{zx} are commutative. We proceed to see that this, made integral by the lowest necessary power z^{ϖ} of z, is a covariant.

Because $\Omega_{xz}S''=0$ we can form from S'' a covariant

$$z^{\varpi}e^{\frac{x}{z}\Omega_{zx}}S''$$

of the system (2). Call this

$$x^{\varpi}S+\varpi x^{\varpi-1}zS_1+\frac{\varpi(\varpi-1)}{1.2}x^{\varpi-2}z^2S_2+\dots$$
$$+\varpi xz^{\varpi-1}S_{\varpi-1}+z^{\varpi}S''. \quad \dots (4)$$

The order ϖ here is given by

$$\varpi=3i_3+2i_2+i_1-2w, \quad \dots (5)$$

where w is the sum of the suffixes in S, or, to express by what is known, $w+\varpi$ is the sum of the suffixes in S'', and i_3, i_2, i_1 are the degrees of S'' in a's, in b's, and in c's respectively. ϖ is non-negative by the known theory of binary quantics. If for different parts of S'' this expression for ϖ has different values, the present and following reasoning applies to those parts separately. By S'' we now mean such a part.

Now S, S_1, S_2, ... $S_{\varpi-1}$ are all seminvariants of the system (1), of which S'' is an invariant. For, § 286 (4), whatever be the function operated on

$$\Omega_{yx}\Omega_{zx}=\Omega_{zx}\Omega_{yx};$$

whence

$$\Omega_{yx}S_{\varpi-1}=\Omega_{yx}\Omega_{zx}S''=\Omega_{zx}\Omega_{yx}S''=0,$$

because Ω_{yx} annihilates S''; and

$$\Omega_{yx}S_{\varpi-2}=\Omega_{yx}\cdot\tfrac{1}{2}\Omega_{zx}S_{\varpi-1}=\tfrac{1}{2}\Omega_{zx}\Omega_{yx}S_{\varpi-1}=0,$$

&c., &c.

Again S, S_1, S_2, ... $S_{\varpi-1}$, S'' are all annihilated by Ω_{yz}. That S'' is so has been seen above. Also it has been seen, § 286 (12), that $\Omega_{yz}\Omega_{zx}-\Omega_{zx}\Omega_{yz}=-\Omega_{yx}$.

Thus

$$\Omega_{yz}S_{\varpi-1}=\Omega_{yz}\Omega_{zx}S''=(\Omega_{zx}\Omega_{yz}-\Omega_{yx})S''=0,$$

because Ω_{yz} and Ω_{yx} annihilate S'';

$$\Omega_{yz}S_{\varpi-2}=\Omega_{yz}\cdot\tfrac{1}{2}\Omega_{zx}S_{\varpi-1}=\tfrac{1}{2}(\Omega_{zx}\Omega_{yz}-\Omega_{yx})S_{\varpi-1}=0,$$

because Ω_{yz} and Ω_{yx} annihilate $S_{\varpi-1}$; and so on.

Thus S, S_1, S_2, ... $S_{\varpi-1}$, S'' are all anti-seminvariants of the system (3). The first, as we shall presently see, is an invariant of the system.

All of these when operated on by $e^{\frac{y}{z}\Omega_{zy}}$ and made integral by multiplication by just adequate powers of z will then produce covariants (invariants a particular case) of the system (3).

Now these covariants are of orders 0, 1, 2, ... $\varpi-1$, ϖ respectively. For in the first place S'', an invariant of the system (1), is unaltered, except at most in sign, when interchanges are made in it equivalent to the interchange of x and y in the system (1). Thus S'' is the same function of the coefficients in the system (3), but for sign at most, as of those in the system (2). It is, as we have seen, an anti-seminvariant of both systems. The covariant of the system (3) of which it is the last coefficient is then of the same order ϖ as that of the system (2) of which it is also the last coefficient, and which has been written above (4). This proves what is wanted as to S''. Now $S_{\varpi-1}$, which is obtained from S'' by operation with Ω_{zx}, i.e. with

$$a_0\frac{\partial}{\partial a_1}+2a_1\frac{\partial}{\partial a_2}+3a_2\frac{\partial}{\partial a_3}+b_0\frac{\partial}{\partial b_1}+2b_1\frac{\partial}{\partial b_2}+c_0\frac{\partial}{\partial c_1},$$

is of weight (sum of suffixes) one less than w' the weight of S''. Also if i_3', i_2', i_1' are the degrees of S'' in the coefficients of the cubic, the quadratic and the linear form of the system (3), so that

$$\begin{aligned}\varpi &= 3i_3'+2i_2'+i_1'-2(w'-\varpi)\\ &= 2w'-3i_3'-2i_2'-i_1',\end{aligned}$$

the sum $3i_3'+2i_2'+i_1'$ for $S_{\varpi-1}$ or $\Omega_{zx}S''$ is $3i_3'+2i_2'+i_1'-1$; for the operation replaces in each term one of the coefficients of the cubic by one in the quadratic, or one in the quadratic by one in the linear, or, &c. Thus the order of the covariant of (3), which $S_{\varpi-1}$ ends, is

$$\begin{aligned}\varpi' &= 2(w'-1)-3i_3'-2i_2'-i_1'+1\\ &= \varpi-1.\end{aligned}$$

In like manner $S_{\varpi-2}, S_{\varpi-3}, \ldots S_2, S_1, S$ produce covariants of (3) of orders $\varpi-2, \varpi-3, \ldots 2, 1, 0$ respectively, the last being therefore an invariant of the set (3).

It hence follows that the covariants of the set (3) in which $S, S_1, \ldots S_{\varpi-1}, S''$ are the last coefficients are respectively

$$S \text{ or } e^{\frac{y}{z}\Omega_{zy}}S,\quad ze^{\frac{y}{z}\Omega_{zy}}S_1, \ldots z^{\varpi-1}e^{\frac{y}{z}\Omega_{zy}}S_{\varpi-1},\quad z^{\varpi}e^{\frac{y}{z}\Omega_{zy}}S''.$$

Thus the expression (4),

$$x^{\varpi}S+\varpi x^{\varpi-1}zS_1+\frac{\varpi(\varpi-1)}{1\,.\,2}x^{\varpi-2}z^2S_2+\ldots+\varpi xz^{\varpi-1}S_{\varpi-1}+z^{\varpi}S'',$$

i.e. $z^{\varpi}e^{\frac{x}{z}\Omega_{zx}}S''$, is the part free from y, and consequently $z^{\varpi}S''$ the part free from x and y, in an integral expression

$$z^{\varpi}e^{\frac{y}{z}\Omega_{zy}}e^{\frac{x}{z}\Omega_{zx}}S'',\quad\text{or}\quad z^{\varpi}e^{\frac{y}{z}\Omega_{zy}+\frac{x}{z}\Omega_{zx}}S'',$$

which is of the form (§ 297) of a covariant of the ternary quantic.

The notation of the cubic has been used, but the argument is general.

The expression found from S'' is easily seen to obey all the conditions for a covariant. It has been constructed so as to be a function of x and covariants of the system (3), so that it is annihilated by $\Omega_{yz}-y\frac{\partial}{\partial z}$ and $\Omega_{zy}-z\frac{\partial}{\partial y}$. The symmetry of its form in x and y tells us that it is also annihilated by $\Omega_{xz}-x\frac{\partial}{\partial z}$ and $\Omega_{zx}-z\frac{\partial}{\partial x}$. Now annihilation by these pairs necessitates annihilation by the third pair $\Omega_{xy}-x\frac{\partial}{\partial y}$, $\Omega_{yx}-y\frac{\partial}{\partial x}$, just as in the case (§ 289) when x, y, z did not occur. This can be seen by the properties of alternants contained in the first example following.

Ex. 10. Prove from §§ 284, 286 the five triads of facts as to alternants of which the types are

$$\left(\Omega_{zy}-z\frac{\partial}{\partial y}\right)\left(\Omega_{yz}-y\frac{\partial}{\partial z}\right)-\left(\Omega_{yz}-y\frac{\partial}{\partial z}\right)\left(\Omega_{zy}-z\frac{\partial}{\partial y}\right)$$
$$=H_1-y\frac{\partial}{\partial y}+z\frac{\partial}{\partial z},$$

$$\left(\Omega_{yx}-y\frac{\partial}{\partial x}\right)\left(\Omega_{zx}-z\frac{\partial}{\partial x}\right)-\left(\Omega_{zx}-z\frac{\partial}{\partial x}\right)\left(\Omega_{yx}-y\frac{\partial}{\partial x}\right)=0,$$

$$\left(\Omega_{xy}-x\frac{\partial}{\partial y}\right)\left(\Omega_{xz}-x\frac{\partial}{\partial z}\right)-\left(\Omega_{xz}-x\frac{\partial}{\partial z}\right)\left(\Omega_{xy}-x\frac{\partial}{\partial y}\right)=0,$$

$$\left(\Omega_{xy}-x\frac{\partial}{\partial y}\right)\left(\Omega_{zx}-z\frac{\partial}{\partial x}\right)-\left(\Omega_{zx}-z\frac{\partial}{\partial x}\right)\left(\Omega_{xy}-x\frac{\partial}{\partial y}\right)=\Omega_{zy}-z\frac{\partial}{\partial y},$$

$$\left(\Omega_{yx}-y\frac{\partial}{\partial x}\right)\left(\Omega_{xz}-x\frac{\partial}{\partial z}\right)-\left(\Omega_{xz}-x\frac{\partial}{\partial z}\right)\left(\Omega_{yx}-y\frac{\partial}{\partial x}\right)$$
$$=-\Omega_{yz}+y\frac{\partial}{\partial z}.$$

Ex. 11. Vary the argument in the preceding article so as to find the covariant whose last coefficient is S'' in the form

$$z^{\varpi}e^{\frac{x}{y}\Omega_{yx}}e^{\frac{y}{z}\Omega_{zy}}S''.$$

Ex. 12. As in § 285 prove the fact already known from Chapter III, that throughout a covariant of degree i, order ϖ, and weight w

$$ip-3w+2\varpi=0,$$

weight being estimated in either of the three ways.

Ex. 13. The order of any covariant of a ternary cubic is a multiple of 3.

Ex. 14. The excess of weight over degree in the coefficient of z^{ϖ} in a covariant of a ternary cubic, z being of weight zero, is non-negative and even.

300. Has a ternary quadratic any covariants? Let us examine for covariants the ternary quadratic

$$u \equiv a_0 x^2 + 2 b_0 xy + c_0 y^2 + 2(a_1 x + b_1 y) z + a_2 z^2.$$

The coefficient S'' of the highest power of z in any covariant is an invariant of the system

$$a_0 x^2 + 2 b_0 xy + c_0 y^2,$$
$$a_1 x + b_1 y,$$
$$a_2.$$

It is consequently a rational integral function of

$$a_0 c_0 - b_0^2 \equiv \alpha, \text{ say},$$
$$a_0 b_1^2 - 2 b_0 a_1 b_1 + c_0 a_1^2 \equiv \beta, \text{ say},$$

and
$$a_2.$$

It is also annihilated by

$$\Omega_{xz} \equiv a_2 \frac{\partial}{\partial a_1} + 2 a_1 \frac{\partial}{\partial a_0} + b_1 \frac{\partial}{\partial b_0}.$$

Now
$$\Omega_{xz} \alpha = 2 a_1 c_0 - 2 b_1 b_0,$$
$$\Omega_{xz} \beta = 2 a_2 (a_1 c_0 - b_1 b_0),$$
and
$$\Omega_{xz} a_2 = 0.$$

If then it be $f(a_2, \alpha, \beta)$,

$$\Omega_{xz} f(a_2, \alpha, \beta) = \frac{\partial f}{\partial a_2} \Omega_{xz} a_2 + \frac{\partial f}{\partial \alpha} \Omega_{xz} \alpha + \frac{\partial f}{\partial \beta} \Omega_{xz} \beta$$
$$= 2 (a_1 c_0 - b_1 b_0) \left(\frac{\partial f}{\partial \alpha} + a_2 \frac{\partial f}{\partial \beta} \right).$$

Thus
$$\frac{\partial f}{\partial \alpha} + a_2 \frac{\partial f}{\partial \beta} = 0,$$

so that α and β only occur in f in the connexion $a_2 \alpha - \beta$. Consequently

$$S'' = F(a_2,\ a_2 a_0 c_0 - a_2 b_0^2 - a_0 b_1^2 + 2 b_0 a_1 b_1 - c_0 a_1^2),$$

where the second argument is the one invariant (§ 290), the discriminant D, of u.

S'' is then such an expression as $a_2^m D^n$, or a sum of such terms. It can, in fact, be only one such term. For it has to be homogeneous and isobaric, the z^ϖ which it multiplies being taken as of weight zero, and these two facts give $m + 3n =$ constant and $2m + 2n =$ constant, so that m and n are constant.

Now the covariant
$$z^\varpi e^{\frac{y}{z}\Omega_{zy} + \frac{x}{z}\Omega_{zx}} S''$$

determined from a final coefficient S'' is unique. Also $u^m D^n$ is a covariant of u with $a_2{}^m D^n$ for final coefficient. There is then no covariant which is not of the form $u^m D^n$.

In other words, a ternary quadratic has no covariant which is not a mere product of powers of its discriminant and itself.

301. **Covariants of the ternary cubic.** The cubic is taken as before to be

$$a_0x^3 + 3b_0x^2y + 3c_0xy^2 + d_0y^3 + 3(a_1x^2 + 2b_1xy + c_1y^2)z + 3(a_2x + b_2y)z^2 + a_3z^3.$$

It contains ten coefficients and three variables, together thirteen. The general scheme of linear substitution contains nine constants. These, eliminated between thirteen equations expressive of the identity of old and new forms, leave four equations connecting old and new coefficients and variables.

We must be prepared then to meet with four absolute covariants and invariants of the cubic, i.e. to meet with five quite independent covariants and invariants, including the cubic itself. We have already met with four, the cubic itself, the invariants S and T, and one covariant the Hessian. Another independent one must be expected.

Before seeking it let us illustrate the methods of §§ 296–299 by finding the one covariant which we already know, i.e. the Hessian, of degree 3 and order 3, and consequently (§ 299, Ex. 12) of whole weight $\frac{1}{3}(9+6) = 5$. This must also be the weight of the coefficient of z^3 in it.

We seek this coefficient of z^3, i.e. an invariant of degree 3 and sum of suffixes 5 of the system

$$\left.\begin{array}{l} a_0x^3 + 3b_0x^2y + 3c_0xy^2 + d_0y^3, \\ a_1x^2 + 2b_1xy \ + c_1y^2, \\ a_2x \ + b_2y, \\ a_3, \end{array}\right\} \qquad \ldots(1)$$

which is annihilated by

$$\Omega_{xz} \equiv a_3\frac{\partial}{\partial a_2} + 2a_2\frac{\partial}{\partial a_1} + 3a_1\frac{\partial}{\partial a_0} + b_2\frac{\partial}{\partial b_1} + 2b_1\frac{\partial}{\partial b_0} + c_1\frac{\partial}{\partial c_0}$$

$$\equiv a_3\frac{\partial}{\partial a_2} + \vartheta, \text{ say.}$$

It must involve a_3. Moreover it cannot involve $a_3{}^2$, for the weight of this exceeds 5. Let it be

$$a_3P + Q.$$

Here P and Q must be separately invariants of the binary system above. P is an invariant of the system whose degree and weight are both 2. It must then be $a_1 c_1 - b_1^2$. Now, expressing the annihilation of

$$a_3 (a_1 c_1 - b_1^2) + Q$$

by $a_3 \dfrac{\partial}{\partial a_2} + \vartheta$, we have, by taking the terms in a_3^2, a_3, 1 separately,

$$\frac{\partial}{\partial a_2} (a_1 c_1 - b_1^2) = 0, \text{ which is obvious,}$$

$$\frac{\partial}{\partial a_2} Q + \vartheta (a_1 c_1 - b_1^2) = 0,$$

$$\vartheta Q = 0;$$

of which the second gives

$$\frac{\partial}{\partial a_2} Q = -2 a_2 c_1 + 2 b_2 a_1,$$

i. e. $$Q = -a_2^2 c_1 + 2 a_2 b_2 b_1 + R,$$

where R is free from a_2, and has so to be chosen that Q is an invariant of the system (1). It is made one by taking $R = - b_2^2 a_1$; for which ϑQ is seen, as it should, to vanish.

Thus $$\{ a_3 (a_1 c_1 - b_1^2) - a_2^2 c_1 + 2 a_2 b_2 b_1 - b_2^2 a_1 \} z^3$$

is the last term in a covariant, the whole expression of which is obtained by operating on the term with

$$e^{\frac{y}{z} \Omega_{zy} + \frac{x}{z} \Omega_{zx}}$$

The coefficient of z^3 is correctly

$$\begin{vmatrix} a_1, & b_1, & a_2 \\ b_1, & c_1, & b_2 \\ a_2, & b_2, & a_3 \end{vmatrix},$$

and the whole covariant is, as it should be,

$$\frac{1}{216} \begin{vmatrix} \dfrac{\partial^2 u}{\partial x^2}, & \dfrac{\partial^2 u}{\partial x\, \partial y}, & \dfrac{\partial^2 u}{\partial x\, \partial z} \\ \dfrac{\partial^2 u}{\partial x\, \partial y}, & \dfrac{\partial^2 u}{\partial y^2}, & \dfrac{\partial^2 u}{\partial y\, \partial z} \\ \dfrac{\partial^2 u}{\partial x\, \partial z}, & \dfrac{\partial^2 u}{\partial y\, \partial z}, & \dfrac{\partial^2 u}{\partial z^2} \end{vmatrix} \equiv H.$$

Ex. 15. Prove that for the canonical form $x^3 + y^3 + z^3 + 6 m x y z$ the covariants $-Tu + 24 SH$ and $8 S^2 u + 3 TH$ are

$$(1 + 8 m^3) \{ (4 m^3 - 1) (x^3 + y^3 + z^3) + 18 m x y z \}$$

and

$$(1 + 8 m^3) \{ m^2 (5 + 4 m^3) (x^3 + y^3 + z^3) + 3 (1 - 10 m^3) x y z \}. \quad (Cayley.)$$

302. We have to seek another covariant of the ternary cubic, independent of u, S, T and the Hessian H.

We have seen that there is no other invariant independent of S and T. Also the covariant H of order 3 has been found as the only one of that order distinct from u itself.

Now (§ 299, Ex. 13) the order of any covariant of the cubic is a multiple of 3. The next possible order is 6. We proceed to see that there is a covariant of order 6 and degree in the coefficients 8, which is independent of u, H, S and T.

We have already two covariants of this order and degree; viz. uHS and u^2T. We seek a third, by looking for the coefficient in it of z^6.

By § 299, Ex. 12 the weight of the covariant is 12, which is the weight of uHS and u^2T. The weights of the coefficients of z^6 are equally 12.

The highest power of a_3 which can occur in the coefficient sought is then a_3^4, whose weight is 12. The coefficient of a_3^4 in it must be of weight zero, so that that coefficient is a function of a_0, b_0, c_0, d_0 only, and, being an invariant of

$$\left.\begin{array}{l} a_0x^3+3b_0x^2y+3c_0xy^2+d_0y^3, \\ a_1x^2+2b_1xy+c_1y^2, \\ a_2x+b_2y, \end{array}\right\} \qquad \ldots (1)$$

must be an invariant of the first only, and so, being of degree 4, must be a numerical multiple of

$$(a_0d_0-b_0c_0)^2-4(a_0c_0-b_0^2)(b_0d_0-c_0^2).$$

Now a_3^4 times this is the corresponding coefficient in u^2T. Thus, after subtracting a numerical multiple of u^2T, we have left in the coefficient of z^6 no term involving a_3^4. It suffices then to look for a covariant in which the coefficient of z^6 is of the form

$$a_3^3P_1+a_3^2Q_1+a_3R_1+S_1.$$

We have to determine P_1, Q_1, R_1, S_1, as invariants of the system (1), in such a way that this may be annihilated by Ω_{xz}, i.e. $a_3\dfrac{\partial}{\partial a_2}+\vartheta$.

As in § 301 we must have

$$\frac{\partial}{\partial a_2}P_1 = 0, \qquad \ldots (2)$$

$$\frac{\partial}{\partial a_2}Q_1+\vartheta P_1 = 0, \qquad \ldots (3)$$

$$\frac{\partial}{\partial a_2}R_1+\vartheta Q_1 = 0, \qquad \ldots (4)$$

$$\frac{\partial}{\partial a_2}S_1+\vartheta R_1 = 0, \qquad \ldots (5)$$

$$\vartheta S_1 = 0. \qquad \ldots (6)$$

The first of these tells us that P_1 does not involve a_2, and consequently that it is an invariant of the cubic and quadratic in the set (1) only. Its degree is 5 and its weight 3. Now (§ 260) the only invariants of the quadratic and cubic of this degree and sum of suffixes are

$$AF \equiv (a_1 c_1 - b_1^2)\{a_1(b_0 d_0 - c_0^2) - b_1(a_0 d_0 - b_0 c_0) + c_1(a_0 c_0 - b_0^2)\}$$

and (§ 261, end)

$$G \equiv a_1^3 d_0^2 + c_1^3 a_0^2 - 6a_1^2 b_1 c_0 d_0 - 6b_1 c_1^2 a_0 b_0 + 2(a_1 c_1 + 2b_1^2)(a_1 b_0 d_0 + c_1 a_0 c_0) + (a_1 c_1 + 8b_1^2)(a_1 c_0^2 + c_1 b_0^2) - 2a_1 b_1 c_1 a_0 d_0 - 2b_1(5a_1 c_1 + 4b_1^2) b_0 c_0;$$

and of these the first is the coefficient of a_3^3, the highest power of a_3 which occurs, in the coefficient of z^6 in uHS. We may subtract this covariant, and look for a covariant in which the coefficient of z^6 has the form

$$a_3^3 G + a_3^2 Q + a_3 R + S.$$

With some labour, by successive use of (3), (4), (5), (6), we can determine Q, R, S as invariants of the system (1). For their expression we need, besides G above and A to F of § 291, the following other invariants of the system, taken from § 260 by aid of § 262,

$$K = c_1 a_2^2 - 2b_1 a_2 b_2 + a_1 b_2^2, \text{ [§ 260 (1)]},$$

$$L = a_0 b_2^3 - 3b_0 a_2 b_2^2 + 3c_0 a_2^2 b_2 - d_0 a_2^3, \text{ [§ 260 (3)]},$$

$$M = (a_1 b_0 - a_0 b_1) b_2^3 - (2a_1 c_0 - b_1 b_0 - c_1 a_0) a_2 b_2^2 + (a_1 d_0 + b_1 c_0 - 2c_1 b_0) a_2^2 b_2 - (b_1 d_0 - c_1 c_0) a_2^3, \text{ [§ 260 (7)]}.$$

We find that

$$Q = 4AB - 3D^2 - 2FK - 8AE + 9A^3,$$

$$R = 3DL + 8AM - BK + 6EK - 11A^2 K,$$

$$S = 3AK^2 - L^2 - 6KM.$$

The only point of difficulty which presents itself in proceeding by means of (3), (4), (5), (6) is the determination of the coefficient of A^3 in Q. This has to be chosen so that the eventual value of S shall be annihilated by ϑ.

The above found are not of course the only, or probably the simplest, expressions for Q, R, S in terms of invariants of the binary quadratic and cubic, of which there are five besides the ten A, B, ... L, M, as these are connected by many syzygies.

303. From this coefficient of z^6 in the new covariant the full expansion of the covariant, which call Φ, may be obtained

by either of the methods already detailed, i.e. by operating on it either with $z^6 e^{\frac{y}{z}\Omega_{zy}+\frac{x}{z}\Omega_{zx}}$ or with $z^6 e^{\frac{x}{y}\Omega_{yx}} e^{\frac{y}{z}\Omega_{zy}}$, or by substituting in it for $a_1, b_1, c_1, a_2, b_2, a_3$ the expressions

$$\frac{1}{6}\frac{\partial^2 u}{\partial x^2},\ \frac{1}{6}\frac{\partial^2 u}{\partial x\,\partial y},\ \frac{1}{6}\frac{\partial^2 u}{\partial y^2},\ \frac{1}{3}\frac{\partial u}{\partial x},\ \frac{1}{3}\frac{\partial u}{\partial y},\ u,$$

and dividing through by the power of z which occurs as a factor in the result, i.e. z^6.

For the canonical form $x^3+y^3+z^3+6mxyz$ we at once see that $A=-m^2$, $C=1$, $F=-m$, while B, D, E, G, K, L, M all vanish, and $a_3=1$. Thus the coefficient of z^6, and therefore of $x^6+y^6+z^6$, in the covariant Φ of the canonical form is $-9m^6$.

For the semi-canonized form $ax^3+by^3+cz^3+6mxyz$ the coefficient of z^6 in Φ is in like manner $-9c^2m^6$, so that Φ has the three terms $-9m^6(a^2x^6+b^2y^6+c^2z^6)$.

For the canonical form the coefficients of z^6 in uHS and u^2T are $-m^3+m^6$ and $1-20m^3-8m^6$ respectively. The covariant Φ is the Θu of Cayley's third memoir. The Θ of Salmon's *Higher Plane Curves*, § 231, has for its z^6 coefficient $3m^3+6m^6$, and is $-(\Phi+3uSH)$. Θ itself might with equal reason be taken as fundamental.

To find the full expression of Φ for the canonical form $x^3+y^3+z^3+6mxyz$ we have to put, in the general expression for the final coefficient found in the last article,

$$x^3+y^3+z^3+6mxyz\,;\ x^2+2myz,\ y^2+2mzx,\ z^2+2mxy\,;$$
$$x,\ mz,\ y\,;\ 1,\ 0,\ 0,\ 1,$$

for $\qquad a_3;\ a_2, b_2;\ a_1, b_1, c_1;\ a_0, b_0, c_0, d_0,$

respectively, and divide by z^6. The result is that for the canonical form

$$\begin{aligned}\Phi = -9m^6(x^3+y^3+z^3)^2 &\\ -(2m+5m^4+20m^7)(x^3+y^3+z^3)\,xyz &\\ -(15m^2+78m^5-12m^8)\,x^2y^2z^2 &\\ +(1+8m^3)^2(y^3z^3+z^3x^3+x^3y^3).&\end{aligned}$$

This is not a quadratic function of $x^3+y^3+z^3$ and xyz. It is then irreducible in terms of u, H, S, T.

304. The system u, H, S, T, Φ is an algebraically complete one of invariants and covariants of the cubic. Any other covariant is a function of them. But there is another covariant which is irreducible. It was obtained by Brioschi, and is, for the semi-canonized form $ax^3+by^3+cz^3+6mxyz$,

$$(abc+8m^3)^3(by^3-cz^3)(cz^3-ax^3)(ax^3-by^3).$$

304 (*bis*). **General theory resumed. A generator of all ternary covariant sources.** For reasons expressed in §§ 297–299, and in keeping with a usage (§ 109) as to binary covariants, we will give the name ternary covariant *sources* to rational integral functions annihilated by Ω_{yx}, Ω_{xy}, Ω_{xz} and Ω_{yz}. A covariant source in the coefficients of a p-ic is not only the coefficient of the highest power z^{ϖ} of z in a covariant of that p-ic, but also the coefficient of the highest power of z in a covariant of any $(p+r)$-ic which has, but for the appropriate multinomial coefficient multipliers, the same coefficients as the p-ic in its terms up to the pth order in x and y.

As in the case of binary quantics, there is convenience in allowing the idea that the order $p+r$ may be increased even to infinity.

Let us use a double suffix notation, and write a ternary p-ic

$$\sum_{r=0\ s=0}^{r+s=p} \frac{p!}{r!\,s!\,(p-r-s)!} c_{rs} z^{p-r-s} x^r y^s;$$

but let us consider an infinitely continued double system of coefficients

$$\begin{array}{c} c_{00} \\ c_{10}\ ,\ c_{01} \\ c_{20}\ ,\ c_{11}\ ,\ c_{02} \\ c_{30}\ ,\ c_{21}\ ,\ c_{12}\ ,\ c_{03} \\ \cdot\ \cdot\ \cdot\ \cdot\ \cdot\ \cdot\ \cdot\ \cdot\ \cdot\ , \end{array}$$

the first p rows containing those present in a p-ic, for any p. Let us also (in this article only) adapt the four operators to this infinitely extended system, writing

$$\Omega_{yx} \equiv \sum_{r=1}^{r\to\infty} \left\{ c_{r\,0}\frac{\partial}{\partial c_{r-1\,1}} + 2c_{r-1\,1}\frac{\partial}{\partial c_{r-2\,2}} + \ldots + rc_{1\,r-1}\frac{\partial}{\partial c_{0\,r}} \right\},$$

$$\Omega_{xy} \equiv \sum_{r=1}^{r\to\infty} \left\{ rc_{r-1\,1}\frac{\partial}{\partial c_{r\,0}} + (r-1)c_{r-2\,2}\frac{\partial}{\partial c_{r-1\,1}} + \ldots + c_{0\,r}\frac{\partial}{\partial c_{1\,r-1}} \right\},$$

$$\Omega_{xz} \equiv \sum_{r=0\ s=0}^{r+s\to\infty} \left\{ (r+1)c_{rs}\frac{\partial}{\partial c_{r+1\,s}} \right\},$$

$$\Omega_{yz} \equiv \sum_{r=0\ s=0}^{r+s\to\infty} \left\{ (s+1)\,c_{rs}\frac{\partial}{\partial c_{r\,s+1}} \right\},$$

so that the Ω_{yx}, Ω_{xy}, Ω_{xz}, Ω_{yz} appropriate to a p-ic are the parts of these which mention no c_{rs} with $r+s>p$. The alternant equalities of §§ 284, 286, 287, with H_1, H_2, H_3 infinitely extended, hold for the extended operators. Any homogeneous rational integral function of the coefficients which is annihilated by the extended Ω_{yx}, Ω_{xy}, Ω_{xz}, Ω_{yz} will be a covariant source for a p-ic and every $(p+r)$-ic if it involves no coefficient for which $r+s>p$.

We can now prove it possible to find by direct operation all covariant sources in the infinite double system of coefficients, though not to dissociate from the rest those appertaining to a p-ic without solving systems of linear equations.

A rational integral homogeneous function of degree i which is annihilated by Ω_{yx} and Ω_{xy}, being an invariant of the binary quantics $c_{00}(x, y)^0$, $(c_{10}, c_{01})(x, y)^1$, $(c_{20}, c_{11}, c_{02})(x, y)^2$, &c., consists of terms in each of which the sums of first and of second suffixes are equal, and the same for all terms: these are the conditions of § 31. Also (§§ 180, 181) every such function is a

$$\phi F,$$

where $$\phi \equiv 1 - \frac{\Omega_{xy}\Omega_{yx}}{1.2} + \frac{\Omega_{xy}{}^2\Omega_{yx}{}^2}{1.2^2.3} - \frac{\Omega_{xy}{}^3\Omega_{yx}{}^3}{1.2^2.3^2.4} + \dots,$$

and F consists of terms of the degree and equal sums of suffixes in question. Conversely every non-vanishing ϕF is annihilated by Ω_{yx} and Ω_{xy}.

If now we take for F a function of the degree and equal sums of suffixes which is annihilated by Ω_{xz} and Ω_{yz}, the derived ϕF will be itself annihilated by Ω_{xz} and Ω_{yz}, as well as by Ω_{yx} and Ω_{xy}. To prove this we will show that if Ω_{xz} and Ω_{yz} annihilate F, they also annihilate $\Omega_{yx}\Omega_{xy}F$, $\Omega_{yx}{}^2\Omega_{xy}{}^2F$, &c. We have

$$\Omega_{xz}\Omega_{yx} - \Omega_{yx}\Omega_{xz} = \Omega_{yz},$$

and

$$\Omega_{yz}\Omega_{yx} - \Omega_{yx}\Omega_{yz} = 0,$$

so that if Ω_{xz} and Ω_{yz} annihilate F they annihilate $\Omega_{yx}F$. Similarly they annihilate $\Omega_{xy}F$. By a succession of uses of these two facts it follows that they annihilate every $\Omega_{xy}{}^m\Omega_{yx}{}^n\Omega_{xy}{}^p \dots F$.

Moreover, conversely, every function with all four annihilators is a ϕF, being the result of operating with ϕ on itself.

It follows that, if we can write down the sum of arbitrary multiples of all functions of the degree i and the given equal sums of suffixes which are annihilated by Ω_{xz} and Ω_{yz}, thus obtaining the most general F of its type which has those annihilators, and if we derive from it the general ϕF, this will be a sum of arbitrary multiples of all the functions of the type which possess all four annihilators.

We have then to look for functions F such that $\Omega_{xz}F=0$ and $\Omega_{yz}F=0$.

Now, if G is any finite rational integral function of coefficients chosen from the double system,

$$\{c_{00}-(c_{10}\Omega_{xz}+c_{01}\Omega_{yz})+\frac{1}{1\,.\,2}(c_{20}\Omega_{xz}{}^2+2c_{11}\Omega_{xz}\Omega_{yz}+c_{02}\Omega_{yz}{}^2) -\ldots\}\,G,$$

which call $$\psi G,$$

is annihilated by Ω_{xz} and by Ω_{yz}. The verification is immediate when we remember that $\Omega_{xz}\Omega_{yz}=\Omega_{yz}\Omega_{xz}$, and that, for some finite and all greater values of r, $\Omega_{xz}{}^r$ and $\Omega_{yz}{}^r$ must annihilate a G of finite degree in given c's.

Conversely, every F annihilated by Ω_{xz} and by Ω_{yz} is a ψG. By § 119 it involves c_{00}; and we will prove the statement by showing that

$$iF=\psi\frac{\partial}{\partial c_{00}}F.$$

From
$$\Omega_{xz}\frac{\partial}{\partial c_{r-1s}}-\frac{\partial}{\partial c_{r-1s}}\Omega_{xz}=-r\frac{\partial}{\partial c_{rs}},$$

and
$$\Omega_{yz}\frac{\partial}{\partial c_{rs-1}}-\frac{\partial}{\partial c_{rs-1}}\Omega_{yz}=-s\frac{\partial}{\partial c_{rs}},$$

it follows that, when the operation is on something annihilated by Ω_{xz} and Ω_{yz},

$$\Omega_{xz}\frac{\partial}{\partial c_{r-1s}}=-r\frac{\partial}{\partial c_{rs}},\quad\text{and}\quad\Omega_{yz}\frac{\partial}{\partial c_{rs-1}}=-s\frac{\partial}{\partial c_{rs}},$$

so that, by $r+s$ repetitions of operation,

$$\frac{1}{r!\,s!}\Omega_{xz}{}^r\Omega_{yz}{}^s\frac{\partial}{\partial c_{00}}=(-1)^{r+s}\frac{\partial}{\partial c_{rs}},\ \text{for every } r \text{ and } s,$$

and consequently

$$\psi\frac{\partial}{\partial c_{00}}=c_{00}\frac{\partial}{\partial c_{00}}+c_{10}\frac{\partial}{\partial c_{10}}+c_{01}\frac{\partial}{\partial c_{01}}+c_{20}\frac{\partial}{\partial c_{20}}+c_{11}\frac{\partial}{\partial c_{11}}+c_{02}\frac{\partial}{\partial c_{02}}+\ldots,$$

which simply multiplies a homogeneous function by its degree.

Accordingly, observing that operation with ψ adds one to degree, while it does not alter either sum of suffixes, we have proved that $\phi\psi$ is an operator which derives from the most general G, of degree $i-1$ and equal sums q of first and of second suffixes throughout, the most general covariant source of degree i and the same sums of suffixes q.

It is not the case that it produces all covariant sources of this type for the p-ic from the most general G which involves only coefficients in the p-ic, except in the very limited class of cases when $2q \not> p$; for in general the result of operation with ψ on this G will involve, to the first degree only, more advanced coefficients c_{rs} than occur in the p-ic.

To obtain all covariant sources appertaining to the p-ic we might, after having obtained the general ψG for a given i and q, equate to zero the coefficients in it of those products which involve letters not present in the p-ic, thus determining some of the arbitraries as linear functions of the rest, and leaving the most general limited ψG which contains only coefficients in the p-ic. Operation with ϕ on this limited ψG would give what is required.

305. **Contravariants.** A contravariant of a ternary quantic u is (§ 66) an invariant of the system consisting of u and the linear form

$$\xi x + \eta y + \zeta z$$

in which the coefficients of the latter are present.

Now the annihilators of invariants of two ternary quantics u, v are

$$\Omega_{yx} + \Omega'_{yx},\ \Omega_{xy} + \Omega'_{xy},\ \Omega_{zy} + \Omega'_{zy},$$
$$\Omega_{yz} + \Omega'_{yz},\ \Omega_{xz} + \Omega'_{xz},\ \Omega_{zx} + \Omega'_{zx},$$

where unaccented Ω's are the annihilators of invariants of u, and accented Ω's are the corresponding annihilators of invariants of v. This is proved exactly as in §§ 281, &c.

A contravariant of u has then the six annihilators

$$\Omega_{yx} + \xi\frac{\partial}{\partial\eta},\ \Omega_{xy} + \eta\frac{\partial}{\partial\xi},\ \Omega_{zy} + \eta\frac{\partial}{\partial\zeta},$$
$$\Omega_{yz} + \zeta\frac{\partial}{\partial\eta},\ \Omega_{xz} + \zeta\frac{\partial}{\partial\xi},\ \Omega_{zx} + \xi\frac{\partial}{\partial\zeta},$$

and all properties of contravariants, except the one fact $ip + \varpi' =$ constant, where ϖ' is the order in ξ, η, ζ, or the *class*, are consequences of these six facts of annihilation.

Notice the distinction between corresponding facts of annihilation as to covariants and contravariants. In corresponding annihilators

$$\Omega_{yx} - y\frac{\partial}{\partial x}, \qquad \Omega_{yx} + \xi\frac{\partial}{\partial\eta},$$

x and y correspond to η and $-\xi$, and not to ξ and η or ξ and $-\eta$.

It is not hard to see, by proceeding as in § 296, that the coefficient of $\zeta^{\varpi'}$, the highest power of ζ which occurs in any *contravariant*, is to be determined so as to have the four annihilators

$$\Omega_{yx},\ \Omega_{xy},\ \Omega_{zx},\ \Omega_{zy},$$

whereas the four annihilators of the last coefficient in a *covariant* are

$$\Omega_{yx},\ \Omega_{xy},\ \Omega_{xz},\ \Omega_{yz}.$$

A function of the coefficients which is annihilated by

$$\Omega_{yx},\ \Omega_{xy},\ \Omega_{zx}$$

is necessarily also annihilated by Ω_{zy} by § 286 (10). Thus three facts of annihilation suffice for the coefficient of $\zeta^{\varpi'}$.

It can also be seen, as in the case of covariants, that, when the final coefficient in a contravariant is known, found as any homogeneous function annihilated by Ω_{yx}, Ω_{xy} and Ω_{zx}, the whole contravariant is determined in the form

$$\zeta^{\varpi'} e^{-\frac{\xi}{\zeta}\Omega_{xz}-\frac{\eta}{\zeta}\Omega_{yz}}\Sigma,$$

where Σ is the coefficient in question.

In a covariant the last coefficient is the one of greatest weight (sum of suffixes). In a contravariant, on the other hand, it is the one of least weight. This is reasonable, for, to make

$$\xi x+\eta y+\zeta z$$

isobaric when we take x, y, z of weights 1, 1, 0, we naturally take ξ, η, ζ of weights 0, 0, 1.

Ex. 16. A ternary p-ic ($p>2$) cannot have more than, and is to be expected to have exactly, $\frac{1}{2}(p+1)(p+2)-5$ algebraically independent contravariants and invariants together, i.e. the same number as of algebraically independent covariants and invariants together.

306. **Contravariant of ternary quadratic.** The method of evectants (§ 67) is a fruitful one for the discovery of contravariants.

The ternary quadratic

$$a_0x^2+2b_0xy+c_0y^2+2(a_1x+b_1y)z+a_2z^2$$

has only one contravariant. It is the evectant of the discriminant

$$a_0c_0a_2+2b_0a_1b_1-a_0b_1^2-c_0a_1^2-b_0^2a_2,$$

i.e. is formed by operation on this with

$$\xi^2\frac{\partial}{\partial a_0}+\xi\eta\frac{\partial}{\partial b_0}+\eta^2\frac{\partial}{\partial c_0}+\xi\zeta\frac{\partial}{\partial a_1}+\eta\zeta\frac{\partial}{\partial b_1}+\zeta^2\frac{\partial}{\partial a_2},$$

and is

$$(c_0a_2-b_1^2)\xi^2+2(a_1b_1-b_0a_2)\xi\eta+(a_0a_2-a_1^2)\eta^2$$
$$+2(b_0b_1-c_0a_1)\xi\zeta+2(b_0a_1-a_0b_1)\eta\zeta+(a_0c_0-b_0^2)\zeta^2.$$

Geometrically its vanishing expresses the tangential equation of the conic denoted by the quadratic, or the point-coordinate equation of a reciprocal conic. Such a contravariant has been called the *reciprocant* of a ternary quantic. This word has been also used by Sylvester and others in a totally different sense of wide application.

Ex. 17. The result of substituting $\partial u/\partial x$, $\partial u/\partial y$, $\partial u/\partial z$ for ξ, η, ζ in the reciprocant of a ternary quadratic u is four times the product of u and its discriminant. (*Cayley.*)

307. **Contravariants of the ternary cubic.** The method of evectants also gives three contravariants of the cubic, in terms of which and the invariants S and T all other contravariants can be expressed, not however rationally and integrally.

We cannot expect more than three contravariants absolutely independent of one another and the invariants. For the cubic

$$a_0x^3 + 3b_0x^2y + 3c_0xy^2 + d_0y^3 + 3(a_1x^2 + 2b_1xy + c_1y^2)z$$
$$+ 3(a_2x + b_2y)z^2 + a_3z^3$$

and

$$\xi x + \eta y + \zeta z$$

contain together thirteen coefficients, and the scheme of linear substitution contains nine. Now elimination of nine quantities from thirteen equations leaves four only; and if there were more than five independent invariants and contravariants there would be more than four independent absolute invariants and contravariants, i.e. more than four independent results of elimination of the nine constants of substitution from the thirteen equations.

Now the first evectant of S, and the first and second evectants of T, are three independent contravariants.

We may readily form two of these three contravariants for the canonical form of the cubic.

For the semi-canonized form

$$ax^3 + by^3 + cz^3 + 6mxyz$$

the invariants are (§§ 292, 293)

$$S = m(abc - m^3),$$
$$T = (abc)^2 - 20m^3abc - 8m^6.$$

Now we know that it is not safe in general to assume that we can correctly obtain, by use of canonical or particularized forms, concomitants from other concomitants by processes which use differentiation with regard to coefficients. For, though a part of a concomitant may vanish when coefficients which vanish in the case of a particularized form are made zero, it is not as a rule the case that the derivatives of that function with regard to those coefficients vanish.

If, however, we regard the expression for S in § 291, we notice that it consists of the part $b_0(a_0d_0a_3 - b_1^3)$, which does not involve coefficients that vanish for the semi-canonized form, and other terms all of which are of the second or higher degrees in these coefficients. The derivatives with regard to all these coefficients will then vanish when the coefficients themselves vanish. Moreover, if we regard the process of formation of T from S by means of the Hessian, we see that the full expression for T also involves, besides the terms which do not vanish for the semi-canonized form, only terms of the second and higher degrees in the coefficients which vanish for that form.

For the semi-canonized form

$$ax^3 + by^3 + cz^3 + 6mxyz$$

we consequently correctly form the first evectants of S and T by operation on the expressions above for those invariants with

$$\xi^3 \frac{\partial}{\partial a} + \eta^3 \frac{\partial}{\partial b} + \zeta^3 \frac{\partial}{\partial c} + \xi\eta\zeta \frac{\partial}{\partial m}.$$

Thus the first evectant of S is

$$P = m(bc\,\xi^3 + ca\,\eta^3 + ab\,\zeta^3) + (abc - 4m^3)\,\xi\eta\zeta,$$

and the first evectant of T, divided by 2, is

$$Q = (abc - 10m^3)(bc\,\xi^3 + ca\,\eta^3 + ab\,\zeta^3) - m^2(30abc + 24m^3)\,\xi\eta\zeta.$$

To obtain correctly the second evectant of T it would be necessary to retain in the full expression for T, not only the terms in a, b, c, m, but those which involve to the second degree coefficients which vanish for the semi-canonized form.

The coefficient of ζ^6 in the full expression for this second evectant of T is

$$(a_0d_0 - b_0c_0)^2 - 4(a_0c_0 - b_0^2)(b_0d_0 - c_0^2);$$

for this is the coefficient of a_3^2 in T. The contravariant is then

$$\zeta^6 e^{-\frac{\xi}{\zeta}\Omega_{xz} - \frac{\eta}{\zeta}\Omega_{yz}} \{(a_0d_0 - b_0c_0)^2 - 4(a_0c_0 - b_0^2)(b_0d_0 - c_0^2)\}.$$

Another way of finding a contravariant which proves to be the same is suggested by geometry. Its vanishing is the condition that the line

$$\xi x + \eta y + \zeta z = 0$$

should touch the cubic. Thus, to find it for the semi-canonized form

$$ax^3 + by^3 + cz^3 + 6mxyz,$$

we may express that

$$\zeta^3(ax^3 + by^3) - c(\xi x + \eta y)^3 - 6m(\xi x + \eta y)\zeta^2 xy,$$

considered as a binary quantic in x, y, may have a square factor, i.e. take the discriminant of this cubic in x, y. This discriminant, divided by ζ^6, is

$$F = b^2c^2\xi^6 + c^2a^2\eta^6 + a^2b^2\zeta^6 - (2abc + 32m^3)(a\eta^3\zeta^3 + b\zeta^3\xi^3 + c\xi^3\eta^3) - 24m^2\xi\eta\zeta(bc\xi^3 + ca\eta^3 + ab\zeta^3) - 24m(abc + 2m^3)\xi^2\eta^2\zeta^2.$$

For the fully canonized form

$$x^3 + y^3 + z^3 + 6mxyz$$

the three contravariants are

$$P = m(\xi^3 + \eta^3 + \zeta^3) + (1 - 4m^3)\xi\eta\zeta,$$
$$Q = (1 - 10m^3)(\xi^3 + \eta^3 + \zeta^3) - m^2(30 + 24m^3)\xi\eta\zeta,$$
$$F = \xi^6 + \eta^6 + \zeta^6 - (2 + 32m^3)(\eta^3\zeta^3 + \zeta^3\xi^3 + \xi^3\eta^3) - 24m^2\xi\eta\zeta(\xi^3 + \eta^3 + \zeta^3) - (24m + 48m^4)\xi^2\eta^2\zeta^2.$$

P is called by Cayley (who takes $-P$) the Pippian, and by other writers the Cayleyan. Q is called the Quippian. F is the reciprocant.

308. In terms of P, Q, F and the invariants S and T all contravariants can be expressed. There is, however, one more irreducible contravariant which is not a rational integral function of them, obtained by Hermite. For the semi-canonized form $ax^3 + by^3 + cz^3 + 6mxyz$ its expression is

$$(abc + 8m^3)^3(c\eta^3 - b\zeta^3)(a\zeta^3 - c\xi^3)(b\xi^3 - a\eta^3).$$

Ex. 18. Prove that $4SQ - 3TP$ and $TQ + 48S^2P$ are cubic contravariants whose canonical forms are

$$(1 + 8m^3)^2\{m(\xi^3 + \eta^3 + \zeta^3) - 3\xi\eta\zeta\},\ (1 + 8m^3)^2\{(1 + 2m^3)(\xi^3 + \eta^3 + \zeta^3) + 18m^2\xi\eta\zeta\}.$$ (*Aronhold.*)

Ex. 19. The result of putting $\partial u/\partial x$, $\partial u/\partial y$, $\partial u/\partial z$ for ξ, η, ζ in F the reciprocant of a ternary cubic u is the product of u and a covariant; and the same is true as to the reciprocant of any ternary quantic. (*Cayley.*)

309. **Mixed concomitants.** A mixed concomitant of a ternary quantic u may be regarded as a covariant of the system consisting of u and the linear form

$$\xi x + \eta y + \zeta z.$$

It has then the six annihilators

$$\Omega_{yx} + \xi\frac{\partial}{\partial\eta} - y\frac{\partial}{\partial x},\quad \Omega_{zy} + \eta\frac{\partial}{\partial\zeta} - z\frac{\partial}{\partial y},\quad \Omega_{xz} + \zeta\frac{\partial}{\partial\xi} - x\frac{\partial}{\partial z},$$
$$\Omega_{xy} + \eta\frac{\partial}{\partial\xi} - x\frac{\partial}{\partial y},\quad \Omega_{yz} + \zeta\frac{\partial}{\partial\eta} - y\frac{\partial}{\partial z},\quad \Omega_{zx} + \xi\frac{\partial}{\partial\zeta} - z\frac{\partial}{\partial x}.$$

If a mixed concomitant of a ternary p-ic is of orders ϖ, ϖ' in x, y, z and ξ, η, ζ respectively, or say of order ϖ and class ϖ', it readily follows that the terms of it in $\zeta^{\varpi'}$ have the annihilators

$$\Omega_{yx} - y\frac{\partial}{\partial x},\quad \Omega_{xy} - x\frac{\partial}{\partial y},\quad \Omega_{zx} - z\frac{\partial}{\partial x},\quad \Omega_{zy} - z\frac{\partial}{\partial y},$$

of which the first two and one of the others necessitate the fourth.

If $P\zeta^{\varpi'}$ denotes the aggregate of these terms, the whole concomitant is

$$\zeta^{\varpi'} e^{-\frac{\xi}{\zeta}\left(\Omega_{xz} - x\frac{\partial}{\partial z}\right) - \frac{\eta}{\zeta}\left(\Omega_{yz} - y\frac{\partial}{\partial z}\right)} P.$$

If Sz^{ϖ} is the highest term in z which occurs in P, then S has the annihilators Ω_{yx}, Ω_{xy}, and is consequently an invariant of the system

$$\begin{aligned}
&(a_0, b_0, c_0, d_0, \ldots)(x, y)^p,\\
&(a_1, b_1, c_1, \ldots)(x, y)^{p-1},\\
&(a_2, b_2, \ldots)(x, y)^{p-2},\\
&\cdot\quad\cdot\quad\cdot\quad\cdot\quad\cdot\quad\cdot\quad\cdot\\
&a_{p-1}x + b_{p-1}y,\\
&a_p.
\end{aligned}$$

The whole expression for P is $z^{\varpi} e^{\frac{x}{z}\Omega_{zx} + \frac{y}{z}\Omega_{zy}} S$.

Consequently, if $Sz^{\varpi}\zeta^{\varpi'}$ is the last term in any concomitant, the whole can be derived from it, and is

$$\zeta^{\varpi'} e^{-\frac{\xi}{\zeta}\left(\Omega_{xz} - x\frac{\partial}{\partial z}\right) - \frac{\eta}{\zeta}\left(\Omega_{yz} - y\frac{\partial}{\partial z}\right)} . z^{\varpi} e^{\frac{x}{z}\Omega_{zx} + \frac{y}{z}\Omega_{zy}} S.$$

As to ϖ and ϖ' the former may be taken arbitrarily not below a certain limit; viz. not below m where m is the first integer for which $(x\Omega_{zx} + y\Omega_{zy})^{m+1} S = 0$. ϖ' is then determinate and has a constant difference from ϖ. If K is the concomitant for the lowest value m of ϖ, the concomitant for any higher value of ϖ is merely $(\xi x + \eta y + \zeta z)^{\varpi - m} K$. In fact the whole concomitant, which may be written

$$\zeta^{\varpi'} e^{\frac{1}{\zeta}(\xi x + \eta y)\frac{\partial}{\partial z}} . z^{\varpi} e^{-\frac{\xi}{\zeta}\Omega_{xz} - \frac{\eta}{\zeta}\Omega_{yz}} e^{\frac{x}{z}\Omega_{zx} + \frac{y}{z}\Omega_{zy}} S,$$

is by Taylor's theorem

$$\zeta^{\varpi' - \varpi} (\xi x + \eta y + \zeta z)^{\varpi} e^{-\frac{\xi}{\zeta}\Omega_{xz} - \frac{\eta}{\zeta}\Omega_{yz}} \left[e^{\frac{x}{z}\Omega_{zx} + \frac{y}{z}\Omega_{zy}} S\right],$$

where in the square brackets $(\xi x + \eta y + \zeta z)/\zeta$ is put for z.

Any invariant of the system of binary quantics written above, i.e. any gradient annihilated by Ω_{yx} and Ω_{xy}, is the final coefficient in a concomitant of some kind, i.e. an invariant, covariant, contravariant, or mixed concomitant.

A valuable authority on this subject is a paper by Forsyth entitled 'Systems of Ternariants that are Algebraically Complete' (*American Journal*, Vol. XII).

Ex. 20. The number of algebraically independent concomitants, including the p-ic itself and $\xi x+\eta y+\zeta z$, of a ternary p-ic is

$$\tfrac{1}{2}(p+1)(p+2)-2. \quad (\textit{Forsyth.})$$

Ex. 21. The ternary quadratic has a mixed concomitant whose last term is $(a_0b_1^2-2b_0a_1b_1+c_0a_1^2)z^2\zeta^2$; and in terms of this, the quadratic itself, the discriminant, and $\xi x+\eta y+\zeta z$ all concomitants whatever of the quadratic can be expressed.

Ex. 22. Any concomitant of the ternary cubic can be algebraically expressed in terms of $\xi x+\eta y+\zeta z$ and seven concomitants whose last coefficients are functions of the results of replacing x, y by b_2, $-a_2$ in

$$(a_0, b_0, c_0, d_0)(x, y)^3,\ (a_1, b_1, c_1)(x, y)^2,\ (a_2, b_2)(x, y),\ a_3$$

and their successive derivatives with regard to x. (Cf. § 263.) (*Forsyth.*)

Ex. 23. Forming the ψG of § 304 (*bis*), with G general of type $i-1$, q, q, and observing that $\Omega_{xy}{}^{q+1}\Omega_{yx}{}^{q+1}\psi G=0$, i.e.

$$\Omega_{yx}\Omega_{xy}(\Omega_{yx}\Omega_{xy}-1\,.\,2)(\Omega_{yx}\Omega_{xy}-2\,.\,3)\ldots(\Omega_{yx}\Omega_{xy}-q\,.\,q+1)\psi G=0,$$

so that ψG is separable, as in § 128 (*bis*), into a sum of $q+1$ parts annihilated by the several operating factors $\Omega_{yx}\Omega_{xy}-r\,.\,r+1$, prove that the first part ($r=0$) is the most general covariant source of type i, q, q (§ 304 (*bis*)), and that the r-th (for $r=1, 2, \ldots q$) is the most general gradient of type i, q, q occurring as the coefficient of $\xi^r\eta^r\zeta^0$ in a quantic $(\xi, \eta, \zeta)^{2r}$ which presents itself as co-factor with the highest power of z in a mixed concomitant of a ternary quantic of high order. (*Cambridge International Congress*, 1912.)

Ex. 24. The whole number of the linearly independent gradients of type i, q, q that are annihilated by Ω_{xz} and by Ω_{yz} is equal to the sum of (1) the number of linearly independent covariant sources of type i, q, q, and (2) the aggregate of the numbers of the linearly independent sources of the q possible types i, $q+r$, $q+r$ $(r=1, 2, \ldots q)$ of those mixed concomitants of the q corresponding classes (dimensions in ξ, η, ζ) $2r$ which contain terms free from ζ in their co-factors with highest powers z^{ϖ} of z. [Mixed concomitants without such terms are results of multiplying other concomitants by powers of the universal concomitant $\xi x+\eta y+\zeta z$.]

310. The whole system of *irreducible*, pure and mixed, concomitants of the ternary cubic has been found to consist of thirty-four forms. This was established by Gordan (*Math. Ann.* I). The system was systematically exhibited by Gundelfinger (*Math. Ann.* VI); and calculated for the form $ax^3+by^3+cz^3+6mxyz$ by Cayley (*Am. J.* IV).

311. **Quantics in more than three variables.** With regard to q-ary quantics in general Sylvester has given a theorem which includes that of § 288.

For a homogeneous function of the coefficients in a q-ary p-ic to be an invariant it is necessary and sufficient that it have a cyclical set of q annihilators of the Ω type.

Let $x_1, x_2, x_3, \ldots, x_q$ be the variables, and denote a cyclical set of Ω's, whose symbolical forms as in § 282 are

$$\left[x_2 \frac{\partial}{\partial x_1}\right], \left[x_3 \frac{\partial}{\partial x_2}\right], \ldots \left[x_q \frac{\partial}{\partial x_{q-1}}\right], \left[x_1 \frac{\partial}{\partial x_q}\right],$$

by $\Omega_{2,1}, \Omega_{3,2}, \ldots, \Omega_{q,q-1}, \Omega_{1,q}$.

It can be readily proved by the theory of multiplication of determinants that the modulus of the resultant substitution which is the equivalent of a succession of substitutions is the product of their moduli. But this is not essential to the argument, in virtue of the theorem of § 23.

By § 22 a homogeneous function of the coefficients has only to be multiplied by a power of l, to become the same function of the coefficients in the quantic which is obtained by substituting $lx_1, lx_2, \ldots, lx_q$ for $x_1, x_2, \ldots, x_q$ in the given quantic.

By Chapter VI, $\Omega_{2,1} I = 0$ is the necessary and sufficient condition for I to persist in form after the substitution of

$$x_1 + mx_2, x_2, x_3, \ldots, x_q$$

for

$$x_1, x_2, x_3, \ldots, x_q.$$

Thus $\Omega_{2,1} I = 0$ is the necessary and sufficient condition for persistence of the homogeneous I, but for a power of l, after the substitution of

$$lx_1 + lmx_2, lx_2, lx_3, \ldots, lx_q.$$

$\Omega_{3,2} I = 0$ is in like manner the necessary and sufficient condition for persistence after the further substitution of $l'x_1, l'x_2 + m'x_3, l'x_3, \ldots, l'x_q$, but for a power of l', i.e. for persistence, but for a function of the constants as factor, after the resultant substitution of

$$ll'x_1 + lml'x_2 + lmm'x_3, ll'x_2 + lm'x_3, ll'x_3, \ldots, ll'x_q.$$

Repeat in like manner for $\Omega_{4,3} I, \Omega_{5,4} I, \ldots \Omega_{q,q-1} I$. We get eventually that there is persistence, but for a function of the constants as factor, if and only if

$$\Omega_{2,1} I = 0, \Omega_{3,2} I = 0, \ldots, \Omega_{q,q-1} I = 0,$$

after substitutions of which that for x_1 is

$$\lambda_1 x_1 + \lambda_2 x_2 + \ldots + \lambda_q x_q,$$

where $\lambda_1, \lambda_2, \ldots, \lambda_q$ are arbitrary, each involving an l or an m

not involved in any previous one of them, while the substitutions for $x_2, x_3, \ldots, x_q$ though restricted are consistent.

In like manner, if and only if

$$\Omega_{3,2}I = 0,\ \Omega_{4,3}I = 0, \ldots, \Omega_{q,q-1}I = 0,\ \Omega_{1,q}I = 0,$$

there is like persistence when for x_2 a general substitution

$$\mu_1 x_1 + \mu_2 x_2 + \ldots + \mu_q x_q$$

is made, and for $x_1, x_3, \ldots, x_q$ restricted but consistent substitutions.

Again, similarly,

$$\Omega_{4,3}I = 0,\ \Omega_{5,4}I = 0, \ldots, \Omega_{2,1}I = 0$$

express that there is like persistence when x_3 is generally substituted for, and $x_1, x_2, x_4, \ldots, x_q$ consistently. And so on. Repeat this process q times.

Now the result of this succession of substitutions is the general substitution of

$$\begin{gathered} \lambda_1' x_1 + \lambda_2' x_2 + \ldots + \lambda_q' x_q, \\ \mu_1' x_1 + \mu_2' x_2 + \ldots + \mu_q' x_q, \\ \cdots\cdots\cdots \\ \omega_1' x_1 + \omega_2' x_2 + \ldots + \omega_q' x_q, \end{gathered}$$

for $x_1, x_2, \ldots, x_q$.

The possession of the q annihilators

$$\Omega_{2,1}, \Omega_{3,2}, \ldots, \Omega_{q,q-1}, \Omega_{1,q}$$

is then necessary and sufficient for a homogeneous function I to persist in form, but for a function of the constants of substitution as factor, after the general linear substitution, i.e. for it to be an invariant of the q-ary p-ic.

In like manner for C, for which $ip - \varpi$ is constant, to be a covariant it is necessary and sufficient that C have q cyclical annihilators

$$\Omega_{2,1} - x_2 \frac{\partial}{\partial x_1}, \text{ \&c.}$$

Also for Γ, for which $ip + \varpi'$ is constant, to be a contravariant it is necessary and sufficient that it have the q cyclical annihilators

$$\Omega_{2,1} + \xi_1 \frac{\partial}{\partial \xi_2}, \text{ \&c.}$$

And for K, for which $ip + \varpi' - \varpi$ is constant, to be a mixed concomitant it is necessary and sufficient that it have the q cyclical annihilators

$$\Omega_{2,1} + \xi_1 \frac{\partial}{\partial \xi_2} - x_2 \frac{\partial}{\partial x_1}, \text{ \&c.}$$

312. Let us denote the general q-ary p-ic by

$$u \equiv \Sigma \frac{p!}{r_1! \, r_2! \dots r_q!} a(r_1 r_2, \dots r_q) \, x_1^{r_1} x_2^{r_2} \dots x_q^{r_q},$$

where $r_1, r_2, \dots, r_q$ take all positive integral and zero values such that

$$r_1 + r_2 + \dots + r_q = p.$$

Let $A(r_1 r_2, \dots r_q)$ be the coefficient corresponding to $a(r_1 r_2, \dots r_q)$ in the transformed p-ic.

There are altogether $q(q-1)$ annihilators $\Omega_{n,m}$ of invariants $I(a)$ of the p-ic—one corresponding to every choice of an n and a different m among 1, 2, ... q.

The form of every $\Omega_{n,m}$ may be obtained as in § 90 by applying the corresponding 'infinitesimal transformation'—ϵ tending to zero—

$$x_1 = X_1,\ x_2 = X_2, \dots, x_m = X_m + \epsilon X_n,\ x_{m+1} = X_{m+1}, \dots, x_q = X_q.$$

We thus get

$$\Omega_{n,m} \, I(a) = 0, \qquad \dots (1)$$

where $\Omega_{n,m} \equiv \Sigma \left\{ r_n \, a(\dots r_m + 1 \dots r_n - 1 \dots) \frac{\partial}{\partial a(\dots r_m \dots r_n \dots)} \right\}.$

In addition to the $q(q-1)$ differential equations (1), all invariants $I(a)$ satisfy q others, expressive of the constancy throughout them, and the equality, of q *weights*. These are, for $n = 1, 2, \dots q$,

$$w_n I(a) = \Sigma r_n \, a(r_1 r_2, \dots r_q) \frac{\partial}{\partial a(r_1 r_2, \dots r_q)} I(a)$$

$$= \frac{ip}{q} I(a). \qquad \dots (2)$$

They can be proved by applying infinitesimal transformations, of which the nth replaces x_n by $(1+\epsilon)X_n$ and every other x_m by the corresponding X_m.

Mr. T. W. Chaundy has derived all the $q(q-1) + q = q^2$ differential equations (1) and (2) from the one fact that the expression of invariancy of $I(a)$ has the form

$$I(A) = M^{ip/q} I(a), \qquad \dots (3)$$

where

$$M = \begin{vmatrix} l_{11}, & l_{12}, & \dots & l_{1q} \\ l_{21}, & l_{22}, & \dots & l_{2q} \\ \cdot & \cdot & \cdot & \cdot \\ l_{q1}, & l_{q2}, & \dots & l_{qq} \end{vmatrix}, \text{ (cf. § 23).}$$

The method might with advantage have been used in dealing with binary and ternary quantics.

Use the notation

$$\omega_{n,m} \equiv l_{1m}\frac{\partial}{\partial l_{1n}} + l_{2m}\frac{\partial}{\partial l_{2n}} + \ldots + l_{qm}\frac{\partial}{\partial l_{qn}},$$

where each of m, n is any one of 1, 2, ..., q.

With m, n the same, we have

$$\omega_{n,n} M = M, \text{ and } \omega_{n,n} M^{ip/q} = \frac{ip}{q} M^{ip/q},$$

and, with m, n different,

$$\omega_{n,m} M = 0, \text{ and } \omega_{n,m} M^{ip/q} = 0.$$

Thus from (3) we obtain

$$\omega_{n,n} I(A) = \frac{ip}{q} I(A), \qquad \ldots (4)$$

and, with m, n different,

$$\omega_{n,m} I(A) = 0. \qquad \ldots (5)$$

Now, the formulae of transformation being

$$x_1 = l_{11}X_1 + l_{12}X_2 + \ldots + l_{1q}X_q,$$
$$x_2 = l_{21}X_1 + l_{22}X_2 + \ldots + l_{2q}X_q,$$
&c., &c.,

the dimensions of any new coefficient $A(r_1 r_2, \ldots r_q)$ in $l_{1n}, l_{2n}, \ldots, l_{qn}$, the coefficients of X_n in the linear expressions for $x_1, x_2, \ldots x_q$, are equal throughout to r_n, the index of the power of X_n which it multiplies. Thus, by Euler's Theorem,

$$\omega_{n,n} A(r_1 r_2, \ldots r_q) = r_n A(r_1 r_2, \ldots r_q),$$

so that by (4)

$$\frac{ip}{q} I(A) = \omega_{n,n} I(A) = \Sigma\left\{\omega_{nn} A \cdot \frac{\partial}{\partial A} I(A)\right\}, \text{ summation for all } A\text{'s},$$

$$= \Sigma\left\{r_n A \frac{\partial}{\partial A} I(A)\right\};$$

which is (2) with large letters for small, so that the q weight-equations are given.

To prove equations (1), observe that, from the formulae of transformation,

$$\omega_{n,m} x_1 = l_{1m} X_n = X_n \frac{\partial}{\partial X_m} x_1,$$

$$\omega_{n,m} x_2 = l_{2m} X_n = X_n \frac{\partial}{\partial X_m} x_2,$$

&c., &c.,

so that

$$\omega_{n,m} u = X_n \frac{\partial}{\partial X_m} x_1 \cdot \frac{\partial u}{\partial x_1} + X_n \frac{\partial}{\partial X_m} x_2 \cdot \frac{\partial u}{\partial x_2} + \ldots + X_n \frac{\partial}{\partial X_m} x_q \cdot \frac{\partial u}{\partial x_q}$$
$$= X_n \frac{\partial}{\partial X_m} u.$$

Now give to u its expression in terms of new coefficients A and variables X, remembering that $\omega_{n,m}$ does not operate on the latter. The left and right thus become two identical polynomials in $X_1, X_2, \ldots X_q$; and, equating coefficients of $X_1^{r_1} X_2^{r_2} \ldots X_q^{r_q}$, we obtain

$$\frac{p!}{r_1!\, r_2! \ldots r_m! \ldots r_n! \ldots r_q!} \omega_{n,m} A(\ldots r_m \ldots r_n \ldots)$$
$$= (r_m + 1) \frac{p!}{r_1! r_2! \ldots (r_m+1)! \ldots (r_n-1)! \ldots r_q!} A(\ldots r_m + 1 \ldots r_n - 1 \ldots),$$

i.e. $\omega_{n,m} A(\ldots r_m \ldots r_n, \ldots) = r_n A(\ldots r_m + 1 \ldots r_n - 1 \ldots)$;

so that, by (5),

$0 = \omega_{n,m} I(A) = \Sigma \left\{ \omega_{n,m} A \cdot \frac{\partial}{\partial A} I(A) \right\}$, summation for all A's,

$=$ the $\Omega_{n,m} I(a)$ of (1), with large letters for small.

Thus the $q(q-1)$ facts of annihilation $\Omega_{n,m} I(a) = 0$ are given.

INDEX

(The references are to pages.)

Absolute covariants, 45.
A rational integral a. c. is a power of a quantic, 45.
A fractional one given by two covariants, 45.
Limit to number of independent, 46.
Absolute invariants, 34.
One given by any two invariants, 35.
Limit to number of independent, 35.
Absolute orthogonal invariants (number of), 348.
Absolute orthogonal covariants, Annihilator of, 349.
led by all products of coefficients, 354.
Algebraically complete systems,
for n linear forms, 329.
for quantics with orders in A. P., 339.
Alternants, defined, 144.
of Ω and O, 144.
of Ω and O^r, 145.
of powers of Ω and O, 146.
of $\Sigma\Omega$ and $(\Sigma O)^r$, 157.
of ternary annihilators, 368, 371, 389.
American Journal, 178.
Anharmonic ratios,
are irrational invariants, 88, 94.
of roots of quartic, 282.
Annihilation, by Ω interpreted, 108.
by O interpreted, 112.
Annihilators, of binary invariants, 108, 112, 116, 121.
expressed by means of roots, 229, 233.
by means of sums of powers of roots, 230, 233.
derive these sums in succession, 232.
of covariants, 122, 133.
of non-unitary parts of invariants, 217.
of orthogonal concomitants, 349.
of Boolian concomitants, 351.
of all gradients, 242.
of all rat. int. functions, 356.
of ternary concomitants, 366, 367, 399, 403.
of end coefficients in the same, 385, 399, 404.
of q-ary concomitants, 406, 407, 410.
Anti-seminvariants, 126.
Apolarity, 266, 284, 286, 290.
Aronhold, 68, 108, 403.
Asyzygetic, or linearly independent, invariants, 119.
seminvariants, 130.

Boole, 24, 55, 342, 344, 346, 349.
Boolian invariants, &c., 344.
Annihilator of, 351.
Boolian complete systems, 352.
Booth, 265.
Brill, 288.
Brioschi, 159, 395.
Burnside and Panton, 29, 92, 188, 230.

Canonical forms, definition of, 254.
of binary cubic, 255, &c.
of binary $(2n-1)$-ic, 260.
of quintic and septimic, 262, 265.
of binary $2n$-ics, 267, 284, 289.
of binary quartic, 269, &c.
of binary sextic, 285, 287.
of binary octavic, 288.
Hammond's of quintic, 297, 298.
of two quadratics, 333.
of ternary cubic, 290, 374, 377.
Canonizants, 21, 23, 263.
with repeated factors, 262, 265.
Canonizing equations of $2n$-ics, 280, 286, 289, 290.
Cartesian geometry, Substitutions of, 343.
Catalecticants, 21, 22, 268, 269.
interpreted, 268.
of ternary &c. quantics, 293, 295.
Cayley, 15, 33, 44, 54, 55, 67, 90, 94, 100, 108, 134, 148, 156, 159, 171, 179, 210, 212, 217, 224, 241, 248, 260, 276, 281, 296, 310, 312, 315, 342, 392, 395, 401, 403, 405.
Cayleyan, of ternary cubic, 403.
Chaundy, 408.
Class, 321, 399, 404.
Clebsch, 68, 211, 296, 311.
Coefficients in quantic freed from second term are seminvariants, 203.
Cogrediency, defined, 55.
of x, y with ∂_y, $-\partial_x$, 51, 80.
of roots with variables, 56.
Orthogonal the same as contragrediency, 346, 349.
Combinants, 340.
Concomitants, defined, 77.
Contragrediency, defined, 74.
Geometrical, 75.
of $x, y, z, \ldots$ and $\partial_x, \partial_y, \partial_z, \ldots$, 75.

Contragrediency, of x, y and $-y$, x, 79.
Orthogonal the same as cogrediency, 346, 349.
Contravariants, defined, 76.
of binary quantics not distinct from covariants, 79.
of binary quantics found as invariants of linear form and the quantics, 78, 319, 321.
of ternary quantics, 399.
Convention as to numerical multiples of concomitants, 82.
Correspondence, of seminvariants and non-unitaries, 236.
of seminvariants and power enders, 243.
Covariants, defined, 3.
to be expected to exist, 6.
of several quantics from those of one, 23, 26.
of one quantic from those of several, 26, 64, &c.
of cubic quartic &c., see Cubic, &c.
Absolute, see Absolute.
of two or more quantics, 48.
of covariants, 49.
derived from emanants, 60.
of second degree in coefficients, 65, 71, 228.
as invariants, 80.
are given by one coefficient, 125, 126, 383.
as functions of differences, 94.
Sum of numerical coefficients in, 97.
are derivable from sources by substitutions, 201, 384.
Covariancy of factors of a binary quantic, 83.
Cubic, Binary,
Canonical form of, 14, 255.
Cubicovariant of, 50, 54.
has only one invariant, 89, 166, 190, 221.
has two covariants besides itself, 98.
has no other irreducible covariant, 132, 168, 213.
has a syzygy among concomitants, 169, 213, 258.
Cubic, Ternary, Canonical form of, 290, 374, 377.
The invariant S of, 375.
The Hessian of, 378, 391.
The invariant T of, 377.
The irreducible system of invariants of, 380.
The sextic covariant of, 395.
The contravariants of, 401.
Cubic equation, solution of, 14, 257.
Cubic protomorphs, 209.
Cubicovariant of cubic, 50, 54.
Degree, of an invariant, 27.
of a covariant, 40.
of an invariant of a binary $(2n+1)$-ic is even, 31.
of a covariant of odd order of a binary quantic is odd, 43.
of a covariant of even order of a binary $(2n+1)$-ic is even, 43.
Constancy of, see Homogeneity.
Differences, Functions of, 101, 103.
Differentiation of seminvariants to produce others, 223, 324, 339.
Use of to obtain irreducible systems, 324.
Diophantine Equations, 182, &c.
Simple sets of solutions of, 183.
Discriminants, are invariants, 15, 18, 89.
freed from numerical factors, 90.
Weight and degree of, 90.
found in succession, 224.
of quadratics, 15.
of binary cubic, 50, 54.
of binary quartic, 93.
of binary quintic, 302.
of ternary cubic, 379.
D'Ocagne, 248.
Dual Substitutions, 75.
Duality in Geometry, 75.
Durfee, 238.

Elemental products of differences, 187.
Eliminants, are invariants, 16.
are combinants, 340.
of linear forms, 9.
Elliptic integrals, 137.
Emanants, 56.
are absolute covariants, 57.
Geometry of, 58.
Invariants of, 61.
Boolian invariants of, 345.
End coefficients in ternary concomitants, 383, 385, 396.
Euler, 159.
Evectants, 26, 77, 401.
Exactness of Cayley's number, 148.
Excess, of a gradient, 141.
of an invariant vanishes, 116, 144.
of a seminvariant is not negative, 129, 146, 157.
Extent of a gradient, 138.

Faà de Bruno, 18, 136, 159, 201, 238, 296, 300.
Factor in expression of covariancy or invariancy a power of the modulus, 4, 28, 37, 41, 49, 117, 408.
an integral power for rational integral concomitants, 31, 37, 43, 48.

Factors of binary quantic, covariancy of, 83.
of a seminvariant are seminvariants, 136.
Ferrers, 154.
Ferrers' diagrams, 154, 158, 241.
Final coefficients in covariants have annihilator O, 126.
Finiteness of systems of concomitants, 72, 189, 192, 193, 197.
of numbers of solutions of Diophantine equations, 182, &c.
Formes-types, 304, 306.
Forms, defined and classified, 1.
Forsyth, 338, 340, 405.
Functional determinants. See Jacobians.
Franklin, 158, 159, 173, 178.

Generating functions, defined, 159.
for $(w; i, p)$, 159.
for numbers of seminvariants, 161, 164, 238, 240.
for concomitants of given degree and order, 171.
Reduced, 172, 174.
Representative, 174, 176.
Real, 180, 361.
in case of two quantics, 178.
for perpetuants, 239, 251.
for orthogonals, 362.
Generators of all seminvariants, 224, 243, 246.
of all ternary sources, 396.
Geometry of binary systems, 6, 59.
of emanants, 58.
of Hessians, 62.
of concomitants of cubic, 259.
of concomitants of quartic, 282.
of a quintic for which $I_{18} = 0$, 308.
of a sextic for which $I_{15} = 0$, 316.
of two quadratics, 334.
of Boolian concomitants, 345, 352.
Metrical, Chap. XV.
Gordan, 37, 68, 72, 171, 182, 296, 311.
Gordan's Theorem, 182, &c.
Proof of for invariants of one binary quantic, 189, 197.
for in- and covariants, 192, 197.
for more quantics than one, 193, 197.
Grace, 72, 240, 251, 267.
Gradients, defined, 138.
annihilated by Ω and O are invariants, 113.
of positive excess are of form ΩG, 118, 148, 150.
always of form ΩG when extent of Ω is infinite, 243, 245.
Gradients, all lead pure or mixed concomitants, 321.
Ground forms, see Irreducible systems.
Gundelfinger, 405.

Hammond, 159, 174, 176, 297, 301, 307, 336, 337.
Hermite, 63, 78, 112, 155, 157, 296, 304, 310, 403.
Hesse, 290.
Hessians, are covariants, 12.
are discriminants of second emanants, 62.
of quadratics are discriminants, 15.
of cubic, Roots of, 100.
of quartic, 279, 284.
of ternary cubic, 378, 391.
Geometry of, 62, 283, 284.
Hilbert, 37, 146, 182, &c., 208, 209, 224.
Hilbert's Theorem, 195.
Hirsch, Meyer, 238.
Homogeneity, of an invariant of one quantic, 27.
of a complete system of invariants of several quantics, 38.
in variables of complete systems of covariants, 40, 48.
in coefficients of the same, 40, 48.
Hyperdeterminants, 66, 131.
give all in- and co-variants, 107, 136.

Independent Covariants, &c., Limit to number of, 46.
Exact number of, 205.
Independent invariants, Limit to number of, 35.
Infinite order, Binary quantic of, 237, &c.
Intermediate invariants and covariants, 23, &c.
are not combinants, 341.
Invariants, defined, 3.
to be expected to exist, 5.
of several quantics from those of one, 24, &c.
of one quantic from those of several, 26, 64.
Homogeneity of, see Homogeneity.
Isobarism of, see Isobarism.
Absolute, see Absolute.
Irreducible, see Irreducible.
of quadratic, cubic, &c., see Quadratic, &c.
Limit to number of independent, 35.
of two or more quantics, 37.
of covariants, 49.
of second degree, 53.
Lineo-linear, 54.

as functions of differences, 86, &c., 100.
Sum of numerical coefficients in, 87.
Irrational, 88.
Symmetry of, 112.
of odd weight are skew, 112.
Formation of by aid of Ω, 118, 121.
Number of Asyzygetic, 119.
involve all coefficients, 141.
of third degree, 156.
of fourth degree, 156.
are transvectants, 247.
of invariants of $\lambda u + \mu v$ are combinants, 342.
of ternary quantics are defined by three cyclical or two pairs of annihilators, 373.
of q-ary quantics, 406.
Involution, Criterion of, 22, 342.
Irreducible concomitants are finite in number, 189, 192, 193, 197.
Irreducible invariants, 36.
covariants, 47.
syzygants, 198.
Irreducible systems,
for linear form, 164.
for quadratic, 97, 165.
for cubic, 134, 166, 167, 212.
for quartic, 169, 173, 213.
for quintic, 170, 175, 298.
for sextic, 170, 176, 311.
for two linear forms, 323.
for linear form and quadratic, 323.
for linear form and cubic, 325.
for linear form and quartic, 328.
for n linear forms, 106, 329.
for two quadratics, 330.
for linear form and two quadratics, 334.
for quadratic and cubic, 335.
of absolute orthogonal concomitants, 361.
Isobarism, of invariants, 32, 34, 37, 369, 408.
of covariants, 43, 44, 48.
Triple of invariants of ternary quantics, 369.

Jacobians, are covariants, 10.
Joubert, 316.

Kempe, 190, 338.

Leading coefficients of covariants are seminvariants, 126.
Linear covariants,
of binary $(2n+1)$-ic, 63.
of binary quintic, 64, 304, 317.
of quadratic and cubic, 133, 134.
Linear form, has no invariant, 164.
Linear substitution, defined, 2.
Linear substitution, Modulus of, 3.
Reversed, 29.
Cartesian, 343.
Dual, 75.
Linear transformation, defined, 2.
Linearly independent, see Asyzygetic.
Lineo-linear invariants, covariants and seminvariants, 54, 64, 71, 121, 134.
of u, v are transvectants of u, v, 134.

MacMahon, 159, 237, 238, 239, 240, 241, 247, 248.
Mixed concomitants, defined, 77.
of binary quantics found as covariants of quantics and linear form, 319, 321, 322.
of ternary quantics, 403.
Modulus of linear substitution, 3.
must not vanish, 3.
irresoluble into factors, 17.
Powers of, 19.
Cartesian, 343.
Orthogonal, 346.
Morley, 317.

Newson, 298.
Non-absolute orthogonal concomitants, 356.
Non-unitary symmetric functions, 236.
Correspondence of with seminvariants, 236.
Non-unitary terms, determine a seminvariant, 203, 215.
in an invariant are given by an annihilator, 219, 220, 234.
Number of asyzygetic invariants of given degree, 119.
of asyzygetic seminvariants of given type, 130, 149, 157.
of seminvariants and invariants of given degree, 163.
of independent covariants, &c., 46, 205.
of independent invariants, 36.
of independent concomitants of ternary p-ic, 400, 405.

Operation with one quantic on another, 52, 299.
with contravariants on covariants, 77.
with covariants on contravariants, 77.
Operational symbolism, 69.
Operators, which effect linear transformation, 111, 116, 123.

Operators, which derive covariants from end coefficients, 126, 133, 384.
which derive ternary concomitants from end coefficients, 384, 400, 404.
which annihilate gradients of positive excess, 118, 149, 224.
which annihilate all gradients, 242, 356.
which derive cubic protomorphs from quadratic, 209.
which derive seminvariants from non-unitary terms, 217.
which derive seminvariants from others, 210, 220, 223, 249.
which generate seminvts., 224, 243.
which derive sums of powers in succession, 232.
which generate orth. invts., 356.
Order, of a quantic, 1.
of a covariant, 40.
of a covariant of a binary $2n$-ic is even, 43.
of a covariant of even degree is even, 43.
of a covariant of a binary $(2n+1)$-ic is even or odd together with its degree, 43.
Orthogonal, invariants, &c., 344, 356.
cogrediency and contragrediency identical, 346, 349.
substitutions direct and skew, 346.
non-absolute, 356.

Partitions, 119.
Conjugate, 154.
Reciprocal, 154, 158, 162.
Perpetuants, 239, 250, 251.
Systems of, 252.
Pippian. See Cayleyan.
Polar curves, 58.
Power ending products, 241.
One to one correspondence of with seminvariants, 244.
Protomorphs, defined, 206.
Systems of, 206, 207, 211.
of lowest degrees, 207, 209.
for systems of quantics, 211.

Quadratic, Binary,
The one invariant of, 89, 165.
has no covariant but itself, 98, 165.
Quadratic, Ternary,
The one invariant of, 373.
Question of covariants of, 390.
Contravariant of, 400.
Quadratic protomorphs, 207, 208.
are irreducible, 215.
Quantics, defined and classified, 1.
Quartic, Binary,
Catalecticant of, 21, 54, 268.
Quadratic invariant of, 53.
The two invariants of, 92, 119.
Discriminant of, 93.
The equi-anharmonic for which $I=0$, 94, 273, 282.
The harmonic for which $J=0$, 94, 274, 282.
transformed into itself, 134.
transformed into its reducing cubic, 134.
has only two irreducible invariants, 134, 169.
Irreducible system and syzygy for, 173, 213, 277.
Canonical form of, 271, 276, 284.
with square factor, 275.
Linear factor of, 281.
Geometry of, 282.
Quartic, Ternary,
Catalecticant of, 293.
not in general a sum of 5 fourth powers, 294.
Quartic equation, Solution of, 280.
Quartics, Quaternary and quinary, not in general sums of 9, 14 fourth powers, 295.
Quintic, Binary,
Canonizant of, 21, 23, 265.
Invariants of, 50, 73, 132, 299, 300.
Linear covariants of, 64, 73, 299, 300, 317.
Generating function for invariants of, 170, 176.
Representative G. F. for, 174.
Canonical form of, 262, 265, 297, 316.
freed from two middle coefficients, 297.
can only be freed from these and another adjacent when $I_{12}=0$, 305.
List of concomitants of, 298.
Forms of concomitants of when $c=0$, $d=0$, 301.
Discriminant of, 302.
Syzygy among invariants of, 303.
expressed with invariant coefficients, 304.
for which $I_{12}=0$, 305, 306, 310.
for which $I_4=0$, 307.
for which $I_8=0$, 307.
for which $I_{18}=0$, 308, 310.
Skew invariant of in terms of roots, 310.
Quippian, of ternary cubic, 403.

Rational integral invariants, &c., form a complete system, 5.
Reciprocant, of ternary quadratic, 400.

Reciprocant, of ternary cubic, 403.
Reciprocity, Hermite's law of, 137, 155, 162, 240.
Resultants. See Eliminants.
Roberts, M., 125, 132, 231.
Roberts, S., 248.
Roots of binary quantic, 83.
  Anharmonic ratios of, 88.

Salmon, 24, 55, 67, 296, 297, 300, 336, 395.
Semi-canonical form of quintic, 297, 301.
  of ternary cubic, 293, 377.
Seminvariants, 126, 127.
  lead covariants, 128, 147.
  Formation of by aid of Ω, 129, 133.
  Number of asyzygetic of given type, 130, 148.
  of second degree, 130, 208.
  of several quantics, 132.
  as particular gradients, 139.
  have no letters absent, 141.
  as eliminants between u and derivatives, 200.
  are given by non-unitary terms, 202, 216.
  as integrals of $\Omega S = 0$, 211.
  as quantics in $a_p : 1$, 221.
  of seminvariants so regarded are seminvariants, 222.
  all generated by certain operators, 224, 243, 245.
  as transvectants, 247.
  One to one correspondence of with power enders, 244.
  derived from others by differentiation, 223.
  as invariants of a quantic and its derivatives, 338.
Seminvariant operators, 220, 249.
Separation by direct operations:
  into coefficients in covariants, 150.
  into orthogonal invariants, 360.
  into ternary sources, &c., 405.
Sextic, Binary,
  Canonical forms of, 285, 287.
  Invariants of, 22, 53, 311, 316.
  Generating function for invariants of, 171, 176.
  The 26 irreducible concomitants of, 312.
  The skew invariant of interpreted, 316.
Skew invariant, 112.
  of a quintic or sextic unique, 309, 316.
Skew orthogonal substitutions, 346.
Solubility of quintic for which $I_{18} = 0$, 308.
Source of a covariant, 126, 396.
Stephanos, 288.
Stroh, 239, 250.
Substitution of derivatives for variables, 55.
  of derivatives for coefficients, 200, 201, 320, 384.
Sufficiency of conditions of annihilation, 113, 124.
Sum of numerical coefficients in invariants, 87.
  in covariants and seminvariants, 97.
Sum of powers, Condition that a $2n$-ic be a, 267, 294, 295.
Sums of powers of roots, 230, &c.
  Differentiation with regard to, 235.
Sylvester, 55, 77, 78, 108, 136, 141, 146, 148, 159, 173, 178, 224, 249, 260, 293, 296, 312, 315, 340, 342, 349, 400, 406.
Symbolical representation, 66, 68, 69.
Symmetry of in- and co-variants, 112, 121, 124, 133.
Syzygants, 198.
Syzygy, for binary cubic, 100, 169, 258.
  for quartic, 173, 215.
  among invariants of quintic, 303.

Tamisage, 175.
Ternary quantics, Triple arrangement of, 365.
  Annihilators of invariants &c. of, 366, 367.
  Covariants of, 382.
Thompson, 223.
Transvectants, 71.
  are lineo-linear invariants of emanants, 71.
  give all covariants and invariants, 72.
  of a p-ic and itself, 131.
  of two binary quantics, 134.
  All invariants are, 247.

Ueberschiebung, 71.
Uniqueness of covariant led by a seminvariant, 128.
Universal Concomitant, The, 77.

Vanishing of all invariants, 208.
von Gall, 314.

Weight, 31, 33, 42, 44, 364, 408.
  Constancy of, see Isobarism.
Wood, 240.

Young, 72, 240, 267.

MODERN PURE SOLID GEOMETRY

By N. ALTSHILLER-COURT

In this second edition of this well-known book on synthetic solid geometry, the author has supplemented several of the chapters with an account of recent results.

—In prep. 2nd ed. xii+330 pp. 5⅜x8. [147] Prob. **$6.00**

STRING FIGURES, and other monographs

By BALL, CAJORI, CARSLAW, and PETERSEN

FOUR VOLUMES IN ONE:

String Figures, *by W. W. Rouse Ball;*

The Elements of Non-Euclidean Plane Geometry, *by H. S. Carslaw;*

A History of the Logarithmic Slide Rule, *by F. Cajori;*

Methods and Theories for the Solution of Problems of Geometrical Construction, *by J. Petersen*

—528 pp. 5¼x8. [130] Four vols. in one. **$3.95**

THÉORIE DES OPERATIONS LINÉAIRES

By S. BANACH

—1933. xii + 250 pp. 5¼x8¼. [110] **$3.95**

THEORIE DER FUNKTIONEN MEHRERER KOMPLEXER VERÄNDERLICHEN

By H. BEHNKE and P. THULLEN

—(Ergeb. der Math.) 1934. vii+115 pp. 5½x8½. [68] **$3.25**

CONFORMAL MAPPING

By L. BIEBERBACH

"The first book in English to give an elementary, readable account of the Riemann Mapping Theorem and the distortion theorems and uniformisation problem with which it is connected. . . . Presented in very attractive and readable form."
—*Math. Gazette.*

"Engineers will profitably use this book for its accurate exposition."—*Appl. Mechanics Reviews.*

". . . thorough and painstaking . . . lucid and clear and well arranged . . . an excellent text."
—*Bulletin of the A. M. S.*

—1952. vi+234 pp. 4½x6½. [90] Cloth **$2.75**
In prep. [176] Paper **$1.50**

ALMOST PERIODIC FUNCTIONS

By H. BOHR

Translated by H. COHN. From the famous series *Ergebnisse der Mathematik und ihrer Grenzgebiete*, a beautiful exposition of the theory of Almost Periodic Functions written by the creator of that theory.

—1951. 120 pp. Lithotyped. [27] **$2.75**

LECTURES ON THE CALCULUS OF VARIATIONS

By O. BOLZA

A standard text by a major contributor to the theory. Suitable for individual study by anyone with a good background in the Calculus and the elements of Real Variables. The present, second edition differs from the first primarily by the inclusion within the text itself of various addenda to the first edition, as well as some notational improvements.

—2nd (corr.) ed. 1961. 280 pp. 5⅜x8. [145] Cloth **$3.25**
[152] Paper **$1.19**

VORLESUNGEN UEBER VARIATIONSRECHNUNG

By O. BOLZA

A standard text and reference work, by one of the major contributors to the theory.

—1963. Corr. repr. of 1st ed. ix+715 pp. 5⅜x8. [160] **$8.00**

THEORIE DER KONVEXEN KÖRPER

By T. BONNESEN and W. FENCHEL

"Remarkable monograph."
—*J. D. Tamarkin, Bulletin of the A. M. S.*

—1934. 171 pp. 5½x8½. Orig. publ. at $7.50 [54] **$3.95**

THE CALCULUS OF FINITE DIFFERENCES

By G. BOOLE

A standard work on the subject of finite differences and difference equations by one of the seminal minds in the field of finite mathematics.

Numerous exercises with answers.

—Fourth edition. 1958. xii + 336 pp. 5x8. [121] Cloth **$3.95**
[148] Paper **$1.39**

A TREATISE ON DIFFERENTIAL EQUATIONS

By G. BOOLE

Including the Supplementary Volume.

—Fifth edition. 1959. xxiv + 735 pp. 5¼x8. [128] **$6.00**

CAJORI, "History of Slide Rule," see Ball

VORLESUNGEN ÜBER REELLE FUNKTIONEN

By C. CARATHÉODORY

This great classic is at once a book for the beginner, a reference work for the advanced scholar and a source of inspiration for the research worker.

—In prep. 2nd ed. 5⅜x8. 728 pp. [38] Prob. **$9.50**

CARSLAW, "Non-Euclidean Plane Geometry," see Ball

ELECTRIC CIRCUIT THEORY and the OPERATIONAL CALCULUS

By J. R. CARSON

—2nd ed. 206 pp. 5¼x8. [92] Cloth **$3.95**
[114] Paper **$1.75**

COLLECTED PAPERS (OEUVRES)

By P. L. CHEBYSHEV

One of Russia's greatest mathematicians, Chebyshev (Tchebycheff) did work of the highest importance in the Theory of Probability, Number Theory, and other subjects. The present work contains his post-doctoral papers (sixty in number) and miscellaneous writings. The language is French, in which most of his work was originally published; those papers originally published in Russian are here presented in French translation.

—1962. Repr. of 1st ed. 1,480 pp. 5⅜x8¼.
[157] Two Vol. set. **$27.50**

TEXTBOOK OF ALGEBRA

By G. CHRYSTAL

The usefulness, both as a textbook and as a work of reference, of this charming classic is attested to by the number of editions it has run through—the present being the sixth. Its richness of content can be only appreciated by an examination of the twelve-hundred-page book itself. **Thousands of valuable exercises (with solutions).**

—Apr., 1964. 6th ed. 2 vols. 1,239 pp. 5⅜x8.
[84] Cloth Each vol. **$3.95**
[181] Paper Each vol. **$2.35**

ALGEBREN

By M. DEURING

—(Ergeb. der Math.) 1935. v + 143 pp. 5½x8½. Orig. pub. at $6.60. [50] **$3.95**

STUDIES IN THE THEORY OF NUMBERS

By L. E. DICKSON

A systematic exposition, starting from first principles, of the arithmetic of quadratic forms, chiefly (but not entirely) ternary forms, including numerous original investigations and correct proofs of a number of classical results that have been stated or proved erroneously in the literature.

—1930-62 viii+230 pp. 5⅜x8. [151] **$3.95**

LECTURES ON ERGODIC THEORY

By P. R. HALMOS

CONTENTS: Introduction. Recurrence. Mean Convergence. Pointwise Convergence. Ergodicity. Mixing. Measure Algebras. Discrete Spectrum. Automorphisms of Compact Groups. Generalized Proper Values. Weak Topology. Weak Approximation. Uniform Topology. Uniform Approximation. Category. Invariant Measures. Generalized Ergodic Theorems. Unsolved Problems.

"Written in the pleasant, relaxed, and clear style usually associated with the author. The material is organized very well and painlessly presented. A usually associated with the author."

—1960. (Repr. of 1956 ed.) viii + 101 pp. 5¼x8. [142] **$2.95**

ALGEBRAIC LOGIC

By P. R. HALMOS

"Algebraic Logic is a modern approach to some of the problems of mathematical logic, and the theory of polyadic Boolean algebras, with which this volume is mostly concerned, is intended to be an efficient way of treating algebraic logic in a unified manner.

"[The material] is accessible to a general mathematical audience; no vast knowledge of algebra or logic is required . . . Except for a slight Boolean foundation, the volume is essentially self-contained."—*From the Preface.*

—1962 271 pp. 6x9 [154] **$3.95**

RAMANUJAN:
Twelve Lectures on His Life and Works

By G. H. HARDY

The book is somewhat more than an account of the mathematical work and personality of Ramanujan; it is one of the very few full-length books of "shop talk" by an important mathematician.

—viii + 236 pp. 6x9. [136] **$3.95**

GRUNDZÜGE DER MENGENLEHRE

By F. HAUSDORFF

Some of the topics in the Grundzüge omitted from later editions:

Symmetric Sets—Principle of Duality—most of the "Algebra" of Sets—most of the "Ordered Sets"—Partially Ordered Sets—Arbitrary Sets of Complexes—Normal Types—Initial and Final Ordering—Complexes of Real Numbers—General Topological Spaces—Euclidean Spaces—the Special Methods Applicable in the Euclidean plane—Jordan's separation Theorem—The Theory of Content and Measure—The Theory of the Lebesgue Integral.

—First edition. viii+476 pp. [61] **$6.00**

SET THEORY

By F. HAUSDORFF

Now for the first time available in English, Hausdorff's classic text-book has been an inspiration and a delight to those who have read it in the original German. The translation is from the Third (latest) German edition.

"We wish to state without qualification that this is an indispensable book for all those interested in the theory of sets and the allied branches of real variable theory."—*Bulletin of A. M. S.*

—2nd ed. 1962. 352 pp. 6x9. [119] **$6.50**

VORLESUNGEN ÜBER DIE THEORIE DER ALGEBRAISCHEN ZAHLEN

By E. HECKE

"An elegant and comprehensive account of the modern theory of algebraic numbers."

—*Bulletin of the A. M. S.*

—1923. 264 pp. 5½x8½. [46] **$3.95**

INTEGRALGLEICHUNGEN UND GLEICHUNGEN MIT UNENDLICHVIELEN UNBEKANNTEN

By E. HELLINGER and O. TOEPLITZ

"Indispensable to anybody who desires to penetrate deeply into this subject."—*Bulletin of A.M.S.*

—With a preface by E. Hilb. 1928. 286 pp. 5¼x8. [89] **$4.50**

Grundzüge Einer Allgemeinen Theorie der LINEAREN INTEGRALGLEICHUNGEN

By D. HILBERT

—306 pp. 5½x8¼. [91] **$4.50**

PRINCIPLES OF MATHEMATICAL LOGIC

By D. HILBERT and W. ACKERMANN

The famous *Grundüge der Theoretischen Logik* translated into English, with added notes and revisions by PROF. R. E. LUCE.

"The best textbook in a Western European language for a student wishing a fairly thorough treatment."—*Bulletin of the A. M. S.*

—1950-59. xii + 172 pp. 6x9. [69] **$3.95**

GEOMETRY AND THE IMAGINATION

By D. HILBERT and S. COHN-VOSSEN

Translated from the German by P. NEMENYI.

"A fascinating tour of the 20th century mathematical zoo. . . . Anyone who would like to see proof of the fact that a sphere with a hole can always be bent (no matter how small the hole), learn the theorems about Klein's bottle—a bottle with no edges, no inside, and no outside—and meet other strange creatures of modern geometry will be delighted with Hilbert and Cohn-Vossen's book."
—*Scientific American.*

"Should provided stimulus and inspiration to every student and teacher of geometry."—*Nature.*

"A mathematical classic. . . . The purpose is to make the reader *see* and *feel* the proofs. . . . readers can penetrate into higher mathematics with . . . pleasure instead of the usual laborious study."
—*American Scientist.*

"Students, particularly, would benefit very much by reading this book . . . they will experience the sensation of being taken into the friendly confidence of a great mathematician and being shown the real significance of things."—*Science Progress.*

"A person with a minimum of formal training can follow the reasoning. . . . an important [book]."
—*The Mathematics Teacher.*

"A remarkable book. . . . A veritable geometric anthology. . . . Over 330 diagrams and every [one] tells a story."—*The Mathematical Gazette.*

—1952. 358 pp. 6x9. [87] **$6.00**

SQUARING THE CIRCLE, and other Monographs

By HOBSON, HUDSON, SINGH, and KEMPE

FOUR VOLUMES IN ONE.

SQUARING THE CIRCLE, by *Hobson.* A fascinating account of one of the three famous problems of antiquity, its significance, its history, the mathematical work it inspired in modern times, and its eventual solution in the closing years of the last century.

RULER AND COMPASSES, by *Hudson.* "An analytical and geometrical investigation of how far Euclidean constructions can take us. It is as thoroughgoing as it is constructive."—*Sci. Monthly.*

THE THEORY AND CONSTRUCTION OF NON-DIFFERENTIABLE FUNCTIONS, by *Singh.* I. Functions Defined by Series. II. Functions Defined Geometrically. III. Functions Defined Arithmetically. IV. Properties of Non-Differentiable Functions.

HOW TO DRAW A STRAIGHT LINE, by *Kempe.* An intriguing monograph on linkages. Describes, among other things, a linkage that will trisect any angle.

"Intriguing, meaty."—*Scientific American.*

—388 pp. 4½x7½. [95] Four Vols. in one **$3.95**

DIFFERENTIAL AND INTEGRAL CALCULUS

By E. LANDAU

A masterpiece of rigor and clarity.

—2nd ed. 1960. 372 pp. 6x9. [78] **$6.00**

ELEMENTARE ZAHLENTHEORIE

By E. LANDAU

"Interest is enlisted at once and sustained by the accuracy, skill, and enthusiasm with which Landau marshals . . . facts and simplifies . . . details."

—*G. D. Birkhoff, Bulletin of the A. M. S.*

—1927. vii + 180 + iv pp. 5½x8¼. [26] **$3.50**

VORLESUNGEN ÜBER ZAHLENTHEORIE

By E. LANDAU

The various sections of this important work (Additive, Analytic, Geometric, and Algebraic Number Theory) can be read independently of one another.

—Vol. I, Pt. 2. * (Additive Number Theory) xii + 180 pp. Vol. II. (Analytical Number Theory and Geometrical Number Theory) viii + 308 pp. Vol. III. (Algebraic Number Theory and Fermat's Last Theorem) viii + 341 pp. 5¼x8¼. * (Vol. I, Pt. 1 is issued as **Elementare Zahlentheorie** (in German) or as **Elementary Number Theory** (in English). Orig. publ. at $26.40. [32] Three Vols. in one. **$14.00**

ELEMENTARY NUMBER THEORY

By E. LANDAU

The present work is a translation of Prof. Landau's famous *Elementare Zahlentheorie,* with added exercises by Prof. Paul T. Bateman.

—1958. 256 pp. 6x9. [125] **$4.95**

GRUNDLAGEN DER ANALYSIS

By E. LANDAU

The student who wishes to study mathematical German will find Landau's famous *Grundlagen der Analysis* ideally suited to his needs.

Only a few score of German words will enable him to read the entire book with only an occasional glance at the Vocabulary! [A COMPLETE German-English vocabulary, prepared with the novice especially in mind, has been appended to the book.]

—3rd ed. 1960. 173 pp. 5⅜x8. [24] Cloth **$3.50**
[141] Paper **$1.95**

FOUNDATIONS OF ANALYSIS

By E. LANDAU

"Certainly no clearer treatment of the foundations of the number system can be offered. . . . One can only be thankful to the author for this fundamental piece of exposition, which is alive with his vitality and genius."—*J. F. Ritt, Amer. Math. Monthly.*

—2nd ed. 1960. 6x9. [79] **$3.95**

ELEMENTS OF ALGEBRA

By HOWARD LEVI

"This book is addressed to beginning students of mathematics. . . . The level of the book, however, is so unusually high, mathematically as well as pedagogically, that it merits the attention of professional mathematicians (as well as of professional pedagogues) interested in the wider dissemination of their subject among cultured people . . . **a closer approximation to the right way to teach mathematics to beginners than anything else now in existence."**—*Bulletin of the A. M. S.*

—4th ed. 1962. 189 pp. 5⅜x8. [103] **$3.50**

THE THEORY OF MATRICES

By C. C. MacDUFFEE

"No mathematical library can afford to be without this book."—*Bulletin of the A. M. S.*

—(Ergeb. der Math.) 2nd edition. 116 pp. 6x9. Orig. publ. at $5.20. [28] **$2.95**

COMBINATORY ANALYSIS, Vols. I and II

By P. A. MACMAHON

TWO VOLUMES IN ONE.

A broad and extensive treatise on an important branch of mathematics.

—xx + 300 + xx + 340 pp. 5⅜x8. [137] Two vols. in one. **$7.50**

MACMAHON, "Introduction . . . ," see Klein

FORMULAS AND THEOREMS FOR THE FUNCTIONS OF MATHEMATICAL PHYSICS

By W. MAGNUS and F. OBERHETTINGER

Gathered into a compact, handy and well-arranged reference work are thousands of results on the many important functions needed by the physicist, engineer and applied mathematician.

Translated by J. WERMER.

—1954. 182 pp. 6x9. [51] **$3.90**

THEORY OF NUMBERS

By G. B. MATHEWS

CHAPTER HEADINGS: I. Elementary Theory of Congruences. II. Quadratic Congruences. III. Binary Quadratic Forms; Analytical Theory. IV. Binary Quadratic Forms; Geometrical Theory. V. Generic Characters of Binary Quadratics. VI. Composition of Forms. VII. Cyclotomy. VIII. Determination of Number of Improperly Primitive Classes for a Given Determinant. IX. Applications of the Theory of Quadratic Forms. X. The Distribution of Primes.

A reprint of the first edition, with correction of errata and some improvements of notation.

—2nd ed. 1892-1962. xii+323 pp. 5⅜x8. [156] **$3.95**

THE DEVELOPMENT OF MATHEMATICS IN CHINA AND JAPAN

By Y. MIKAMI

"Filled with valuable information. Mikami's [account of the mathematicians he knew personally] is an attractive features."

—*Scientific American.*

—1913-62. x + 347 pp. 5⅜x8. [149] **$4.95**

KURVENTHEORIE

By K. MENGER

—1932-63. vi+376 pp. 5⅜x8¼. [172] **In prep.**

GEOMETRIE DER ZAHLEN

By H. MINKOWSKI

—viii + 256 pp. 5½x8¼. [93] **$4.50**

DIOPHANTISCHE APPROXIMATIONEN

By H. MINKOWSKI

—viii + 235 pp. 5¼x8¼. [118] **$4.50**

MORDELL, "Fermat's Last Theorem," *see Klein*

INVERSIVE GEOMETRY

By F. MORLEY and F. V. MORLEY

—xi + 273 pp. 5¼x8¼. [101] **$3.95**

INTRODUCTION TO NUMBER THEORY

By T. NAGELL

A special feature of Nagell's well-known text is the rather extensive treatment of Diophantine equations of second and higher degree. A large number of non-routine problems are given.

—1951-64. Corr. repr. of 1st ed. 309 pp. 5⅜x8. [163] Prob. **$4.95**

THE THEORY OF SUBSTITUTIONS

By E. NETTO

Partial Contents: CHAP. I. Symmetric and Alternating Functions. II. Multiple- valued Functions and Groups of Substitutions. III. The Different Values of a Multiple-valued Function and their Algebraic Relation to One Another. IV. Transitivity and Primitivity; Simple and Compound Groups; Isomorphism. V. Algebraic Relations between Functions Belonging to the Same Group . . . VII. Certain Special Classes of Groups. VIII. Analytical Representation of Substitutions. The Linear Group. IX. Equations of Second, Third, Fourth Degrees. Groups of an Equation. X. Cyclotomic Equations. XI. Abelian Equations . . . XIII. Algebraic Solution of Equations. XIV. Group of an Algebraic Equation. XV. Algebraically Solvable Equations.

—In prep. Corr. repr. of 1st ed. 310 pp. 5⅜x8. Prob. **$3.95**

KONTINUUUM,
andere Monographien

By H. WEYL, E. LANDAU, and B. RIEMANN

FOUR VOLUMES IN ONE.

DAS KONTINUUM (Kritische Untersuchungen ueber die Grundlagen der Analysis), by *H. Weyl.* Reprint of 2nd edition.

MATHEMATISCHE ANALYSE DES RAUMPROBLEMS, by *H. Weyl.*

DARSTELLUNG UND BEGRUENDUNG EINIGER NEURER ERGEBNISSE DER FUNKTIONENTHEORIE, by *E. Landau.* Reprint of 2nd edition.

UEBER DIE HYPOTHESEN, WELCHE DER GEOMETRIE ZU GRUNDE LIEGEN, by *B. Riemann.* Reprint of 3rd edition, edited and with comments by H. Weyl.

—83 + 117 + 120 + 48 pp. 5¼x8. [134] Four vols. in one **$6.00**

LEHRBUCH DER ALGEBRA

By H. WEBER

The bible of classical algebra, still unsurpassed for its clarity and completeness. Much of the material on elliptic functions is not available elsewhere in connected form.

PARTIAL CONTENTS: *VOL. I.* CHAP. I. Rational Functions. II. Determinants. III. Roots of Algebraic Equations. V. Symmetric Functions. V. Linear Transformations. Invariants. VI. Tchirnhaus Transformation. VII. Reality of Roots. VIII. Sturm's Theorem. X. Limits on Roots. X. Approximate Computation of Roots. XI. Continued Fractions. XII. Roots of Unity. XIII. Galois Theory. XIV. Applications of Permutation Group to Equations. XV. Cyclic Equations. XVI. Kreisteilung. XVII. Algebraic Solution of Equations. XVIII. Roots of Metacyclic Equations.

VOL. II. CHAPS. I.-V. Group Theory. VI.-X. Theory of Linear Groups. XI.-XVI. Applications of Group Theory (General Equation of Fifth Degree. The Group G_{168} and Equations of Seventh Degree . . .). XVII.-XXIV. Algebraic Numbers. XXV. Transcendental Numbers.

VOL. III. CHAP. I. Elliptic Integral. II. Theta Functions. III. Transformation of Theta Functions. IV. Elliptic Functions. V. Modular Function. V. Multiplication of Elliptic Functions. Division. VII. Equations of Transformation. VIII. Groups of the Transformation Equations and the Equation of Fifth Degree... XI.-XVI. Quadratic Fields. XVII. Elliptic Functions and Quadratic Forms. XVIII. Galois Group of Class Equation. XIX. Computation of Class Invariant . . . XII. Cayley's Development of Modular Function. XXIII. Class Fields. XXIV.-XXVI. Algebraic Functions. XXVII. Algebraic and Abelian Differentials.

—3rd ed. (C. repr. of 2nd ed.) 1908-62. 2,345 pp. 5⅜x8.
[144] Each Vol. **$8.00**
Three Vol. set **$19.50**